COURSE OF THEORETICAL PHYSICS

Volume 2

THE CLASSICAL THEORY OF FIELDS

Revised Second Edition

THE CLASSICAL THEORY OF FIELDS

REVISED SECOND EDITION

by

L. D. LANDAU and E. M. LIFSHITZ
Institute for Physical Problems
Academy of Sciences of the U.S.S.R.

Translated from the Russian

by

MORTON HAMERMESH
Argonne National Laboratory

PERGAMON PRESS
OXFORD · LONDON · PARIS · FRANKFURT

ADDISON-WESLEY PUBLISHING COMPANY, INC.
READING, MASSACHUSETTS U. S. A.

First Published in English 1951
Revised Second Edition 1962
Revised Second Edition, Second Impression 1965

U. S. A. edition distributed by
Addison-Wesley Publishing Company Inc.
Reading, Massachusetts, U.S.A ,

Library of Congress Card Number 62–9181

PRINTED PHOTO-LITHO IN GREAT BRITAIN
BY D. R. HILLMAN & SONS LTD., FROME

PREFACE
TO THE SECOND ENGLISH EDITION

This book is devoted to the presentation of the theory of the electromagnetic and gravitational fields. In accordance with the general plan of our "Course of Theoretical Physics", we exclude from this volume problems of the electrodynamics of continuous media, and restrict the exposition to "microscopic electrodynamics", the electrodynamics of the vacuum and of point charges.

A complete, logically connected theory of the electromagnetic field includes the special theory of relativity, so the latter has been taken as the basis of the presentation. As the starting point of the derivation of the fundamental equations we take the variational principles, which make possible the achievement of maximum generality, unity and simplicity of the presentation.

The last two chapters are devoted to the presentation of the theory of gravitational fields, i.e., the general theory of relativity. The reader is not assumed to have any previous knowledge of tensor analysis, which is presented in parallel with the development of the theory.

The present edition has been extensively revised from the first English edition, which appeared in 1951.

We express our sincere gratitude to L. P. Gor'kov, I. E. Dzyaloshinskiĭ and L. P. Pitaevskiĭ for their assistance in checking formulas.

L. D. LANDAU, E. M. LIFSHITZ

Moscow, September 1961

CONTENTS

CHAPTER 1

THE PRINCIPLE OF RELATIVITY

§ 1. Velocity of propagation of interaction

For the description of processes taking place in nature, one must have a *system of reference*. By a system of reference we understand a system of coordinates serving to indicate the position of a particle in space, as well as clocks fixed in this system serving to indicate the time.

There exist systems of reference in which a freely moving body, i.e., a moving body which is not acted upon by external forces, proceeds with constant velocity. Such reference systems are said to be *inertial*.

If two reference systems move uniformly relative to each other, and if one of them is an inertial system, then clearly the other is also inertial (in this system too every free motion will be linear and uniform). In this way one can obtain arbitrarily many inertial systems of reference, moving uniformly relative to one another.

Experiment shows that the so-called *principle of relativity* is valid. According to this principle all the laws of nature are identical in all inertial systems of reference. In other words, the equations expressing the laws of nature are invariant with respect to transformations of coordinates and time from one inertial system to another. This means that the equation describing any law of nature, when written in terms of coordinates and time in different inertial reference systems, has one and the same form.

The interaction of material particles is described in ordinary mechanics by means of a potential energy of interaction, which appears as a function of the coordinates of the interacting particles. It is easy to see that this manner of describing interactions contains the assumption of instantaneous propagation of interactions. For the forces exerted on each of the particles by the other particles at a particular instant of time depend, according to this description, only on the positions of the particles at this one instant. A change in the position of any of the interacting particles influences the other particles immediately.

However, experiment shows that instantaneous interactions do not exist in nature. Thus a mechanics based on the assumption of instantaneous propagation of interactions contains within itself a certain inaccuracy. In actuality, if any change takes place in one of the interacting bodies, it will influence the other bodies only after the lapse of a certain interval of time. It is only after this time interval that processes caused by the initial change begin to take place in the second body. Dividing the distance between the two bodies by this time interval, we obtain the *velocity of propagation of the interaction.*

We note that this velocity should, strictly speaking, be called the *maximum* velocity of propagation of interaction. It determines only that interval of time after which a change occurring in one body *begins* to manifest itself in another. It is clear that the existence of a maximum velocity of propagation of interactions implies, at the same time, that motions of bodies with greater velocity than this are in general impossible in nature. For if such a motion could occur, then by means of it one could realize an interaction with a velocity exceeding the maximum possible velocity of propagation of interactions.

Interactions propagating from one particle to another are frequently called "signals", sent out from the first particle and "informing" the second particle of changes which the first has experienced. The velocity of propagation of interaction is then referred to as the *signal velocity.*

From the principle of relativity it follows in particular that the velocity of propagation of interactions is the *same* in *all* inertial systems of reference. Thus the velocity of propagation of interactions is a universal constant. This constant velocity (as we shall show later) is also the velocity of light in empty space. The velocity of light is usually designated by the letter c, and its numerical value according to the latest measurements is

$$c = 2.99792 \times 10^{10} \text{ cm/sec.} \tag{1.1}$$

The large value of this velocity explains the fact that in practice classical mechanics appears to be sufficiently accurate in most cases. The velocities with which we have occasion to deal are usually so small compared with the velocity of light that the assumption that the latter is infinite does not materially affect the accuracy of the results.

The combination of the principle of relativity with the finiteness of the velocity of propagation of interactions is called the *principle of relativity of Einstein* (it was formulated by Einstein in 1905) in contrast to the principle of relativity of Galileo, which was based on an infinite velocity of propagation of interactions.

The mechanics based on the Einsteinian principle of relativity (we shall usually refer to it simply as the principle of relativity) is called *relativistic.* In the limiting case when the velocities of the moving bodies are small compared with the velocity of light we can neglect the effect on the motion of the finiteness of the velocity of propagation. Then relativistic mechanics goes over into the usual mechanics, based on the assumption of instantaneous propagation of interactions; this mechanics is called *Newtonian* or *classical.* The limiting transition from relativistic to classical mechanics can be produced formally by the transition to the limit $c \to \infty$ in the formulas of relativistic mechanics.

In classical mechanics distance is already relative, i.e., the spatial relations between different events depend on the system of reference in which they are described. The statement that two nonsimultaneous events occur at one and the same point in space or, in general, at a definite distance from each other, acquires a meaning only when we indicate the system of reference which is used.

On the other hand, time is absolute in classical mechanics; in other words, the properties of time are assumed to be independent of the system of reference; there is one time for all reference frames. This means that if any two phenomena occur simultaneously for any one observer, then they occur simultaneously also for all others. In general, the interval of time between two given events must be identical for all systems of reference.

It is easy to show, however, that the idea of an absolute time is in complete contradiction to the Einstein principle of relativity. For this it is sufficient to recall that in classical mechanics, based on the concept of an absolute time, a general law of combination of velocities is valid, according to which the velocity of a composite motion is simply equal to the (vector) sum of the velocities which constitute this motion. This law, being universal, should also be applicable to the propagation of interactions. From this it would follow that the velocity of propagation must be different in different inertial systems of reference, in contradiction to the principle of relativity. In this matter experiment completely confirms the principle of relativity. Measurements first performed by Michelson (1881) showed complete lack of dependence of the velocity of light on its direction of propagation; whereas according to classical mechanics the velocity of light should be smaller in the direction of the earth's motion than in the opposite direction.

Thus the principle of relativity leads to the result that time is not absolute. Time elapses differently in different systems of reference. Consequently the statement that a definite time interval has elapsed between two given events acquires meaning only when the reference frame to which this statement applies is indicated. In particular, events which are simultaneous in one reference frame will not be simultaneous in other frames.

To clarify this, it is instructive to consider the following simple example. Let us look at two inertial reference systems K and K' with coordinate axes XYZ and $X'Y'Z'$ respectively, where the system K' moves relative to K along the $X(X')$ axis (Fig. 1.1).

Suppose signals start out from some point A on the X' axis in two opposite directions. Since the velocity of propagation of a signal in the K' system, as in all inertial systems, is equal (for both directions) to c, the signals will reach points B and C, equidistant from A, at one and the same time (in the K' system). But it is easy to see that the same two events (arrival of the signal at B and C) can by no means be simultaneous for an observer in the K system.

In fact, the velocity of the signal relative to the K system has, according to the principle of relativity, the same value c, and since the point B moves (relative to the K system) toward the source of its signal, while the point C moves in the direction away from the signal (sent from A to C), in the K system the signal will reach point B earlier than point C.

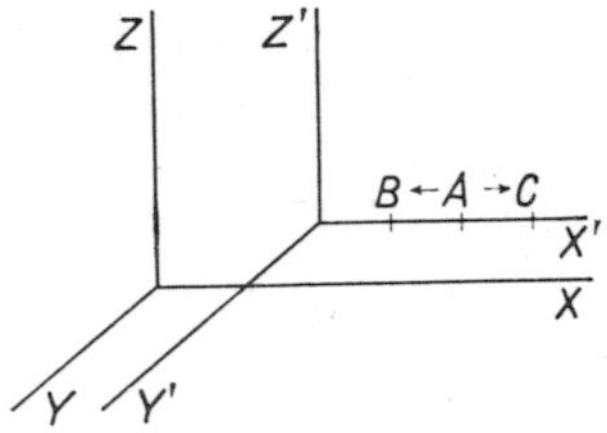

FIG. 1.

Thus the principle of relativity of Einstein introduces very drastic and fundamental changes in basic physical concepts. The notions of space and time derived by us from our daily experiences are only approximations linked to the fact that in daily life we happen to deal only with velocities which are very small compared with the velocity of light.

§ 2. **Intervals**

In what follows we shall frequently use the concept of an *event*. An event is described by the place where it occurred and the time when it occurred. Thus an event occurring in a certain material particle is defined by the three coordinates of that particle and the time when the event occurs.

It is frequently useful for reasons of presentation to use a fictitious four-dimensional space, on the axes of which are marked three space coordinates and the time. In this space events are represented by points, called *world points*. In this fictitious four-dimensional space there corresponds to each particle a certain line, called a *world line*. The points of this line determine the coordinates of the particle at all moments of time. It is easy to show that to a particle in uniform rectilinear motion there corresponds a straight world line.

We now express the principle of the invariance of the velocity of light in mathematical form. For this purpose we consider two reference systems K and K' moving relative to each other with constant velocity. We choose the coordinate axes, so that the axes X and X' coincide, while the Y and Z axes are parallel to Y' and Z'; we designate the time in the systems K and K' by t and t'.

Let the first event consist of sending out a signal, propagating with light velocity, from a point having coordinates $x_1 y_1 z_1$ in the K system, at time t_1 in this system. We observe the propagation of this signal in the K system.

Let the second event consist of the arrival of the signal at point $x_2y_2z_2$ at the moment of time t_2. The signal propagates with velocity c; the distance covered by it is therefore $c(t_1-t_2)$. On the other hand, this same distance equals $[(x_2-x_1)^2+(y_2-y_1)^2+(z_2-z_1)^2]^{\frac{1}{2}}$. Thus we can write the following relation between the coordinates of the two events in the K system:

$$(x_2-x_1)^2+(y_2-y_1)^2+(z_2-z_1)^2-c^2(t_2-t_1)^2 = 0. \tag{2.1}$$

The same two events, i.e., the propagation of the signal, can be observed from the K' system:

Let the coordinates of the first event in the K' system be $x_1'y_1'z_1't_1'$, and of the second: $x_2'y_2'z_2't_2'$. Since the velocity of light is the same in the K and K' systems, we have, similarly to (2.1):

$$(x_2'-x_1')^2+(y_2'-y_1')^2+(z_2'-z_1')^2-c^2(t_2'-t_1')^2 = 0. \tag{2.2}$$

If $x_1y_1z_1t_1$ and $x_2y_2z_2t_2$ are the coordinates of *any* two events, then the quantity

$$s_{12} = [c^2(t_2-t_1)^2-(x_2-x_1)^2-(y_2-y_1)^2-(z_2-z_1)^2]^{\frac{1}{2}} \tag{2.3}$$

is called the *interval* between these two events.

Thus it follows from the principle of invariance of the velocity of light that if the interval between two events is zero in one coordinate system, then it is equal to zero in all other systems.

If two events are infinitely close to each other, then the interval ds between them is

$$ds^2 = c^2\,dt^2-dx^2-dy^2-dz^2. \tag{2.4}$$

For mathematical convenience and to give our equations a more symmetrical form, we shall frequently use in place of the time t another variable τ, associated with t by the relation:

$$\tau = ict. \tag{2.5}$$

Then

$$s_{12}^2 = -[(x_2-x_1)^2+(y_2-y_1)^2+(z_2-z_1)^2+(\tau_2-\tau_1)^2], \tag{2.6}$$

$$ds^2 = -(dx^2+dy^2+dz^2+d\tau^2). \tag{2.7}$$

In accordance with this derivation we now mark the coordinate axes in our fictitious four-dimensional space not with x, y, z, t, but with x, y, z, τ. As is easily seen, $-s_{12}^2$ can be interpreted as the square of the distance between the points $x_1y_1z_1\tau_1$ and $x_2y_2z_2\tau_2$ in this space, and $-ds^2$ as the square of the line element.†

As already shown, if $ds = 0$ in one inertial system, then $ds' = 0$ in any other system. On the other hand, ds and ds' are infinitesimals of the same

† The four-dimensional geometry described by the quadratic forms (2·4) and (2·7) was introduced by H. Minkowski, in connection with the theory of relativity.

order. From these two conditions it follows that ds^2 and ds'^2 must be proportional to each other:

$$ds^2 = a\,ds'^2$$

where the coefficient a can depdnd only on the absolute value of the relative velocity of the two inertial systems. It cannot depend on the coordinates or the time, since then different points in space and different moments in time would not be equivalent, which would be in contradiction to the homogeneity of space and time. Similarly, it cannot depend on the direction of the relative velocity, since that would contradict the isotropy of space.

Let us consider three reference systems K, K_1, K_2, and let V_1 and V_2 be the velocities of systems K_1 and K_2 relative to K. We then have:

$$ds^2 = a(V_1)\,ds_1^2, \qquad ds^2 = a(V_2)\,ds_2^2.$$

Similarly we can write

$$ds_1^2 = a(V_{12})\,ds_2^2,$$

where V_{12} is the absolute value of the velocity of K_2 relative to K_1. Comparing these relations with one another, we find that we must have

$$\frac{a(V_2)}{a(V_1)} = a(V_{12}). \tag{2.8}$$

But V_{12} depends not only on the absolute values of the vectors $\mathbf{V}_1$ and $\mathbf{V}_2$, but also on the angle between them. However, this angle does not appear on the left side of formula (2.8). It is therefore clear that this formula can be correct only if the function $a(V)$ reduces to a constant, which is equal to unity according to this same formula.

Thus,

$$ds^2 = ds'^2,$$

and from the equality of the infinitesimal intervals there follows the equality of finite intervals: $s = s'$.

Thus we arrive at a very important result: the interval between two events is the same in all inertial systems of reference, i.e., it is invariant under transformation from one inertial system to any other. This invariance is the mathematical expression of the constancy of the velocity of light.

Again let $x_1y_1z_1t_1$ and $x_2y_2z_2t_2$ be the coordinates of two events in a certain reference system K. Does there exist a coordinate system K', in which these two events occur at one and the same point in space?

We introduce the notation

$$t_2 - t_1 = t_{12}, \quad (x_2-x_1)^2+(y^2-y_1)^2+(z_2-z_1)^2 = l_{12}^2.$$

Then the interval between events in the K system is:

$$s_{12}^2 = c^2 t_{12}^2 - l_{12}^2$$

and in the K' system

$$s'^2_{12} = c^2 t'^2_{12} - l'^2_{12},$$

whereupon, because of the invariance of intervals,

$$c^2 t^2_{12} - l^2_{12} = c^2 t'^2_{12} - l'^2_{12}.$$

We want the two events to occur at the same point in the K' system, that is, we require $l'_{12} = 0$. Then

$$s^2_{12} = c^2 t^2_{12} - l^2_{12} = c^2 t'^2_{12} > 0.$$

Consequently a system of reference with the required property exists if $s^2_{12} > 0$, that is, if the interval between the two events is a real number. Real intervals are said to be *timelike*.

Thus, if the interval between two events is timelike, then there exists a system of reference in which the two events occur at one and the same place. The time which elapses between the two events in this system is

$$t'_{12} = \frac{1}{c}\sqrt{c^2 t^2_{12} - l^2_{12}} = \frac{s_{12}}{c}. \tag{2.9}$$

If two events occur in one and the same body, then the interval between them is always timelike, for the distance which the body moves between the two events cannot be greater than ct_{12}, since the velocity of the body cannot exceed c. So we have always

$$l_{12} < ct_{12}.$$

Let us now ask whether or not we can find a system of reference in which the two events occur at one and the same time. As before, we have for the K and K' systems $c^2 t^2_{12} - l^2_{12} = c^2 t'^2_{12} - l'^2_{12}$. We want to have $t'_{12} = 0$, so that

$$s^2_{12} = -l'^2_{12} < 0.$$

Consequently the required system can be found only for the case when the interval s_{12} between the two events is an imaginary number. Imaginary intervals are said to be *spacelike*.

Thus if the interval between two events is spacelike, there exists a reference system in which the two events occur simultaneously. The distance between the points where the events occur in this system is

$$l'_{12} = \sqrt{l^2_{12} - c^2 t^2_{12}} = is_{12}. \tag{2.10}$$

The division of intervals into space-and timelike intervals is, because of their invariance, an absolute concept. This means that the timelike or spacelike character of an interval is independent of the reference system.

Let us take some event O as our origin of time and space coordinates. In other words, in the four-dimensional system of coordinates, the axes of which are marked x, y, z, t, the world point of the event O is the origin of coordinates. Let us now consider what relation other events bear to the given event O. For visualization, we shall consider only one space dimension and the time, marking them on two axes (Fig. 2). Uniform rectilinear motion of a particle, passing through $x = 0$ at $t = 0$, is represented by a straight line going through O and inclined to the t axis at an angle whose tangent is the velocity of the particle. Since the maximum possible velocity

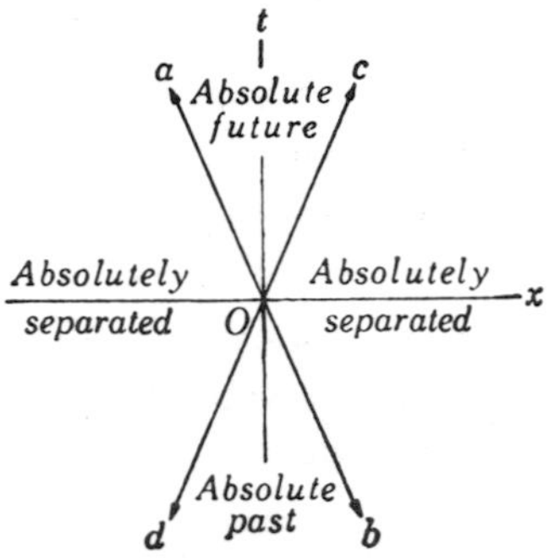

FIG. 2.

is c, there is a maximum angle which this line can subtend with the t axis. In Fig. 2 are shown the two lines representing the propagation of two signals (with the velocity of light) in opposite directions passing through the event O (i.e., going through $x=0$ at $t=0$). All lines representing the motion of particles can lie only in the regions aOc and dOb. On the lines ab and cd, $x = \pm ct$. First consider events whose world points lie within the region aOc. It is easy to show that for all the points of this region $c^2t^2 - x^2 > 0$. In other words, the interval between any event in this region and the event O is timelike. In this region $t > 0$, i.e., all the events in this region occur "after" the event O. But two events which are separated by a timelike interval cannot occur simultaneously in any reference system. Consequently it is impossible to find a reference system in which any of the events in region aOc occurred "before" the event O, i.e., at time $t < 0$. Thus all the events in region aOc are future events relative to O in *all* reference systems. Therefore this region can be called the *absolute future* relative to O.

In exactly the same way, all events in the region bOd are in the *absolute past* relative to O; i.e., events in this region occur before the event O in all systems of reference.

Next consider regions dOa and cOb. The interval between any event in this region and the event O is spacelike. These events occur at different points in space in every reference system. Therefore these regions can be said to be *absolutely remote* relative to O. However, the concepts "simultaneous," "earlier," and "later" are relative for these regions. For any event in these regions there exist systems of reference in which it occurs after the event

O, systems in which it occurs earlier than O, and finally one reference system in which it occurs simultaneously with O.

Note that if we consider all three space coordinates instead of just one, then instead of the two intersecting lines of Fig. 2 we would have a "cone" $x^2+y^2+z^2-c^2t^2 = 0$ in the four-dimensional coordinate system x, y, z, t, the axis of the cone coinciding with the t axis. (This cone is called the *light cone.*) The regions of absolute future and absolute past are then represented by the two interior portions of this cone.

Two events can be related causally to each other only if the interval between them is timelike; this follows immediately from the fact that no interaction can propagate with a velocity greater than the velocity of light. As we have just seen, it is precisely for these events that the concepts "earlier" and "later" have an absolute significance, which is a necessary condition for the concepts of cause and effect to have meaning.

§ 3. Proper time

Suppose that in a certain inertial reference system we observe clocks which are moving relative to us in an arbitrary manner. At each different moment of time this motion can be considered as uniform. Thus at each moment of time we can introduce a coordinate system rigidly linked to the moving clocks, which with the clocks constitutes an inertial reference system.

In the course of an infinitesimal time interval dt (as read by a clock in our rest frame) the moving clocks go a distance $\sqrt{dx^2+dy^2+dz^2}$. Let us ask what time interval dt' is indicated for this period by the moving clocks. In a system of coordinates linked to the moving clocks, the latter are at rest, i.e., $dx' = dy' = dz' = 0$. Because of the invariance of intervals

$$ds^2 = c^2\,dt^2-dx^2-dy^2-dz^2 = c^2\,dt'^2,$$

from which

$$dt' = \frac{ds}{c} = \frac{1}{c}\sqrt{c^2\,dt^2-dx^2-dy^2-dz^2}$$

or else

$$dt' = dt\sqrt{1-\frac{dx^2+dy^2+dz^2}{c^2\,dt^2}}.$$

But

$$\frac{dx^2+dy^2+dz^2}{dt^2} = v^2,$$

where v is the velocity of the moving clocks; therefore

$$dt' = \frac{ds}{c} = dt\sqrt{1-\frac{v^2}{c^2}}. \tag{3.1}$$

Integrating this expression, we can obtain the time interval indicated by the moving clocks when the elapsed time according to a clock at rest is $t_2 - t_1$:

$$t_2' - t_1' = \int_{t_1}^{t_2} dt \sqrt{1 - \frac{v^2}{c^2}}. \tag{3.2}$$

The time read by a clock moving with a given object is called the *proper time* for this object. Formulas (3.1) and (3.2) express the proper time in terms of the time for a system of reference from which the motion is observed.

As we see from (3.1) or (3.2), the proper time of a moving object is always less than the corresponding interval in the rest system. In other words, moving clocks go more slowly than those at rest.

Suppose some clocks are moving in uniform rectilinear motion relative to an inertial system K. A reference frame K' linked to the latter is also inertial. Then from the point of view of an observer in the K system the clocks in the K' system fall behind. And conversely, from the point of view of the K' system, the clocks in K lag. To convince ourselves that there is no contradiction, let us note the following. In order to establish that the clocks in the K' system lag behind those in the K system, we must proceed in the following fashion. Suppose that at a certain moment the clock in K' passes by the clock in K, and at that moment the readings of the two clocks coincide. To compare the rates of the two clocks in K and K' we must once more compare the readings of the same moving clock with the clocks in K. But now we compare this clock with *different* clocks in K—with those past which the clock in K' goes at this new time. Then we find that the clock in K' lags behind the clock in K with which it is being compared. We see that to compare the rates of clocks in two reference frames we require several clocks in one frame and one in the other, and that therefore this process is not symmetric with respect to the two systems. The clock that appears to lag is always the one which is being compared with different clocks in the other system.

If we have two clocks, one of which describes a closed path returning to the starting point (the position of the clock which remained at rest), then clearly the moving clock appears to lag relative to the one at rest. The converse reasoning, in which the moving clock would be considered to be at rest (and vice versa) is now impossible, since the clock describing a closed trajectory does not carry out a uniform rectilinear motion, so that a coordinate system linked to it will not be inertial.

Since the laws of nature are the same only for inertial reference frames, the frames linked to the clock at rest (inertial frame) and to the moving clock (non-inertial) have different properties, and the argument which leads to the result that the clock at rest must lag is not valid.

The time interval read by a clock is equal to the integral $\frac{1}{c}\int_a^b ds$, taken along the world line of the clock. If the clock is at rest then its world line is clearly a line parallel to the t axis; if the clock carries out a nonuniform motion in a closed path and returns to its starting point, then its world line will be a curve passing through the two points, on the straight world line of a clock at rest, corresponding to the beginning and end of the motion. On the other hand, we saw that the clock at rest always indicates a greater time interval than the moving one. Thus we arrive at the result that the integral $\int_a^b ds$, taken between a given pair of world points, has its maximum value if it is taken along the straight world line joining these two points.†

§ 4. The Lorentz transformation

Our purpose is now to obtain the formula of transformation from one inertial reference system to another, that is, a formula by means of which, knowing the coordinates x, y, z, t, of a certain event in the K system, we can find the coordinates x', y', z', t' of the same event in another inertial system K'.

In classical mechanics this question is resolved very simply. Because of the absolute nature of time we there have $t = t'$; if, furthermore, the coordinate axes are chosen as usual (axes X, X' coincident, Y, Z axes parallel to Y', Z', motion along X, X') then the coordinates y, z clearly are equal to y', z', while the coordinates x and x' differ by the distance traversed by one system relative to the other. If the time origin is chosen as the moment when the two coordinate systems coincide, and if the velocity of the K' system relative to K is V, then this distance is Vt. Thus

$$x = x' + Vt, \quad y = y', \quad z = z', \quad t = t'. \tag{4.1}$$

This formula is called the *Galileo transformation*. It is easy to verify that this transformation, as was to be expected, does not satisfy the requirements of the theory of relativity; it does not leave the interval between events invariant.

We shall obtain the relativistic transformation precisely as a consequence of the requirement that it leave the interval between events invariant.

If we use the quantity $\tau = ict$, which is convenient for the following presentation, then as we saw in § 2, the interval between events can be looked

† It is assumed, of course, that the points a and b and the curves joining them are such that all elements ds along the curves are timelike.

This property of the integral $\int_a^b ds$ is connected with the fact that one of the coordinates is imaginary ($\tau = ict$); if all four coordinates were real then the integral would, of course, be a minimum along the straight line.

on as the distance between the corresponding pair of world points in a four-dimensional system of coordinates. Consequently we may say that the required transformation must leave unchanged all distances in the four-dimensional x, y, z, τ, space. But such transformations consist only of parallel displacements, and rotations of the coordinate system. Of these the displacement of the coordinate system parallel to itself is of no interest, since it leads only to a shift in the origin of the space coordinates and a change in the time reference point. Thus the required transformation must be expressible mathematically as a rotation of the four-dimensional x, y, z, τ, coordinate system.

Every rotation in the four-dimensional space can be resolved into six rotations, in the planes xy, zy, xz, τx, τy, τz (just as every rotation in ordinary space can be resolved into three rotations in the planes xy, zy, and xz). The first three of these rotations transform only the space coordinates; they correspond to the usual space rotations.

Let us consider a rotation in the τx plane; under this, the y and z coordinates do not change. If ψ is the angle of rotation, then the relation between the old and the new coordinates is given by the formula:

$$x = x' \cos\psi - \tau' \sin\psi, \qquad \tau = x' \sin\psi + \tau' \cos\psi. \tag{4.2}$$

We try to find the formula of transformation from an inertial reference frame K to a system K' moving relative to K with velocity V along the x axis. In this case clearly only the coordinate x and the time τ are subject to change. Therefore this transformation must have the form (4.2). Now it remains only to determine the angle ψ, which can depend only on the relative velocity V.†

Let us consider the motion, in the K system, of the origin of the K' system. Then $x' = 0$ and formulas (4.2) take the form:

$$x = -\tau' \sin\psi, \qquad \tau = \tau' \cos\psi,$$

or dividing one by the other,

$$\frac{x}{\tau} = -\tan\psi.$$

But $\tau = ict$, and x/t is clearly the velocity V of the K' system relative to K. So

$$\tan\psi = i\frac{V}{c}.$$

From this

$$\sin\psi = \frac{i\dfrac{V}{c}}{\sqrt{1-\dfrac{V^2}{c^2}}}, \qquad \cos\psi = \frac{1}{\sqrt{1-\dfrac{V^2}{c^2}}}.$$

† Note that to avoid confusion we shall always use V to signify the constant relative velocity of two intertial systems, and v for the velocity of a moving particle, not necessarily constant.

Substituting in (4.2), we find:

$$x = \frac{x' - i\frac{V}{c}\tau'}{\sqrt{1-\frac{V^2}{c^2}}}, \quad y = y', \quad z = z', \quad \tau = \frac{\tau' + i\frac{V}{c}x'}{\sqrt{1-\frac{V^2}{c^2}}}.$$

Now setting $\tau = ict$, $\tau' = ict'$, we have finally

$$x = \frac{x' + Vt'}{\sqrt{1-\frac{V^2}{c^2}}}, \quad y = y', \quad z = z', \quad t = \frac{t' + \frac{V}{c^2}x'}{\sqrt{1-\frac{V^2}{c^2}}}. \tag{4.3}$$

This is the required transformation formula. It is called the *Lorentz transformation*, and is of fundamental importance for what follows.

The inverse formulas, expressing x', y', z', t' in terms of x, y, z, t, are most easily obtained by changing V to $-V$ (since the K system moves with velocity $-V$ relative to the K' system). The same formulas can be obtained directly by solving equations (4.3) for x', y', z', t'.

It is easy to see from (4.3) that on making the transition to the limit $c \to \infty$ and classical mechanics, the formula for the Lorentz transformation actually goes over into the Galileo transformation.

For $V > c$ in formula (4.3) the coordinates x, t are imaginary; this corresponds to the fact that motion with a velocity greater than the velocity of light is impossible. Moreover, one cannot use a reference system moving with the velocity of light — in that case the denominators in (4.3) would go to zero.

For velocities V small compared with the velocity of light, we can use in place of (4.3) the approximate formulas:

$$x = x' + Vt', \quad y = y', \quad z = z', \quad t = t' + \frac{V}{c^2}x'. \tag{4.4}$$

Suppose there is a rod at rest in the K system, parallel to the X axis. Let its length, measured in this system, be $\Delta x = x_2 - x_1$ (x_2 and x_1 are the coordinates of the two ends of the rod in the K system). We now determine the length of this rod as measured in the K' system. To do this we must find the coordinates of the two ends of the rod (x_2' and x_1') in this system at one and the same time t'. From (4.3) we find:

$$x_1 = \frac{x_1' + Vt'}{\sqrt{1-\frac{V^2}{c^2}}}, \quad x_2 = \frac{x_2' + Vt'}{\sqrt{1-\frac{V^2}{c^2}}}.$$

The length of the rod in the K' system is $\Delta x' = x_2' - x_1'$; subtracting x_1 from x_2, we find

$$\Delta x = \frac{\Delta x'}{\sqrt{1-\frac{V^2}{c^2}}}.$$

The *proper length* of a rod is its length in a reference system in which it is at rest. Let us denote it by $l_0 = \Delta x$, and the length of the rod in any other reference frame K' by l. Then

$$l = l_0\sqrt{1-\frac{V^2}{c^2}}. \tag{4.5}$$

Thus a rod has its greatest length in the reference system in which it is at rest. Its length in a system in which it moves with velocity V is decreased by the factor $\sqrt{1-V^2/c^2}$. This result of the theory of relativity is called the *Lorentz contraction.*

Since the transverse dimensions do not change because of its motion, the volume $\mathcal{V}$ of a body decreases according to the similar formula

$$\mathcal{V} = \mathcal{V}_0\sqrt{1-\frac{V^2}{c^2}}, \tag{4.6}$$

where $\mathcal{V}_0$ is the *proper volume* of the body.

From the Lorentz transformation we can obtain anew the results already known to us concerning the proper time (§ 3). Suppose a clock to be at rest in the K' system. We take two events occurring at one and the same point x', y', z' in space in the K' system. The time between these events in the K' system is $\Delta t' = t_2' - t_1'$. Now we find the time Δt which elapses between these two events in the K system. From (4.3), we have

$$t_1 = \frac{t_1' + \frac{V}{c^2}x'}{\sqrt{1-\frac{V^2}{c^2}}}, \qquad t_2 = \frac{t_2' + \frac{V}{c^2}x'}{\sqrt{1-\frac{V^2}{c^2}}},$$

or, subtracting one from the other,

$$t_2 - t_1 = \Delta t = \frac{\Delta t'}{\sqrt{1-\frac{V^2}{c^2}}},$$

in complete agreement with (3.1).

Finally we mention another general property of Lorentz transformations which distinguishes them from Galilean transformations. The latter have the general property of commutativity, i.e. the combined result of two successive Galilean transformations (with different velocities $\mathbf{V}_1$ and $\mathbf{V}_2$) does not depend on the order in which the transformations are performed. On the other hand, the result of two successive Lorentz transformations does depend, in general, on their order. This is already apparent purely mathematically from our formal description of these transformations as rotations of the four-dimensional coordinate system: we know that the result of two rotations (about different axes) depends on the order in which they are carried out. The sole exception is the case of transformations with parallel vectors $\mathbf{V}_1$ and $\mathbf{V}_2$ (which are equivalent to two rotations of the four-dimensional coordinate system about the same axis).

§ 5. Transformation of velocities

In the preceding section we obtained formulas which enable us to find from the coordinates of an event in one reference frame, the coordinates of the same event in a second reference frame. Now we find formulas relating the velocity of a material particle in one reference system to its velocity in a second reference system.

Let us suppose once again that the K' system moves relative to the K system with velocity V along the x axis. Let $v_x = dx/dt$ be the component of the particle velocity in the K system and $v'_x = dx'/dt'$ the velocity component of the same particle in the K' system. From (4.3), we have

$$dx = \frac{dx' + V\,dt'}{\sqrt{1-\frac{V^2}{c^2}}}, \quad dy = dy', \quad dz = dz', \quad dt = \frac{dt' + \frac{V}{c^2}dx'}{\sqrt{1-\frac{V^2}{c^2}}}.$$

Dividing the first three equations by the fourth, we find

$$\frac{dx}{dt} = \frac{dx' + V\,dt'}{dt' + \frac{V}{c^2}dx'}, \quad \frac{dy}{dt} = \frac{dy'\sqrt{1-\frac{V^2}{c^2}}}{dt' + \frac{V}{c^2}dx'}, \quad \frac{dz}{dt} = \frac{dz'\sqrt{1-\frac{V^2}{c^2}}}{dt' + \frac{V}{c^2}dx'},$$

or dividing the numerator and denominator of the right sides of these equations by dt',

$$v_x = \frac{v'_x + V}{1 + v'_x\frac{V}{c^2}}, \quad v_y = \frac{v'_y\sqrt{1-\frac{V^2}{c^2}}}{1 + v'_x\frac{V}{c^2}}, \quad v_z = \frac{v'_z\sqrt{1-\frac{V^2}{c^2}}}{1 + v'_x\frac{V}{c^2}}. \tag{5.1}$$

These formulas determine the transformation of velocities. They describe the law of composition of velocities in the theory of relativity. In the limiting case of $c \to \infty$, they go over into the formulas $v_x = v'_x + V$, $v_y = v'_y$, $v_z = v'_z$ of classical mechanics.

In the special case of motion of a particle parallel to the X axis, $v_x = v$, $v_y = v_z = 0$. Then $v'_y = v'_z = 0$, $v'_x = v'$, to that

$$v = \frac{v'+V}{1+v'\dfrac{V}{c^2}}. \tag{5.2}$$

It is easy to convince oneself that, according to this formula, the sum of two velocities each smaller than the velocity of light is again not greater than the light velocity.

For a velocity V significantly smaller than the velocity of light (the velocity v can be arbitrary), we have approximately, two terms of order V/c:

$$v_x = v'_x+V\left(1-\frac{v'^2_x}{c^2}\right), \quad v_y = v'_y-v'_x v'_y\frac{V}{c^2}, \quad v_z = v'_z-v'_x v'_z\frac{V}{c^2}.$$

These three formulas can be written as a single vector formula

$$\mathbf{v} = \mathbf{v}'+\mathbf{V}-\frac{1}{c^2}(\mathbf{V}\cdot\mathbf{v}')\mathbf{v}' \tag{5.3}$$

We may point out that in the relativistic law of addition of velocities (5.1) the two velocities $\mathbf{v}'$ and $\mathbf{V}$ which are combined enter unsymmetrically (provided they are not both directed along the x axis). This fact is related to the noncommutativity of Lorentz transformations which we mentioned in the preceding Section.

Let us choose our coordinate axes so that the velocity of the particle at the given moment lies in the XY plane. Then the velocity of the particle in the K system has components $v_x = v\cos\theta$, $v_y = v\sin\theta$, and in the K' system $v'_x = v'\cos\theta'$, $v'_y = v'\sin\theta'$ (v, v', θ, θ' are the absolute values and the angles subtended with the X, X' axes respectively in the K, K' systems). With the help of formula (5.1), we then find

$$\tan\theta = \frac{v'\sqrt{1-\dfrac{V^2}{c^2}}\sin\theta'}{v'\cos\theta'+V}. \tag{5.4}$$

This formula describes the change in the direction of the velocity on transforming from one reference system to another.

Let us consider a very important special case of this formula, namely, the deviation of light in transforming to a new reference system — a phenomenon known as the *aberration of light*. In this case $v = v' = c$, so that the preceding formula goes over into

$$\tan\theta = \frac{\sqrt{1-\dfrac{V^2}{c^2}}}{\dfrac{V}{c}+\cos\theta'}\sin\theta'. \tag{5.5}$$

From the same transformation formulas (5.1) it is easy to obtain for $\sin\theta$ and $\cos\theta$:

$$\sin\theta = \frac{\sqrt{1-\dfrac{V^2}{c^2}}}{1+\dfrac{V}{c}\cos\theta'}\sin\theta', \qquad \cos\theta = \frac{\cos\theta'+\dfrac{V}{c}}{1+\dfrac{V}{c}\cos\theta'}. \tag{5.6}$$

In case $V \ll c$, we find from this formula, correct to terms of order V/c:

$$\sin\theta - \sin\theta' = -\frac{V}{c}\sin\theta'\cos\theta'.$$

Introducing the angle $\Delta\theta = \theta'-\theta$ (the aberration angle), we find to the same order of accuracy

$$\Delta\theta = \frac{V}{c}\sin\theta', \tag{5.7}$$

which is the well-known elementary formula for the aberration of light.

PROBLEMS

1. The relative velocity of two particles is defined in relativistic mechanics as the velocity of one of them in the system of reference in which the other is at rest. Find the absolute magnitude of this velocity.

Solution: The components of the relative velocity are given by formulas (5.1), in which we must set $\mathbf{v}' = \mathbf{v}_1$, $\mathbf{V} = -\mathbf{v}_2$, where $\mathbf{v}_1, \mathbf{v}_2$ are the velocities of the two particles in the original coordinate system. The square of its absolute value can be written as:

$$v_{\text{rel}}^2 = \frac{(\mathbf{v}_1-\mathbf{v}_2)^2 - \dfrac{1}{c^2}(\mathbf{v}_1\times\mathbf{v}_2)^2}{\left(1-\dfrac{\mathbf{v}_1\cdot\mathbf{v}_2}{c^2}\right)^2}. \tag{1}$$

Note that this expression is symmetric in $\mathbf{v}_1$ and $\mathbf{v}_2$, i.e. the absolute value of the relative velocity does not depend on our choice of the particle with respect to which is it defined. (Of course, the direction of the vector $\mathbf{v}_{\text{rel}}$ does depend on this choice).

2. Find the "element of length" in relativistic "velocity space".

Solution: The required "element of length" dl_v is the relative velocity of two points having velocities $\mathbf{v}$ and $\mathbf{v}+d\mathbf{v}$. We therefore find from (1):

$$dl_v^2 = \frac{(d\mathbf{v})^2 - \dfrac{1}{c^2}(\mathbf{v}\times d\mathbf{v})^2}{\left(1-\dfrac{v^2}{c^2}\right)^2} = \frac{dv^2}{\left(1-\dfrac{v^2}{c^2}\right)^2} + \frac{v^2}{\left(1-\dfrac{v^2}{c^2}\right)}(d\theta^2+\sin^2\theta\, d\phi^2),$$

where θ, ϕ are the polar angle and azimuth of $\mathbf{v}$. If we introduce the variable χ in place of v by the equation $v/c = \tanh\chi$, the element of length becomes

$$dl_v^2 = c^2[d\chi^2 + \sinh^2\chi\,(d\theta^2+\sin^2\theta\, d\phi^2)].$$

From the geometrical point of view, this is the element of length in the three-dimensional space of Lobachevskii — the space of constant negative curvature (see § 106).

§ 6. Four-vectors

If we use as coordinates of an event the quantities x, y, z, τ, then we may consider x, y, z, τ, as components of a vector in four-dimensional space. The sum of the squares of these components, i.e. the square of the "length" of the vector, $x^2+y^2+z^2+\tau^2$, does not change under rotations of the four-dimensional system of coordinates, which include the Lorentz transformations as a special case.

The vector with components, x, y, z, τ, is called the *four-dimensional radius vector*. We shall denote its components by x_i, where $i = 1, 2, 3, 4$, so that

$$x_1 = x, \quad x_2 = y, \quad x_3 = z, \quad x_4 = \tau = ict.$$

Under a transformation from one inertial reference system to another i.e., under a Lorentz transformation, the components of the four-dimensional radius vector (or, as we shall write for brevity, the radius four-vector), transform according to (4.3), as follows:

$$x_1 = \frac{x_1' - i\frac{V}{c}x_4'}{\sqrt{1-\frac{V^2}{c^2}}}, \quad x_2 = x_2', \quad x_3 = x_3', \quad x_4 = \frac{x_4' + i\frac{V}{c}x_1'}{\sqrt{1-\frac{V^2}{c^2}}}. \tag{6.1}$$

A set of four quantities A_1, A_2, A_3, A_4, which under transformations of the four-dimensional coordinate system transform like the components x_i, is called a *four-vector* A_i. Under a Lorentz transformation,

$$A_1 = \frac{A_1' - i\frac{V}{c}A_4'}{\sqrt{1-\frac{V^2}{c^2}}}, \quad A_2 = A_2', \quad A_3 = A_3', \quad A_4 = \frac{A_4' + i\frac{V}{c}A_1'}{\sqrt{1-\frac{V^2}{c^2}}}. \tag{6.2}$$

Four-vectors have properties which are very similar to those of ordinary vectors. Thus it is easy to show that, like the ordinary scalar product of vectors, the sum of the products of the components of two four-vectors $A_1B_1+A_2B_2+A_3B_3+A_4B_4$ is a scalar. We shall denote this scalar product of vectors by A_iB_i, and in general we shall assume that if a particular Latin index appears twice then summation over this index from 1 to 4 is understood. Thus the square of the "absolute value" of a four-vector is expressed in the form A_iA_i or A_i^2. This method for denoting summation over "dummy" indices (in which the summation sign is omitted) is convenient and greatly simplifies the formulas.

We shall denote the components of three-dimensional vectors by Greek indices; repetition of a Greek index implies summation from 1 to 3 (e.g., $\mathbf{A}\cdot\mathbf{B} = A_\alpha B_\alpha$).

The first three components of a four-vector are called *space components* and the fourth a *time component*, in analogy to the radius four-vector. The time components of all four-vectors with which we have to deal are imaginary. We note that the square A_i^2 can be positive, negative or equal to zero, since there are imaginary quantities among the components A_i; such four-vectors are called spacelike, timelike and null-vectors, respectively.

A *four-dimensional tensor* (four-tensor) of the second rank is defined as an aggregate of sixteen quantities A_{ik} ($i, k = 1, 2, 3, 4$), which under a coordinate transformation

$$x_i = a_{ik} x'_k \tag{6.3}$$

transforms like a product of coordinates, that is, according to the formula:

$$A_{ik} = a_{im} a_{kl} A'_{ml}\,. \tag{6.4}$$

For the Lorentz transformation

$$(a_{ik}) = \left\{\begin{matrix} \dfrac{1}{\sqrt{1-\dfrac{V^2}{c^2}}} & 0 & 0 & \dfrac{-i\dfrac{V}{c}}{\sqrt{1-\dfrac{V^2}{c^2}}} \\ 0 & 1 & 0 & 0 \\ 0 & 0 & 1 & 0 \\ \dfrac{i\dfrac{V}{c}}{\sqrt{1-\dfrac{V^2}{c^2}}} & 0 & 0 & \dfrac{1}{\sqrt{1-\dfrac{V^2}{c^2}}} \end{matrix}\right\}. \tag{6.5}$$

The *unit four-tensor* δ_{ik} is defined as the tensor satisfying the condition that for any vector A_i,

$$\delta_{ik} A_k = A_i\,. \tag{6.6}$$

It is easy to see that the components of this tensor are

$$\delta_{ik} = \left\{\begin{matrix} 0 & \text{if} & i \neq k \\ 1 & \text{if} & i = k \end{matrix}\right\}. \tag{6.7}$$

From any tensor A_{ik}, we can form a scalar $A_{ii} = A_{11}+A_{22}+A_{33}+A_{44}$ called the *trace* of the tensor; clearly

$$\delta_{ii} = 4. \tag{6.8}$$

A tensor is said to be *symmetric* if $A_{ik} = A_{ki}$, and *antisymmetric* if $A_{ik} = -A_{ki}$. In an antisymmetric tensor the diagonal components, i.e., the components A_{11}, A_{22}, A_{33}, A_{44} equal zero, since, for example, we must have $A_{11} = -A_{11}$.

Tensor of higher rank can be defined by analogy to those of the second rank.

The completely antisymmetric unit four-tensor of the fourth rank is a tensor e_{iklm}, whose components change sign upon interchange of any two indices, so that the components different from zero are equal to ± 1. From the antisymmetry it follows that all components of this tensor for which two indices coincide are zero, so that only those components for which all four indices are different differ from zero. Let $e_{1234} = 1$; then clearly all the nonzero components of e_{iklm} equal $+1$ or -1, according as an even or odd number of interchanges (transpositions) brings the numbers i, k, l, m into the order 1, 2, 3, 4. We note, as is easily verified, that $e^2_{iklm} = 4!$

With respect to rotations of the coordinate system, the quantities e_{iklm} behave like the components of a tensor; but if we change the sign of one (or of three) coordinates, the components of e_{iklm}, being defined in the same way for all coordinate systems, do not change sign, whereas the components of a tensor should change sign. Therefore e_{iklm} is, strictly speaking, not a tensor, but is called a *pseudotensor*. Pseudotensors of arbitrary rank, in particular *pseudoscalars*, behave like tensors under all orthogonal transformations, except for those which cannot be produced by rotations (i.e., except under inversions — changes in the sign of the coordinates not reducible to a rotation).

If A_{ik} is an antisymmetric tensor, then the tensor A_{ik} and the pseudotensor $\frac{1}{2}e_{iklm}A_{lm}$ are said to be *dual* to each other. Similarly, $e_{iklm}A_m$ is an antisymmetric pseudotensor of the third rank, dual to the vector A_i. The product $\frac{1}{2}e_{iklm}A_{ik}A_{lm}$ of a tensor of the second rank and its dual is clearly a pseudoscalar.

In connection with this discussion we note certain analogous properties of three-dimensional vectors and tensors. The completely antisymmetric unit pseudotensor of the third rank is an aggregate of quantities $e_{\alpha\beta\gamma}$, which change sign for any interchange of two indices. Just as for e_{iklm}, all the components of $e_{\alpha\beta\gamma}$ are zero except those for which $\alpha \neq \beta \neq \gamma$. As for these components, $e_{123} = 1$; the others are clearly equal to 1 or -1, according as an even or odd number of transpositions change the order α, β, γ to 1, 2, 3.†

† For reference purposes, we give the formula for the product $e_{\alpha\beta\gamma}e_{\lambda\mu\nu}$. This product is a proper tensor of sixth rank and can therefore be expressed as a combination of products of components of the unit tensor $\delta_{\alpha\beta}$:

$$e_{\alpha\beta\gamma}e_{\lambda\mu\nu} = \delta_{\alpha\lambda}\delta_{\beta\mu}\delta_{\gamma\nu}+\delta_{\alpha\mu}\delta_{\beta\nu}\delta_{\gamma\lambda}+\delta_{\alpha\nu}\delta_{\beta\lambda}\delta_{\gamma\mu}-\delta_{\alpha\lambda}\delta_{\beta\nu}\delta_{\gamma\mu}-\delta_{\alpha\nu}\delta_{\beta\mu}\delta_{\gamma\lambda}-\delta_{\alpha\mu}\delta_{\beta\lambda}\delta_{\gamma\nu}.$$

Contracting this tensor on one, two, and three pairs of indices, we obtain:

$$e_{\alpha\beta\nu}e_{\lambda\mu\nu} = \delta_{\alpha\lambda}\delta_{\beta\mu}-\delta_{\alpha\mu}\delta_{\beta\lambda},$$
$$e_{\alpha\mu\nu}e_{\lambda\mu\nu} = 2\delta_{\alpha\lambda},$$
$$e_{\lambda\mu\nu}e_{\lambda\mu\nu} = 6.$$

Similar formulas can be written for the four-tensor e_{iklm}.

Under an inversion of the coordinate system, i.e., for a change in sing of all three coordinates, the components of an ordinary vector also change sign. Such vectors are said to be *polar*. The components of a vector which can be expressed as the vector product of two polar vectors do not change sign under inversion. Such vectors are said to be *axial*. The scalar product of a polar and an axial vector is not a true scalar but a *pseudoscalar*; it changes sign under inversion of the coordinate system. An axial vector is a pseudo-vector, dual to a certain antisymmetric tensor. Thus if $\mathbf{C} = \mathbf{A} \times \mathbf{B}$, then $C_\alpha = \frac{1}{2} e_{\alpha\beta\gamma} C_{\beta\gamma}$, where

$$C_{\beta\gamma} = A_\beta B_\gamma - A_\gamma B_\beta .$$

In three-space, integrations can be extended over volumes, surfaces, and curves. In four-dimensional space four types of integration are possible:

(1) Integral over a curve in four-space; the element of integration is the element of arc, i.e., the four-vector dx_i.

(2) Integral over a (two-dimensional) surface in four-space. As we know, in three-dimensional space the projected areas of the parallelogram spanned by the vectors d_r and $d_{r'}$ on the coordinate planes $x_\alpha x_\beta$ are $dx_\alpha dx'_\beta - dx_\beta dx'_\alpha$. Similarly in four-space an infinitesimal surface element is determined by the antisymmetric tensor of second rank, $df_{ik} = dx_i dx'_k - dx_k dx'_i$, whose components are equal to the projected area of the surface element on the coordinate planes. In three-space, as is well known, one uses as surface element in place of the tensor $df_{\alpha\beta}$, the vector df_α, dual to the tensor $df_{\alpha\beta}$; i.e., $df_\alpha = \frac{1}{2} e_{\alpha\beta\gamma}\, df_{\beta\gamma}$. Geometrically this is a vector normal to the surface element and equal in absolute magnitude to the area of the element. In four-sqace we cannot construct such a vector, but we can construct the tensor df^*_{ik} dual to the tensor df_{ik}, that is,

$$df^*_{ik} = \tfrac{1}{2} e_{iklm}\, df_{lm} . \tag{6.9}$$

Geometrically it describes an element of surface which is equal to and "normal" to the element df_{ik}. All lines lying in it are perpendicular to all lines on the element df_{ik}. It is easy to see that $df_{ik} df^*_{ik} = 0$.

(3) Integral over a hypersurface, i.e., over a three-dimensicnal manifold (three-dimensional volume). In three-dimensional space, the volume of the parallelepiped spanned by three vectors is equal to the determinant of the third rank made up of the components of these vectors. In four-space the projected volumes of the parallelepiped (i.e., the "ereas" of the hypersurface) spanned by three four-vectors dx_i, dx'_i, dx''_i are given by the determinants

$$dS_{ikl} = \begin{vmatrix} dx_i & dx'_i & dx''_i \\ dx_k & dx'_k & dx''_k \\ dx_l & dx'_l & dx''_l \end{vmatrix},$$

making up a tensor of rank three, antisymmetric in all three indices. As element of integration over the hypersurface, it is convenient to use the four-vector dS_i dual to the tensor dS_{ikl}:

$$dS_i = \tfrac{1}{6}\, e_{iklm}\, dS_{klm}, \qquad dS_{ikl} = e_{klmi}\, dS_m. \tag{6.10}$$

(It is easy to verify that the components dS_i are: $dS_1 = dS_{234}$, $dS_2 = dS_{143}$, etc.) Geometrically this four-vector is equal in absolute magnitude to the "area" of the element of hypersurface and is in the direction normal to this element (perpendicular to all lines lying in this element of hypersurface). It is clear that $dS_4 = dx\,dy\,dz$ is equal to the three-dimensional volume element dV, the projection of the hypersurface on the hyperplane $x_4 =$ const.

(4) Integral over a four-dimensional volume; the element of integration is the element of four-volume $d\Omega = dx_1 dx_2 dx_3 dx_4$.

A hypersurface is called spacelike if the normal at any of its points has a timelike direction (lies inside the light cone with its vertex at the same point); all the interval elements on such a hypersurface are spacelike. On the other hand, if the normal directions to a hypersurface lie outside the light cones, interval elements on it can be either timelike or spacelike.

Analogous to the theorems of Gauss and Stokes for three-dimensional integrals, there are theorems which enable us to transform four-dimensional integrals. Of these theorems, the following two will be useful to us later on. An integral over a closed hypersurface can be converted into an integral over the four-volume enclosed by it, by replacing the element of integration dS_i by the operator

$$dS_i \to d\Omega \frac{\partial}{\partial x_i}. \tag{6.11}$$

For example, for the integral of the vector A_i, we have

$$\oint A_i\, dS_i = \int \frac{\partial A_i}{\partial x_i}\, d\Omega.$$

This theorem is clearly the generalization of Gauss' theorem.

An integral over an ordinary surface is transformed into an integral over the hypersurface "spanning" it by replacing the element of integration df^*_{ik} by the operator

$$df^*_{ik} \to \left(dS_i \frac{\partial}{\partial x_k} - dS_k \frac{\partial}{\partial x_i}\right). \tag{6.12}$$

For example, for the integral of the antisymmetric tensor A_{ik}, we have

$$\tfrac{1}{2}\int A_{ik}\, df^*_{ik} = \tfrac{1}{2}\int \left(dS_i \frac{\partial A_{ik}}{\partial x_k} - dS_k \frac{\partial A_{ik}}{\partial x_i}\right) = \int dS_i \frac{\partial A_{ik}}{\partial x_k}. \tag{6.13}$$

For completeness we also give the rule for transformation of an integral over a closed four-dimensional curve into an integral over a surface spanning it; it consists of the replacement

$$dx_i \to df_{ki} \frac{\partial}{\partial x_k}. \tag{6.14}$$

For example, for the integral of a vector,

$$\oint A_i\, dx_i = \int df_{ki} \frac{\partial A_i}{\partial x_k} = \tfrac{1}{2} \int df_{ik} \left(\frac{\partial A_k}{\partial x_i} - \frac{\partial A_i}{\partial x_k} \right), \tag{6.15}$$

which is the generalization of Stokes' theorem.

§ 7. Four-dimensional velocity and acceleration

From the ordinary three-dimensional velocity vector one can form a four-vector. This four-dimensional velocity (*four-velocity*) of a particle is the vector

$$u_i = \frac{dx_i}{ds}. \tag{7.1}$$

To find its components, we note that according to (3.1),

$$ds = c\, dt \sqrt{1 - \frac{v^2}{c^2}},$$

where v is the ordinary three-dimensional velocity of the particle. Thus

$$u_1 = \frac{dx_1}{ds} = \frac{dx}{c\, dt \sqrt{1 - \frac{v^2}{c^2}}} = \frac{v_x}{c \sqrt{1 - \frac{v^2}{c^2}}}.$$

We find u_2, u_3, u_4 similarly, with the final result:

$$u_\alpha = \frac{v_\alpha}{c \sqrt{1 - \frac{v^2}{c^2}}}, \qquad u_4 = \frac{i}{\sqrt{1 - \frac{v^2}{c^2}}}. \tag{7.2}$$

Note that the four-velocity is a dimensionless quantity.

The components of the four-velocity are not independent. Noting that $dx_i^2 = -ds^2$, we have

$$u_i^2 = -1. \tag{7.3}$$

Geometrically, we may therefore say that u_i is a unit four-vector.

Similarly to the definition of the four-velocity, the second derivative

$$\frac{d^2 x_i}{ds^2} = \frac{du_i}{ds}$$

may be called the four-acceleration. Differentiating formula (7.3), we find:

$$u_i \frac{du_i}{ds} = 0, \tag{7.4}$$

i.e. the four-vectors of velocity and acceleration are "mutually perpendicular".

PROBLEM

Determine the relativistic uniformly accelerated motion, i.e. the rectilinear motion for which the acceleration w_0 in the proper reference frame (at each instant of time) remains constant.

Solution: In the reference frame in which the particle velocity is $v = 0$, it is easily shown that the components of the four-acceleration are w_0/c^2, 0, 0, 0 (where w_0 is the ordinary three-dimensional acceleration, which is assumed to be directed along the x axis). The relativistically invariant condition for uniform acceleration must be expressed by the constancy of the four-scalar which coincides with w_0 in the proper reference frame:

$$\left(\frac{du_i}{ds}\right)^2 = \text{const} \equiv \frac{w_0^2}{c^4}.$$

In the "fixed" frame, with respect to which the motion is observed, writing out the expression for $\left(\frac{du_i}{ds}\right)^2$ gives the equation

$$\frac{d}{dt}\frac{v}{\sqrt{1-\frac{v^2}{c^2}}} = w_0, \quad \text{or} \quad \frac{v}{\sqrt{1-\frac{v^2}{c^2}}} = w_0 t + \text{const}.$$

Setting $v = 0$ for $t = 0$, we find that const = 0, so that

$$v = \frac{w_0 t}{\sqrt{1+\frac{w_0^2 t^2}{c^2}}}.$$

Integrating once more and setting $x = 0$ for $t = 0$, we find:

$$x = \frac{c^2}{w_0}\left(\sqrt{1+\frac{w_0^2 t^2}{c^2}} - 1\right).$$

For $w_0 t \ll c$, these formulas go over into the classical expressions $v = w_0 t$, $x = w_0 t^2/2$. For $w_0 t \to \infty$, the velocity tends toward the constant value c.

The proper time of a uniformly accelerated particle is given by the integral

$$\int_0^t \sqrt{1-\frac{v^2}{c^2}}\, dt = \frac{c}{w_0}\sinh^{-1}\left(\frac{w_0 t}{c}\right).$$

As $t \to \infty$, it increases much more slowly than t, according to the law $\frac{c}{w_0}\ln\frac{2w_0 t}{c}$.

CHAPTER 2

RELATIVISTIC MECHANICS

§ 8. The principle of least action

In studying the motion of material particles, we shall start from the Principle of Least Action. The *principle of least action* is defined, as we know, by the statement that for each mechanical system there exists a certain integral S, called the *action*, which has a minimum value for the actual motion, so that its variation δS is zero.†

To determine the action integral for a free material particle (a particle not under the influence of any external force), we note that this integral must not depend on our choice of reference system, that is, it must be invariant under Lorentz transformations. Then it follows that it must depend on a scalar. Furthermore, it is clear that the integrand must be a differential of the first order. But the only scalar of this kind that one can construct for a free particle is the interval ds, or $\alpha\, ds$, where α is some constant. So for a free particle the action must have the form

$$S = -\alpha \int_a^b ds,$$

where $\int_a^b$ is an integral along the world line of the particle between the two particular events of the arrival of the particle at the initial position and at the final position at definite times t_1 and t_2, i.e., between two given world points; and α is some constant characterizing the particle. It is easy to see that α must be a positive quantity for all particles. In fact, as we saw in § 3, $\int_a^b ds$ has its maximum value along a straight world line; by integrating along a curved world line we can make the integral arbitrarily small. Thus the integral $\int_a^b ds$ with the positive sign cannot have a minimum; with the opposite sign it clearly has a minimum, along the straight world line.

The action integral can be represented as an integral with respect to the time

$$S = \int_{t_1}^{t_2} L\, dt.$$

† Strictly speaking, the principle of least action asserts that the integral S must be a minimum only for infinitesima lengths of the path of integration. For paths of arbitrary length we can say only that S must be an extremum, not necessarily a minimum. (See *Mechanics*, § 2.)

The coefficient L represents the *Lagrange function* of the mechanical system. With the aid of (3.1), we find:

$$S = -\int_{t_1}^{t_2} ac\sqrt{1-\frac{v^2}{c^2}}\,dt,$$

where v is the velocity of the material particle. Consequently the Lagrangian for the particle is

$$L = -ac\sqrt{1-v^2/c^2}.$$

The quantity a, as already mentioned, characterizes the particle. In classical mechanics each particle is characterized by its mass m. Let us find the relation between a and m. It can be determined from the fact that in the limit as $c\to\infty$, our expression for L must go over into the classical expression $L = mv^2/2$. To carry out this transition we expand L in powers of v/c. Then, neglecting terms of higher order, we find

$$L = -ac\sqrt{1-\frac{v^2}{c^2}} \approx -ac+\frac{av^2}{2c}.$$

As is well known, terms which are exact differentials with respect to the time are of no importance in the Lagrangian, and can be omitted from it.† Any constant is the exact differential of the product of the constant with t; it can therefore be omitted from L. Omitting the constant ac, we get $L = av^2/2c$, while in classical mechanics $L = mv^2/2$. Consequently, we must have $a = mc$.

Thus the action for a free material point is

$$S = -mc\int_a^b ds \tag{8.1}$$

and the Lagrangian is

$$L = -mc^2\sqrt{1-\frac{v^2}{c^2}}. \tag{8.2}$$

§ 9. **Energy and momentum**

By the *momentum* of a particle we mean the vector $\mathbf{p} = \partial L/\partial \mathbf{v}$ ($\partial L/\partial \mathbf{v}$ is the symbolic representation of the vector whose components are the derivatives of L with respect to the corresponding components of $\mathbf{v}$). Using (8.2), we find:

$$\mathbf{p} = \frac{m\mathbf{v}}{\sqrt{1-\dfrac{v^2}{c^2}}}. \tag{9.1}$$

For small velocities ($v \ll c$) or, in the limit as $c\to\infty$, this expression goes over into the classical $\mathbf{p} = m\mathbf{v}$. For $v = c$, the momentum becomes infinite.

† In the action integral exact differentials with respect to time give quantities not depending on the path of integration, and do not contribute to the variation of the action.

The time derivative of the momentum is the force acting on the particle. Suppose the velocity of the particle changes only in direction, that is, suppose the force is directed perpendicular to the velocity. Then

$$\frac{d\mathbf{p}}{dt} = \frac{m}{\sqrt{1-\frac{v^2}{c^2}}}\frac{d\mathbf{v}}{dt}. \tag{9.2}$$

If the velocity changes only in magnitude, that is, if the force is parallel to the velocity, then

$$\frac{d\mathbf{p}}{dt} = \frac{m}{\left(1-\frac{v^2}{c^2}\right)^{\frac{3}{2}}}\frac{d\mathbf{v}}{dt}. \tag{9.3}$$

We see that the ratio of force to acceleration is different in the two cases.

The *energy* $\mathcal{E}$ of the particle is defined as the quantity†

$$\mathcal{E} = \mathbf{p}\cdot\mathbf{v} - L.$$

Substituting the expressions (8.2) and (9.1) for L and $\mathbf{p}$, we find

$$\mathcal{E} = \frac{mc^2}{\sqrt{1-\frac{v^2}{c^2}}}. \tag{9.4}$$

This very important formula shows, in particular, that in relativistic mechanics the energy of a free particle does not go to zero for $v = 0$, but rather takes on a finite value

$$\mathcal{E} = mc^2. \tag{9.5}$$

This quantity is called the *rest energy* of the particle.

For small velocities ($v/c \ll 1$), we have, expanding (9.4) in series in powers of v/c,

$$\mathcal{E} \approx mc^2 + \frac{mv^2}{2},$$

which, except for the rest energy, is the classical expression for the kinetic energy of a particle.

We emphasize that, although we speak of a "particle", we have nowhere made use of the fact that it is "elementary". Thus the formulas are equally applicable to any composite body, consisting of many particles, where by m we mean the total mass of the body and by v the velocity of its motion as a whole. In particular, formula (9.5) is valid for any body which is at rest as a whole. We call attention to the fact that in relativistic mechanics the energy of a free body (i.e. the energy of any closed system) is a completely definite quantity which is always positive and is directly related to the mass

† See *Mechanics*, § 6.

of the body. In this connection we recall that in classical mechanics the energy of a body is defined only to within an arbitrary additive constant, and can be either positive or negative.

The energy of a body at rest contains, in addition to the rest energies of its constituent particles, the kinetic energy of the particles and the energy of their interactions with one another. In other words, mc^2 is not equal to $\sum m_a c^2$ (where m_a are the masses of the particles), and so m is not equal to $\sum m_a$. Thus in relativistic mechanics the law of conservation of mass does not hold: the mass of a composite body is not equal to the sum of the masses of its parts. Instead only the law of conservation of energy, in which the rest energies of the particles are included, is valid.

Squaring (9.1) and (9.4) and comparing the results, we get the following relation between the energy and momentum of a particle:

$$\frac{\mathcal{E}^2}{c^2} = p^2 + m^2c^2. \tag{9.6}$$

The energy expressed in terms of the momentum is called the Hamiltonian function $\mathcal{H}$:

$$\mathcal{H} = c\sqrt{p^2 + m^2c^2}. \tag{9.7}$$

For low velocities, $p \ll mc$, and we have approximately

$$\mathcal{H} \approx mc^2 + \frac{p^2}{2m},$$

i.e., except for the rest energy we get the familiar classical expression for the Hamiltonian.

From (9.1) and (9.4) we get the following relation between the energy, momentum, and velocity of a free particle:

$$\mathbf{p} = \mathcal{E}\frac{\mathbf{v}}{c^2}. \tag{9.8}$$

For $v = c$, the momentum and energy of the particle become infinite. This means that a particle with mass m different from zero cannot move with the velocity of light. Nevertheless, in relativistic mechanics, particles of zero mass moving with the velocity of light can exist. From (9.8) we have for such particles:

$$p = \frac{\mathcal{E}}{c}. \tag{9.9}$$

The same formula also holds approximately for particles with nonzero mass in the so-called *ultrarelativistic* case, when the particle energy $\mathcal{E}$ is large compared to its rest energy mc^2.

We now write all our formulas in four-dimensional form. According to the principle of least action,

$$\delta S = -mc\delta \int_a^b ds = 0.$$

To set up the expression for δS, we note that $ds = \sqrt{-dx_i^2}$ and therefore

$$\delta S = -mc\delta \int_a^b \sqrt{-dx_i^2} = -mc \int_a^b \frac{-dx_i\,\delta dx_i}{\sqrt{-dx_i^2}} = mc \int_a^b u_i\, d\delta x_i,$$

since dx_i/ds are the components of the four-velocity. Integrating by parts, we obtain

$$\delta S = mcu_i\,\delta x_i \Big|_a^b - mc \int_a^b \delta x_i \frac{du_i}{ds} ds. \tag{9.10}$$

As we know, to get the equations of motion we compare different trajectories between the same two points, i.e., at the limits $(\delta x_i)_a = (\delta x_i)_b = 0$. The actual trajectory is then determined from the condition $\delta S = 0$. From (9.10) we thus obtain the equations $\dfrac{du_i}{ds} = 0$; that is, a constant velocity for the free particle in four-dimensional form.

To determine the variation of the action as a function of the coordinates, one must consider the point a as fixed, so that $(\delta x_i)_a = 0$. The second point is to be considered as variable, but only actual trajectories are admissible, i.e., those which satisfy the equations of motion. Therefore the integral in expression (9.10) for δS is zero. In place of $(\delta x_i)_b$ we may write simply δx_i, and thus obtain

$$\delta S = mcu_i\,\delta x_i. \tag{9.11}$$

The four-vector with components $\partial S/\partial x_i$ is called the *four-vector of momentum*. We shall denote it by p_i. From (9.11) we see that the components of the four-momentum of a free material particle are

$$p_i = mcu_i. \tag{9.12}$$

As is shown in mechanics, the derivatives $\delta S/\delta x$, $\partial S/\partial y$, $\partial S/\partial z$ are the three components of the momentum of the particle, and the derivative $-\dfrac{\partial S}{\partial t} = -ic\dfrac{\partial S}{\partial \tau}$ is the energy of the particle. Using expression (7.2) for the components of the four-velocity, it is easy to show that the space components of p_i actually are identical with the momentum $\mathbf{p}$ and that the time component is $i\mathcal{E}/c$:

$$p_\alpha = p_\alpha, \quad p_4 = \frac{i\mathcal{E}}{c}. \tag{9.13}$$

Thus in relativistic mechanics, momentum and energy are the components of a single four-vector. From this we immediately get the transformation formulas for momentum and energy when we go over from one inertial system to another. In fact, substituting (9.13) in the general formula (6.2) for the transformation of four-vectors, we find

$$p_x = \frac{p'_x + \frac{V}{c^2}\mathcal{E}'}{\sqrt{1-\frac{V^2}{c^2}}}, \quad p_y = p'_y, \quad p_z = p'_z, \quad \mathcal{E} = \frac{\mathcal{E}' + Vp'_x}{\sqrt{1-\frac{V^2}{c^2}}}. \tag{9.14}$$

By analogy with the usual definition of force, we define the force four-vector as the derivative

$$g_i = \frac{dp_i}{ds} = mc\frac{du_i}{ds}. \tag{9.15}$$

Since $u_i \dfrac{du_i}{ds} = 0$, the same identity

$$g_i u_i = 0 \tag{9.16}$$

is satisfied by the components of the four-force. The space and time components of this four-vector are related to the usual three-dimensional force vector $\mathbf{f}$ by the equations

$$g_\alpha = \frac{f_\alpha}{c\sqrt{1-\frac{v^2}{c^2}}}, \quad g_4 = \frac{i\mathbf{f}\cdot\mathbf{v}}{c^2\sqrt{1-\frac{v^2}{c^2}}}. \tag{9.17}$$

From the definition (9.12) of the four-momentum and the identity $u_i^2 = -1$; we have:

$$p_i^2 = -m^2c^2. \tag{9.18}$$

If we substitute the expressions (9.13) for the components p_i, we get back (9.6).

Replacing p_i by $\dfrac{\partial S}{\partial x_i}$ in (9.18), we find

$$\left(\frac{\partial S}{\partial x_i}\right)^2 = -m^2c^2, \tag{9.19}$$

or, writing the sum explicitly:

$$\left(\frac{\partial S}{\partial x}\right)^2 + \left(\frac{\partial S}{\partial y}\right)^2 + \left(\frac{\partial S}{\partial z}\right)^2 - \frac{1}{c^2}\left(\frac{\partial S}{\partial t}\right)^2 + m^2c^2 = 0. \tag{9.20}$$

This is the *Hamilton-Jacobi equation* of relativistic mechanics.

The transition to the limiting case of classical mechanics in equation (9.19) is made as follows. First of all we must notice that just as in the corresponding transition with (9.7), the energy of a particle in relativistic mechanics contains the term mc^2, which it does not in classical mechanics. Inasmuch as the action S is related to the energy by $\mathcal{E} = -\frac{\partial S}{\partial t}$, in making the transition to classical mechanics we must in place of S substitute a new action S' according to the relation:

$$S = S' - mc^2 t.$$

Substituting this in (9.20), we find

$$\frac{1}{2m}\left[\left(\frac{\partial S'}{\partial x}\right)^2 + \left(\frac{\partial S'}{\partial y}\right)^2 + \left(\frac{\partial S'}{\partial z}\right)^2\right] - \frac{1}{2mc^2}\left(\frac{\partial S'}{\partial t}\right)^2 + \frac{\partial S'}{\partial t} = 0.$$

In the limit as $c \to \infty$, this equation goes over into the classical Hamilton-Jacobi equation.

§ 10. Transformation of distribution functions

In various physical problems we have to deal with distribution functions for the momenta of particles: $f(\mathbf{p})\, dp_x\, dp_y\, dp_z$ is the number of particles having momenta with components in given intervals dp_x, dp_y, dp_z (or, as we say for brevity, the number of particles in a given volume element $dp_x\, dp_y\, dp_z$ in "momentum space"). We are then faced with the problem of finding the law of transformation of the distribution function $f(\mathbf{p})$ when we transform from one reference system to another.

To solve this problem, we first determine the properties of the "volume element" $dp_x\, dp_y\, dp_z$ with respect to Lorentz transformations. If we introduce a four-dimensional coordinate system, on whose axes are marked the components of the four-momentum of a particle, then $dp_x\, dp_y\, dp_z$ can be considered as the fourth component of an element of the hypersurface defined by equation (9.18): $p_i^2 = -m^2c^2$. The element of hypersurface is a four-vector directed along the normal to the hypersurface; in our case the direction of the normal obviously coincides with the direction of the four-vector p_i. From this it follows that the ratio

$$\frac{dp_x\, dp_y\, dp_z}{\mathcal{E}} \tag{10.1}$$

is an invariant quantity, since it is the ratio of corresponding components of two parallel four-vectors.†

† The integration with respect to the element (10.1) can be expressed in four-dimensional form by means of the δ-function (cf. the footnote on p. 78) as an integration with respect to

$$\frac{2}{ic}\delta(p_i^2 + m^2c^2)\, d^4p, \qquad d^4p = dp_1\, dp_2\, dp_3\, dp_4\,. \tag{10.1a}$$

The number of particles, $f\,dp_x\,dp_y\,dp_z$, is also obviously an invariant, since it does not depend on the choice of reference frame. Writing it in the form

$$f(\mathbf{p})\mathcal{E}\frac{dp_x\,dp_y\,dp_z}{\mathcal{E}}$$

and using the invariance of the ratio (10.1), we conclude that the product $f(\mathbf{p})\mathcal{E}$ is invariant. Thus the distribution function in the K' system is related to the distribution function in the K system by the formula

$$f'(\mathbf{p}') = \frac{f(\mathbf{p})\mathcal{E}}{\mathcal{E}'}, \tag{10.2}$$

where $\mathbf{p}$ and $\mathcal{E}$ must be expressed in terms of $\mathbf{p}'$ and $\mathcal{E}'$ by using the transformation formulas (9.14).

Let us now return to the invariant expression (10.1). If we introduce "spherical coordinates" in momentum space, the volume element $dp_x\,dp_y\,dp_z$ becomes $p^2\,dp\,do$, where do is the element of solid angle around the direction of the vector p. Noting that $pdp = \mathcal{E}\,d\mathcal{E}/c^2$ [from (9.6)], we have:

$$\frac{p^2\,dp\,do}{\mathcal{E}} = \frac{p\,d\mathcal{E}\,do}{c^2}.$$

Thus we find that the expression

$$p\,d\mathcal{E}\,do \tag{10.3}$$

is also invariant.

If we are dealing with particles moving with the velocity of light, so that the relation $\mathcal{E} = pc$ (9.9) is valid, the invariant quantity (10.3) can be written as $p\,dp\,do$ or $\mathcal{E}\,d\mathcal{E}\,do$.

§ 11. Decay of particles

Let us consider the spontaneous decay of a body of mass M into two parts with masses m_1 and m_2. The law of conservation of energy in the decay, applied in the system of reference in which the body is at rest, gives:

$$Mc^2 = \mathcal{E}_{10}+\mathcal{E}_{20}, \tag{11.1}$$

where $\mathcal{E}_{10}$ and $\mathcal{E}_{20}$ are the energies of the emerging particles. Since $\mathcal{E}_{10} > m_1c^2$ and $\mathcal{E}_{20} > m_2c^2$, the equality (11.1) can be satisfied only if $M > m_1+m_2$, i.e. a body can disintegrate spontaneously into parts the sum of whose masses is less than the mass of the body. On the other hand, if $M < m_1+m_2$, the body is stable (with respect to the particular decay) and does not decay spontaneously. To cause the decay in this case, we would have to supply to the body from outside an amount of energy at least equal to its "binding energy" $(m_1+m_2-M)c^2$.

Momentum as well as energy must be conserved in the decay process. Since the initial momentum of the body was zero, the sum of the momenta of the emerging particles must be zero: $\mathbf{p}_{10}+\mathbf{p}_{20}=0$. Consequently $p_{10}^2=p_{20}^2$, or

$$\mathcal{E}_{10}^2-m_1^2c^4=\mathcal{E}_{20}^2-m_2^2c^4. \tag{11.2}$$

The two equations (11.1) and (11.2) uniquely determine the energies of the emerging particles:

$$\mathcal{E}_{10}=c^2\frac{M^2+m_1^2-m_2^2}{2M}, \qquad \mathcal{E}_{20}=c^2\frac{M^2-m_1^2+m_2^2}{2M}. \tag{11.3}$$

In a certain sense the inverse of this problem is the calculation of the total energy Mc^2 of two colliding particles in the system of reference in which their total momentum is zero. (This is abbreviated as the "system of the center of inertia" or the "C-system"). The computation of this quantity gives a criterion for the possible occurrence of various inelastic collision processes, accompanied by a change in state of the colliding particles, or the "creation" of new particles. A process of this type can occur only if the sum of the masses of the "reaction products" does not exceed M.

Suppose that in the initial reference system (the "laboratory" system) a particle with mass m_1 and energy $\mathcal{E}_1$ collides with a particle of mass m_2 which is at rest. The total energy of the two particles is

$$\mathcal{E}=\mathcal{E}_1+\mathcal{E}_2=\mathcal{E}_1+m_2c^2,$$

and their total momentum is $\mathbf{p}=\mathbf{p}_1+\mathbf{p}_2=\mathbf{p}_1$. Considering the two particles together as a single composite system, we find the velocity of its motion as a whole from (9.8):

$$\mathbf{V}=\frac{\mathbf{p}c^2}{\mathcal{E}}=\frac{\mathbf{p}_1c^2}{\mathcal{E}_1+m_2c^2}. \tag{11.4}$$

This quantity is the velocity of the C-system with respect to the laboratory system (the L-system).

However, in determining the mass M, there is no need to transform from one reference frame to the other. Instead we can make direct use of formula (9.6), which is applicable to the composite system just as it is to each particle individually. We thus have

$$M\cdot c^4=\mathcal{E}^2-p^2c^2=(\mathcal{E}_1+m_2c^2)^2-(\mathcal{E}_1^2-m_1^2c^4),$$

from which

$$M^2=m_1^2+m_2^2+2m_2\frac{\mathcal{E}_1}{c^2}. \tag{11.5}$$

Problems

1. A particle moving with velocity V dissociates "in flight" into two particles. Determine the relation between the angles of emergence of these particles and their energies.

Solution: Let $\mathcal{E}_0$ be the energy of one of the decay particles in the C-system [i.e. $\mathcal{E}_{10}$ or $\mathcal{E}_{20}$ in (11.3)], $\mathcal{E}$ the energy of this same particle in the L-system, and θ its angle of emergence in the L-system (with respect to the direction of **V**). By using the transformation formulas we find:

$$\mathcal{E}_0 = \frac{\mathcal{E} - Vp\cos\theta}{\sqrt{1-\frac{V^2}{c^2}}},$$

so that

$$\cos\theta = \frac{\mathcal{E} - \mathcal{E}_0\sqrt{1-\frac{V^2}{c^2}}}{V\sqrt{\frac{\mathcal{E}^2}{c^2} - m^2c^2}}. \tag{1}$$

For the determination of $\mathcal{E}$ from $\cos\theta$ we then get the quadratic equation

$$\mathcal{E}^2\left(1-\frac{V^2}{c^2}\cos^2\theta\right) - 2\mathcal{E}\mathcal{E}_0\sqrt{1-\frac{V^2}{c^2}} + \mathcal{E}_0^2\left(1-\frac{V^2}{c^2}\right) + V^2m^2c^2\cos^2\theta = 0, \tag{2}$$

which has one positive root (if the velocity v_0 of the decay particle in the C-system satisfies $v_0 > V$) or two positive roots (if $v_0 < V$).

The source of this ambiguity is clear from the following graphical construction. According to (9.14), the momentum components in the L-system are expressed in terms of quantities referring to the C-system by the formulas

$$p_x = \frac{p_0\cos\theta_0 + \frac{\mathcal{E}_0 V}{c^2}}{\sqrt{1-\frac{V^2}{c^2}}}, \qquad p_y = p_0\sin\theta_0.$$

Eliminating θ_0, we get

$$p_y^2 + \left(p_x\sqrt{1-\frac{V^2}{c^2}} - \mathcal{E}_0\frac{V}{c^2}\right)^2 = p_0^2.$$

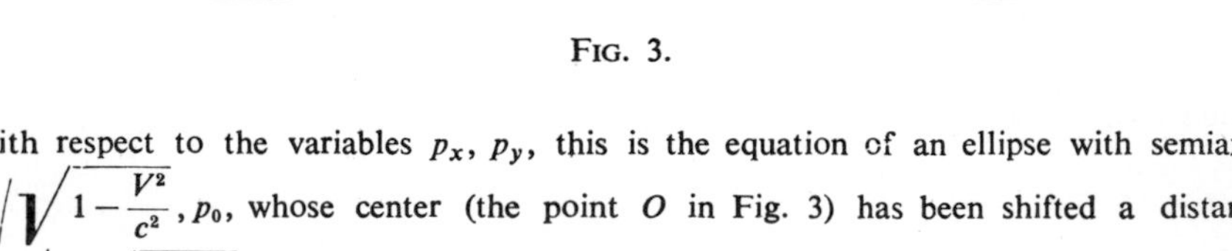

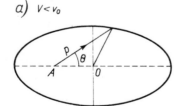

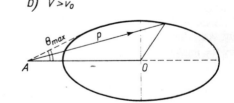

FIG. 3.

With respect to the variables p_x, p_y, this is the equation of an ellipse with semiaxes $p_0\Big/\sqrt{1-\frac{V^2}{c^2}}$, p_0, whose center (the point O in Fig. 3) has been shifted a distance $\mathcal{E}_0 V\Big/c^2\sqrt{1-\frac{V^2}{c^2}}$ from the point $\mathbf{p} = 0$ (point A in Fig. 3).†

If $V > \frac{p_0 c^2}{\mathcal{E}_0} = v_0$, the point A lies outside the ellipse (Fig. 3b), so that for a fixed angle θ the vector $\boldsymbol{p}$ (and consequently the energy $\mathcal{E}$) can have two different values. It is also clear

† In the classical limit, the ellipse reduces to a circle. (See *Mechanics*, § 16).

from the construction that in this case the angle θ cannot exceed a definite value θ_{max} (corresponding to the position of the vector **p** in which it is tangent to the ellipse). The value of θ_{max} is most easily determined analytically from the condition that the discriminant of the quadratic equation (2) go to zero:

$$\sin\theta_{max} = \frac{p_0\sqrt{1-\frac{V^2}{c^2}}}{mV}.$$

2. Find the energy distribution of the decay particles in the *L*-system.

Solution: In the *C*-system the decay particles are distributed isotropically in direction, i.e. the number of particles within the element of solid angle $do_0 = 2\pi\sin\theta_0\, d\theta_0$ is

$$dN = \frac{1}{4\pi}do_0 = \tfrac{1}{2}d|\cos\theta_0|. \tag{1}$$

The energy in the *L*-system is given in terms of quantities referring to the *C*-system by

$$\mathcal{E} = \frac{\mathcal{E}_0 + p_0 V\cos\theta_0}{\sqrt{1-\frac{V^2}{c^2}}}$$

and runs through the range of values from

$$\frac{\mathcal{E}_0 - Vp_0}{\sqrt{1-\frac{V^2}{c^2}}} \quad \text{to} \quad \frac{\mathcal{E}_0 + Vp_0}{\sqrt{1-\frac{V^2}{c^2}}}.$$

Expressing $d|\cos\theta_0|$ in terms of $d\mathcal{E}$, we obtain the normalized energy distribution (for each of the two types of decay particles):

$$dN = \frac{1}{2Vp_0}\sqrt{1-\frac{V^2}{c^2}}\,d\mathcal{E}.$$

3. Determine the range of values in the *L*-system for the angle between the two decay particles (their separation angle) for the case of decay into two identical particles.

Solution: In the *C*-system, the particles fly off in opposite directions, so that $\theta_{10} = \pi - \theta_{20} = \theta_0$. According to (5.4), the connection between angles in the *C*- and *L*-systems is given by the formulas:

$$\cot\theta_1 = \frac{v_0\cos\theta_0 + V}{v_0\sin\theta_0\sqrt{1-\frac{V^2}{c^2}}}, \quad \cot\theta_2 = \frac{-v_0\cos\theta_0 + V}{v_0\sin\theta_0\sqrt{1-\frac{V^2}{c^2}}}$$

(since $v_{10} = v_{20} = v_0$ in the present case). The required separation angle is $\Theta = \theta_1 + \theta_2$, and a simple calculation gives:

$$\cot\Theta = \frac{V^2 - v_0^2 + \frac{V^2 v_0^2}{c^2}\sin^2\theta_0}{2Vv_0\sqrt{1-\frac{V^2}{c^2}}\sin\theta_0}.$$

An examination of the extreme for this expression gives the following ranges of possible values of Θ:

$$\text{for } V < v_0:\ 2\tan^{-1}\left(\frac{v_0}{V}\sqrt{1-\frac{V^2}{c^2}}\right) < \Theta < \pi;$$

$$\text{for } v_0 < V < \frac{v_0}{\sqrt{1-\frac{v_0^2}{c^2}}} : 0 < \Theta < \sin^{-1}\sqrt{\frac{c^2-V^2}{c^2-v_0^2}} < \frac{\pi}{2};$$

$$\text{for } V > \frac{v_0}{\sqrt{1-\frac{v_0^2}{c^2}}} : 0 < \Theta < 2\tan^{-1}\left(\frac{v_0}{V}\sqrt{1-\frac{V^2}{c^2}}\right) < \frac{\pi}{2}.$$

4. Find the angular distribution in the L-system for decay particles of zero mass.

Solution: According to (5.6) the connection between the angles of emergence in the C- and L-systems for particles with $m = 0$ is

$$\cos\theta_0 = \frac{\cos\theta - \frac{V}{c}}{1 - \frac{V}{c}\cos\theta}.$$

Substituting this expression in formula (1) of Problem 2, we find:

$$dN = \frac{\left(1-\frac{V^2}{c^2}\right)do}{4\pi\left(1-\frac{V}{c}\cos\theta\right)^2}.$$

5. Find the distribution of separation angles in the L-system for a decay into two particles of zero mass.

Solution: The relation between the angles of emergence, θ_1, θ_2 in the L-system and the angles $\theta_{10} = \theta_0$, $\theta_{20} = \pi - \theta_0$ in the C-system is given by (5.6), so that we have for the separation angle $\Theta = \theta_1 + \theta_2$:

$$\cos\Theta = \frac{2\frac{V^2}{c^2} - 1 - \frac{V^2}{c^2}\cos^2\theta_0}{1 - \frac{V^2}{c^2}\cos^2\theta_0}$$

and conversely,

$$\cos\theta_0 = \sqrt{1 - \frac{c^2-V^2}{V^2}\cot^2\frac{\Theta}{2}}.$$

Substituting thus expression in formula (1) of Problem 2, we find:

$$dN = \frac{1-\frac{V^2}{c^2}}{16\pi\frac{V}{c}} \frac{do}{\sin^3\frac{\Theta}{2}\sqrt{\frac{V^2}{c^2}-\cos^2\frac{\Theta}{2}}}.$$

The angle Θ takes on values from 0 to $\Theta_{\max} = 2\cos^{-1}\frac{V}{c}$.

6. Determine the maximum energy which can be carried off by one of the decay particles, when a particle of mass M at rest decays into three particles with masses m_1, m_2, and m_3.

Solution: The particle m_1 has its maximum energy if the system of the other two particles m_2 and m_3 has the least possible mass; the latter is equal to the sum $m_2 + m_3$ (and corresponds to the case where the two particles move together with the same velocity). Having thus reduced the problem to the decay of a body into two parts, we obtain from (11.3):

$$\mathscr{E}_{1\,\max} = c^2 \frac{M^2+m_1^2-(m_2+m_3)^2}{2M}.$$

§12. Transformation of effective cross sections

Collision processes are characterized by their *effective cross sections*, which determine the number of collisions (of the particular type) occurring between beams of colliding particles.

Suppose that there are two colliding beams for which the particle densities (i.e., the numbers of particles per unit volume) are n_1 and n_2. We denote the difference between the velocities of the particles in the two beams by $v_{12} = |\mathbf{v}_2-\mathbf{v}_1|$. (For the collision of a beam with a target at rest, v_{12} is simply the velocity of the particles in the beam.) According to the definition of the effective cross section, σ, the number of collisions occurring in the volume dV during the time dt is

$$d\nu = \sigma v_{12} n_1 n_2 \, dV \, dt. \tag{12.1}$$

The number $d\nu$ is, by its very nature, an invariant quantity. The product $dV\,dt = d\Omega/ic$ is also a four-dimensional scalar. From this we conclude that the quantity

$$\sigma v_{12} n_1 n_2 = \text{inv} \tag{12.2}$$

is invariant.

The transformation law for the particle density n is easily found by noting that, by definition, the number of particles $n\,dV$ in a given volume element dV is an invariant. Writing $n\,dV = n_0\,dV_0$, where the subscript 0 denotes "proper" values of quantities (in the reference frame in which the particles are at rest) and using formula (4.6) for the transformation of the volume, we find:

$$n = \frac{n_0}{\sqrt{1-\dfrac{v^2}{c^2}}}. \tag{12.3}$$

Considering this relation, we see that the statement of the invariance of (12.2) is equivalent to the invariance of the expression

$$\frac{\sigma v_{12}}{\sqrt{1-\dfrac{v_1^2}{c^2}}\sqrt{1-\dfrac{v_2^2}{c^2}}} = \text{inv},$$

in which the particle densities no longer appear. This invariant can be written in a more convenient form by dividing it by the scalar product of the four-velocities of the particles in the two beams:

$$u_{i1}u_{i2} = \frac{\dfrac{\mathbf{v}_1\cdot\mathbf{v}_2}{c^2} - 1}{\sqrt{1-\dfrac{v_1^2}{c^2}}\sqrt{1-\dfrac{v_2^2}{c^2}}}.$$

Thus we arrive at the result that the ratio

$$\frac{\sigma v_{12}}{1-\dfrac{\mathbf{v}_1\cdot\mathbf{v}_2}{c^2}} = \text{inv} \tag{12.4}$$

is an invariant. (W. Pauli, 1933.)

By using this result we can write a formula for the number of collisions of particles with velocities $\mathbf{v}_1$ and $\mathbf{v}_2$, expressed in terms of the effective cross section σ_0 in the system of reference in which one of the colliding particles is at rest. We write the expression (12.4) in the two reference systems and use the formula for the relative velocity which was found in the problem of § 5:

$$\frac{\sigma v_{12}}{1-\dfrac{\mathbf{v}_1\cdot\mathbf{v}_2}{c^2}} = \sigma_0 v_{\text{rel}} = \sigma_0 \frac{\sqrt{(\mathbf{v}_1-\mathbf{v}_2)^2-\dfrac{1}{c^2}(\mathbf{v}_1\times\mathbf{v}_2)^2}}{1-\dfrac{\mathbf{v}_1\cdot\mathbf{v}_2}{c^2}}.$$

Finally, substituting this expression for σv_{12} into (12.1), we obtain:

$$d\nu = \sigma_0\sqrt{(\mathbf{v}_1-\mathbf{v}_2)^2-\frac{1}{c^2}(\mathbf{v}_1\times\mathbf{v}_2)^2}\, n_1 n_2\, dV\, dt. \tag{12.5}$$

We may point out that, if the velocities $\mathbf{v}_1$ and $\mathbf{v}_2$ are parallel,

$$d\nu = \sigma_0 |\mathbf{v}_1-\mathbf{v}_2| n_1 n_2\, dV\, dt,$$

which differs from (12.1) only in the replacement of σ by σ_0; in other words, the effective cross section is unchanged by transformations which leave the directions of the velocities of the two particles unchanged; this fact was more or less obvious to begin with.

§ 13. Elastic collisions of particles

We shall now consider the *elastic collision* of two particles, that is, a collision in which the internal state of the particles does not change. Let the energy and momentum of the particles before the collision be $\mathbf{p}_1$, $\mathcal{E}_1$ and $\mathbf{p}_2$, $\mathcal{E}_2$ respectively in the L-system of reference. The x axis of the L-system is chosen along the direction of the total momentum of the particles, $\mathbf{p}_1+\mathbf{p}_2$. We denote by a prime the values of quantities after collision.

To study the collision it is convenient to go over to the C-system, in which the total momentum of the two particles is zero. From (9.8) the velocity $\mathbf{V}$ of the C-system relative to the L-system is

$$\mathbf{V} = \frac{(\mathbf{p}_1+\mathbf{p}_2)c^2}{\mathcal{E}_1+\mathcal{E}_2}. \tag{13.1}$$

From the general transformation formula (9.14), and (13.1), it is easy to calculate the energy and momentum of the two particles in the C-system; we designate them by $\mathcal{E}_{10}$, $\mathcal{E}_{20}$, $\mathbf{p}_{10} = -\mathbf{p}_{20}$.

During the collision, the total momentum and energy of the particles remain unchanged. In the C-system, the momenta are equal in magnitude and opposite in direction. During the collision the momenta $\mathbf{p}_{10}$ and $\mathbf{p}_{20}$ can only rotate, remaining equal and opposite in direction. So because of the energy conservation law, the momentum of each particle remains unchanged.

Let us assume that one of the particles (the second) was at rest before the collision (in the L-system). In the C-system, before the collision, this particle has velocity $-V$ along the x axis and a corresponding momentum $\dfrac{m_2 V}{\sqrt{1-\dfrac{V^2}{c^2}}}$. Let χ be the angle through which the momenta $\mathbf{p}_{10}$ and $\mathbf{p}_{20}$ are rotated by the collision, in the C-system (angle of scattering in the L-system). Since the absolute value of $\mathbf{p}_{20}$ is not changed because of the collision, the x component of the momentum of the particle after the collision is

$$\frac{m_2 V}{\sqrt{1-\dfrac{V^2}{c^2}}}\cos\chi.$$

The energy of this particle in the C-system is

$$\mathcal{E}_{20} = \frac{m_2 c^2}{\sqrt{1-\dfrac{V^2}{c^2}}}.$$

With the aid of the last transformation formula of (9.14), we find the energy $\mathcal{E}_2'$ (in the L-system), after collision, of the particle which was initially at rest:

$$\mathcal{E}_2' = \frac{m_2 c^2\left(1-\dfrac{V^2}{c^2}\cos\chi\right)}{1-\dfrac{V^2}{c^2}}.$$

We obtain the final formula for $\mathcal{E}_2'$ by eliminating the auxiliary quantity V, using formula (13.1) in the form

$$V = \frac{p_1 c^2}{\mathcal{E}_1+m_2c^2} = c\,\frac{\sqrt{\mathcal{E}_1^2-m_1^2c^4}}{\mathcal{E}_1+m_2c^2} \tag{13.2}$$

(before the collision $p_2 = 0$, $\mathcal{E}_2 = m_2c^2$). An elementary calculation gives:

$$\mathcal{E}'_2 = m_2c^2 + \frac{m_2(\mathcal{E}_1^2 - m_1^2c^4)}{m_1^2c^2 + m_2^2c^2 + 2m_2\mathcal{E}_1}(1-\cos\chi). \tag{13.3}$$

The second term represents the energy taken by the second particle from the first during the collision. Remembering that the sum of the energies of the two particles is conserved in the collision, we can immediately write for the energy of the first particle after the collision:

$$\mathcal{E}'_1 = \mathcal{E}_1 - \frac{m_2(\mathcal{E}_1^2 - m_1^2c^4)}{m_1^2c^2 + m_2^2c^2 + 2m_2\mathcal{E}_1}(1-\cos\chi). \tag{13.4}$$

The maximum possible energy transfer in the collision occurs for $\chi = \pi$. The corresponding value of $\mathcal{E}'_2$ is

$$\mathcal{E}'_{2\,\max} = m_2c^2 + \frac{2m_2(\mathcal{E}_1^2 - m_1^2c^4)}{m_1^2c^2 + m_2^2c^2 + 2m_2\mathcal{E}_1}. \tag{13.5}$$

The particle m_1 will then have its minimum energy

$$\mathcal{E}'_{1\,\min} = m_1c^2 + \frac{(\mathcal{E}_1 - m_1c^2)(m_2 - m_1)^2c^2}{m_1^2c^2 + m_2^2c^2 + 2m_2\mathcal{E}_1}. \tag{13.6}$$

We want to point out a certain consequence of these formulas. Writing formula (13.6) in the form

$$\frac{\mathcal{E}'_{1\,\min} - m_1c^2}{\mathcal{E}_1 - m_1c^2} = \frac{(m_2 - m_1)^2}{m_1^2 + m_2^2 + \frac{2}{c^2}m_2\mathcal{E}_1},$$

we see that in the limiting case of small velocities (when $\mathcal{E} \cong mc^2 + mv^2/2$), we obtain the well-known result of nonrelativistic mechanics that the ratio of the minimum kinetic energy of the impinging particle to its initial kinetic energy approaches the limiting value $(m_1 - m_2)^2/(m_1 + m_2)^2$. In the opposite limiting case, where the velocity of the particle m_1 is close to c (i.e., large $\mathcal{E}_1$), the ratio approaches zero; the quantity $\mathcal{E}'_{1\,\min}$ also approaches a constant limit. This limit is

$$\mathcal{E}'_{1\,\min} = \frac{m_1^2 + m_2^2}{2m_2}c^2.$$

Let us assume that $m_2 \gg m_1$, that is, the mass of the impinging particle is small compared with the mass of the particle at rest. In this case, according to classical mechanics, the light particle can transfer only a negligible part of its energy to the heavy one.† This is not the case in relativistic mechanics. From formula (13.5) it is clear that for sufficiently large energies $\mathcal{E}_1$, the fraction of the energy transferred can become of the order of unity. For

† See *Mechanics*, § 17.

this to occur, however, it is not enough that the velocity of particle m_1 be of order c, but rather it is necessary that the energy be of order

$$\mathcal{E}_1 \sim m_2 c^2,$$

that is, the light particle must have an energy of the order of the rest energy of the heavy particle.

An analogous situation exists for $m_2 \ll m_1$, that is, when a heavy particle impinges on a light one. Here, too, according to classical mechanics, only a negligible energy transfer would occur. The fraction of the energy transferred begins to become significant only when the energy becomes of order

$$\mathcal{E}_1 \sim \frac{m_1^2}{m_2} c^2.$$

We note that here, too, what is required is not simply a velocity of the order of the light velocity, but rather an energy large compared with $m_1 c^2$.

Next we derive relations between the angle of scattering of the particle in the L-system (angle of deflection of the mass m_1 from its initial direction of motion) and the change in its energy due to the collision. To do this, we note that for each of the particles we have the relation

$$(p_i - p'_i)U_i = 0, \tag{13.7}$$

where p_i, p'_i are the four-momentum of the particle before and after the collision, and U_i is the velocity of the center of inertia. In fact, the left side of this equation is a scalar quantity and it is therefore sufficient to verify this relation in any one system of reference. In the C-system we have $U_\alpha = 0$, so that

$$(p_i - p'_i)U_i = i/c(\mathcal{E} - \mathcal{E}'),$$

but in the C-system the energy of the particle is not changed by the collision, that is, $\mathcal{E} = \mathcal{E}'$, which proves relation (13.7)

First let us apply (13.7) to the particle m_2 initially at rest. Let θ_2 be the angle of scattering of this particle in the L-system. Then, substituting the values of the components of the vectors p_{i2}, p'_{i2}, U_i in the L-system, we get

$$\mathcal{E}'_2 - m_2 c^2 = V p'_2 \cos\theta_2$$

or, using (13.2) for V,

$$\cos\theta_2 = \frac{(\mathcal{E}_1 + m_2 c^2)(\mathcal{E}'_2 - m_2 c^2)}{p_1 p'_2 c^2}. \tag{13.8}$$

Similarly, applying (13.7) to the impinging particle, we get

$$\mathcal{E}_1 - \mathcal{E}'_1 = V(p_1 - p'_1 \cos\theta_1),$$

from which, using the expression for V, we find

$$\cos\theta_1 = \frac{\mathcal{E}'_1(\mathcal{E}_1 + m_2 c^2) - \mathcal{E}_1 m_2 c^2 - m_1^2 c^4}{p_1 p'_1 c^2}. \tag{13.9}$$

Formulas (13.8) and (13.9) solve the problem we have set. We note that if $m_1 > m_2$, that is, if the impinging particle is heavier than the one at rest, the scattering angle θ_1 cannot exceed a certain maximum value. An elementary calculation gives for this quantity the equation

$$\sin\theta_{1\,\max} = \frac{m_2}{m_1},$$

in complete agreement with the classical result.

Formulas (13.8) and (13.9) simplify in case the impinging particle has zero mass and so moves with the velocity of light. Setting $m_1 = 0$, $p_1 = \mathcal{E}_1/c$, $p_1' = \mathcal{E}_1'/c$, we find:

$$\begin{aligned} \cos\theta_1 &= \frac{\mathcal{E}_1'(\mathcal{E}_1+m_2c^2)-\mathcal{E}_1 m_2 c^2}{\mathcal{E}_1\mathcal{E}_1'}, \\ \cos\theta_2 &= \frac{(\mathcal{E}_1+m_2c^2)(\mathcal{E}_2'-m_2c^2)}{\mathcal{E}_1 p_2' c}. \end{aligned} \tag{13.10}$$

We also give the inverse formula for the energy of the impinging particle after the collision, as expressed in terms of the deflection angle:

$$\mathcal{E}_1' = \frac{m_2c^2}{1-\cos\theta_1+\dfrac{m_2c^2}{\mathcal{E}_1}}. \tag{13.11}$$

PROBLEMS

1. The triangle ABC in Fig. 4 is formed by the momentum vector $\mathbf{p}$ of the impinging particle and the momenta $\mathbf{p}_1'$, $\mathbf{p}_2'$ of the two particles after the collision. Find the locus of the points C corresponding to all possible values of $\mathbf{p}_1'$, $\mathbf{p}_2'$.

Solution: The required curve is an ellipse whose semiaxes can be found by using the formulas obtained in problem 1 of § 11. In fact, the construction given there determined the locus of the vectors $\mathbf{p}$ in the L-system which are obtained from arbitrarily directed vectors $\mathbf{p}_0$ with given length p_0 in the C-system.

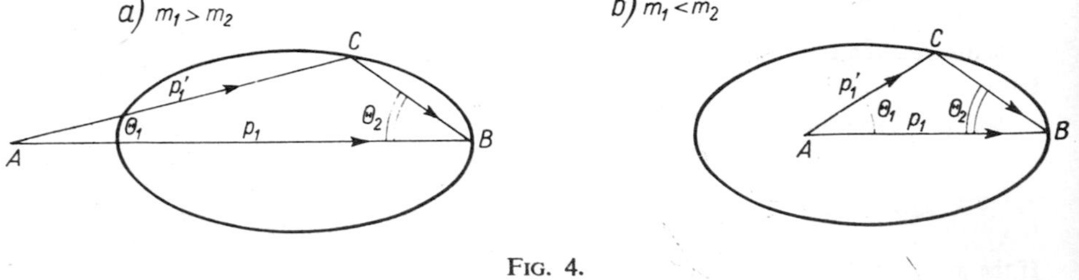

FIG. 4.

Since the absolute values of the momenta of the colliding particles are identical in the C-system, and do not change in the collision, we are dealing with a similar construction for the vector $\mathbf{p}_1'$, for which

$$p_0 = p_{10} = p_{20} = \frac{m_2 V}{\sqrt{1-\dfrac{V^2}{c^2}}}$$

in the C-system, where V is given by formula (13.2). We find that the minor and major semiaxes of the ellipse are equal respectively to

$$\frac{m_2 p_1}{\sqrt{m_1^2+m_2^2+2\frac{m_2\mathcal{E}_1}{c^2}}} \quad \text{and} \quad \frac{m_2 p_1\left(\frac{\mathcal{E}_1}{c^2}+m_2\right)}{m_1^2+m_2^2+2\frac{m_2\mathcal{E}_1}{c^2}},$$

For $\theta_1 = 0$, the vector $\mathbf{p}_1'$ coincides with $\mathbf{p}_1$, so that the distance AB is equal to p_1. Comparing p_1 with the length of the major axis of the ellipse, it is easily shown that the point A lies outside the ellipse If $m_1 > m_2$ (Fig. 4a), and inside it if $m_1 < m_2$ (Fig. 4b).

2. Determine the minimum separation angle Θ_{min} of two particles after collision if the masses of the two particles are the same ($m_1 = m_2 = m$).

Solution: If $m_1 = m_2$, the point A of the diagram lies on the ellipse, while the minimum separation angle corresponds to the situation where point C is at the end of the minor axis (Fig. 5). From the construction it is clear that tan ($\Theta_{min}/2$) is the ratio of the lengths of the semiaxes, and we find:

$$\tan\frac{\Theta_{min}}{2} = \sqrt{\frac{2mc^2}{\mathcal{E}_1+mc^2}},$$

or

$$\cos\Theta_{min} = \frac{\mathcal{E}_1-mc^2}{\mathcal{E}_1+3mc^2}.$$

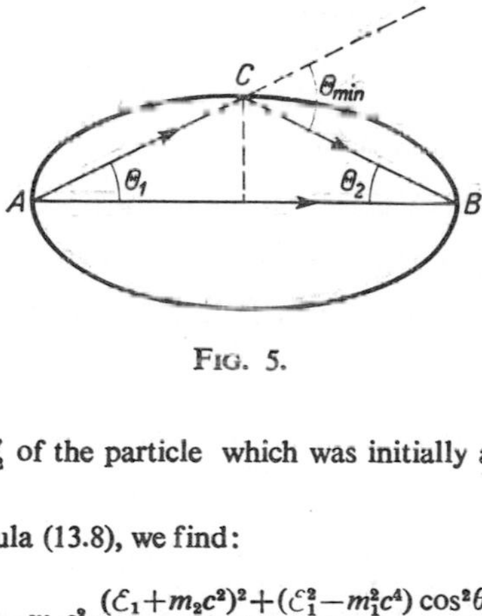

FIG. 5.

3. Express the energy $\mathcal{E}_2'$ of the particle which was initially at rest in terms of its scattering angle θ_2.

Solution: Inverting formula (13.8), we find:

$$\mathcal{E}_2' = m_2c^2\frac{(\mathcal{E}_1+m_2c^2)^2+(\mathcal{E}_1^2-m_1^2c^4)\cos^2\theta_2}{(\mathcal{E}_1+m_2c^2)^2-(\mathcal{E}_1^2-m_1^2c^4)\cos^2\theta_2}.$$

If the masses of the particles are the same ($m_1 = m_2 = m$),

$$\mathcal{E}' = mc^2\frac{\mathcal{E}+mc^2+(\mathcal{E}-mc^2)\cos^2\theta}{\mathcal{E}+mc^2-(\mathcal{E}-mc^2)\cos^2\theta}.$$

This formula can be applied either to the particle which was initially at rest or to the impinging particle, by using either θ_2 or θ_1 in place of θ. (In the general case, the inversion of (13.9) leads to an extremely complicated expression for $\mathcal{E}_1'$ in terms of θ_1).

§ 14. Angular momentum

As is well known from classical mechanics, for a closed system, in addition to conservation of energy and momentum, there is conservation of angular momentum, that is, of the vector

$$\mathbf{M} = \sum \mathbf{r} \times \mathbf{p}$$

where **r** and **p** are the radius vector and momentum of the particle; the summation runs over all the particles making up the system. The conservation of angular momentum is a consequence of the fact that because of the isotropy of space, the Lagrangian of a closed system does not change under a rotation of the system as a whole.

By carrying through a similar derivation in four-dimensional form, we obtain the relativistic expression for the angular momentum. Let x_i be the coordinates of one of the particles of the system. We make an infinitesimal rotation in the four-dimensional space. Under such a transformation, the coordinates x_i take on new values x'_i such that the differences $x'_i - x_i$ are linear functions

$$x'_i - x_i = x_k \, \delta\Omega_{ik} \tag{14.1}$$

with infinitesimal coefficients $\delta\Omega_{ik}$. The components of the four-tensor $\delta\Omega_{ik}$ are connected to one another by the relations resulting from the requirement that, under a rotation, the length x_i^2 of the radius vector must remain unchanged, that is, $x_i^2 = x_i'^2$. Substituting for x'_i from (14.1) and dropping terms quadratic in $\delta\Omega_{ik}$, as infinitesimals of higher order, we find

$$x_i x_k \, \delta\Omega_{ik} = 0.$$

This equation must be fulfilled for arbitrary x_i. Since $x_i x_k$ is a symmetric tensor, $\delta\Omega_{ik}$ must be an antisymmetric tensor (the product of a symmetrical and an antisymmetrical tensor is clearly identically zero). Thus we find that

$$\delta\Omega_{ki} = -\delta\Omega_{ik}. \tag{14.2}$$

The change δS in the action S for an infinitesimal change in coordinates has the form (see 9.11):

$$\delta S = \sum p_i \, \delta x_i$$

(the summation extends over all the particles of the system). In the case of rotation which we are now considering, $\delta x_i = \delta\Omega_{ik} x_k$, and so

$$\delta S = \delta\Omega_{ik} \sum p_i x_k.$$

If we resolve the tensor $\sum p_i x_k$ into symmetric and antisymmetric parts, then the first of these when multiplied by an antisymmetric tensor gives identically zero. Therefore, taking the antisymmetric part of $\sum p_i x_k$, we can write the preceding equality in the form

$$\delta S = \delta\Omega_{ik} \cdot \tfrac{1}{2} \sum (p_i x_k - p_k x_i). \tag{14.3}$$

For a closed system, because of the isotropy of space and time, the Lagrangian does not change under a rotation in four-space, i.e., the parameters $\delta\Omega_{ik}$ for the rotation are cyclic coordinates. Therefore the corresponding generalized momenta are conserved. These generalized momenta are the quantities $\delta S/\delta\Omega_{ik}$. From (14.3), we have

$$\frac{\delta S}{\delta\Omega_{ik}} = \frac{1}{2}\sum (p_i x_k - p_k x_i).$$

Consequently we see that for a closed system the tensor

$$M_{ik} = \sum (x_i p_k - x_k p_i) \tag{14.4}$$

is conserved. This antisymmetric tensor is called the *four-tensor of angular momentum*. The space components of this tensor ($i, k = 1, 2, 3$) are obviously the components of the three-dimensional angular momentum vector:

$$\mathbf{M} = \sum \mathbf{r} \times \mathbf{p}, \tag{14.5}$$

$$M_{zx} = -M_{xz} = M_y, \quad M_{xy} = -M_{yx} = M_z, \quad M_{yz} = -M_{zy} = M_x.$$

As for the components $M_{4\alpha}$ ($\alpha = 1, 2, 3$) it is easy to verify that

$$M_{4\alpha} = ic\sum\left(tp_\alpha - \frac{\mathcal{E}x_\alpha}{c^2}\right). \tag{14.6}$$

These three components therefore form a three-dimensional vector $ic\sum(t\mathbf{p} - \mathcal{E}\mathbf{r}/c^2)$.

Because of the conservation of M_{ik} for a closed system, we have, in particular,

$$\sum\left(t\mathbf{p} - \frac{\mathcal{E}\mathbf{r}}{c^2}\right) = \text{const}.$$

Since, on the other hand, the total energy $\sum\mathcal{E}$ is also conserved, this equality can be written in the form

$$\frac{\sum\mathcal{E}\mathbf{r}}{\sum\mathcal{E}} - \frac{c^2\sum\mathbf{p}}{\sum\mathcal{E}}t = \text{const}. \tag{14.7}$$

From this we see that the point with the radius vector

$$\mathbf{R} = \frac{\sum\mathcal{E}\mathbf{r}}{\sum\mathcal{E}} \tag{14.8}$$

moves uniformly with the velocity

$$\mathbf{V} = \frac{c^2\sum\mathbf{p}}{\sum\mathcal{E}}, \tag{14.9}$$

which is none other than the velocity of motion of the system as a whole. [It relates the total energy and momentum, according to formula (9.8).]

Formula (14.8) gives the relativistic definition of the coordinates of the *center of inertia* of the system. If the velocities of all the particles are small compared to c, we can approximately set $\mathcal{E} \approx mc^2$ so that (14.8) goes over into the usual classical expression $\mathbf{R} = \frac{\sum m\mathbf{r}}{\sum m}$.†

Let $\mathbf{M}_0$ be the angular momentum of a body (a system of particles) in the reference frame K_0 in which it is at rest as a whole, and $\mathbf{M}$ its angular momentum with respect to its center of inertia in the reference frame K in which the body moves with velocity $\mathbf{V}$. In the K system, the angular momentum of the body with respect to an arbitrary point $\mathbf{a}$ is $\mathbf{M}+\mathbf{a}\times\sum\mathbf{p}$; in the K_0 system, in which $\sum\mathbf{p} = 0$, the value of the angular momentum is independent of the point with respect to which it is defined.

Let us examine the relation between $\mathbf{M}$ and $\mathbf{M}_0$. Since the components of the vector $\mathbf{M}$ are the space components of the four-tensor M_{ik}, we must make use of the transformation formulas for these quantities.

The K system moves with respect to K_0 with the velocity $-\mathbf{V}$; we choose the direction of $\mathbf{V}$ as the x axis. The components of a tensor transform like the products of the corresponding components of vectors. Since under the Lorentz transformation (6.2) the y- and z-components of a four-vector are not changed, the components M_{xy} and M_{xz} of the angular momentum tensor transform like the x-component of a four-vector, while M_{yz} is not changed at all:

$$M_{xy}^{(0)} = \frac{M_{xy}+i\frac{V}{c}M_{\tau y}}{\sqrt{1-\frac{V^2}{c^2}}}, \qquad M_{xz}^{(0)} = \frac{M_{xz}+i\frac{V}{c}M_{\tau z}}{\sqrt{1-\frac{V^2}{c^2}}}, \qquad M_{yz}^{(0)} = M_{yz}.$$

Since the origin of coordinates of the K system was chosen at the center of inertia of the body, $\sum\mathcal{E}y = \sum\mathcal{E}z = 0$, and since the velocity $\mathbf{V}$ is directed along the x axis, $\sum p_y = \sum p_z = 0$. Consequently, we have $M_{\tau y} = M_{\tau z} = 0$ in the K system, and we obtain finally:

$$M_x = M_{x0}, \quad M_y = M_{y0}\sqrt{1-\frac{V^2}{c^2}}, \quad M_z = M_{z0}\sqrt{1-\frac{V^2}{c^2}}. \tag{14.10}$$

For the absolute value of the angular momentum, we have:

$$M^2 = M_0^2\left(1-\frac{V^2}{c^2}\right)+\frac{V^2}{c^2}M_{x0}^2. \tag{14.11}$$

† See *Mechanics*, § 8. We note that whereas the classical formula for the center of inertia applies equally well to interacting and non-interacting particles, formula (14.8) is valid only if we neglect interaction. In relativistic mechanics, the definition of the center of inertia of a system of interacting particles requires us to include explicitly the momentum and energy of the field produced by the particles.

CHAPTER 3

CHARGES IN ELECTROMAGNETIC FIELDS

§ 15. Elementary particles in the theory of relativity

The interaction of particles can be described with the help of the concept of a *field* of force. Namely, instead of saying that one particle acts on another, we may say that the particle creates a field around itself; a certain force then acts on every other particle located in this field. In classical mechanics, the field is merely a mode of description of the physical phenomenon — the interaction of particles. In the theory of relativity, because of the finite velocity of propagation of interactions, the situation is changed fundamentally The forces acting on a particle at a given moment are not determined by the positions at that same moment. A change in the position of one of the particles influences other particles only after the lapse of a certain time interval. This means that the field itself acquires physical reality. We cannot speak of a direct interaction of particles located at a distance from one another. Interactions can occur at any one moment only between neighboring points in space (contact interaction). Therefore we must speak of the interaction of the one particle with the field, and of the subsequent interaction of the field with the second particle.

We shall consider two types of fields, gravitational and electromagnetic. The study of gravitational fields is left to Chapters 10 to 12 and in the other chapters we consider only electromagnetic fields.

Before considering the interactions of particles with the electromagnetic field, we shall make some general remarks concerning the concept of a "particle" in relativistic mechanics.

In classical mechanics one can introduce the concept of a rigid body, i.e., a body which is not deformable under any conditions. In the theory of relativity it should follow similarly that we would consider as rigid those bodies whose dimensions all remain unchanged in the reference system in which they are at rest. However, it is easy to see that the theory of relativity makes the existence of rigid bodies impossible in general.

Consider, for example, a circular disk rotating around its axis, and let us assume that it is rigid. A reference frame fixed in the disk is clearly not inertial. It is possible, however, to introduce for each of the infinitesimal elements of the disk an inertial system in which this element would be at rest at the moment; for different elements of the disk, having different velocities, these systems will, of course, also be different. Let us consider a series of line elements, lying along a particular radius vector. Because of the rigidity of the disk, the length of each of these segments (in the corresponding inertial system of reference) will be the same as it was when the disk was at rest. This same length would be measured by an observer at rest, past whom this radius swings at the given moment, since each of its segments is perpendicular to its velocity and consequently a Lorentz contraction does not occur. Therefore the total length of the radius as measured by the observer at rest, being the sum of its segments, will be the same as when the disk was at rest. On the other hand, the length of each element of the circumference of the disk, passing by the observer at rest at a given moment, undergoes a Lorentz contraction, so that the length of the whole circumference (measured by the observer at rest as the sum of the lengths of its various segments) turns out to be smaller than the length of the circumference of the disk at rest. Thus we arrive at the result that due to the rotation of the disk, the ratio of circumference to radius (as measured by an observer at rest) must change, and not remain equal to 2π. The absurdity of this result shows that actually the disk cannot be rigid, and that in rotation it must necessarily undergo some complex deformation depending on the elastic properties of the material of the disk.

The impossibility of the existence of rigid bodies can be demonstrated in another way. Suppose some solid body is set in motion by an external force acting at one of its points. If the body were rigid, all of its points would have to be set in motion at the same time as the point to which the force is applied; if this were not so the body would be deformed. However, the theory of relativity makes this impossible, since the force at the particular point is transmitted to the others with a finite velocity, so that all the points cannot begin moving simultaneously.

From this discussion we can draw certain conclusions concerning the treatment of "*elementary*" particles, i.e., particles whose state we assume to be described completely by giving its three coordinates and the three components of its velocity as a whole. It is obvious that if an elementary particle had finite dimensions, i.e., if it were extended in space, it could not be deformable, since the concept of deformability is related to the possibility of independent motion of individual parts of the body. But, as we have seen, the theory of relativity shows that it is impossible for absolutely rigid bodies to exist.

Thus we come to the conclusion that in classical (non-quantum) relativistic mechanics, we cannot ascribe finite dimensions to particles which we regard as elementary. In other words, within the framework of classical theory elementary particles must be treated as points.†

---

† Quantum mechanics makes a fundamental change in this situation, but here again relativity theory makes it extremely difficult to introduce anything other than point interactions.

§ 16. Four-potential of a field

For a particle moving in a given electromagnetic field, the action is made up of two parts: the action (8.1) for the free particle, and a term describing the interaction of the particle with the field. The latter term must contain quantities characterizing the particle and quantities characterizing the field.

It turns out† that the properties of a particle with respect to interaction with the electromagnetic field are determined by a single parameter — the *charge* e of the particle, which can be either positive or negative (or equal to zero). The properties of the field are characterized by a four-vector A_i, the *four-potential*, whose components are functions of the coordinates and time. These quantities appear in the action function in the term.

$$\frac{e}{c}\int_a^b A_i\, dx_i,$$

where the functions A_i are taken at points on the world line of the particle. The factor $1/c$ has been introduced for convenience. It should be pointed out that, so long as we have no formulas relating the charge or the potentials with already known quantities, the units for measuring these new quantities can be chosen arbitrarily.‡

Thus the action function for a charge in an electromagnetic field has the form

$$S = \int_a^b \left(-mc\, ds + \frac{e}{c} A_i\, dx_i\right). \tag{16.1}$$

The three space components of the four-vector A_i form a three-dimensional vector $\mathbf{A}$ called the *vector potential* of the field. The time component of the vector A_i is imaginary, i.e., it has the form $A_4 = i\phi$. The real quantity ϕ is called the *scalar potential* of the field. Thus

$$A_{1,2,3} = A_{x,y,z}, \qquad A_4 = i\phi. \tag{16.2}$$

Therefore the action integral can be written in the form

$$S = \int_a^b \left(-mc\, ds + \frac{e}{c}\mathbf{A}\cdot d\mathbf{r} - e\phi\, dt\right).$$

† The assertions which follow should be regarded as being, to a certain extent, the consequence of experimental data. The form of the action for a particle in an electromagnetic field cannot be fixed on the basis of general considerations alone (such as, for example, the requirement of relativistic invariance). The latter would permit the occurrence in formula (16.1) of terms of the form $\int A\, ds$, where A is a scalar function.

To avoid any misunderstanding, we repeat that we are considering classical (and not quantum) theory, and therefore do not include effects which are related to the spins of particles.

‡ Concerning the establishment of these units, see § 27.

Introducing $d\mathbf{r}/dt = \mathbf{v}$, where $\mathbf{v}$ is the velocity of the particle, and changing to an integration over t,

$$S = \int_{t_1}^{t_2} \left(-mc^2 \sqrt{1 - \frac{v^2}{c^2}} + \frac{e}{c} \mathbf{A} \cdot \mathbf{v} - e\phi \right) dt. \tag{16.3}$$

The integrand is just the Lagrangian for a charge in an electromagnetic field:

$$L = -mc^2 \sqrt{1 - \frac{v^2}{c^2}} + \frac{e}{c} \mathbf{A} \cdot \mathbf{v} - e\phi. \tag{16.4}$$

This function differs from the Lagrangian for a free particle (8.2) by the terms $\frac{e}{c} \mathbf{A} \cdot \mathbf{v} - e\phi$, which describe the interaction of the charge with the field.

The derivative $\partial L / \partial \mathbf{v}$ is the generalized momentum of the particle; we denote it by $\mathbf{P}$. Carrying out the differentiation, we find

$$\mathbf{P} = \frac{m\mathbf{v}}{\sqrt{1 - \frac{v^2}{c^2}}} + \frac{e}{c} \mathbf{A} = \mathbf{p} + \frac{e}{c} \mathbf{A}. \tag{16.5}$$

Here we have denoted by $\mathbf{p}$ the ordinary momentum of the particle, which we shall refer to simply as its momentum.

From the Lagrangian we can find the Hamiltonian function for a particle in a field from the general formula

$$\mathcal{H} = \mathbf{v} \cdot \frac{\partial L}{\partial \mathbf{v}} - L.$$

Substituting (16.4), we get

$$\mathcal{H} = \frac{mc^2}{\sqrt{1 - \frac{v^2}{c^2}}} + e\phi. \tag{16.6}$$

However, the Hamiltonian must be expressed not in terms of the velocity, but rather in terms of the generalized momentum of the particle.

From (16.5) and (16.6) it is clear that the relation between $\mathcal{H} - e\phi$ and $\mathbf{P} - \frac{e}{c} \mathbf{A}$ is the same as the relation between $\mathcal{H}$ and $\mathbf{P}$ in the absence of the field, i.e.

$$\left(\frac{\mathcal{H} - e\phi}{c} \right)^2 = m^2 c^2 + \left(\mathbf{P} - \frac{e}{c} \mathbf{A} \right)^2, \tag{16.7}$$

or else

$$\mathcal{H} = \sqrt{m^2 c^4 + c^2 \left(\mathbf{P} - \frac{e}{c} \mathbf{A} \right)^2} + e\phi. \tag{16.8}$$

For low velocities, i.e., for classical mechanics, the Lagrangian (16.4) goes over into

$$L = \frac{mv^2}{2} + \frac{e}{c}\mathbf{A}\cdot\mathbf{v} - e\phi. \tag{16.9}$$

In this approximation

$$\mathbf{p} = m\mathbf{v} = \mathbf{P} - \frac{e}{c}\mathbf{A},$$

and we find the following expression for the Hamiltonian:

$$\mathcal{H} = \frac{1}{2m}\left(\mathbf{P} - \frac{e}{c}\mathbf{A}\right)^2 + e\phi. \tag{16.10}$$

Finally we write the Hamilton-Jacobi equation for a particle in an electromagnetic field. It is obtained by replacing, in the equation for the Hamiltonian, $\mathbf{P}$ by $\partial S/\partial \mathbf{r}$, and $\mathcal{H}$ by $-\dfrac{\partial S}{\partial t}$. Thus we get from (17.6)

$$\left(\nabla S - \frac{e}{c}\mathbf{A}\right)^2 - \frac{1}{c^2}\left(\frac{\partial S}{\partial t} + e\phi\right)^2 + m^2c^2 = 0. \tag{16.11}$$

§ 17. Equations of motion of a charge in a field

A charge located in a field not only is subjected to a force exerted by the field, but also in turn acts on the field, changing it. However, if the charge e is not large, the action of the charge on the field can be neglected. In this case, when considering the motion of the charge in a given field, we may assume that the field itself does not depend on the coordinates or the velocity of the charge. The precise conditions which the charge must fulfil in order to be considered as small in the present sense, will be clarified later on (see § 75). In what follows we shall assume that this condition is fulfilled.

So we must find the equations of motion of a charge in a given electromagnetic field. These equations are obtained by varying the action, i.e., they are given by the Lagrange equations

$$\frac{\partial}{\partial t}\left(\frac{\partial L}{\partial \mathbf{v}}\right) = \frac{\partial L}{\partial \mathbf{r}}, \tag{17.1}$$

where L is given by formula (16.4).

The derivative $\partial L/\partial \mathbf{v}$ is the generalized momentum of the particle (16.5). Further, we write

$$\frac{\partial L}{\partial \mathbf{r}} = \nabla L = \frac{e}{c}\,\text{grad}\,\mathbf{A}\cdot\mathbf{v} - e\,\text{grad}\,\phi.$$

But from a familiar formula of vector analysis.

$$\text{grad}\,(\mathbf{a}\cdot\mathbf{b}) = (\mathbf{a}\cdot\nabla)\mathbf{b} + (\mathbf{b}\cdot\nabla)\mathbf{a} + \mathbf{b}\times\text{curl}\,\mathbf{a} + \mathbf{a}\times\text{curl}\,\mathbf{b},$$

where **a** and **b** are two arbitrary vectors. Applying this formula to $\mathbf{A}\cdot\mathbf{v}$, and remembering that differentiation with respect to **r** is carried out for constant **v**, we find

$$\frac{\partial L}{\partial \mathbf{r}} = \frac{e}{c}(\mathbf{v}\cdot\nabla)\mathbf{A} + \frac{e}{c}\mathbf{v}\times\text{curl}\,\mathbf{A} - e\,\text{grad}\,\phi.$$

So the Lagrange equation has the form:

$$\frac{d}{dt}\left(\mathbf{p}+\frac{e}{e}\mathbf{A}\right) = \frac{e}{c}(\mathbf{v}\cdot\nabla)\mathbf{A} + \frac{e}{c}\mathbf{v}\times\text{curl}\,\mathbf{A} - e\,\text{grad}\,\phi.$$

But the total differential $\frac{d\mathbf{A}}{dt}dt$ consists of two parts: the change $\frac{\partial\mathbf{A}}{dt}dt$ of the vector potential with time at a fixed point in space, and the change due to motion from one point in space to another at distance $d\mathbf{r}$. This second part, as is known from vector analysis, is $(d\mathbf{r}\cdot\nabla)\mathbf{A}$. Thus

$$\frac{d\mathbf{A}}{dt} = \frac{\partial\mathbf{A}}{\partial t} + (\mathbf{v}\cdot\nabla)\mathbf{A}.$$

Substituting this in the previous equation, we find

$$\frac{d\mathbf{p}}{dt} = -\frac{e}{c}\frac{\partial\mathbf{A}}{\partial t} - e\,\text{grad}\,\phi + \frac{e}{c}\mathbf{v}\times\text{curl}\,\mathbf{A}. \tag{17.2}$$

This is the equation of motion of a particle in an electromagnetic field. On the left side stands the derivative of the particle's momentum with respect to the time. Therefore the expression on the right of (17.2) is the force exerted on the charge in an electromagnetic field. We see that this force consists of two parts. The first part (first and second terms on the right side of 17.2) does not depend on the velocity of the particle. The second part (third term) depends on the velocity, being proportional to the velocity and perpendicular to it.

The force of the first type, per unit charge, is called the *electric field intensity*; we denote it by **E**. So by definition,

$$\mathbf{E} = -\frac{1}{c}\frac{\partial\mathbf{A}}{\partial t} - \text{grad}\,\phi. \tag{17.3}$$

The factor of $\mathbf{v}/c$ in the force of the second type, per unit charge, is called the *magnetic field intensity*. We designate it by **H**. So by definition,

$$\mathbf{H} = \text{curl}\,\mathbf{A}. \tag{17.4}$$

If in an electromagnetic field, $\mathbf{E} \neq 0$ but $\mathbf{H} = 0$, then we speak of an electric field; if $\mathbf{E} = 0$ but $\mathbf{H} \neq 0$, then the field is said to be magnetic. In general, the electromagnetic field is a superposition of electric and magnetic fields.

The equation of motion of a charge in an electromagnetic field can now be written as

$$\frac{d\mathbf{p}}{dt} = e\mathbf{E} + \frac{e}{c}\mathbf{v}\times\mathbf{H}. \tag{17.5}$$

The expression on the right is called the *Lorentz force*. The first term (the force which the electric field exerts on the charge) does not depend on the velocity of the charge, and is along the direction of **E**. The second part (the force exerted by the magnetic field on the charge) is proportional to the velocity of the charge and is directed perpendicular to the velocity and to the magnetic field **H**.

For velocities small compared with the velocity of light, the momentum **p** is approximately equal to its classical expression $m\mathbf{v}$, and the equation of motion (17.5) becomes

$$m\frac{d\mathbf{v}}{dt} = e\mathbf{E} + \frac{e}{c}\mathbf{v}\times\mathbf{H}, \tag{17.6}$$

Next we derive the equation for the rate of change of the kinetic energy of the particle† with time, i.e., the derivative

$$\frac{d\mathcal{E}_{\text{kin}}}{dt} = \frac{d}{dt}\left(\frac{mc^2}{\sqrt{1-\frac{v^2}{c^2}}}\right).$$

It is easy to check that

$$d\mathcal{E}_{\text{kin}} = \mathbf{v}\cdot d\mathbf{p},$$

so that

$$\frac{d\mathcal{E}_{\text{kin}}}{dt} = \mathbf{v}\cdot\frac{d\mathbf{p}}{dt}.$$

Substituting $d\mathbf{p}/dt$ from (17.5) and noting that $\mathbf{v}\times\mathbf{H}\cdot\mathbf{v} = 0$, we have

$$\frac{d\mathcal{E}_{\text{kin}}}{dt} = e\mathbf{E}\cdot\mathbf{v}. \tag{17.7}$$

The rate of change of the kinetic energy is the work done by the field on the particle per unit time. From (17.7) we see that this work is equal to the product of the velocity by the force which the electric field exerts on the charge. The work done by the field during a time dt, i.e., during a displacement of the charge by $d\mathbf{r}$, is clearly equal to $e\mathbf{E}\cdot d\mathbf{r}$.

We emphasize the fact that work is done on the charge only by the electric field; the magnetic field does no work on a charge moving in it. This is connected with the fact that the force which the magnetic field exerts on a charge is always perpendicular to the velocity of the charge.

† By "kinetic" we mean the energy (9.4), which includes the rest energy.

The equations of mechanics are invariant with respect to a change in sign of the time, that is, with respect to interchange of future and past. In other words, in mechanics the two time directions are equivalent, i.e., time is isotropic. This means that if a certain motion is possible according to the equations of mechanics, then the reverse motion is also possible, in which the system passes through the same states in reverse order.

It is easy to see that this is also valid for the electromagnetic field in the theory of relativity. In this case, however, in addition to changing t into $-t$, we must reverse the sign of the magnetic field. In fact it is easy to see that the equatiors of motion (17.5) are not altered if we make the changes

$$t \to -t, \quad \mathbf{E} \to \mathbf{E}, \quad \mathbf{H} \to -\mathbf{H}. \tag{17.8}$$

According to (17.3) and (17.4), this does not change the scalar potential, while the vector potential changes sign:

$$\phi \to \phi, \quad \mathbf{A} \to -\mathbf{A}, \tag{17.9}$$

Thus, if a certain motion is possible in an electromagnetic field, then the reversed motion is possible in a field in which the direction of $\mathbf{H}$ is reversed.

Problem

Express the acceleration of a particle in terms of its velocity and the electric and magnetic field intensities.

Solution. Substitute in the equation of motion (17.5) $\mathbf{p} = \mathbf{v}\mathcal{E}_{\text{kin}}/c^2$, and take the expression for $d\mathcal{E}_{\text{kin}}/dt$ from (17.7). As a result, we get

$$\dot{\mathbf{v}} = \frac{e}{m}\sqrt{1-\frac{v^2}{c^2}}\left\{\mathbf{E} + \frac{1}{c}\mathbf{v}\times\mathbf{H} - \frac{1}{c^2}\mathbf{v}(\mathbf{v}\cdot\mathbf{E})\right\}.$$

§ 18. Gauge invariance

Let us consider to what extent the potentials are uniquely determined. First of all we call attention to the fact that the field is characterized by the effect which it produces on the motion of a charge located in it. But in the equation of motion (17.5) there appear not the potentials, but the field intensities $\mathbf{E}$ and $\mathbf{H}$. Therefore two fields are physically identical if they are characterized by the same vectors $\mathbf{E}$ and $\mathbf{H}$.

If we are given potentials $\mathbf{A}$ and ϕ, then these uniquely determine (according to (17.3) and (17.4)) the fields $\mathbf{E}$ and $\mathbf{H}$. However, to one and the same field there can correspond different potentials. To show this, let us add to each component of the potential the quantity $\partial f/\partial x_k$, where f is an arbitrary function of the coordinates and the time. Then the potential A_k goes over into

$$A'_k = A_k + \frac{\partial f}{\partial x_k}. \tag{18.1}$$

As a result of this change there appears in the action integral (16.1) the additional term

$$\frac{e}{c}\frac{\partial f}{\partial x_k}dx_k = \frac{e}{c}\,df,$$

which is a total differential† and has no effect on the equations of motion. (See the footnote on p. 26.)

If in place of the four-potential we introduce the scalar and vector potentials, and in place of x_i, the coordinates x, y, z, t, then the four equations (18.1) can be written in the form

$$\mathbf{A}' = \mathbf{A} + \operatorname{grad} f, \qquad \phi' = \phi - \frac{1}{c}\frac{\partial f}{\partial t}. \tag{18.2}$$

It is easy to check that electric and magnetic fields determined from equations (17.3) and (17.4) actually do not change upon replacement of **A** and ϕ by **A**′ and ϕ', defined by (18.2). Thus the transformation of potentials (18.2) does not change the fields. The potentials are therefore not uniquely defined; the vector potential is determined to within the gradient of an arbitrary function, and the scalar potential to within the time derivative of the same function.

In particular, we see that we can add an arbitrary constant vector to the vector potential, and an arbitrary constant to the scalar potential. This is also clear directly from the fact that the definitions of **E** and **H** contain only derivatives of **A** and ϕ, and therefore the addition of constants to the latter does not affect the field intensities.

Only those quantities have physical meaning which are invariant with respect to the transformation (18.2) of the potentials; in particular all equations must be invariant under this transformation. This invariance is called *gauge invariance* (in German, eichinvarianz).

This nonuniqueness of the potentials gives us the possibility of choosing them so that they fulfill one auxiliary condition chosen by us. We emphasize that we can set one condition, since we may choose the function f in (18.2) arbitrarily. In particular, it is always possible to choose the potentials so that the scalar potential ϕ is zero. If the vector potential is not zero, then it is not generally possible to make it zero, since the condition $\mathbf{A} = 0$ represents three auxiliary conditions (for the three components of **A**).

§ 19. Constant electromagnetic field

By a constant electromagnetic field we mean a field which does not depend on the time. Clearly the potentials of a constant field can be chosen so that they are functions only of the coordinates and not of the time. A constant

† We emphasize that this is related to the assumed constancy of e. Thus the gauge invariance of the equations of electrodynamics (see below) and the conservation of charge are closely related to one another.

magnetic field is equal, as before, to $\mathbf{H} = \operatorname{curl} \mathbf{A}$. A constant electric field is equal to

$$\mathbf{E} = -\operatorname{grad} \phi. \tag{19.1}$$

Thus a constant electric field is determined only by the scalar potential and a constant magnetic field only by the vector potential.

We saw in the preceding section that the potentials are not uniquely determined. However it is easy to convince oneself that if we describe the constant electromagnetic field in terms of potentials which do not depend on the time, then we can add to the scalar potential, without changing the fields, only an arbitrary constant (not depending on either the coordinates or the time). Usually ϕ is subjected to the additional requirement that it have a definite value at some particular point in space; most frequently ϕ is chosen to be zero at infinity. Thus the arbitrary constant previously mentioned is determined, and the scalar potential of the constant field is thus determined uniquely.

On the other hand, just as before, the vector potential is not uniquely determined even for the constant electromagnetic field; namely, we can add to it the gradient of an arbitrary function of the coordinates.

We now determine the energy of a charge in a constant electromagnetic field. If the field is constant, then the Lagrangian for the charge also does not depend explicitly on the time. As we know, in this case the energy is conserved and coincides with the Hamiltonian.

According to (16.6), we have

$$\mathcal{E} = \frac{mc^2}{\sqrt{1-\frac{v^2}{c^2}}} + e\phi. \tag{19.2}$$

Thus the presence of the field adds to the energy of the particle the term $e\phi$, the potential energy of the charge in the field. We note the important fact that the energy depends only on the scalar and not on the vector potential. This means that the magnetic field does not affect the energy of the charge. Only the electric field can change the energy of the particle. This is related to the fact that the magnetic field, unlike the electric field, does no work on the charge.

If the field intensities are the same at all points in space, then the field is said to be uniform. The scalar potential of a uniform electric field can be expressed in terms of the field intensity as

$$\phi = -\mathbf{E}\cdot\mathbf{r}. \tag{19.3}$$

In fact, since $\mathbf{E} = \text{const}$, $\nabla(\mathbf{E}\cdot\mathbf{r}) = (\mathbf{E}\cdot\nabla)\mathbf{r} = \mathbf{E}$.

The vector potential of a uniform magnetic field can be expressed in terms of its field intensity as

$$\mathbf{A} = \tfrac{1}{2}\mathbf{H}\times\mathbf{r}. \tag{19.4}$$

In fact, recalling that $\mathbf{H} = \text{const}$, we obtain with the aid of well-known formulas of vector analysis:

$$\text{curl}\,(\mathbf{H}\times\mathbf{r}) = \mathbf{H}\,\text{div}\,\mathbf{r} - (\mathbf{H}\cdot\nabla)\mathbf{r} = 2\mathbf{H}$$

(noting that $\text{div}\,\mathbf{r} = 3$).

The vector potential of a uniform magnetic field can also be chosen in the form

$$A_x = -Hy, \qquad A_y = A_z = 0 \tag{19.5}$$

(the z axis is along the direction of $\mathbf{H}$). It is easily verified that with this choice for $\mathbf{A}$ we have $\mathbf{H} = \text{curl}\,\mathbf{A}$. In accordance with the transformation formulas (18.2), the potentials (19.4) and (19.5) differ from one another by the gradient of some function: formula (19.5) is obtained from (19.4) by adding ∇f, where $f = -xyH/2$.

Problem

Give the variational principle for the trajectory of a particle (Maupertuis' principle) in a constant electromagnetic field in relativistic mechanics.

Solution: Maupertuis' principle consists in the statement that if the energy of a particle is conserved (motion in a constant field), then its trajectory can be determined from the variational equation

$$\delta\int \mathbf{P}\cdot d\mathbf{r} = 0,$$

where $\mathbf{P}$ is the generalized momentum of the particle, expressed in terms of the energy and the coordinate differentials, and the integral is taken along the trajectory of the particle†. Substituting $\mathbf{P} = \mathbf{p} + \frac{e}{c}\mathbf{A}$ and noting that the directions of $\mathbf{p}$ and $d\mathbf{r}$ coincide, we have

$$\delta\int\left(p\,dl + \frac{e}{c}\mathbf{A}\cdot d\mathbf{r}\right) = 0,$$

where $dl = \sqrt{d\mathbf{r}^2}$ is the element of arc. Determining p from $p^2 + m^2c^2 = \left(\frac{\mathcal{E} - e\varphi}{c}\right)^2$, we obtain finally

$$\delta\int\left\{\sqrt{\left(\frac{\mathcal{E} - e\varphi}{c}\right)^2 - m^2c^2}\,dl + \frac{e}{c}\mathbf{A}\cdot d\mathbf{r}\right\} = 0.$$

§ 20. Motion in a constant uniform electric field

Let us consider the motion of a charge e in a uniform constant electric field $\mathbf{E}$. We take the direction of the field as the X axis. The motion will obviously proceed in a plane, which we choose as the XY plane. Then the equations of motion (17.5) become

$$\dot{p}_x = eE, \qquad \dot{p}_y = 0$$

(where the dot denotes differentiation with respect to t), so that

$$p_x = eEt, \qquad p_y = p_0. \tag{20.1}$$

† See *Mechanics*, § 44.

The time reference point has been chosen at the moment when $p_x = 0$; p_0 is the momentum of the particle at that moment.

The kinetic energy of the particle (the energy omitting the potential energy in the field) is $\mathcal{E}_{\text{kin}} = c\sqrt{m^2c^2+p^2}$. Substituting (20.1), we find in our case

$$\mathcal{E}_{\text{kin}} = \sqrt{m^2c^4+c^2p_0^2+(ceEt)^2} = \sqrt{\mathcal{E}_0^2+(ceEt)^2}, \tag{20.2}$$

where $\mathcal{E}_0$ is the energy at $t = 0$.

According to (9.8) the velocity of the particle is $\mathbf{v} = \mathbf{p}c^2/\mathcal{E}_{\text{kin}}$. For the velocity $v_x = \dot{x}$, we have therefore

$$\frac{dx}{dt} = \frac{c^2eEt}{\sqrt{\mathcal{E}_0^2+(ceEt)^2}}.$$

Integrating, we find

$$x = \frac{1}{eE}\sqrt{\mathcal{E}_0^2+(ceEt)^2}. \tag{20.3}$$

The constant of integration we set equal to zero.†

For determining y, we have

$$\frac{dy}{dt} = \frac{p_yc^2}{\mathcal{E}} = \frac{p_0c^2}{\sqrt{\mathcal{E}_0^2+(ceEt)^2}},$$

from which

$$y = \frac{p_0c}{eE} = \sinh^{-1}\left(\frac{ceEt}{\mathcal{E}_0}\right). \tag{20.4}$$

We obtain the equation of the trajectory by expressing t in terms of y from (20.4) and substituting in (20.3). This gives:

$$x = \frac{\mathcal{E}_0}{eE}\cosh\frac{eEy}{p_0c}. \tag{20.5}$$

Thus in a uniform electric field a charge moves along a catenary curve.

If the velocity of the particle is $v \ll c$, then we can set $p_0 = mv_0$, $\mathcal{E}_0 = mc^2$, and expand (20.5) in series in powers of $1/c$. Then we get, to within terms of higher order,

$$x = \frac{eE}{2mv_0^2}y^2 + \text{const},$$

that is, the charge moves along a parabola, a result well known from classical mechanics.

† This result (for $p_0 = 0$) coincides with the solution of the problem of relativistic motion with constant "proper acceleration" $w_0 = eE/m$ (see the problem in § 7). For the present case, the constancy of the acceleration is related to the fact that the electric field does not change for Lorentz transformations having velocities $\mathbf{V}$ along the direction of the field (see § 24).

§ 21. Motion in a constant uniform magnetic field

We now consider the motion of a charge e in a uniform magnetic field **H**. We choose the direction of the field as the Z axis. We rewrite the equation of motion

$$\dot{\mathbf{p}} = \frac{e}{c}\mathbf{v}\times\mathbf{H}$$

in another form, by substituting for the momentum, from (9.8),

$$\mathbf{p} = \frac{\mathcal{E}\mathbf{v}}{c^2},$$

where $\mathcal{E}$ is the energy of the particle, which we know from § 19 is a constant in the magnetic field. The equation of motion then goes over into the form

$$\frac{\mathcal{E}}{c^2}\frac{d\mathbf{v}}{dt} = \frac{e}{c}\mathbf{v}\times\mathbf{H} \tag{21.1}$$

or, expressed in terms of components,

$$\dot{v}_x = \omega v_y, \qquad \dot{v}_y = -\omega v_x, \qquad \dot{v}_z = 0, \tag{21.2}$$

where we have introduced the notation

$$\omega = \frac{ecH}{\mathcal{E}}. \tag{21.3}$$

We multiply the second equation of (21.2) by i, and add it to the first:

$$\frac{d}{dt}(v_x+iv_y) = -i\omega(v_x+iv_y),$$

so that

$$v_x+iv_y = ae^{-i\omega t},$$

where a is a complex constant. This can be written in the form $a = v_{0t}e^{-i\alpha}$ where v_{0t} and α are real. Then

$$v_z+iv_y = v_{0t}e^{-i(\omega t+\alpha)}$$

and, separating real and imaginary parts, we find

$$v_x = v_{0t}\cos(\omega t+\alpha), \qquad v_y = -v_{0t}\sin(\omega t+\alpha). \tag{21.4}$$

The constants v_{0t} and α are determined by the initial conditions; α is the initial phase, and as for v_{0t}, from (21.4) it is clear that

$$v_{0t} = \sqrt{v_x^2+v_y^2},$$

that is, v_{0t} is the velocity of the particle in the XY plane, and stays constant throughout the motion.

From (21.4) we find, integrating once more,

$$x = x_0+r\sin(\omega t+\alpha), \qquad y = y_0+r\cos(\omega t+\alpha), \tag{21.5}$$

where

$$r = \frac{v_{0t}}{\omega} = \frac{v_{0t}\mathcal{E}}{ecH} = \frac{cp_t}{eH} \tag{21.6}$$

(p_t is the projection of the momentum on the XY plane). From the third equation of (21.2), we find $v_z = v_{0z}$ and

$$z = z_0 + v_{0z}t. \tag{21.7}$$

From (21.5) and (21.7), it is clear that the charge moves in a uniform magnetic field along a helix having its axis along the direction of the magnetic field and with a radius r given by (21.6). The velocity of the particle is constant. In the special case where $v_{0z} = 0$, that is, the charge has no velocity component along the field, it moves along a circle in the plane perpendicular to the field.

The quantity ω, as we see from the formulas, is the angular frequency of rotation of the particle in the plane perpendicular to the field.

If the velocity of the particle is low, then we can approximately set $\mathcal{E} = mc^2$. Then the frequency ω is changed to

$$\omega = \frac{eH}{mc}. \tag{21.8}$$

We shall now assume that the magnetic field remains uniform but varies slowly in magnitude and direction. Let us see how the motion of a charged particle changes in this case.

We know that when the conditions of the motion are changed slowly, certain quantities called adiabatic invariants remain constant. Since the motion in the plane perpendicular to the magnetic field is periodic, the adiabatic invariant is the integral $I = \frac{1}{2\pi}\oint \mathbf{P}_t \cdot d\mathbf{r}$, taken over a complete period of the motion, i.e. over the circumference of a circle in the present case ($\mathbf{P}_t$ is the projection of the generalized momentum on the plane perpendicular to $\mathbf{H}$†). Substituting $\mathbf{P}_t = \mathbf{p}_t + \frac{e}{c}\mathbf{A}$, we have:

$$I = \frac{1}{2\pi}\oint \mathbf{P}_t \cdot d\mathbf{r} = \frac{1}{2\pi}\oint \mathbf{p}_t \cdot d\mathbf{r} + \frac{e}{2\pi c}\oint \mathbf{A} \cdot d\mathbf{r}.$$

† See *Mechanics*, § 49. In general the integrals $\oint p\, dq$, taken over a period of the particular coordinate q, are adiabatic invariants. In the present case the periods for the two coordinates in the plane perpendicular to $\mathbf{H}$ coincide, and the integral I which we have written is the sum of the two corresponding adiabatic invariants. However each of these invariants individually has no special significance, sinc eit depends on the (non-unique) choice of the vector potential of the field. The nonuniqueness of the adiabatic invariants which results from this, is a reflection of the fact that, when we regard the magnetic field as uniform over all of space, we cannot in principle determine the electric field which results from changes in $\mathbf{H}$, since it will actually depend on the specific conditions at infinity.

In the first term we note that $\mathbf{p}_t$ is constant in magnitude and directed along $d\mathbf{r}$; we apply Stokes' theorem to the second term and write curl $\mathbf{A} = \mathbf{H}$:

$$I = rp_t + \frac{e}{2c} Hr^2,$$

where r is the radius of the orbit. Substituting the expression (21.6) for r, we find:

$$I = \frac{3cp_t^2}{2eH}. \tag{21.9}$$

From this we see that, for slow variation of H, the tangential momentum p_t varies proportionally to $\sqrt{H}$.

This result can be applied approximately to another case — when the particle moves in a constant field which is not uniform (but varies little over distances comparable to the radius of the particle's orbit). For the motion in such a quasiuniform field, the circular orbit is displaced in the course of time, and the field as seen from it appears to vary with time while remaining uniform. Then the component of momentum transverse to the direction of the field varies according to the law $p_t = \sqrt{CH}$, where C is a constant and H is a given function of the coordinates. On the other hand, just as for any motion in a constant magnetic field, the energy of the particle (and so also the square of its momentum p^2) remains constant. We therefore have for the longitudinal component of the momentum:

$$p_l^2 = p^2 - p_t^2 = p^2 - CH(x, y, z).$$

Since $p_l^2 \geqslant 0$, we see that penetration of the particle into certain portions of space (those in which $CH > p^2$) may be impossible.

Problem

Determine the frequency of vibration of a charged spatial oscillator, placed in a constant, uniform magnetic field; the proper frequency of vibration of the oscillator (in the absence of the field) is ω_0.

Solution. The equations of forced vibration of the oscillator in a magnetic field (directed along the Z axis) are:

$$\ddot{x} + \omega_0^2 x = \frac{eH}{mc}\dot{y}, \qquad \ddot{y} + \omega_0^2 y = -\frac{eH}{mc}\dot{x}, \qquad \ddot{z} + \omega_0^2 z = 0.$$

Multiplying the second equation by i and combining with the first, we find

$$\ddot{\zeta} + \omega_0^2 \zeta = -i\frac{eH}{mc}\dot{\zeta},$$

where $\zeta = x + iy$. From this we find that the frequency of vibration of the oscillator in a plane perpendicular to the field is

$$\omega = \sqrt{\omega_0^2 + \frac{1}{4}\left(\frac{eH}{mc}\right)^2} \pm \frac{eH}{2mc}.$$

If the field H is weak, this formula goes over into

$$\omega = \omega_0 \pm eH/2mc.$$

The vibration along the direction of the field remains unchanged.

§ 22. Motion of a charge in constant uniform electric and magnetic fields

Finally we consider the motion of a charge in the case where there are present both electric and magnetic fields, constant and uniform. We limit ourselves to the case where the velocity of the charge $v \ll c$, so that its momentum $\mathbf{p} = m\mathbf{v}$; as we shall see later, it is necessary for this that the electric field be small compared to the magnetic.

We choose the direction of **H** as the Z axis, and the plane passing through **H** and **E** as the YZ plane. Then the equation of motion

$$m\dot{\mathbf{v}} = e\mathbf{E} + \frac{e}{c}\mathbf{v}\times\mathbf{H}$$

can be written in the form

$$m\ddot{x} = \frac{e}{c}\dot{y}H, \qquad m\ddot{y} = eE_y - \frac{e}{c}\dot{x}H, \qquad m\ddot{z} = eE_z. \tag{22.1}$$

From the third equation we see that the charge moves with uniform acceleration in the Z direction, that is,

$$z = \frac{eE_z}{2m}t^2 + v_{0z}t. \tag{22.2}$$

Multiplying the second equation of (22.1) by i and combining with the first, we find

$$\frac{d}{dt}(\dot{x} + i\dot{y}) + i\omega(\dot{x} + i\dot{y}) = i\frac{e}{m}E_y$$

($\omega = eH/mc$). The integral of this equation, where $\dot{x}+i\dot{y}$ is considered as the unknown, is equal to the sum of the integral of the same equation without the right-hand term and a particular integral of the equation with the right-hand term. The first of these is $ae^{-i\omega t}$, the second is $eE_y/m\omega = cE_y/H$. Thus

$$\dot{x} + i\dot{y} = ae^{-i\omega t} + \frac{cE_y}{H}.$$

The constant a is in general complex. Writing it in the form $a = be^{i\alpha}$, with real b and α, we see that since a is multiplied by $e^{-i\omega t}$, we can, by a suitable choice of the time origin, give the phase α any arbitrary value. We choose this so that a is real. Then breaking up $\dot{x}+i\dot{y}$ into real and imaginary parts, we find

$$\dot{x} = a\cos\omega t + \frac{cE_y}{H}, \qquad \dot{y} = -a\sin\omega t. \tag{22.3}$$

At $t = 0$ the velocity is along the X axis.

We see that the components of the velocity of the particle are periodic functions of the time.

$$\bar{\dot{x}} = \frac{cE_y}{H}, \quad \bar{\dot{y}} = 0. \tag{22.4}$$

Thus the average velocity along the Y axis is zero, while the average velocity along the X axis, i.e., perpendicular to the magnetic and electric fields, is different from zero.

All the formulas of this section assume that the velocity of the particle is small compared with the velocity of light; we see that for this to be so, it is necessary in particular that the electric and magnetic fields satisfy the condition

$$\frac{E_y}{H} \ll 1, \tag{22.5}$$

while the absolute magnitudes of E_0 and H can be arbitrary.

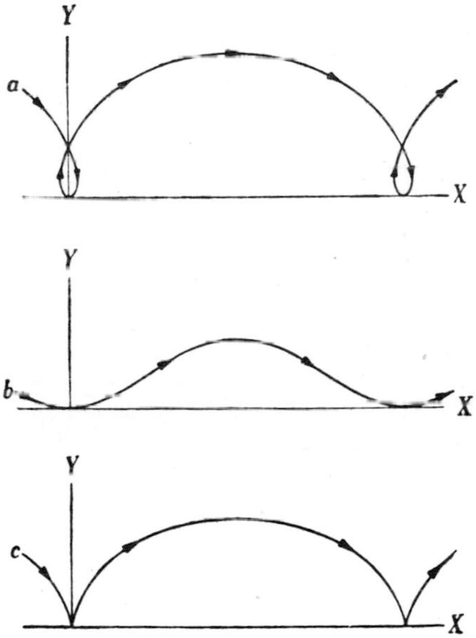

FIG. 6.

Integrating equation (22.3) again, and choosing the constant of integration so that at $t = 0$, $x = y = 0$, we obtain

$$x = \frac{a}{\omega}\sin\omega t + \frac{cE_y}{H}t; \quad y = \frac{a}{\omega}(\cos\omega t - 1). \tag{22.6}$$

Considered as parametric equations of a curve, these equations define a trochoid. Depending on whether a is larger or smaller in absolute value than the quantity cE_y/H, the projection of the trajectory on the plane XY has the forms shown in Figs. 6a and 6b, respectively.

If $a = -cE_y/H$, then (22.6) becomes

$$x = \frac{cE_y}{\omega H}(\omega t - \sin \omega t),$$

$$y = \frac{cE_y}{\omega H}(1 - \cos \omega t) \qquad (22.7)$$

that is, the projection of the trajectory on the XY plane is a cycloid (Fig. 6c).

PROBLEMS

1. Determine the relativistic motion of a charge in parallel uniform electric and magnetic fields.

Solution: The magnetic field has no influence on the motion along the common direction of **E** and **H** (the z axis), which therefore occurs under the influence of the electric field alone; therefore according to § 20 we find:

$$z = \frac{\mathcal{E}_{\text{kin}}}{eE}, \qquad \mathcal{E}_{\text{kin}} = \sqrt{\mathcal{E}_0^2 + (ceEt)^2}\,.$$

For the motion in the xy plane we have the equation

$$\dot{p}_x = \frac{e}{c}Hv_y, \quad \dot{p}_y = -\frac{e}{c}Hv_x,$$

or

$$\frac{d}{dt}(p_x + ip_y) = -i\frac{eH}{c}(v_x + iv_y) = -\frac{ieHc}{\mathcal{E}_{\text{kin}}}(p_x + ip_y).$$

Consequently

$$p_x + ip_y = p_t e^{-i\varphi},$$

where p_t is the constant value of the projection of the momentum on the xy plane, and the auxiliary quantity φ is defined by the relation

$$d\varphi = eHc\frac{dt}{\mathcal{E}_{\text{kin}}},$$

from which

$$ct = \frac{\mathcal{E}_0}{eE}\sinh\frac{E}{H}\varphi. \qquad (1)$$

Furthermore we have:

$$p_x + ip_y = p_t e^{-i\varphi} = \frac{\mathcal{E}_{\text{kin}}}{c^2}(\dot{x} + i\dot{y}) = \frac{eH}{c}\frac{d(x+iy)}{d\varphi},$$

so that

$$x = \frac{cp_t}{eH}\sin\varphi, \qquad y = \frac{cp_t}{eH}\cos\varphi. \qquad (2)$$

Formulas (1), (2) together with the formula

$$z = \frac{\mathcal{E}_0}{eE}\cosh\frac{E}{H}\varphi, \qquad (3)$$

determine the motion of the particle in parametric form. The trajectory is a helix with radius cp_t/eH and monotonically increasing step, along which the particle moves with decreasing angular velocity $\dot{\varphi} = eHc/\mathcal{E}_{\text{kin}}$ and with a velocity along the z axis which tends toward the value c.

2. Determine the relativistic motion of a charge in electric and magnetic fields which are mutually perpendicular and equal in magnitude.†

Solution: Choosing the z axis along **H** and the y axis along **E** and setting $E = H$, we write the equations of motion:

$$\frac{dp_x}{dt} = \frac{e}{c} E v_y, \qquad \frac{dp_y}{dt} = eE\left(1 - \frac{v_x}{c}\right), \qquad \frac{dp_z}{dt} = 0$$

and, as a consequence of them, formula (17.7),

$$\frac{d\mathcal{E}_{\text{kin}}}{dt} = eEv_y.$$

From these equations we have:

$$p_z = \text{const}, \qquad \mathcal{E}_{\text{kin}} - cp_x = \text{const} \equiv \alpha.$$

Also using the equation

$$\mathcal{E}_{\text{kin}}^2 - c^2 p_x^2 = (\mathcal{E}_{\text{kin}} + cp_x)(\mathcal{E}_{\text{kin}} - cp_x) = c^2 p_y^2 + \varepsilon^2$$

(where $\varepsilon^2 = m^2c^4 + c^2p_z^2 = \text{const}$), we find:

$$\mathcal{E}_{\text{kin}} + cp_x = \frac{1}{\alpha}(c^2p_y^2 + \varepsilon^2),$$

and so

$$\mathcal{E}_{\text{kin}} = \frac{\alpha}{2} + \frac{c^2p_y^2 + \varepsilon^2}{2\alpha},$$

$$p_x = -\frac{\alpha}{2c} + \frac{c^2p_y^2 + \varepsilon^2}{2\alpha c}.$$

Furthermore we write

$$\mathcal{E}_{\text{kin}} \frac{dp_y}{dt} = eE\left(\mathcal{E}_{\text{kin}} - \frac{\mathcal{E}_{\text{kin}} v_x}{c}\right) = eE(\mathcal{E}_{\text{kin}} - cp_x) = eE\alpha,$$

from which

$$2eEt = \left(1 + \frac{\varepsilon^2}{\alpha^2}\right)p_y + \frac{c^2}{3\alpha^2}p_y^3. \tag{1}$$

To determine the trajectory, we make a transformation of variables in the equations

$$\frac{dx}{dt} = \frac{c^2p_x}{\mathcal{E}_{\text{kin}}}, \ldots$$

to the variable p_y by using the relation $dt = \dfrac{\mathcal{E}_{\text{kin}}\, dp_y}{eE\alpha}$, after which integration gives the formulas:

$$x = \frac{c}{2eE}\left(-1 + \frac{\varepsilon^2}{\alpha^2}\right)p_y + \frac{c^3}{6\alpha^2 eE}p_y^3, \tag{2}$$

$$y = \frac{c^2}{2\alpha eE}p_y^2, \qquad z = \frac{p_z c^2}{eE\alpha}p_y.$$

Formulas (1) and (2) completely determine the motion of the particle in parametric form (parameter p_y). We call attention to the fact that the velocity increases most rapidly in the direction perpendicular to **E** and **H** (the x axis).

† The problem of motion in mutually perpendicular fields **E** and **H** which are not equal in magnitude can, by a suitable transformation of the reference system, be reduced to the problem of motion in a pure electric or a pure magnetic field (see § 25).

§ 23. The electromagnetic field tensor

In § 17, we derived the equation of motion of a charge in a field, starting from the Lagrangian (16.4) written in three-dimensional form. We now derive the same equation directly from the action (16.1) written in four-dimensional notation.

The principle of least action states

$$\delta S = \delta \int_a^b \left(-mc\, ds + \frac{e}{c} A_i\, dx_i\right) = 0. \tag{23.1}$$

Noting that $ds = \sqrt{-dx_i^2}$, we find (the limits of integration a and b are omitted for brevity):

$$\begin{aligned}\delta S &= \int \left[-mc\,\delta ds + \frac{e}{c}\delta(A_i\, dx_i)\right]\\ &= \int \left(mc \frac{dx_i\, \delta dx_i}{ds} + \frac{e}{c} A_i\, \delta dx_i + \frac{e}{c}\delta A_i\, dx_i\right)\\ &= \int \left(mc \frac{dx_i\, d\delta x_i}{ds} + \frac{e}{c} A_i\, d\delta x_i + \frac{e}{c}\delta A_i\, dx_i\right) = 0.\end{aligned}$$

We integrate the first two terms in the integrand by parts. Also, in the first term we set $dx_i/ds = u_i$, where u_i are the components of the four-velocity. Then

$$\int \left(-mc\, du_i\, \delta x_i - \frac{e}{c}\delta x_i\, dA_i + \frac{e}{c}\delta A_i\, dx_i\right) + \left[\left(mcu_i + \frac{e}{c}A_i\right)\delta x_i\right] = 0. \tag{23.2}$$

The second term in this equation is zero, since the integral is varied between fixed limits, that is, $(\delta x_i)_b = (\delta x_i)_a = 0$. Furthermore:

$$\delta A_i = \frac{\partial A_i}{\partial x_k}\delta x_k, \qquad dA_i = \frac{\partial A_i}{\partial x_k} dx_k,$$

and therefore

$$\int \left(-mc\, du_i\, \delta x_i - \frac{e}{c}\frac{\partial A_i}{\partial x_k}\delta x_i\, dx_k + \frac{e}{c}\frac{\partial A_i}{\partial x_k} dx_i\, \delta x_k\right) = 0.$$

In the first term we write $du_i = \dfrac{du_i}{ds} ds$, in the second and third, $dx_i = u_i\, ds$. In addition, in the third term we interchange the indices i and k (this changes nothing since the indices i and k are summed over). Then

$$\int \left[-mc\frac{du_i}{ds} + \frac{e}{c}\left(\frac{\partial A_k}{\partial x_i} - \frac{\partial A_i}{\partial x_k}\right)u_k\right]\delta x_i\, ds = 0.$$

In view of the arbitrariness of δx_i, it follows that the integrand is zero, that is,

$$mc\frac{du_i}{ds} = \frac{e}{c}\left(\frac{\partial A_k}{\partial x_i} - \frac{\partial A_i}{\partial x_k}\right)u_k. \tag{23.3}$$

We now introduce the notation

$$F_{ik} = \frac{\partial A_k}{\partial x_i} - \frac{\partial A_i}{\partial x_k}. \tag{23.4}$$

The tensor F_{ik} is called the *electromagnetic field tensor*. The equation of motion (23.3) then takes the form:

$$mc \frac{du_i}{ds} = \frac{e}{c} F_{ik} u_k. \tag{23.5}$$

These four equations (for $i = 1, 2, 3, 4$) are the equations of motion of a charge in the electromagnetic field in four-dimensional form.

From the definition of the tensor F_{ik} it follows that

$$F_{ik} = -F_{ki}, \tag{23.6}$$

that is, the electromagnetic field tensor is antisymmetric. Therefore $F_{ik} = 0$, for $i = k$.

Substituting in (23.4) $A_{1,2,3} = A_{x,y,z}$; $A_4 = i\phi$, we easily find the following values for the various components of the tensor F_{ik}:

$$F_{11} = F_{22} = F_{33} = F_{44} = 0$$

$$\begin{aligned} F_{12} &= -F_{21} = H_z, & F_{14} &= -F_{41} = -iE_x \\ F_{13} &= -F_{31} = -H_y, & F_{24} &= -F_{42} = -iE_y \\ F_{23} &= -F_{32} = H_x, & F_{34} &= -F_{43} = -iE_z. \end{aligned}$$

This can be written in the form of a table:

$$(F_{ik}) = \begin{pmatrix} 0 & H_z & H_y & -iE_x \\ -H_z & 0 & H_x & -iE_y \\ -H_y & -H_x & 0 & -iE_z \\ iE_x & iE_y & iE_z & 0 \end{pmatrix}. \tag{23.7}$$

Thus the components of the electric and magnetic field intensities are the components of a single four-tensor for the electromagnetic field.

From (23.7) we see that the space components of the tensor F_{ik} (i.e., the components with $i, k = 1, 2, 3$) are associated with the magnetic field: the components of the magnetic field **H** form a three-dimensional antisymmetric tensor of the second rank. This means, as we know, that the vector **H** is an axial vector (see § 6).

As for the components of the electricf ield **E**, they are the time components of F_{ik} (either i or $k = 4$). The vector **E** is clearly an ordinary (polar) vector.

Changing to three-dimensional notation, it is easy to verify that the first three equations of (23.5) are identical with the equations of motion (17.5), and the fourth with equation (17.7). The last equation is a consequence of (17.5). The fact that only three of these four equations are independent can be shown directly by multiplying both sides of (23.5) by u_i. Then in view of (7.4) and (23.6), both sides of the equation become identically zero.

If in considering variations δS, we admit only possible trajectories, then the first term in (23.2) is identically zero. Then the second term, in which the upper limit is considered as variable, gives the differential of the action as a function of the coordinates. Thus

$$\delta S = \left(mcu_i + \frac{e}{c}A_i\right)\delta x_i, \tag{23.8}$$

so that

$$\frac{\delta S}{\partial x_i} = mcu_i + \frac{e}{c}A_i = p_i + \frac{e}{c}A_i. \tag{23.9}$$

The four-vector with components $\partial S/\partial x_i$ is the four-vector of generalized momentum P_i. Using the expressions for the four-velocity and four-potential which make it up, we find the following expressions for the components P_i:

$$P_\alpha = p_\alpha + \frac{e}{c}A_\alpha, \quad P_4 = \frac{i}{c}(\mathscr{E}_{\text{kin}} + e\phi). \tag{23.10}$$

As expected, the space components of the four-vector P_i form the three-dimensional generalized momentum vector (16.5). The time component is $i\mathscr{E}/c$, where $\mathscr{E}$ is the total energy of the charge in the field.

In view of the fact that $u_i^2 = -1$, we have

$$\left(P_i - \frac{e}{c}A_i\right)^2 = -m^2c^2, \tag{23.11}$$

a relation which coincides with (16.7). Changing P_i to $\partial S/\partial x_i$, we obtain the Hamilton-Jacobi equation (16.11) in four-dimensional form:

$$\left(\frac{\partial S}{\partial x_i} - \frac{e}{c}A_i\right)^2 + m^2c^2 = 0. \tag{23.12}$$

§ 24. **Lorentz transformation of the field**

In this section we find the transformation formulas for fields, that is, formulas by means of which we can determine the field in one inertial system of reference, knowing the same field in another system.

The formulas for transformation of the potentials are obtained directly from the general formulas for transformation of four-vectors (6.2). Remembering that the components of the vector A_i are $A_{x,y,z}$, $i\phi$, we get easily

$$A_x = \frac{A'_x + \frac{V}{c}\phi'}{\sqrt{1-\frac{V^2}{c^2}}}, \quad A_y = A'_y, \quad A_z = A'_z, \quad \phi = \frac{\phi' + \frac{V}{c}A'_x}{\sqrt{1-\frac{V^2}{c^2}}}. \tag{24.1}$$

The transformation formulas for the components of the tensor F_{ik} could be gotten from the general formula (6.2) for transformation of four-tensors. However, it is easier to proceed in the following way.

We recall that the transformation from the reference system K to the K' system, moving relative to K along the X axis, is equivalent to a rotation in the $X\tau$ plane in the four-dimensional space x, y, z, τ (see § 4). The components of a tensor transform like the products of the corresponding coordinates. The coordinates $x_2 = y$ and $x_3 = z$ do not change under this transformation. For the same reason F_{23} does not change:

$$F_{23} = F'_{23}. \tag{24.2}$$

Furthermore, for the same reason, since the coordinates y and z do not change, the components F_{12}, F_{13} and F_{42}, F_{43} transform simply like the corresponding coordinates $x_1 = x$ and $x_4 = \tau$. In accordance with (6.2) we find:

$$\begin{aligned} F_{12} &= \frac{F'_{12} - i\frac{V}{c}F'_{42}}{\sqrt{1-\frac{V^2}{c^2}}}, \quad F_{42} = \frac{F'_{42} + i\frac{V}{c}F'_{12}}{\sqrt{1-\frac{V^2}{c^2}}}, \\ F_{13} &= \frac{F'_{13} - i\frac{V}{c}F'_{43}}{\sqrt{1-\frac{V^2}{c^2}}}, \quad F_{43} = \frac{F'_{43} + i\frac{V}{c}F'_{13}}{\sqrt{1-\frac{V^2}{c^2}}}. \end{aligned} \tag{24.3}$$

In order to determine the transformation of the component F_{14}, we note the following: an antisymmetric tensor having a rank equal to the number of dimensions of the space (cf., in § 6, the tensors e_{iklm} and $e_{\alpha\beta\gamma}$) remains invariant under rotations of the coordinate system in this space. The rotation of the system of coordinates x, y, z, τ, in the plane $X\tau$, can be considered as a rotation of the two-dimensional system of coordinates x, τ in this two-dimensional space. The tensor with components $F_{11} = F_{44} = 0$, $F_{14} = -F_{41}$, in this system, is precisely one with its rank equal to the number of dimensions. Therefore under rotation in the $X\tau$ plane

$$F_{14} = F'_{14} \tag{24.4}$$

Now we substitute in (24.2)–(24.4), in place of the components F_{ik}, their expressions in terms of the components of the fields **E** and **H**, according to (23.7). We then find the following formulas of transformation for the electric field:

$$E_x = E'_x, \quad E_y = \frac{E'_y + \frac{V}{c}H'_z}{\sqrt{1-\frac{V^2}{c^2}}}, \quad E_z = \frac{E'_z - \frac{V}{c}H'_y}{\sqrt{1-\frac{V^2}{c^2}}}, \tag{24.5}$$

and for the magnetic field:

$$H_x = H'_x,\ H_y = \frac{H'_y - \dfrac{V}{c} E'_z}{\sqrt{1 - \dfrac{V^2}{c^2}}},\ H_z = \frac{H'_z + \dfrac{V}{c} E'_y}{\sqrt{1 - \dfrac{V^2}{c^2}}}. \tag{24.6}$$

Thus the electric and magnetic fields, like the majority of physical quantities, are relative; that is, their properties are different in different reference systems. In particular, the electric or the magnetic field can be equal to zero in one reference system and at the same time be present in another system.

The formulas (24.5), (24.6) simplify considerably for the case $V \ll c$. To terms of order V/c, we have:

$$E_x = E'_x,\ E_y = E'_y + \frac{V}{c} H'_z,\ E_z = E'_z - \frac{V}{c} H'_y;$$

$$H_x = H'_x,\ H_y = H'_y - \frac{V}{c} E'_z,\ H_z = H'_z + \frac{V}{c} E'_y.$$

These formulas can be written in vector form

$$\mathbf{E} = \mathbf{E}' + \frac{1}{c}\mathbf{H}' \times \mathbf{V},\ \mathbf{H} = \mathbf{H}' - \frac{1}{c}\mathbf{E}' \times \mathbf{V}. \tag{24.7}$$

The formulas for the inverse transformation from K' to K are obtained directly from (24.5)–(24.7) by changing the sign of V and shifting the prime.

If the magnetic field $\mathbf{H}' = 0$ in the K' system, then, as we easily verify on the basis of (24.5) and (24.6), the following relation exists between the electric and magnetic fields in the K system:

$$\mathbf{H} = \frac{1}{c}\mathbf{V} \times \mathbf{E}. \tag{24.8}$$

If in the K' system, $\mathbf{E}' = 0$, then in the K system

$$\mathbf{E} = -\frac{1}{c}\mathbf{V} \times \mathbf{H}. \tag{24.9}$$

Consequently, in both cases, in the K system the magnetic and electric fields are mutually perpendicular.

These formulas also have a significance when used in the reverse direction: if the fields $\mathbf{E}$ and $\mathbf{H}$ are mutually perpendicular (but not equal in magnitude) in some reference system K, then there exists a reference system K' in which the field is pure electric or pure magnetic. The velocity $\mathbf{V}$ of this system (relative to K) is perpendicular to $\mathbf{E}$ and $\mathbf{H}$ and equal in magnitude to cH/E in the first case (where we must have $H < E$) and to cE/H in the second case (where $E < H$).

§ 25. Invariants of the field

From the electric and magnetic field intensities we can form invariant quantities, which remain unchanged in the transition from one inertial reference system to another.

The form of these invariants is easily found starting from the four-dimensional representation of the field using the antisymmetric four-tensor F_{ik}. It is obvious that we can form the following invariant quantities from the components of this tensor:

$$F_{ik}^2 = \text{inv}, \tag{25.1}$$

$$e_{iklm} F_{ik} F_{lm} = \text{inv}, \tag{25.2}$$

where e_{iklm} is the completely antisymmetric unit tensor of the fourth rank (cf. § 6). It should be noted that the second of these quantities is not a true scalar, but a pseudoscalar (the product of the tensor F_{ik} with its dual tensor, cf. § 6).

Writing out expressions (25.1—2) using (23.7), it is easily shown that, in three-dimensional form, these invariants have the form:

$$H^2 - E^2 = \text{inv}, \tag{23.3}$$

$$\mathbf{E} \cdot \mathbf{H} = \text{inv}. \tag{25.4}$$

The pseudoscalar character of the second of these is here apparent from the fact that it is the product of the polar vector **E** with the axial vector **H** (whereas its square $(\mathbf{E} \cdot \mathbf{H})^2$ is a true scalar).

From the invariance of the two expressions presented, we get the following theorems. If the electric and magnetic fields are mutually perpendicular in any reference system, that is, $\mathbf{E} \cdot \mathbf{H} = 0$, then they are also perpendicular in every other inertial reference system. If the absolute values of **E** and **H** are equal to each other in any reference system, then they are the same in any other system.

The following inequalities are also clearly valid. If in any reference system $E > H$ (or $H > E$), then in every other system we will have $E > H$ (or $H > E$). If in any system of reference the vectors **E** and **H** make an acute (or obtuse) angle, then they will make an acute (or obtuse) angle in every other reference system.

By means of a Lorentz transformation we can always give **E** and **H** any arbitrary values, subject only to the condition that $E^2 - H^2$ and $\mathbf{E} \cdot \mathbf{H}$ have fixed values. In particular, we can always find an inertial system in which the electric and magnetic fields are parallel to each other at a given point. In this system $\mathbf{E} \cdot \mathbf{H} = EH$, and from the two equations

$$E^2 - H^2 = E_0^2 - H_0^2, \qquad EH = \mathbf{E}_0 \cdot \mathbf{H}_0,$$

we can find the values of **E** and **H** in this system of reference ($\mathbf{E}_0$ and $\mathbf{H}_0$ are the electric and magnetic fields in the original system of reference).

The case where both invariants are zero is excluded. In this case, **E** and **H** are equal and mutually perpendicular in all reference systems.

If $\mathbf{E}\cdot\mathbf{H} = 0$, then we can always find a reference system in which $\mathbf{E} = 0$ or $\mathbf{H} = 0$ (according as $E^2 - H^2 <$ or > 0), that is, the field is purely magnetic or purely electric. Conversely, if in any reference system $\mathbf{E} = 0$ or $\mathbf{H} = 0$, then they are mutually perpendicular in every other system, in accordance with the statement at the end of the preceding section.

We shall give still another approach to the problem of finding the invariants of an antisymmetric four-tensor. From this method we shall, in particular, see that (25.3—4) are actually the only two independent invariants and at the same time we will explain some instructive mathematical properties of the Lorentz transformation when applied to such a four-tensor.

Let us consider the complex vector

$$\mathbf{F} = \mathbf{E} + i\mathbf{H}. \tag{25.5}$$

Using formulas (24.5—6), it is easy to see that a Lorentz transformation (along the x axis) for this vector has the form

$$F_x = F'_x,\ F_y = F'_y \cosh\phi - iF'_z \sinh\phi = F'_y \cos i\phi - F'_z \sin i\phi.$$

$$F_z = F'_z \cos i\phi + F'_y \sin i\phi,\ \tanh\phi = \frac{V}{c}. \tag{25.6}$$

We see that a rotation in the x, t plane in four-space (which is what this Lorentz transformation is, cf. p. 13) for the vector **F** is equivalent to a rotation through an imaginary angle in three-dimensional space. The set of all possible rotations in four-space (including also the simple rotations around the x,y, and z axes) is equivalent to the set of all possible rotations, through complex angles in three-dimensional space (where the six angles of rotation in four-space correspond to the three complex angles of rotation of the three-dimensional system.

The only invariant of the vector with respect to rotation is its square: $F^2 = E^2 - H^2 + 2\, i\, \mathbf{E}\cdot\mathbf{H}$; thus the real quantities $E^2 - H^2$ and $\mathbf{E}\cdot\mathbf{H}$ are the only two independent invariants of the tensor F_{ik}.

If $\mathbf{F}^2 \neq 0$, the vector **F** can be written as $\mathbf{E} = a\ \mathbf{n}$, where **n** is a unit vector ($\mathbf{n}^2 = 1$). By a suitable rotation we can point **n** along one of the coordinate axes; it is clear that then **n** becomes real and $\mathbf{F} = (E + iH)\,\mathbf{n}$; in other words we get the result that **E** and **H** become parallel to one another.

Problem

Determine the velocity of the system of reference in which the electric and magnetic fields are parallel.

Solution: Systems of reference K', satisfying the required condition, exist in infinite numbers. If we have found one such, then the same property will be had by any other system moving relative to the first with its velocity directed along the common direction of **E** and **H**. Therefore it is sufficient to find one of these systems which has a velocity perpendicular to both fields. Choosing the direction of the velocity as the x axis, and making use of the fact that in K': $E'_x = H'_x = 0$, $E'_y H'_z - E'_z H'_y = 0$, we obtain with the aid of formulas (24.5) and (24.6) for the velocity **V** of the K' system relative to the original system the following equation:

$$\frac{\dfrac{\mathbf{V}}{c}}{1-\dfrac{\mathbf{V}^2}{c^2}} = \frac{\mathbf{E}\times\mathbf{H}}{E^2+H^2}$$

(we must choose that root of the quadratic equation for which $V < c$).

CHAPTER 4

THE ELECTROMAGNETIC FIELD EQUATIONS

§ 26. The first pair of Maxwell's equations

From the expressions

$$\mathbf{H} = \operatorname{curl} \mathbf{A}, \qquad \mathbf{E} = -\frac{1}{c}\frac{\partial \mathbf{A}}{\partial t} - \operatorname{grad} \phi$$

it is easy to obtain equations containing only **E** and **H**. To do this we find curl **E**:

$$\operatorname{curl} \mathbf{E} = -\frac{1}{c}\frac{\partial}{\partial t} \operatorname{curl} \mathbf{A} - \operatorname{curl} \operatorname{grad} \phi .$$

But the curl of any gradient is zero. Consequently,

$$\operatorname{curl} \mathbf{E} = -\frac{1}{c}\frac{\partial \mathbf{H}}{\partial t}. \tag{26.1}$$

Taking the divergence of both sides of the equation curl $\mathbf{A} = \mathbf{H}$, and recalling that div curl $= 0$, we find

$$\operatorname{div} \mathbf{H} = 0. \tag{26.2}$$

The equations (26.1) and (26.2) are called the first pair of Maxwell's equations.† We note that these two equations still do not completely determine the properties of the fields. This is clear from the fact that they determine the change of the magnetic field with time (the derivative $\partial \mathbf{H}/\partial t$), but do not determine the derivative $\partial \mathbf{E}/\partial t$.

Equations (26.1) and (26.2) can be written in integral form. According to Gauss' theorem

$$\int \operatorname{div} \mathbf{H}\, dV = \oint \mathbf{H} \cdot d\mathbf{f},$$

where the integral on the right goes over the entire closed surface surrounding the volume over which the integral on the left is extended. On the basis of (26.2), we have

$$\oint \mathbf{H} \cdot d\mathbf{f} = 0. \tag{26.3}$$

The integral of a vector over a surface is called the *flux of the vector* through the surface. Thus the flux of the magnetic field through every closed surface is zero.

---

† Maxwell's equations (the fundamental equations of electrodynamics) were first formulated by him in the 1860's.

According to Stokes' theorem,

$$\int \operatorname{curl} \mathbf{E} \cdot d\mathbf{f} = \oint \mathbf{E} \cdot d\mathbf{l},$$

where the integral on the right is taken over the closed contour bounding the surface over which the left side is integrated. From (26.1) we find, integrating both sides for any surface,

$$\oint \mathbf{E} \cdot d\mathbf{l} = -\frac{1}{c}\frac{\partial}{\partial t}\int \mathbf{H} \cdot d\mathbf{f}. \tag{26.4}$$

The integral of a vector over a closed contour is called the *circulation* of the vector around the contour. The circulation of the electric field is also called the *electromotive force* in the given contour. Thus the electromotive force in any contour is equal to minus the time derivative of the magnetic flux through a surface bounded by this contour.

The Maxwell equations (26.1) and (26.2) can be expressed in four-dimensional notation. Using the definition of the electromagnetic field tensor

$$F_{ik} = \partial A_k/\partial x_i - \partial A_i/\partial x_k,$$

it is easy to verify that

$$\frac{\partial F_{ik}}{\partial x_l} + \frac{\partial F_{kl}}{\partial x_i} + \frac{\partial F_{li}}{\partial x_k} = 0. \tag{26.5}$$

The expression on the left is a tensor of third rank, which is antisymmetric in all three indices. The only components which are not identically zero are those with $i \neq k \neq l$. Thus there are altogether four different equations which we can easily show [by substituting from (23.7)] coincide with equations (26.1) and (26.2).

We can construct the four-vector which is dual to this antisymmetric four-tensor of rank three by multiplying the tensor by e^{iklm} and contracting on three pairs of indices (see § 6). Thus (26.5) can be written in the form

$$e^{iklm}\frac{\partial F_{lm}}{\partial x_k} = 0, \tag{26.6}$$

which shows explicitly that there are only three independent equations.

§ 27. The action function of the electromagnetic field

The action function S for the whole system, consisting of an electromagnetic field as well as the particles located in it, must consist of three parts:

$$S = S_f + S_m + S_{mf}, \tag{27.1}$$

where S_m is that part of the action which depends only on the properties of the particles. This part is clearly just the action for the free particles, that is, for the particles in the absence of the field. The action for a free particle is given by (8.1). If there are several particles, then their total action is the sum of the actions for each of the individual particles. Thus,

$$S_m = -\sum mc \int ds. \tag{27.2}$$

The quantity S_{mf} is that part of the action which depends on the interaction between the particles and the field. According to § 16, we have for a system of particles:

$$S_{mf} = \sum \frac{e}{c} \int A_k \, dx_k. \tag{27.3}$$

In each term of this sum, A_k is the potential of the field at that point of space-time at which the corresponding particle is located. The sum $S_m + S_{mf}$ is already familiar to us as the action (16.1) for a charge in a field.

Finally S_f is that part of the action which depends only on the properties of the field itself, that is, S_f is the action for a field in the absence of charges. Up to now, because we were interested only in the motion of charges in a *given* electromagnetic field, the quantity S_f, which does not depend on the particles, did not concern us, since this term cannot affect the motion of the particles. Nevertheless this term is necessary when we want to find equations determining the field itself. This corresponds to the fact that from the parts $S_m + S_{mf}$ of the action we found only two equations for the field, (26.1) and (26.2), which are not yet sufficient for complete determination of the field.

To establish the form of the action S_f for the field, we start from the following very important property of electromagnetic fields. As experiment shows, the electromagnetic field satisfies the so-called *principle of superposition*. This principle consists in the statement that if one charge produces a certain field, and another charge produces a second field, then the field produced by the two particles together is the result of a simple composition of the fields produced by each of the particles individually. This means that the resultant field intensity at each point is equal to the vector sum of the individual field intensities at that point.

Every solution of the field equations gives a field that can exist in nature. According to the principle of superposition, the sum of any such fields must be a field that can exist in nature, that is, must satisfy the field equations.

As is well known, linear differential equations have just this property, that the sum of any solutions is also a solution. Consequently the field equations must be linear differential equations.

From the discussion, it follows that under the integral sign for the action S_f there must stand an expression quadratic in the field. Only in this case will the field equations be linear; the field equations are obtained by varying the action, and in the variation the degree of the expression under the integral sign decreases by unity.

The potentials cannot enter into the expression for the action S_f, since they are not uniquely determined (in S_{mf} this lack of uniqueness was not important). Therefore S_f must be the integral of some function of the electromagnetic field tensor F_{ik}.† But the action must be a scalar and must therefore be the integral of some scalar.

There exists only one scalar of the second degree that can be formed from F_{ik} (§ 25); this is F_{ik}^2 (the quantity $e_{iklm}F_{ik}F_{lm}$ is a *pseudoscalar*).

Thus S_f must have the form:

$$S_f = a\int\int F_{ik}^2\,dV\,dt, \qquad dV = dx\,dy\,dz,$$

where the integral extends over all of space and the time between two given moments; a is some constant. Under the integral stands $F_{ik}^2 = 2(H^2-E^2)$. The field $\mathbf{E}$ contains the derivative $\partial\mathbf{A}/\partial t$; but it is easy to see that $(\partial\mathbf{A}/\partial t)^2$ must appear in the action with the positive sign (and therefore E^2 must have a positive sign). For if $(\partial\mathbf{A}/\partial t)^2$ appeared in S_f with a minus sign, then sufficiently rapid change of the potential with time (in the time interval under consideration) could always make S_f a negative quantity with arbitrarily large absolute value. Consequently S_f could not have a minimum, as is required by the principle of least action. Thus, a must be negative.

The numerical value of a depends on the choice of units for measurement of the field. We note that after the choice of a definite value for a and for the units of measurement of field, the units for measurement of all other electromagnetic quantities are determined.

From now on we shall use so-called *Gaussian system of units*; in this system a is a dimensionless quantity, equal to $-\frac{1}{16\pi}$††.

Thus the action for the field has the form

$$S_f = \frac{i}{16\pi c}\int F_{ik}^2\,d\Omega, \qquad d\Omega = dx\,dy\,dz\,d\tau. \tag{27.4}$$

---

† The function in the integrand of S_f must not include derivatives of F_{ik}, since the Lagrangian can contain, aside from the coordinates, only their first time derivatives, the role of "coordinates" (i.e., parameters to be varied in the principle of least action) is in this case played by the field potential A_k; this is analogous to the situation in mechanics where the Lagrangian of a mechanical system contains only the coordinates of the particles and their first time derivatives.

†† In addition to the Gaussian system, one also uses the so-called Heaviside system, in which $a = -{}^1/_4$. In this system of units the field equations have a more convenient form (π does not appear) but on the other hand, π appears in the Coulomb law. Conversely, in the Gaussian system the field equations contain π, but the Coulomb law has a simple form.

Here we have written $d\Omega$ in place of $dV\,dt$ and divided the whole expression by ic. In three-dimensional form:

$$S_f = \frac{1}{8\pi}\int (E^2 - H^2)\,dV\,dt. \tag{27.5}$$

In other words, the Lagrangian for the field is

$$L_f = \frac{1}{8\pi}\int (E^2 - H^2)\,dV. \tag{27.6}$$

The action for field plus particles has the form

$$S = -\sum\int mc\,ds + \sum\int \frac{e}{c}A_k\,dx_k + \frac{i}{16\pi c}\int F_{ik}^2\,d\Omega. \tag{27.7}$$

We note that now the charges are not assumed to be small, as in the derivation of the equation of motion of a charge in a given field. Therefore A_k and F_{ik} refer to the actual field, that is, the external field plus the field produced by the particles themselves; A_k and F_{ik} now depend on the positions and velocities of the charges.

§ 28. The four-dimensional current vector

Instead of treating charges as points, for mathematical convenience we frequently consider them to be distributed continuously in space. Then we can introduce the "charge density" ϱ such that $\varrho\,dV$ is the charge contained in the volume dV. The density ϱ is in general a function of the coordinates and the time.

The integral of ϱ over a certain volume is the charge contained in that volume.

Here we must remember that charges are actually pointlike, so that the density ϱ is zero everywhere except at points where the point charges are located, and the integral $\int \varrho\,dV$ must be equal to the sum of the charges contained in the given volume.† Therefore ϱ can be expressed with the help of the δ-function in the following form:

$$\varrho = \sum_a e_a \delta(\mathbf{r} - \mathbf{r}_a) \tag{28.1}$$

where the sum goes over all the charges and $\mathbf{r}_a$ is the radius vector of the charge e_a.

---

† The δ-function $\delta(x)$ is defined as follows: $\delta(x) = 0$, for all nonzero values of x; for $x = 0$, $\delta(0) = \infty$, in such a way that the integral

$$\int_{-\infty}^{+\infty} \delta(x)\,dx = 1.$$

The charge on a particle is, from its very definition, an invariant quantity, that is, it does not depend on the choice of reference system. On the other hand, the density ϱ is not generally an invariant — only the product $\varrho\, dV$ is invariant.

Multiplying the equality $de = \varrho\, dV$ on both sides with dx_i:

$$de\, dx_i = \varrho\, dV\, dx_i = \varrho\, dV\, dt \frac{dx_i}{dt}.$$

On the left stands a four-vector (since de is a scalar and dx_i is a four-vector). This means that the right side must be a four-vector. But $dV\, dt$ must be a scalar (see § 6), and so $\varrho \frac{dx_i}{dt}$ is a four-vector. This vector (we denote it by j_i) is called the *current four-vector*:

$$j_i = \varrho \frac{dx_i}{dt}. \qquad (28.2)$$

The first three components of this vector form a vector in ordinary space,

$$\mathbf{j} = \varrho \mathbf{v}, \qquad (28.3)$$

From this definition there result the following properties: if $f(x)$ is any continuous function, then

$$\int_{-\infty}^{+\infty} f(x)\, \delta(x-a)\, dx = f(a),$$

and in particular,

$$\int_{-\infty}^{+\infty} f(x)\, \delta(x)\, dx = f(0).$$

(The limits of integration, it is understood, need not be $\pm\infty$, the range of integration can be arbitrary, provided it includes the point at which the δ-function does not vanish.)

The meaning of the following equalities is that the left and right sides give the same result when introduced as factors under an integral sign:

$$\delta(-x) = \delta(x), \quad \delta(ax) = \frac{1}{|a|}\, \delta(x).$$

The last equality is a special case of the more general relation

$$\delta[\phi(x)] = \sum_i \frac{1}{|\phi'(a_i)|} \delta(x - a_i),$$

where $\phi(x)$ is a single-valued function (whose inverse need not be single-valued) and the a_i are the roots of the equation $\phi(x) = 0$.

Just as $\delta(x)$ was defined for one variable x, we can introduce a three-dimensional δ-function, $\delta(\mathbf{r})$, equal to zero everywhere except at the origin of the three-dimensional coordinate system, and whose integral over all space is unity. As such a function we can clearly use the product $\delta(x)\, \delta(y)\, \delta(z)$.

where **v** is the velocity of the charge at the given point. The vector **j** is called the *current-density vector*. The fourth component of the current four-vector is $ic\varrho$. Thus

$$j_{1,2,3} = j_{x,y,z}, \quad j_4 = ic\varrho. \tag{28.4}$$

The total charge present in all of space is equal to the integral $\int \varrho \, dV$ over all space. We can write this integral in four-dimensional form:

$$\int \varrho \, dV = \frac{1}{ic} \int j_4 \, dV = \frac{1}{ic} \int j_i \, dS_i, \tag{28.5}$$

where the integral is taken over the entire four-dimensional hyperplane perpendicular to the x_4 axis (clearly this integration means integration over the whole three-dimensional space).

Generally, the integral $\frac{1}{ic} \int j_i \, dS_i$ over an arbitrary hypersurface is the sum of the charges whose world lines pass through this surface.

Let us introduce the current four-vector into the expression (27.7) for the action. Namely, let us transform the second term in that expression. Introducing in place of the point charges e a continuous distribution of charge with density ϱ, we must write this term as

$$\frac{1}{c} \int \varrho A_i \, dx_i \, dV,$$

replacing the sum over the charges by an integral over the whole volume. Rewriting in the form

$$\frac{1}{c} \int \varrho \frac{dx_i}{dt} A_i \, dV \, dt,$$

we see that this term is equal to

$$-\frac{i}{c^2} \int A_i j_i \, d\Omega.$$

Thus the action S takes the form

$$S = -\sum \int mc \, ds - \frac{i}{c^2} \int A_i j_i \, d\Omega + \frac{i}{16\pi c} \int F_{ik}^2 \, d\Omega. \tag{28.6}$$

§ 29. The equation of continuity

The change with time of the charge contained in a certain volume is determined by the derivative

$$\frac{\partial}{\partial t} \int \varrho \, dV.$$

On the other hand, the change in unit time, say, is determined by the quantity of charge which in unit time leaves the volume and goes to the outside or, conversely, passes to its interior. The quantity of charge which passes in unit time though the element $d\mathbf{f}$ of the surface bounding our volume is equal to $\varrho\mathbf{v}.\,d\mathbf{f}$, where $\mathbf{v}$ is the velocity of the charge at the point in space where the element $d\mathbf{f}$ is located. The vector $d\mathbf{f}$ is directed, as always, along the external normal to the surface, that is, along the normal toward the outside of the volume under consideration. Therefore $\varrho\mathbf{v}\cdot d\mathbf{f}$ is positive if charge leaves the volume, and negative if charge enters the volume. The total amount of charge leaving the given volume per unit time is consequently $\oint \varrho\mathbf{v}\cdot d\mathbf{f}$, where the integral extends over the whole of the closed surface bounding the volume.

From the equality of these two expressions, we get

$$\frac{\partial}{\partial t}\int \varrho\, dV = -\oint \varrho\mathbf{v}\cdot d\mathbf{f}. \tag{29.1}$$

The minus sign appears on the right, since the left side is positive if the total charge in the given volume increases. The equation (29.1) is the so-called *equation of continuity*, expressing the conservation of charge in integral form. Noting that $\varrho\mathbf{v}$ is the current density, we can rewrite (29.1) in the form

$$\frac{\partial}{\partial t}\int \varrho\, dV = -\oint \mathbf{j}\cdot d\mathbf{f}. \tag{29.2}$$

We also write this equation in differential form. To do this we apply Gauss' theorem:

$$\oint \mathbf{j}\cdot d\mathbf{f} = \int \operatorname{div}\mathbf{j}\, dV.$$

Substituting this in (29.2) we find

$$\int \left(\operatorname{div}\mathbf{j} + \frac{\partial\varrho}{\partial t}\right) dV = 0.$$

Since this must hold for integration over an arbitrary volume, the integrand must be zero:

$$\operatorname{div}\mathbf{j} + \frac{\partial\varrho}{\partial t} = 0. \tag{29.3}$$

This is the equation of continuity in differential form.

It is easy to check that the expression (28.1) for ϱ in δ-function form automatically satisfies the equation (29.3). For simplicity we assume that we have altogether only one charge, so that

$$\varrho = e\delta(\mathbf{r}-\mathbf{r}_0).$$

The current $\mathbf{j}$ is then

$$\mathbf{j} = e\mathbf{v}\,\delta(\mathbf{r}-\mathbf{r}_0),$$

where $\mathbf{v}$ is the velocity of the charge. We determine the derivative $\partial\varrho/\partial t$. During the motion of the charge its coordinates change, that is, the vector $\mathbf{r}_0$ changes. Therefore

$$\frac{\partial\varrho}{\partial t} = \frac{\partial\varrho}{\partial\mathbf{r}_0}\cdot\frac{\partial\mathbf{r}_0}{\partial t}.$$

But $\partial\mathbf{r}_0/\partial t$ is just the velocity $\mathbf{v}$ of the charge. Furthermore since ϱ is a function of $\mathbf{r}-\mathbf{r}_0$,

$$\frac{\partial\varrho}{\partial\mathbf{r}_0} = -\frac{\partial\varrho}{\partial\mathbf{r}}.$$

Consequently

$$\frac{\partial\varrho}{\partial t} = -\mathbf{v}\cdot\mathbf{grad}\,\varrho = -\mathrm{div}\,(\varrho\mathbf{v})$$

(the velocity $\mathbf{v}$ of the charge of course does not depend on $\mathbf{r}$). Thus we arrive at the equation (29.3).

It is easily verified that, in four-dimensional form, the continuity equation (29.3) is expressed by the statement that the four-divergence of the current four-vector is zero:

$$\frac{\partial j_i}{\partial x_i} = 0. \tag{29.4}$$

In the preceding section we saw that the total charge present in all of space can be written as

$$\frac{1}{ic}\int j_i\,dS_i,$$

where the integration is extended over the hyperplane $x_4 = \text{const}$. At each moment of time, the total charge is given by such an integral taken over a different hyperplane perpendicular to the x_4 axis. It is easy to verify that the equation (29.4) actually leads to conservation of charge, that is, to the result that the integral $\int j_i\,dS_i$ is the same no matter what hyperplane $x_4 = \text{const}$ we integrate over. The difference between the integrals $\int j_i\,dS_i$ taken over two such hyperplanes can be written in the form $\oint j_i\,dS_i$, where the integral is taken over the whole closed hypersurface surrounding the four-volume between the two hyperplanes under consideration (this integral differs from the required integral because of the presence of the integral over the infinitely distant "sides" of the hypersurface which, however, drop out, since there are no charges at infinity). Using Gauss' theorem (6.11) we can transform this to an integral over the four-volume between the two hyperplanes and using (29.4) verify that

$$\oint j_i\,dS_i = \int\frac{\partial j_i}{\partial x_i}\,d\Omega = 0. \tag{29.5}$$

The proof presented clearly remains valid also for any two integrals $\int j_i\, dS_i$, in which the integration is extended over any two infinite hypersurfaces (and not just the hyperplanes $x_4 = \text{const}$) which each contain all of three-dimensional space. From this it follows that the integral $\frac{1}{ic}\int j_i\, dS_i$ is actually identical in value (and equal to the total charge in space) no matter over what such hypersurface the integration is taken.

§ 30. The second pair of Maxwell equations

In finding the field equations with the aid of the principle of least action we must assume the motion of the charges to be given and vary only the field, that is, the potentials†; on the other hand, to find the equations of motion we assumed the field to be given and varied the trajectory of the particle. Therefore the variation of the first term in (28.6) is zero, and in the second we must not vary the current j_i. Thus,

$$\delta S = \int\left(\frac{1}{ic^2} j_i\, \delta A_i - \frac{1}{16\pi ic}\, \delta(F_{ik}^2)\right) d\Omega = \int \frac{1}{ic}\left\{\frac{1}{c} j_i\, \delta A_i - \frac{1}{8\pi} F_{ik}\, \delta F_{ik}\right\} d\Omega = 0.$$

Substituting $F_{ik} = \partial A_k/\partial x_i - \partial A_i/\partial x_k$, we have

$$\delta S = \int \frac{1}{ic}\left\{\frac{1}{c} j_i\, \delta A_i - \frac{1}{8\pi} F_{ik}\, \delta\left(\frac{\partial A_k}{\partial x_i} - \frac{\partial A_i}{\partial x_k}\right)\right\} d\Omega$$

$$= \int \frac{1}{ic}\left\{\frac{1}{c} j_i\, \delta A_i - \frac{1}{8\pi} F_{ik} \frac{\partial}{\partial x_i}\, \delta A_k + \frac{1}{8\pi} F_{ik} \frac{\partial}{\partial x_k}\, \delta A_i\right\} d\Omega.$$

In the second term we interchange the indices i and k, over which the expressions are summed, and in addition replace F_{ik} by $-F_{ki}$. Then we obtain

$$\delta S = \int \frac{1}{ic}\left\{\frac{1}{c} j_i\, \delta A_i + \frac{1}{4\pi} F_{ik} \frac{\partial}{\partial x_k}\, \delta A_i\right\} d\Omega.$$

The second of these integrals we integrate by parts, that is, we apply Gauss' theorem:

$$dS = \frac{1}{ic}\int\left\{\frac{1}{c} j_i - \frac{1}{4\pi}\frac{\partial F_{ik}}{\partial x_k}\right\} \delta A_i\, d\Omega + \frac{1}{4\pi ic}\int F_{ik}\, \delta A_i\, dS_k \Bigg| . \qquad (30.1)$$

In the second term we must insert the values at the limits of integration. The limits for the coordinates are at infinity, where the field is zero. At the limits of the time integration, that is, at the given initial and final time values, the variation of the potentials is zero, since in accord with the principle of

† The potentials are the "coordinates" of the system (see the footnote on p. 77)

least action the fields are given at these times. Thus the second term in (30.1) is zero, and we find

$$\int \left(\frac{1}{c} j_i - \frac{1}{4\pi} \frac{\partial F_{ik}}{\partial x_k} \right) \delta A_i \, d\Omega = 0 .$$

Since according to the principle of least action, the variations δA_i are arbitrary, the coefficients of the δA_i must be set equal to zero:

$$\frac{\partial F_{ik}}{\partial x_k} = \frac{4\pi}{c} j_i . \tag{30.2}$$

Let us express these four ($i = 1$–4) equations in three-dimensional form. The first of them ($i = 1$) is:

$$\frac{\partial F_{11}}{\partial x} + \frac{\partial F_{12}}{\partial y} + \frac{\partial F_{13}}{\partial z} + \frac{1}{ic} \frac{\partial F_{14}}{\partial t} = \frac{4\pi}{c} j_1 .$$

Substituting the values for the components of F_{ik} from (23.7), we find

$$\frac{\partial H_z}{\partial y} - \frac{\partial H_y}{\partial z} - \frac{1}{c} \frac{\partial E_x}{\partial t} = \frac{4\pi}{c} j_x .$$

This together with the two succeeding equations ($i = 2, 3$) can be written as one vector equation:

$$\text{curl}\, \mathbf{H} = \frac{1}{c} \frac{\partial \mathbf{E}}{\partial t} + \frac{4\pi}{c} \mathbf{j} . \tag{30.3}$$

Finally, the fourth equation ($i = 4$) gives

$$\frac{\partial iE_x}{\partial x} + \frac{\partial iE_y}{\partial y} + \frac{\partial iE_z}{\partial z} = \frac{4\pi}{c} ic\varrho$$

or

$$\text{div}\, \mathbf{E} = 4\pi\varrho . \tag{30.4}$$

Equations (30.3) and (30.4) are the second pair of Maxwell equations.† Together with the first pair of Maxwell equations they completely determine the electromagnetic field, and are the fundamental equations of the theory of such fields, i.e., of *electrodynamics.*

Let us write these equations in integral form. Integrating (30.4) over a volume and applying Gauss' theorem

$$\int \text{div}\, \mathbf{E}\, dV = \oint \mathbf{E} \cdot d\mathbf{f},$$

we get

$$\oint \mathbf{E} \cdot d\mathbf{f} = 4\pi \int \varrho \, dV . \tag{30.5}$$

Thus the flux of the electric field through a closed surface is equal to 4π times the total charge contained in the volume bounded by the surface.

† The Maxwell equations in a form applicable to point charges in the electromagnetic field in vacuum were formulated by Lorentz.

Integrating (30.3) over an open surface and applying Stokes' theorem

$$\int \operatorname{curl} \mathbf{H} \cdot d\mathbf{f} = \oint \mathbf{H} \cdot d\mathbf{l},$$

we find

$$\oint \mathbf{H} \cdot d\mathbf{l} = \frac{1}{c} \frac{\partial}{\partial t} \int \mathbf{E} \cdot d\mathbf{f} + \frac{4\pi}{c} \int \mathbf{j} \cdot d\mathbf{f}. \tag{30.6}$$

The quantity

$$\frac{1}{4\pi} \frac{\partial \mathbf{E}}{\partial t} \tag{30.7}$$

is called the "*displacement current*". From (30.6) written in the form

$$\oint \mathbf{H} \cdot d\mathbf{l} = \frac{4\pi}{c} \int \left(\mathbf{j} + \frac{1}{4\pi} \frac{\partial \mathbf{E}}{\partial t} \right) \cdot d\mathbf{f}, \tag{30.8}$$

we see that the circulation of the magnetic field around any contour is equal to $4\pi/c$ times the sum of the true current and displacement current passing through a surface bounded by this contour.

From the Maxwell equations we can obtain the already familiar continuity equation (29.3). Taking the divergence of both sides of (30.3), we find

$$\operatorname{div} \operatorname{curl} \mathbf{H} = \frac{1}{c} \frac{\partial}{\partial t} \operatorname{div} \mathbf{E} + \frac{4\pi}{c} \operatorname{div} \mathbf{j}.$$

But $\operatorname{div} \operatorname{curl} \mathbf{H} = 0$ and $\operatorname{div} \mathbf{E} = 4\pi\varrho$, according to (30.4). Thus we arrive once more at equation (29.3). In four-dimensional form, from (30.2), we have:

$$\frac{\partial^2 F_{ik}}{\partial x_i \, \partial x_k} = \frac{4\pi}{c} \frac{\partial j_i}{\partial x_i}.$$

But because of the antisymmetry of F_{ik}, we have, replacing F_{ik} by $-F_{ki}$ and also interchanging indices,

$$\frac{\partial^2 F_{ik}}{\partial x_i \, \partial x_k} = -\frac{\partial^2 F_{ki}}{\partial x_i \, \partial x_k} = -\frac{\partial^2 F_{ik}}{\partial x_k \, \partial x_i},$$

from which it follows that $\partial^2 F_{ik}/\partial x_i \, \partial x_k = 0$, and we arrive at the continuity equation (29.4) expressed in four-dimensional form.

§ 31. Energy density and energy flux

Let us multiply both sides of (30.3) by $\mathbf{E}$ and both sides of (26.1) by $\mathbf{H}$ and combine the resultant equations. Then we get

$$\frac{1}{c} \mathbf{E} \cdot \frac{\partial \mathbf{E}}{\partial t} + \frac{1}{c} \mathbf{H} \cdot \frac{\partial \mathbf{H}}{\partial t} = -\frac{4\pi}{c} \mathbf{j} \cdot \mathbf{E} - (\mathbf{H} \cdot \operatorname{curl} \mathbf{E} - \mathbf{E} \cdot \operatorname{curl} \mathbf{H}).$$

Using the well-known formula of vector analysis,

$$\operatorname{div} (\mathbf{a} \times \mathbf{b}) = \mathbf{b} \cdot \operatorname{curl} \mathbf{a} - \mathbf{a} \cdot \operatorname{curl} \mathbf{b},$$

we rewrite this relation in the form

$$\frac{1}{2c}\frac{\partial}{\partial t}(E^2+H^2) = -\frac{4\pi}{c}\mathbf{j}\cdot\mathbf{E}-\text{div}\,(\mathbf{E}\times\mathbf{H})$$

or

$$\frac{\partial}{\partial t}\left(\frac{E^2+H^2}{8\pi}\right) = -\mathbf{j}\cdot\mathbf{E}-\text{div}\,\mathbf{S}. \tag{31.1}$$

The vector

$$\mathbf{S} = \frac{c}{4\pi}\mathbf{E}\times\mathbf{H} \tag{31.2}$$

is called the *Poynting vector.*

We integrate (31.1) over a volume and apply Gauss' theorem to the second term on the right. Then we obtain

$$\frac{\partial}{\partial t}\int\frac{E^2+H^2}{8\pi}dV = -\int\mathbf{j}\cdot\mathbf{E}\,dV-\oint\mathbf{S}\cdot d\mathbf{f}. \tag{31.3}$$

If the integral extends over all space, then the surface integral vanishes (the field is zero at infinity). Furthermore, we can express the integral $\int\mathbf{j}\cdot\mathbf{E}\,dV$ as a sum $\sum e\mathbf{v}\cdot\mathbf{E}$ over all the charges, and substitute from (17.7):

$$e\mathbf{v}\cdot\mathbf{E} = \frac{\partial}{\partial t}\mathcal{E}_{\text{kin}}.$$

Then (31.3) becomes

$$\frac{\partial}{\partial t}\left\{\int\frac{E^2+H^2}{8\pi}dV+\sum\mathcal{E}_{\text{kin}}\right\} = 0. \tag{31.4}$$

Thus for the closed system consisting of the electromagnetic field and particles present in it, the quantity in brackets in this equation is conserved. The second term in this expression is the kinetic energy (including the rest energy of all the particles; see the footnote on p. 53), the first term is consequently the energy of the field itself. We can therefore call the quantity

$$W = \frac{E^2+H^2}{8\pi} \tag{31.5}$$

the *energy density* of the electromagnetic field; it is the energy per unit volume of the field.

If we integrate over any finite volume, then the surface integral in (31.3) generally does not vanish, so that we can write the equation in the form

$$\frac{\partial}{\partial t}\left\{\int\frac{E^2+H^2}{8\pi}dV+\sum\mathcal{E}_{\text{kin}}\right\} = -\oint\mathbf{S}\cdot d\mathbf{f}, \tag{31.6}$$

where now the second term in the brackets is summed only over the particles present in the volume under consideration. On the left stands the change in the total energy of field and particles per unit time. Therefore the integral

$\oint \mathbf{S}\cdot d\mathbf{f}$ must be interpreted as the flux of field energy across the surface bounding the given volume, so that the Poynting vector **S** is this flux density — the amount of field energy passing through unit area of the surface in unit time.†

§ 32. The energy-momentum tensor

In the preceding section we derived an expression for the energy of the electromagnetic field. Now we derive this expression, together with one for the field momentum, in four-dimensional form. In doing this we shall for simplicity consider for the present an electromagnetic field without charges. Having in mind later applications (to the gravitational field), and also to simplify the calculation, we present the derivation in a general form, not specializing the nature of the system. So we consider any system whose action integral has the form

$$S = \int \Lambda\left(q, \frac{\partial q}{\partial x_i}\right) dV\,dt = \frac{1}{ic}\int \Lambda\,d\Omega, \tag{32.1}$$

where Λ is some function of the quantities q, describing the state of the system, and of their first derivatives with respect to coordinates and time (for the electromagnetic field the components of the four-potential are the quantities q); for brevity we write here only one of the q's. We note that the space integral $\int \Lambda\,dV$ is the Lagrangian of the system, so that Λ can be considered as the *Lagrangian "density."* The mathematical expression of the fact that the system is closed is the absence of any explicit dependence of Λ on the x_i, similarly to the situation for a closed system in mechanics, where the Lagrangian does not depend explicitly on the time.

The "equations of motion" (i.e., the field equations, if we are dealing with some field) are obtained in accordance with the principle of least action by varying S. We have (for brevity we write $q_{,i} = \partial q/\partial x_i$),

$$\delta S = \frac{1}{ic}\int\left(\frac{\partial\Lambda}{\partial q}\delta q + \frac{\partial\Lambda}{\partial q_{,i}}\delta q_{,i}\right) d\Omega$$

$$= \frac{1}{ic}\int\left[\frac{\partial\Lambda}{\partial q}\delta q + \frac{\partial}{\partial x_i}\left(\frac{\partial\Lambda}{\partial q_{,i}}\delta q\right) - \delta q\frac{\partial}{\partial x_i}\frac{\partial\Lambda}{\partial q_{,i}}\right] d\Omega = 0.$$

The second term in the integrand, after transformation by Gauss' theorem, vanishes upon integration over all space, and we then find the following "equations of motion":

$$\frac{\partial}{\partial x_i}\frac{\partial\Lambda}{\partial q_{,i}} - \frac{\partial\Lambda}{\partial q} = 0 \tag{32.2}$$

(it is, of course, understood that we sum over any repeated index).

†We assume that at the given moment there are no charges on the surface itself. It this were not the case, then on the right we would have to include the energy flux due to particles passing through the surface.

The remainder of the derivation is similar to the procedure in mechanics for deriving the conservation of energy. Namely, we write:

$$\frac{\partial \Lambda}{\partial x_i} = \frac{\partial \Lambda}{\partial q}\frac{\partial q}{\partial x_i} + \frac{\partial \Lambda}{\partial q_{,k}}\frac{\partial q_{,k}}{\partial x_i}.$$

Substituting (32.2) and noting that $\partial q_{,k}/\partial x_i = \partial^2 q/\partial x_i\,\partial x_k = \partial q_{,i}/\partial x_k$, we find

$$\frac{\partial \Lambda}{\partial x_i} = \frac{\partial}{\partial x_k}\left(\frac{\partial \Lambda}{\partial q_{,k}}\right) q_{,i} + \frac{\partial \Lambda}{\partial q_{,k}}\frac{\partial q_{,i}}{\partial x_k} = \frac{\partial}{\partial x_k}\left(q_{,i}\frac{\partial \Lambda}{\partial q_{,k}}\right).$$

On the other hand, we can write $\dfrac{\partial \Lambda}{\partial x_i} = \delta_{ik}\dfrac{\partial \Lambda}{\partial x_k}$, so that

$$\frac{\partial \Lambda}{\partial x_k}\delta_{ik} = \frac{\partial}{\partial x_k}\left(\frac{\partial \Lambda}{\partial q_{,k}} q_{,i}\right).$$

Introducing the notation

$$T_{ik} = \delta_{ik}\Lambda - q_{,i}\frac{\partial \Lambda}{\partial q_{,k}} \tag{32.3}$$

we can express the relation in the form

$$\frac{\partial T_{ik}}{\partial x_k} = 0. \tag{32.4}$$

We note that if there is not one but several quantities $q^{(l)}$, then in place of (32.3) we must write

$$T_{ik} = \delta_{ik}\Lambda - \sum_l q^{(l)}_{,i}\frac{\partial \Lambda}{\partial q^{(l)}_{,k}}. \tag{32.5}$$

But in § 29 we saw that an equation of the form $\partial A_k/\partial x_k = 0$, i.e., the vanishing of the four-divergence of a vector, is equivalent to the statement that the integral $\int A_k\, dS_k$ of the vector over a hypersurface which contains all of three-dimensional space is conserved. It is clear that an analogous result holds for the divergence of a tensor; the equation $\partial T_{ik}/\partial x_k = 0$ asserts that the vector P_i whose components are the integral of T_{ik} over such a hypersurface

$$P_i = \text{const}\int T_{ik}\, dS_k$$

is conserved.

This vector must be identified with the four-vector of momentum of the system. We choose the constant factor in front of the integral so that, in accord with our previous definition, the fourth component of the vector

P_i is equal to the energy of the system multiplied by i/c. To do this we note that P_4 can be written in the form

$$P_4 = \text{const}\int T_{4k}\,dS_k = \text{const}\int T_{44}\,dV$$

if the integration is extended over the hyperplane $x_4 = \text{const}$. On the other hand, according to (32.3),

$$T_{44} = -\dot{q}\frac{\partial\Lambda}{\partial\dot{q}} + \Lambda. \qquad \left(\dot{q} = \frac{\partial q}{\partial t}\right)$$

Comparing with the usual formulas relating the energy and the Lagrangian, we see that this quantity must be considered as the energy density of the system, and therefore $-\int T_{44}\,dV$ is the total energy of the system. Thus we must set const $= -i/c$, and we get finally for the four-momentum of the system the expression

$$P_i = -\frac{i}{c}\int T_{ik}\,dS_k. \tag{32.6}$$

The tensor T_{ik} is called the *energy-momentum tensor* of the system.

It is necessary to point out that the definition of the tensor T_{ik} is not unique. In fact, to the tensor T_{ik} defined by equation (32.3) we can add a quantity of the form $\frac{\partial}{\partial x_l}\psi_{ikl}$, where ψ_{ikl} is an arbitrary tensor antisymmetric in the indices k, l. After this change, the new tensor T_{ik} will also satisfy equation (32.4), since we have identically $\partial^2\psi_{ikl}/\partial x_k\partial x_l = 0$. The total four-momentum of the system, P_i, does not change, since according to (6.12), we can write

$$\int\frac{\partial\psi_{ikl}}{\partial x_l}\,dS_k = \frac{1}{2}\int\left(dS_k\frac{\partial\psi_{ikl}}{\partial x_l} - dS_l\frac{\partial\psi_{ikl}}{\partial x_k}\right) = \frac{1}{2}\int\psi_{ikl}\,df^*_{ki},$$

where the integration on the right side of the equation is extended over the (ordinary) surface which "bounds" the hypersurface over which the integration on the left is taken. This surface is clearly located at infinity in the three-dimensional space, and since neither field nor particles are present at infinity this integral is zero. Thus the four-momentum of the system is, as it must be, a uniquely determined quantity. To define the tensor T_{ik} uniquely we can use the requirement that the four-tensor of angular momentum (see § 14) of the system be expressed in terms of the four-momentum by

$$M_{ik} = \int(x_i\,dP_k - x_k\,dP_i) = -\frac{i}{c}\int(x_i T_{kl} - x_k T_{il})\,dS_l, \tag{32.7}$$

that is, not only the total angular momentum of the system, but also its "density" is expressed in terms of the "density" of momentum by the usual formula.

It is easy to determine what conditions the energy-momentum tensor must satisfy in order that this be valid. We note that the law of conservation of angular momentum can be expressed, as we already know, by setting equal to zero the divergence of the expression under the integral sign in M_{ik}. Thus

$$\frac{\partial}{\partial x_l}(x_i T_{kl}-x_k T_{il}) = 0.$$

Noting that $\partial x_i/\partial x_l = \delta_{il}$ and that $\partial T_{kl}/\partial x_l = 0$, we find from this

$$\delta_{il} T_{kl}-\delta_{kl} T_{il} = T_{ki}-T_{ik} = 0$$

or

$$T_{ik} = T_{ki}, \tag{32.8}$$

that is, the energy-momentum tensor must be symmetric.

We note that T_{ik}, defined by formula (32.5), is generally speaking not symmetric, but can be made so by adding an expression of the form $\frac{\partial}{\partial x_l}\psi_{ikl}$ with suitable ψ_{ikl}. Later on (§ 94) we shall see that there is a direct method for obtaining a symmetric tensor T_{ik}.

As we mentioned above, if we carry out the integration in (32.6) over the hyperplane $x_4 =$ const, then P_i takes on the form

$$P_i = -\frac{i}{c}\int T_{i4}\, dV, \tag{32.9}$$

where the integration extends over the whole (three-dimensional) space. The space components of P_i form the three-dimensional momentum vector of the system and the time component is its energy multiplied by i/c. Thus the vector with components

$$-\frac{i}{c}T_{\alpha 4} \tag{32.10}$$

may be called the "*momentum density*", and the quantity

$$W = -T_{44} \tag{32.11}$$

the "*energy density*".

To clarify the meaning of the remaining components of T_{ik}, we write the conservation equation (32.4) in three-dimensional form:

$$\frac{1}{ic}\frac{\partial T_{44}}{\partial t}+\frac{\partial T_{4\alpha}}{\partial x_\alpha} = 0, \qquad \frac{1}{ic}\frac{\partial T_{\alpha 4}}{\partial t}+\frac{\partial T_{\alpha\beta}}{\partial x_\beta} = 0. \tag{32.12}$$

We integrate these equations over a volume V in space. From the first equation

$$\frac{1}{ic}\frac{\partial}{\partial t}\int T_{44}\, dV+\int \frac{\partial T_{4\alpha}}{\partial x_\alpha}\, dV = 0$$

or, transforming the second integral by Gauss' theorem,

$$\frac{\partial}{\partial t}\int (-T_{44})\, dV = ic \oint T_{4\alpha}\, df_\alpha, \tag{32.13}$$

where the integral on the right is taken over the surface surrounding the volume V. The expression on the left is the rate of change of the energy contained in the volume V; from this it is clear that the expression on the right is the amount of energy transferred across the boundary of the volume V, and the vector $\mathbf{S}$ with components

$$S_\alpha = -i\,c\,T_{4\alpha} \tag{32.14}$$

is its flux density—the amount of energy passing through unit surface in unit time. Thus we arrive at the important conclusion that the requirements of relativistic invariance, as expressed by the tensor character of the quantities T_{ik}, automatically lead to a definite connection between the energy flux and the momentum flux: the energy flux density is equal to the momentum flux density multiplied by c^2.

From the second equation, we find similarly

$$\frac{\partial}{\partial t}\int\left(-\frac{i}{c}T_{\alpha 4}\right)dV = -\oint T_{\alpha\beta}\,df_\beta. \tag{32.15}$$

On the left is the change of the momentum of the system in volume V per unit time; therefore $\oint T_{\alpha\beta}\,df_\beta$ is the momentum emerging from the volume V per unit time, and $T_{\alpha\beta}$ is the momentum flux density. The density of energy flux is a vector; the density of momentum flux, which is itself a vector, must be a tensor. (The component $T_{\alpha\beta}$ of this tensor is the amount of the α-component of the momentum passing in unit time through a unit surface perpendicular to the x_β axis.)

Problem

Find the formulas for the Lorentz transformation of the components of the energy-momentum tensor of the electromagnetic field.

Solution: From the general formulas (6.4) and (6.5), we get:

$$T_{xx} = \frac{1}{1-\frac{V^2}{c^2}}\left(T'_{xx}+2\frac{V}{c^2}S'_x+\frac{V^2}{c^2}W'\right), \qquad T_{yy} = T'_{yy}, \qquad T_{yz} = T'_{yz},$$

$$T_{xy} = \frac{1}{\sqrt{1-\frac{V^2}{c^2}}}\left(T'_{xy}+\frac{V}{c^2}S'_y\right), \qquad S_x = \frac{1}{1-\frac{V^2}{c^2}}\left[S'_x\left(1+\frac{V^2}{c^2}\right)+VW'+VT'_{xx}\right],$$

$$S_y = \frac{1}{\sqrt{1-\frac{V^2}{c^2}}}(S'_y-VT'_{xy}), \qquad W = \frac{1}{1-\frac{V^2}{c^2}}\left(W'+2\frac{V}{c^2}S'_x+\frac{V^2}{c^2}T'_{xx}\right),$$

and similar formulas for S_z, T_{xz}, T_{zz}.

§ 33. Energy-momentum tensor of the electromagnetic field

We now apply the general relations obtained in the previous section to the electromagnetic field. For the electromagnetic field, the quantity standing under the integral sign in (32.1) is equal, according to (27.4), to

$$\Lambda = -\frac{1}{16\pi}F^2_{kl} = -\frac{1}{16\pi}\left(\frac{\partial A_l}{\partial x_k}-\frac{\partial A_k}{\partial x_l}\right)^2.$$

The quantities q are the components of the four-potential of the field, A_k, so that the definition (32.5) of the tensor T_{ik} becomes

$$T_{ik} = -\frac{\partial A_l}{\partial x_i}\frac{\partial \Lambda}{\partial\left(\dfrac{\partial A_l}{\partial x_k}\right)}+\delta_{ik}\Lambda.$$

To calculate the derivatives of Λ which appear here, we find the variation $\delta\Lambda$. We have

$$\delta\Lambda = -\frac{1}{8\pi}\left(\frac{\partial A_l}{\partial x_k}-\frac{\partial A_k}{\partial x_l}\right)\delta\left(\frac{\partial A_l}{\partial x_k}-\frac{\partial A_k}{\partial x_l}\right) = -\frac{1}{8\pi}F_{kl}\left(\delta\frac{\partial A_l}{\partial x_k}-\delta\frac{\partial A_k}{\partial x_l}\right)$$

or, interchanging indices and making use of the fact that $F_{kl} = -F_{lk}$,

$$\delta\Lambda = -\frac{1}{4\pi}F_{kl}\delta\frac{\partial A_l}{\partial x_k}.$$

From this we see that

$$\frac{\partial\Lambda}{\partial\left(\dfrac{\partial A_l}{\partial x_k}\right)} = -\frac{1}{4\pi}F_{kl},$$

and therefore

$$T_{ik} = \frac{1}{4\pi}\frac{\partial A_l}{\partial x_i}F_{kl}-\frac{1}{16\pi}\delta_{ik}F_{lm}^2.$$

In order to make this expression symmetric in the indices i and k, we subtract the term $\dfrac{1}{4\pi}\dfrac{\partial A_i}{\partial x_l}F_{kl}$; this term has the form of a derivative $\dfrac{\partial}{\partial x_l}\psi_{ikl}$ since

$$\frac{\partial A_i}{\partial x_l}F_{kl} = \frac{\partial(A_iF_{kl})}{\partial x_l}-A_i\frac{\partial F_{kl}}{\partial x_l} = \frac{\partial(A_iF_{kl})}{\partial x_l}$$

(according to Maxwell's equation 30.2, at points where there are no charges, $\partial F_{kl}/\partial x_l = 0$). Therefore, as we made clear in the preceding section, this term may actually be added to the energy-momentum tensor. Since $\partial A_l/\partial x_i - \partial A_i/\partial x_l = F_{il}$, we get finally the following expression for the energy-momentum tensor of the electromagnetic field:

$$T_{ik} = \frac{1}{4\pi}(F_{il}F_{kl}-\tfrac{1}{4}F_{lm}^2\delta_{ik}). \tag{33.1}$$

This tensor is obviously symmetric. In addition it has the property that

$$T_{ii} = 0, \tag{33.2}$$

i.e., the sum of its diagonal terms is zero.

Let us express the components of the tensor T_{ik} in terms of the electric and magnetic field intensities. By using the values (23.7) for the components F_{ik}, we easily verify that, in accordance with the general rules (32.11) and

(32.14), the quantity $-T_{44}$ coincides with the energy density W of the electromagnetic field (31.5), while the components $S_\alpha = -icT_{4\alpha}$ are the same as the components of the Poynting vector (31.2). The space components form a three-dimensional tensor with components

$$T_{xx} = \frac{1}{8\pi}(E_y^2+E_z^2-E_x^2+H_y^2+H_z^2-H_x^2),$$

$$T_{xy} = -\frac{1}{4\pi}(E_x E_y+H_x H_y),$$

etc, or

$$T_{\alpha\beta} = \frac{1}{4\pi}\{-E_\alpha E_\beta-H_\alpha H_\beta+\tfrac{1}{2}\delta_{\alpha\beta}(E^2+H^2)\}. \tag{33.3}$$

This tensor is called the *Maxwell stress tensor*.

To bring the tensor T_{ik} to diagonal form, we must transform to a reference system in which the vectors **E** and **H** (at the given point in space and moment in time) are parallel to one another or where one of them is equal to zero; as we know (§ 25), such a transformation is always possible except when **E** and **H** are mutually perpendicular and equal in magnitude. It is easy to see that after the transformation the only non zero components of T_{ik} will be

$$-T_{11} = T_{22} = T_{33} = -T_{44} = W$$

(the x axis has been taken along the direction of the field).

But if the vectors **E** and **H** are mutually perpendicular and equal in magnitude, the tensor T_{ik} cannot be brought to diagonal form.† The non zero components in this case are

$$-T_{44} = T_{33} = -iT_{34} = W$$

(where the x axis is taken along the direction of **E** and the y axis along **H**).

Up to now we have considered fields in the absence of charges. When charged particles are present, the energy-momentum tensor of the whole system is the sum of the energy-momentum tensors for the electromagnetic field and for the particles, where in the latter the particles are assumed not to interact with one another.

To determine the form of the energy-momentum tensor of the particles we must describe their mass distribution in space by using a "mass density" in the same way as we describe a distribution of point charges in terms of their density. Analogously to formula (28.1) for the charge density, we can write the mass density in the form

$$\mu = -\sum_a m_a\,\delta(\mathbf{r}-\mathbf{r}_a), \tag{33.4}$$

†The fact that the reduction of the symmetric tensor T_{ik} to principal axes may be impossible is related to the fact that one of the coordinates of the four-space in which the four-tensor is defined is imaginary.

where $\mathbf{r}_a$ are the radius-vectors of the particles, and the summation extends over all the particles of the system.

The "four-momentum density" of the particles is given by $\mu c u_i$. We know that this density is the component $-iT_{4\alpha}/c$ of the energy-momentum tensor, i.e., $T_{4\alpha} = i\mu c^2 u_\alpha$. But the mass density is the time component of the four-vector $\frac{\mu}{ic}\frac{dx_k}{dt}$ (in analogy to the charge density; see § 28). Therefore the energy-momentum tensor of the system of noninteracting particles is

$$T_{ik} = \mu c \frac{dx_i}{ds}\frac{dx_k}{dt} = \mu c u_i u_k \frac{ds}{dt}. \tag{33.5}$$

As expected, this tensor is symmetric.

We verify by a direct computation that the energy and momentum of the system, defined as the sum of the energies and momenta of field and particles, are actually conserved. In other words we shall verify the equations

$$\frac{\partial}{\partial x_k}(T_{ik}^{(f)} + T_{ik}^{(p)}) = 0, \tag{33.6}$$

which express these conservation laws.

By substituting (33.1), we write for the energy-momentum tensor of the electromagnetic field

$$\frac{\partial T_{ik}^{(f)}}{\partial x_k} = \frac{1}{4\pi}\left(-\frac{1}{4}\frac{\partial F_{lm}^2}{\partial x_k}\delta_{ik} + \frac{\partial}{\partial x_k}F_{il}F_{kl}\right) =$$

$$= \frac{1}{4\pi}\left(-\frac{1}{2}\frac{\partial F_{lm}}{\partial x_i}F_{lm} + \frac{\partial F_{il}}{\partial x_k}F_{kl} + \frac{\partial F_{kl}}{\partial x_k}F_{il}\right).$$

Substituting from the Maxwell equations (26.5) and (30.2),

$$\frac{\partial F_{lk}}{\partial x_k} = \frac{4\pi}{c}j_l, \qquad \frac{\partial F_{lm}}{\partial x_i} = -\frac{\partial F_{mi}}{\partial x_l} - \frac{\partial F_{il}}{\partial x_m}$$

and using the fact that the tensor F_{ik} is antisymmetric, we have:

$$\frac{\partial T_{ik}^{(f)}}{\partial x_k} = \frac{1}{4\pi}\left(\frac{1}{2}\frac{\partial F_{mi}}{\partial x_l}F_{lm} + \frac{1}{2}\frac{\partial F_{il}}{\partial x_m}F_{lm} + \frac{\partial F_{il}}{\partial x_k}F_{kl} - \frac{4\pi}{c}F_{il}j_l\right).$$

By permuting the indices, we easily show that the first three terms on the right cancel one another, and we arrive at the result:

$$\frac{\partial T_{ik}^{(f)}}{\partial x_k} = -\frac{1}{c}F_{ik}j_k. \tag{33.7}$$

Differentiating the expression (33.5) for the energy-momentum tensor of the particles gives

$$\frac{\partial T_{ik}^{(p)}}{\partial x_k} = cu_i\frac{\partial}{\partial x_k}\left(\mu\frac{dx_k}{dt}\right) + \mu c\frac{dx_k}{dt}\frac{\partial u_i}{\partial x_k}.$$

The first term in this expression is zero because of the conservation of mass for noninteracting particles. In fact, the quantities $\mu \frac{dx_k}{dt}$ constitute the "mass current" four-vector, analogous to the charge current four-vector (28.2); the conservation of mass is expressed by equating to zero the divergence of this four-vector:

$$\frac{\partial}{\partial x_k}\left(\mu \frac{dx_k}{dt}\right) = 0, \tag{33.8}$$

just as the conservation of charge is expressed by equation (29.4).

Thus we have:

$$\frac{\partial T_{ik}^{(p)}}{\partial x_k} = \mu c \frac{dx_k}{dt}\frac{\partial u_i}{\partial x_k} = \mu c \frac{du_i}{dt}.$$

Next we use the equation of motion of the charges in the field, expressed in the four-dimensional form (23.5),

$$mc \frac{du_i}{ds} = \frac{e}{c} F_{ik} u_k.$$

Changing to continuous distributions of charge and mass, we have, from the definitions of the densities μ and ϱ: $\mu/m = \varrho/e$. We can therefore write the equation of motion in the form

$$\mu c \frac{du_i}{ds} = \frac{\varrho}{c} F_{ik} u_k$$

or

$$\mu c \frac{du_i}{dt} = \frac{1}{c} F_{ik} \varrho u_k \frac{ds}{dt} = \frac{1}{c} F_{ik} j_k.$$

Thus,

$$\frac{\partial T_{ik}^{(p)}}{\partial x_k} = \frac{1}{c} F_{ik} j_k. \tag{33.9}$$

Combining this with (33.7), we find that we actually get zero, i.e. we arrive at equation (33.6).

§ 34. The virial theorem

Since the sum of the diagonal terms of the energy-momentum tensor of the electromagnetic field is equal to zero, the sum T_{ii} for any system of interacting particles reduces to the trace of the energy-momentum tensor for the particles alone. Using (33.5), we therefore have:

$$T_{ii} = T_{ii}^{(p)} = \mu c u_i u_i \frac{ds}{dt} = -\mu c \frac{ds}{dt} = -\mu c^2 \sqrt{1-\frac{v^2}{c^2}}.$$

Let us rewrite this result, shifting to a summation over the particles, i.e. writing μ as the sum (33.4). We then get finally:

$$T_{ii} = -\sum_a m_a c^2 \sqrt{1-\frac{v_a^2}{c^2}}\,\delta(\mathbf{r}-\mathbf{r}_a). \tag{34.1}$$

We note that, according to this formula, we have for every system:

$$T_{ii} \leqslant 0, \tag{34.2}$$

where the equality sign holds only for the electromagnetic field without charges.

Let us consider a closed system of charged particles carrying out a finite motion, in which all the quantities (coordinates, momenta) characterizing the system vary over finite ranges.†

We average the equation

$$\frac{1}{ic}\frac{\partial T_{\alpha 4}}{\partial t} + \frac{\partial T_{\alpha\beta}}{\partial x_\beta} = 0$$

[see (32.12)] with respect to the time. The average of the derivative $\partial T_{\alpha 4}/\partial t$, like the average of the derivative of any bounded quantity, is zero.‡ Therefore we get

$$\frac{\partial}{\partial x_\beta}\overline{T_{\alpha\beta}} = 0.$$

We multiply this equation by x_α and integrate over all space. We transform the integral by Gauss' theorem, keeping in mind that at infinity $T_{\alpha\beta} = 0$, and so the surface integral vanishes:

$$\int x_\alpha \overline{\frac{\partial T_{\alpha\beta}}{\partial x_\beta}}\, dV = -\int \frac{\partial x_\alpha}{\partial x_\beta}\overline{T_{\alpha\beta}}\, dV = -\int \delta_{\alpha\beta}\overline{T_{\alpha\beta}}\, dV = 0,$$

or finally,

$$\int \overline{T_{\alpha\alpha}}\, dV = 0. \tag{34.3}$$

On the basis of this equality we can write for the integral of $\overline{T_{ii}} = \overline{T_{\alpha\alpha}} + \overline{T_{44}}$:

$$\int \overline{T_{ii}}\, dV = \int \overline{T_{44}}\, dV = -\mathcal{E},$$

where $\mathcal{E}$ is the total energy o^c the system.

---

† Here we also assume that the electromagnetic field of the system also vanishes at infinity. This means that, if there is a radiation of electromagnetic waves by the system, it is assumed that special "reflecting walls" prevent these waves from going off to infinity.

‡ Let $f(t)$ be su:h a quantity. Then the average value of the derivative df/dt over a certain time interval T is

$$\overline{\frac{df}{dt}} = \frac{1}{T}\int_0^T \frac{df}{dt}\,dt = \frac{f(T)-f(0)}{T}.$$

Since $f(t)$ varies only within finite limits, then as T increases without limit, the average value of df/dt clearly goes to zero.

Finally, substituting (34.1) we get:

$$\mathcal{E} = \sum_a m_a c^2 \overline{\sqrt{1-\frac{v_a^2}{c^2}}}. \tag{34.4}$$

This relation is the relativistic generalization of the *virial theorem* of classical mechanics.† For low velocities, it becomes

$$\mathcal{E} - \sum_a m_a c^2 = -\sum_a \frac{\overline{m_a v_a^2}}{2},$$

that is, the total energy (minus the rest energy) is equal to the negative of the average value of the kinetic energy — in agreement with the result given by the classical virial theorem for a system of charged particles (interacting according to the Coulomb law).

§ 35. The energy-momentum tensor for macroscopic bodies

In addition to the energy-momentum tensor for a system of point particles (33.5), we shall also need the expression for this tensor for macroscopic bodies which are treated as being continuous.

The flux of momentum through the element $d\mathbf{f}$ of the surface of the body is just the force acting on this surface element. Therefore $T_{\alpha\beta}\, df_\beta$ is the α-component of the force acting on the element. Now we introduce a reference system in which a given element of volume of the body is at rest. In such a reference system, Pascal's law is valid, that is, the pressure applied to a given portion of the body is transmitted equally in all directions and is everywhere perpendicular to the surface on which it acts.†† Therefore we can write $T_{\alpha\beta}\, df_\beta = p\, df_\alpha$, so that

$$T_{\alpha\beta} = p\delta_{\alpha\beta},$$

where p is the pressure. As for the components $T_{\alpha 4}$, which represent the momentum density, they are equal to zero for the given volume element in the reference system we are using. The component $-T_{44}$ is as always the energy density of the body, which we denote by ϵ; ϵ/c^2 is then the mass density of the body, i.e., the mass per unit volume. We emphasize that we are talking here about the unit "proper" volume, that is, the volume in the reference system in which the given portion of the body is at rest.

† See *Mechanics*, § 10.

†† Strictly speaking, Pascal's law is valid only for liquids and gases. However for solid bodies the maximum possible difference in the stress in different directions is negligible in comparison with the stresses which can play a role in the theory of relativity, so that its consideration is of no interest.

Thus, in the reference system under consideration, the energy-momentum tensor (for the given portion of the body) has the form:

$$T_{ik} = \begin{pmatrix} p & 0 & 0 & 0 \\ 0 & p & 0 & 0 \\ 0 & 0 & p & 0 \\ 0 & 0 & 0 & -\epsilon \end{pmatrix} \tag{35.1}$$

Now it is easy to find the expression for the energy-momentum tensor in an arbitrary reference system. To do this we introduce the four-velocity u_i for the macroscopic motion of an element of volume of the body. In the reference frame in which the particular element is at rest, the components of its four-velocity are $u_\alpha = 0$, $u_4 = i$. The expression for T_{ik} must be chosen so that in this reference system it takes on the form (35.1). It is easy to verify that this is

$$T_{ik} = (p+\epsilon)u_i u_k + p\delta_{ik}. \tag{35.2}$$

This expression gives the energy-momentum tensor for a macroscopic body. Its components, written in three-dimensional form, are

$$T_{\alpha\beta} = \frac{(p+\epsilon)v_\alpha v_\beta}{c^2\left(1-\dfrac{v^2}{c^2}\right)} + p\delta_{\alpha\beta},$$

$$T_{\alpha 4} = \frac{i(p+\epsilon)v_\alpha}{c\left(1-\dfrac{v^2}{c^2}\right)}, \qquad T_{44} = -\frac{\epsilon + p\dfrac{v^2}{c^2}}{1-\dfrac{v^2}{c^2}}. \tag{35.3}$$

If the velocity v of the macroscopic motion is small compared with the velocity of light, then we have approximately:

$$T_{\alpha 4} = \frac{i}{c}(p+\epsilon)v_\alpha.$$

Since $-\dfrac{i}{c}T_{\alpha 4}$ is the momentum density, we see that in this case the sum $\dfrac{1}{c^2}(p+\epsilon)$ plays the role of the mass density of the body.

The expression for T_{ik} simplifies in the case where the velocities of all the particles making up the body are small compared with the velocity of light (the velocity of the macroscopic motion itself can be arbitrary). In this case we can neglect, in the energy density ϵ, all terms small compared with the rest energy, that is, we can write $\mu_0 c^2$ in place of ϵ, where μ_0 is the sum of the masses of the particles present in unit (proper) volume of the body (we emphasize that in the general case, μ_0 must differ from the actual mass density

ϵ/c^2 of the body, which includes also the mass corresponding to the energy of microscopic motion of the particles in the body and the energy of their interactions). As for the pressure determined by the energy of microscopic motion of the molecules, in the case under consideration it is also clearly small compared with the rest energy $\mu_0 c^2$. Thus we find for T_{ik} the expression

$$T_{ik} = \mu_0 c^2 u_i u_k. \tag{35.4}$$

From the expression (34.2), we get

$$T_{ii} = -\epsilon + 3p. \tag{35.5}$$

The general property (34.2) of the energy-momentum tensor of an arbitrary system now shows that the following inequality is always valid for the pressure and density of a macroscopic body:

$$p < \frac{\epsilon}{3}. \tag{35.6}$$

Let us compare the relation (35.5) with the general formula (34.1) which we saw was valid for an arbitrary system. Since we are at present considering a macroscopic body, the expression (34.1) must be averaged over all the values of **r** in unit volume. We obtain the result

$$\epsilon - 3p = \sum_a m_a c^2 \sqrt{1 - \frac{v_a^2}{c^2}} \tag{35.7}$$

(the summation extends over all particles in unit volume).

We apply our formula to an ideal gas, which we assume to consist of identical particles. Since the particles of an ideal gas do not interact with one another, we can use formula (33.5) after averaging it. Thus for an ideal gas,

$$T_{ik} = nmc \overline{\frac{dx_i}{dt} \frac{dx_k}{ds}},$$

where n is the number of particles in unit volume and the dash means an average over all the particles. If there is no macroscopic motion in the gas then we can use for T_{ik} the expression (35.1). Comparing the two formulas, we arrive at the equations:

$$\epsilon = nm \overline{\left(\frac{c^2}{\sqrt{1 - \frac{v^2}{c^2}}}\right)}, \quad p = \frac{nm}{3} \overline{\left(\frac{v^2}{\sqrt{1 - \frac{v^2}{c^2}}}\right)}. \tag{35.8}$$

These equations determine the density and pressure of a relativistic ideal gas in terms of the velocity of its particles; the second of these replaces the well-known formula $p = nm\overline{v^2}/3$ of the nonrelativistic kinetic theory of gases.

CHAPTER 5

CONSTANT ELECTROMAGNETIC FIELDS

§ 36. Coulomb's law

For a constant electric, or as it usually called, *electrostatic* field, the Maxwell equations have the form:

$$\operatorname{div} \mathbf{E} = 4\pi\varrho, \tag{36.1}$$

$$\operatorname{curl} \mathbf{E} = 0. \tag{36.2}$$

The electric field **E** is expressed in terms of the scalar potential alone by the relation

$$\mathbf{E} = -\operatorname{grad} \phi. \tag{36.3}$$

Substituting (36.3) in (36.1), we get the equation which is satisfied by the potential of a constant electric field:

$$\Delta\phi = -4\pi\varrho. \tag{36.4}$$

This equation is called the *Poisson equation*. In particular, in vacuum, i.e., for $\varrho = 0$, the potential satisfies the *Laplace equation*

$$\Delta\phi = 0. \tag{36.5}$$

From the last equation it follows, in particular, that the potential of the electric field can nowhere have a maximum or a minimum. For in order that ϕ have an extreme value, it would be necessary that the first derivatives of ϕ with respect to the coordinates be zero, and that the second derivatives $\partial^2\phi/\partial x^2$, $\partial^2\phi/\partial y^2$, $\partial^2\phi/\partial z^2$ all have the same sign. The last is impossible, since in that case (36.5) could not be satisfied.

We now determine the field produced by a point charge. From symmetry considerations, it is clear that it is directed along the radius-vector from the point at which the charge e is located. From the same consideration it is clear that the value E of the field depends only on the distance R from the charge. To find this absolute value, we apply equation (36.1) in the integral form (30.5). The flux of the electric field through a spherical surface of radius R circumscribed around the charge e is equal to $4\pi R^2 E$; this flux must equal $4\pi e$. From this we get

$$E = \frac{e}{R^2}.$$

In vector notation:

$$\mathbf{E} = \frac{e\mathbf{R}}{R^3}. \tag{36.6}$$

Thus the field produced by a point charge is inversely proportional to the square of the distance from the charge. This is the *Coulomb law*. The potential of this field is, clearly,

$$\phi = \frac{e}{R}. \tag{36.7}$$

If we have a system of charges, then the field produced by this system is equal, according to the principle of superposition, to the sum of the fields produced by each of the particles individually. In particular, the potential of such a field is

$$\phi = \sum_a \frac{e_a}{R_a},$$

where R_a is the distance from the charge e_a to the point at which we are determining the potential. If we introduce the charge density ϱ, this formula takes on the form

$$\phi = \int \frac{\varrho}{R}\, dV, \tag{36.8}$$

where R is the distance from the volume element dV to the given point of the field.

We note a mathematical relation which is obtained from (36.4) by substituting the values of ϱ and ϕ for a point charge, i.e., $\varrho = e\,\delta(\mathbf{R})$ and $\phi = e/R$. We then find

$$\Delta\left(\frac{1}{R}\right) = -4\pi\,\delta(\mathbf{R}). \tag{36.9}$$

§ 37. Electrostatic energy of charges

We determine the energy of a system of charges. We start from the energy of the field, that is, from the expression (31.5) for the energy density. Namely, the energy of the system of charges must be equal to

$$U = \frac{1}{8\pi}\int E^2\, dV,$$

where $\mathbf{E}$ is the field produced by these charges, and the integral goes over all space. Substituting $\mathbf{E} = -\operatorname{grad}\phi$, U can be changed to the following form:

$$U = -\frac{1}{8\pi}\int \mathbf{E}\cdot\operatorname{grad}\phi\, dV = -\frac{1}{8\pi}\int \operatorname{div}(\mathbf{E}\phi)\, dV + \frac{1}{8\pi}\int \phi\operatorname{div}\mathbf{E}\, dV.$$

According to Gauss' theorem, the first integral is equal to the integral of $\mathbf{E}\phi$ over the surface bounding the volume of integration, but since the integral is taken over all space and since the field is zero at infinity, this integral vanishes. Substituting in the second integral, div $\mathbf{E} = 4\pi\varrho$, we find the following expression for the energy of a system of charges:

$$U = \tfrac{1}{2}\int \varrho\phi \, dV. \tag{37.1}$$

For a system of point charges, e_a, we can write in place of the integral a sum over the charges

$$U = \tfrac{1}{2}\sum_a e_a\phi_a, \tag{37.2}$$

where ϕ_a is the potential of the field produced by all the charges, at the point where the charge e_a is located.

If we apply our formula to a single elementary charged particle (say, an electron), and the field which the charge itself produces, we arrive at the result that the charge must have a certain "self"-potential energy equal to $e\phi/2$, where ϕ is the potential of the field produced by the charge at the point where it is located. But we know that in the theory of relativity every elementary particle must be considered as pointlike. The potential $\phi = e/R$ of its field becomes infinite at the point $R = 0$. Thus according to electrodynamics, the electron would have to have an infinite "self-energy", and consequently also an infinite mass (equal to the energy divided by c^2). The physical absurdity of this result shows that the basic principles of electrodynamics itself lead to the result that its application must be restricted to definite limits.

We note that in view of the infinity obtained from electrodynamics for the self-energy and mass, it is impossible within the frame work of classical electrodynamics itself to pose the question of whether the total mass of the electron is electrodynamic (that is, associated with the electromagnetic self-energy of the particle).†

Since the occurrence of the physically meaningless infinite self-energy of the elementary particle is related to the fact that such a particle must be considered as pointlike, we can conclude that electrodynamics as a logically closed physical theory presents internal contradictions when we go to sufficiently small distances. We can pose the question as to the order of magnitude of such distances. We can answer this question by noting that for the electromagnetic self-energy of the electron we should obtain a value of the order of the rest energy mc^2. If, on the other hand, we consider an electron

†From the purely formal point of view, the finiteness of the electron mass can be handled by introducing an infinite negative mass of nonelectromagnetic origin which compensates the infinity of the electromagnetic mass (mass "renormalization"). However, we shall see later (§ 75) that this does not eliminate all the internal contradictions of classical electrodynamics.

as possessing a certain radius R_0, then its self-potential energy would be of order e^2/R_0. From the requirement that these two quantities be of the same order, $e^2/R_0 \sim mc^2$, we find

$$R_0 \sim \frac{e^2}{mc^2}. \tag{37.3}$$

This dimension (the "radius" of the electron) determines the limit of applicability of electrodynamics to the electron, and follows already from its fundamental principles. We must, however, keep in mind that actually the limits of applicability of the classical electrodynamics which is presented here lie much higher, because of the occurrence of quantum phenomena.†

We now turn again to formula (37.2). The potentials ϕ_a which appear there are equal, from Coulomb's law, to

$$\phi_a = \sum \frac{e_b}{R_{ab}}, \tag{37.4}$$

where R_{ab} is the distance between the charges e_a, e_b. The expression for the energy (37.2) consists of two parts. First, it contains an infinite constant, the self-energy of the charges, not depending on their mutual separations. The second part is the energy of interaction of the charges, depending on their separations. Only this part has physical interest. It is equal to

$$U' = \tfrac{1}{2} \sum e_a \phi'_a, \tag{37.5}$$

where

$$\phi'_a = \sum_{b \neq a} \frac{e_b}{R_{ab}} \tag{37.6}$$

is the potential at the point of location of e_a, produced by all the charges other than e_a. In other words, we can write

$$U' = \frac{1}{2} \sum_{a \neq b} \frac{e_a e_b}{R_{ab}}. \tag{37.7}$$

In particular, the energy of interaction of two charges is

$$U' = \frac{e_1 e_2}{R_{12}}. \tag{37.8}$$

38. The field of a uniformly moving charge

We determine the field produced by a charge e, moving uniformly with velocity V. We call the laboratory frame the system K; the system of reference moving with the charge is the K' system. Let the charge be located at the origin of coordinates of the K' system. The system K' moves relative to K

† Quantum effects become important for distances of the order of $\hbar/mc$, where $\hbar$ is Planck's constant.

along the X axis; the axes Y and Z are parallel to Y' and Z'. At the time $t = 0$ the origins of the two systems coincide. The coordinates of the charge in the K system are consequently $x = Vt$, $y = z = 0$. In the K' system, we have a constant electric field with vector potential $\mathbf{A}' = 0$, and scalar potential equal to $\phi' = e/R'$, where $R'^2 = x'^2+y'^2+z'^2$. In the K system, according to (24.1) for $\mathbf{A}' = 0$,

$$\phi = \frac{\phi'}{\sqrt{1-\frac{V^2}{c^2}}} = \frac{e}{R'\sqrt{1-\frac{V^2}{c^2}}}. \tag{38.1}$$

We must now express R' in terms of the coordinates x, y, z, in the K system. According to the formulas for the Lorentz transformation

$$x' = \frac{x-Vt}{\sqrt{1-\frac{V^2}{c^2}}}, \quad y' = y, \quad z' = z,$$

from which

$$R'^2 = \frac{(x-Vt)^2+\left(1-\frac{V^2}{c^2}\right)(y^2+z^2)}{1-\frac{V^2}{c^2}}. \tag{38.2}$$

Substituting this in (38.1) we find

$$\phi = \frac{e}{R^*} \tag{38.3}$$

where we have introduced the notation

$$R^{*2} = (x-Vt)^2+\left(1-\frac{V^2}{c^2}\right)(y^2+z^2). \tag{38.4}$$

The vector potential in the K system is equal to

$$\mathbf{A} = \phi\frac{\mathbf{V}}{c} = \frac{e\mathbf{V}}{cR^*}. \tag{38.5}$$

In the K' system the magnetic field $\mathbf{H}'$ is absent and the electric field is

$$\mathbf{E}' = \frac{e\mathbf{R}'}{R'^3}.$$

From formula (24.5), we find

$$E_x = E'_x = \frac{ex'}{R'^3}, \quad E_y = \frac{E'_y}{\sqrt{1-\frac{V^2}{c^2}}} = \frac{ey'}{R'^3\sqrt{1-\frac{V^2}{c^2}}},$$

$$E_z = \frac{ez'}{R'^3\sqrt{1-\frac{V^2}{c^2}}}.$$

Substituting for R', x', y', z', their expressions in terms of x, y, z, we obtain

$$\mathbf{E} = \left(1-\frac{V^2}{c^2}\right)\frac{e\mathbf{R}}{R^{*3}}, \tag{38.6}$$

where $\mathbf{R}$ is the radius vector from the charge e to the field point with coordinates x, y, z, (its components are $x-Vt$, y, z).

This expression for $\mathbf{E}$ can be written in another form by introducing the angle θ between the direction of motion and the radius vector $\mathbf{R}$. It is clear that $y^2+z^2 = R^2 \sin^2\theta$, and therefore R^{*2} can be written in the form:

$$R^{*2} = R^2\left(1-\frac{V^2}{c^2}\sin^2\theta\right). \tag{38.7}$$

Then we have for $\mathbf{E}$,

$$\mathbf{E} = \frac{e\mathbf{R}}{R^3}\frac{1-\frac{V^2}{c^2}}{\left(1-\frac{V^2}{c^2}\sin^2\theta\right)^{\frac{3}{2}}}. \tag{38.8}$$

For a fixed distance R from the charge, the value of the field E increases as θ increases from 0 to $\pi/2$ (or as θ decreases from π to $\pi/2$). The field along the direction of motion ($\theta = 0, \pi$) has the smallest value; it is equal to

$$E_{||} = \frac{e}{R^2}\left(1-\frac{V^2}{c^2}\right).$$

The largest field is that perpendicular to the velocity ($\theta = \pi/2$), equal to

$$E_{\perp} = \frac{e}{R^2}\frac{1}{\sqrt{1-\frac{V^2}{c^2}}}.$$

We note that as the velocity increases, the field $E_{||}$ decreases, while $E_{\perp}$ increases. We can describe this pictorially by saying that the electric field of a moving charge is "contracted" in the direction of motion. For velocities V close to the velocity of light, the denominator in formula (38.8) is close to zero in a narrow interval of values θ around the value $\theta = \pi/2$. The "width" of this interval is, in order of magnitude,

$$\Delta\theta \sim \sqrt{1-\frac{V^2}{c^2}}.$$

Thus the electric field of a rapidly moving charge at a given distance from it is large only in a narrow range of angles in the neighborhood of the equatorial plane, and the width of this interval decreases with increasing V like $\sqrt{1-(V^2/c^2)}$.

The magnetic field in the K system is

$$\mathbf{H} = \frac{1}{c}\mathbf{V}\times\mathbf{E} \tag{38.9}$$

[see (24.8)]. In particular, for $V \ll c$ the electric field is given approximately by the usual formula for the Coulomb law, $\mathbf{E} = e\mathbf{r}/\mathbf{R}^3$, and the magnetic field is

$$\mathbf{H} = \frac{e}{c}\frac{\mathbf{V}\times\mathbf{R}}{R^3}, \tag{38.10}$$

Problem

Determine the force (in the K system) between two charges moving with the same velocity $\mathbf{V}$.

Solution: We shall determine the force $\mathbf{F}$ by computing the force acting on one of the charges (e_1) in the field produced by the other (e_2). Using (38.9), we have

$$\mathbf{F} = e_1\mathbf{E}_2 + \frac{e_1}{c}\mathbf{V}\times\mathbf{H}_2 = e_1\left(1-\frac{V^2}{c^2}\right)\mathbf{E}_2 + \frac{e_1}{c^2}\mathbf{V}(\mathbf{V}\cdot\mathbf{E}_2).$$

Substituting for $\mathbf{E}_2$ from (38.8), we get for the components of the force in the direction of motion (F_x) and perpendicular to it (F_y):

$$F_x = \frac{e_1 e_2}{R^2}\frac{\left(1-\frac{V^2}{c^2}\right)\cos\theta}{\left(1-\frac{V^2}{c^2}\sin^2\theta\right)^{3/2}}, \quad F_y = \frac{e_1 e_2}{R^2}\frac{\left(1-\frac{V^2}{c^2}\right)^2\sin\theta}{\left(1-\frac{V^2}{c^2}\sin^2\theta\right)^{3/2}},$$

where $\mathbf{R}$ is the radius vector from e_2 to e_1, and θ is the angle between $\mathbf{R}$ and $\mathbf{V}$.

§ 39. Motion in the Coulomb field

We consider the motion of a particle with mass m and charge e in the field produced by a second charge e'; we assume that the mass of this second charge is so large that it can be considered as fixed. Then our problem becomes the study of the motion of a charge e in a centrally symmetric electric field with potential $\phi = e'/r$.

The total energy $\mathcal{E}$ of the particle is equal to

$$\mathcal{E} = c\sqrt{p^2+m^2c^2} + \frac{\alpha}{r},$$

where $\alpha = ee'$. If we use polar coordinates in the plane of motion of the particle, then as we know from mechanics,

$$p^2 = (M^2/r^2)+p_r^2,$$

where p_r is the radial component of the momentum, and M is the constant angular momentum of the particle. Then

$$\mathcal{E} = c\sqrt{p_r^2+\frac{M^2}{r^2}+m^2c^2}+\frac{\alpha}{r}. \tag{39.1}$$

We discuss the question whether the particle during its motion can approach arbitrarily close to the center. First of all, it is clear that this is never possible if the charges e and e' repel each other, that is, if e and e' have the same sign. Furthermore, in the case of attraction (e and e' of opposite sign), arbitrarily close approach to the center is not possible if $Mc > |a|$, for in this case the first term in (39.1) is always larger than the second, and for $r \to 0$ the right side of the equation would approach infinity. On the other hand, if $Mc < |a|$, then as $r \to 0$, this expression can remain finite (here it is understood that p_r approaches infinity). Thus, if

$$cM < |a|, \tag{39.2}$$

the particle during its motion "falls in" toward the charge attracting it, in contrast to nonrelativistic mechanics, where for the Coulomb field such a collapse is generally impossible (with the exception of the one case $M = 0$, where the particle e moves on a line toward the particle e').

A complete determination of the motion of a charge in a Coulomb field starts most conveniently from the Hamilton-Jacobi equation. We choose polar coordinates r, ϕ, in the plane of the motion. The Hamilton-Jacobi equation (16.11) has the form

$$-\frac{1}{c^2}\left(\frac{\partial S}{\partial t}+\frac{a}{r}\right)^2+\left(\frac{\partial S}{\partial r}\right)^2+\frac{1}{r^2}\left(\frac{\partial S}{\partial \phi}\right)^2+m^2c^2 = 0.$$

We seek an S of the form

$$S = -\mathcal{E}t+M\phi+f(r),$$

where $\mathcal{E}$ and M are the constant energy and angular momentum of the moving particle. The result is

$$S = -\mathcal{E}t+M\phi+\int\sqrt{\frac{1}{c^2}\left(\mathcal{E}-\frac{a}{r}\right)^2-\frac{M^2}{r^2}-m^2c^2}\,dr. \tag{39.3}$$

The trajectory is determined by the equation $\partial S/\partial M = \text{const}$. Integration of (39.3) leads to the following results for the trajectory:

(a) If $Mc > |a|$,

$$(c^2M^2-a^2)\frac{1}{r} = c\sqrt{(M\mathcal{E})^2-m^2c^2(M^2c^2-a^2)}\cos\left(\phi\sqrt{1-\frac{a^2}{c^2M^2}}\right)-\mathcal{E}a. \tag{39.4}$$

(b) If $Mc < |a|$,

$$(a^2-M^2c^2)\frac{1}{r} = \pm c\sqrt{(M\mathcal{E})^2+m^2c^2(a^2-M^2c^2)}\cosh\left(\phi\sqrt{\frac{a^2}{c^2M^2}-1}\right)+\mathcal{E}a. \tag{39.5}$$

(c) If $Mc = |a|$,

$$\frac{2\mathcal{E}a}{r} = \mathcal{E}^2-m^2c^4-\phi^2\left(\frac{\mathcal{E}a}{cM}\right)^2. \tag{39.6}$$

The integration constant is contained in the arbitrary choice of the reference line for measurement of the angle ϕ.

In (39.4) the ambiguity of sign in front of the square root is unimportant, since it already contains the arbitrary reference origin of the angle ϕ under the cos. In the case of attraction ($\alpha < 0$) the trajectory corresponding to this equation lies entirely at finite values of r (finite motion), if $\mathcal{E} < mc^2$. If $\mathcal{E} > mc^2$, then r can go to infinity (infinite motion). The finite motion corresponds to motion in a closed orbit (ellipse) in nonrelativistic mechanics. From (39.4) it is clear that in relativistic mechanics the trajectory can never be closed; when the angle ϕ changes by 2π, the distance r from the center does not return to its initial value. In place of ellipses we here get orbits in the form of open "rosettes". Thus, whereas in nonrelativistic mechanics the finite motion in a Coulomb field leads to a closed orbit, in relativistic mechanics the Coulomb field loses this property.

In (39.5) we must choose the positive sign for the root in case $\alpha < 0$, and the negative sign if $\alpha > 0$ [the opposite choice of sign would correspond to a reversal of the sign of the root in (39.1)].

For $\alpha < 0$ the trajectories (39.5) and (39.6) are spirals in which the distance r approaches 0 as $\phi \to \infty$. The time required for the "falling in" of the charge to the coordinate origin is finite. This can be verified by noting that the dependence of the coordinate r on the time is determined by the equation $\partial S/\partial \mathcal{E} = \text{const}$; substituting (39.3), we see that the time is determined by an integral which converges for $r \to 0$.

Problems

1. Determine the angle of deflection of a charge passing through a repulsive Coulomb field ($\alpha > 0$).

Solution: The angle of deflection χ equals $\chi = \pi - 2\phi_0$, where ϕ_0 is the angle between the two asymptotes of the trajectory (39.4). We find

$$\chi = \pi - \frac{2cM}{\sqrt{c^2M^2-\alpha^2}} \tan^{-1}\left(\frac{v\sqrt{c^2M^2-\alpha^2}}{c\alpha}\right),$$

where v is the velocity of the charge at infinity.

2. Determine the effective scattering cross section at small angles for the scattering of particles in a Coulomb field.

Solution: The effective cross section $d\sigma$ is the ratio of the number of particles scattered per second into a given element do of solid angle to the flux density of impinging particles (i.e., to the number of particles crossing one square centimeter, per second, of a surface perpendicular to the beam of particles).†

Since the angle of deflection χ of the particle during its passage through the field is determined by the *impact parameter* ϱ (i.e., the distance from the center to the line along which the particle would move in the absence of the field),

$$d\sigma = 2\pi\varrho\, d\varrho = 2\pi\varrho \frac{d\varrho}{d\chi} d\chi = \varrho \frac{d\varrho}{d\chi} \frac{do}{\sin\chi},$$

where $do = 2\pi \sin\chi\, d\chi$. The angle of deflection (for small angles) can be taken equal to the ratio of the change in momentum to its initial value. The change in momentum is equal

† See *Mechanics*, § 18.

to the time integral of the force acting on the charge, in the direction perpendicular to the direction of motion; it is approximately $\frac{a}{r^2}\frac{\varrho}{r}$. Thus we have

$$\chi = \frac{1}{p}\int_{-\infty}^{+\infty} \frac{a\varrho\, dt}{(\varrho^2+v^2 t^2)^{\frac{3}{2}}} = \frac{2a}{p\varrho v}$$

(v is the velocity of the particles). From this we find the effective cross section for small χ:

$$d\sigma = 4\left(\frac{a}{pv}\right)^2 \frac{do}{\chi^4}.$$

In the nonrelativistic case, $p \simeq mv$, and this expression coincides with the one obtained from the Rutherford formula † for small χ.

§ 40. The dipole moment

We consider the field produced by a system of charges at large distances, that is, at distances large compared with the dimensions of the system.

We introduce a coordinate system with origin anywhere within the system of charges. Let the radius vectors of the various charges be r_a. The potential of the field produced by all the charges at the point having the radius vector $\mathbf{R}_0$ is

$$\phi = \sum_a \frac{e_a}{|\mathbf{R}_0-\mathbf{r}_a|} \tag{40.1}$$

(the summation goes over all charges); here $\mathbf{R}_0-\mathbf{r}_a$ are the radius vectors from the charges e_a to the point where we are finding the potential.

We must investigate this expression for large $\mathbf{R}_0(\mathbf{R}_0 \gg \mathbf{r}_a)$. To do this, we expand it in powers of $\mathbf{r}_a/R_0$, using the formula

$$f(\mathbf{R}_0-\mathbf{r}) = f(\mathbf{R}_0)-\mathbf{r}\cdot \text{grad}\, f(\mathbf{R}_0)$$

(in the grad, the differentiation applies to the coordinates of the vector $\mathbf{R}_0$). To terms of first order,

$$\phi = \frac{\sum e_a}{R_0} - \sum e_a\mathbf{r}_a\cdot \text{grad}\, \frac{1}{R_0}. \tag{40.2}$$

The sum

$$\mathbf{d} = \sum e_a\mathbf{r}_a \tag{40.3}$$

is called the *dipole moment* of the system of charges. It is important to note that if the sum of all the charges, $\sum e_a$, is zero, then the dipole moment does not depend on the choice of the origin of coordinates, for the radius vectors $\mathbf{r}_a$ and $\mathbf{r}'_a$ of one and the same charge in two different coordinate systems are related by

$$\mathbf{r}'_a = \mathbf{r}_a+\mathbf{a},$$

†See *Mechanics*, § 19.

where **a** is some constant vector. Therefore if $\sum e_a = 0$, the dipole moment is the same in both systems:

$$\mathbf{d}' = \sum e_a \mathbf{r}'_a = \sum e_a \mathbf{r}_a + \mathbf{a} \sum e_a = \mathbf{d}.$$

If we denote by e_a^+, $\mathbf{r}_a^+$ and e_a^-, $\mathbf{r}_a^-$ the positive and negative charges of the system and their radius vectors, then we can write the dipole moment in the form

$$\mathbf{d} = \sum e_a^+ \mathbf{r}_a^+ - \sum e_a^- \mathbf{r}_a^- + \mathbf{R}_a^+ \sum e_a^+ - \mathbf{R}^- \sum e_a^- \tag{40.4}$$

where

$$\mathbf{R}^+ = \frac{\sum e_a^+ \mathbf{r}_a^+}{\sum e_a^+}, \qquad \mathbf{R}^- = \frac{\sum e_a^- \mathbf{r}_a^-}{\sum e_a^-} \tag{40.5}$$

are the radius vectors of the "charge centers" for the positive and negative charges. If $\sum e_a^+ = \sum e_a^- = e$, then

$$\mathbf{d} = e\mathbf{R}_{+-}, \tag{40.6}$$

where $\mathbf{R}_{+-} = \mathbf{R}^+ - \mathbf{R}^-$ is the radius vector from the center of negative to the center of positive charge. In particular, if we have altogether two charges, then $\mathbf{R}_{+-}$ is the radius vector between them.

If the total charge of the system is zero, then the potential of the field of this system at large distances is

$$\phi = -\mathbf{d} \cdot \nabla \frac{1}{\mathbf{R}_0} = \frac{\mathbf{d} \cdot \mathbf{R}_0}{R_0^3}. \tag{40.7}$$

The field intensity is:

$$\mathbf{E} = -\text{grad} \frac{\mathbf{d} \cdot \mathbf{R}_0}{R_0^3} = -\frac{1}{R_0^3} \text{grad } (\mathbf{d} \cdot \mathbf{R}_0) - (\mathbf{d} \cdot \mathbf{R}_0) \text{ grad } \frac{1}{R_0^3},$$

or finally,

$$\mathbf{E} = \frac{3(\mathbf{n} \cdot \mathbf{d})\mathbf{n} - \mathbf{d}}{R_0^3}, \tag{40.8}$$

where **n** is a unit vector along $\mathbf{R}_0$. Another useful expression for the field is

$$\mathbf{E} = (\mathbf{d} \cdot \nabla) \nabla \frac{1}{R_0}. \tag{40.9}$$

Thus the potential of the field at large distances produced by a system of charges with total charge equal to zero is inversely proportional to the square of the distance, and the field intensity is inversely proportional to the cube of the distance. This field has axial symmetry around the direction of **d**. In a plane passing through this direction (which we choose as the z axis), the components of the vector **E** are:

$$E_z = d\frac{3\cos^2\theta - 1}{R_0^3}, \quad E_x = d\frac{3\sin\theta\cos\theta}{R_0^3}. \tag{40.10}$$

The radial and tangential components in this plane are

$$E_R = d\frac{2\cos\theta}{R_0^3}, \quad E_\theta = -d\frac{\sin\theta}{R_0^3}. \tag{40.11}$$

§ 41. Multipole moments

In the expansion of the potential in powers of $1/R_0$,

$$\phi = \phi^{(0)} + \phi^{(1)} + \phi^{(2)} + \dots, \tag{41.1}$$

the term $\phi^{(n)}$ is proportional to $1/R_0^{n+1}$. We saw that the first term, $\phi^{(0)}$, is determined by the sum of all the charges; the second term, $\phi^{(1)}$, sometimes called the dipole potential of the system, is determined by the dipole moment of the system.

The third term in the expansion, $\phi^{(2)}$, is clearly equal to

$$\phi^{(2)} = \frac{1}{2}\sum e x_\alpha x_\beta \frac{\partial^2}{\partial X_\alpha \partial X_\beta}\left(\frac{1}{R_0}\right), \tag{41.2}$$

where the sum goes over all charges; we here drop the index numbering the charges; x_α are the components of the vector **r**, and X_α those of the vector $\mathbf{R}_0$.

This part of the potential is usually called the *quadrupole potential.* If the sum of the charges and the dipole moment of the system are both equal to zero, the expansion begins with $\phi^{(2)}$.

In the expression (41.2) there enter the six quantities $\sum e x_\alpha x_\beta$. However, it is easy to see that the field actually depends not on six independent quantities, but only on five. This follows from the fact that the function $1/R_0$ satisfies the Laplace equation, that is,

$$\Delta\left(\frac{1}{R_0}\right) = \frac{\partial^2}{\partial X_\beta^2}\left(\frac{1}{R_0}\right) = 0.$$

This equality can be written in the form

$$\delta_{\alpha\beta}\frac{\partial^2}{\partial X_\alpha \partial X_\beta}\left(\frac{1}{R_0}\right) = 0.$$

We can therefore write $\phi^{(2)}$ in the form

$$\phi^{(2)} = \frac{1}{2}\sum e\left(x_\alpha x_\beta - \frac{1}{3}r^2\delta_{\alpha\beta}\right)\frac{\partial^2}{\partial X_\alpha \partial X_\beta}\left(\frac{1}{R_0}\right).$$

The tensor

$$D_{\alpha\beta} = \sum e(3x_\alpha x_\beta - r^2\delta_{\alpha\beta}) \tag{41.3}$$

is called the *quadrupole moment* of the system. From the definition of $D_{\alpha\beta}$ it is clear that the sum of its diagonal elements is zero:

$$D_{\alpha\alpha} = 0. \tag{41.4}$$

Therefore the symmetric tensor $D_{\alpha\beta}$ has altogether five independent components. With the aid of $D_{\alpha\beta}$, we can write

$$\phi^{(2)} = \frac{D_{\alpha\beta}}{6} \frac{\partial^2}{\partial X_\alpha \partial X_\beta} \left(\frac{1}{R_0}\right), \tag{41.5}$$

or, performing the differentiation,

$$\frac{\partial^2}{\partial X_\alpha \partial X_\beta} \frac{1}{R_0} = \frac{3X_\alpha X_\beta}{R_0^5} - \frac{\delta_{\alpha\beta}}{R_0^3},$$

and using the fact that, because of (41.4), $\delta_{\alpha\beta} D_{\alpha\beta} = D_{\alpha\alpha} = 0$,

$$\phi^{(2)} = \frac{D_{\alpha\beta} n_\alpha n_\beta}{2R_0^3}. \tag{41.6}$$

Like every symmetric three-dimensional tensor, the tensor $D_{\alpha\beta}$ can be brought to principal axes. Because of (41.4), in general only two of the three principal values will be independent. If it happens that the system of charges is symmetric around some axis (the z axis)† then this axis must be one of the principal axes of the tensor $D_{\alpha\beta}$, the location of the other two axes in the x, y plane is arbitrary, and the three principal values are related to one another:

$$D_{xx} = D_{yy} = -\tfrac{1}{2} D_{zz}. \tag{41.7}$$

Denoting the component D_{zz} by D (in this case it is simply called the quadrupole moment), we get for the potential

$$\phi^{(2)} = \frac{D}{4R_0^3}(3\cos^2\theta - 1) = \frac{D}{2R_0^3} P_2(\cos\theta), \tag{41.8}$$

where θ is the angle between $\boldsymbol{R}_0$ and the z axis, and P_2 is a Legendre polynomial.

Just as we did for the dipole moment in the preceding section, we can easily show that the quadrupole moment of a system does not depend on the choice of the coordinate origin, if both the total charge and the dipole moment of the system are equal to zero.

In similar fashion we could also write the succeeding terms of the expansion (41.1). The l'th term of the expansion defines a tensor (which is called the tensor of the 2^l-pole moment) of rank l, symmetric in all its indices and vanishing when contracted on any pair of indices;‡ it can be shown that such a tensor has $2l+1$ independent components.

---

†We are assuming a symmetry axis of any order higher than the second.

‡The contraction of a tensor on a pair of indices means that two indices are set equal to one another and then are summed over; as a result the rank of the tensor is reduced by two units.

We shall express the general term in the expansion of the potential in another form, by using the well known formula of the theory of spherical harmonics

$$\frac{1}{|\mathbf{R}_0-\mathbf{r}|} = \frac{1}{\sqrt{R_0^2+r^2-2rR_0\cos\chi}} = \sum_{l=0}^{\infty} \frac{r^l}{R_0^{l+1}} P_l(\cos\chi), \qquad (41.9)$$

where χ is the angle between $\mathbf{R}_0$ and $\mathbf{r}$. We introduce the spherical angles Θ, Φ and θ, ϕ, formed by the vectors $\mathbf{R}_0$ and $\mathbf{r}$, respectively, with the fixed coordinate axes, and use the addition theorem for the spherical harmonics:

$$P_l(\cos\chi) = \sum_{m=-l}^{l} \frac{(l-|m|)!}{(l+|m|)!} P_l^{|m|}(\cos\Theta) P_l^{|m|}(\cos\theta) e^{-im(\Phi-\phi)}, \qquad (41.10)$$

where the P_l^m are the associated Legendre polynomials. The expansion (41.9) then takes the form:

$$\frac{1}{|\mathbf{R}_0-\mathbf{r}|} = \sum_{l=0}^{\infty} \sum_{m=-l}^{l} \frac{r^l}{R_0^{l+1}} \frac{(l-|m|)!}{(l+|m|)!} P_l^{|m|}(\cos\Theta) P_l^{|m|}(\cos\theta) e^{-im(\Phi-\phi)}.$$

Performing such an expansion in each term of the sum (40.1), we finally get the following expression for the l'th term in the expansion of the potential:

$$\phi^{(l)} = \frac{1}{R_0^{l+1}} \sum_{m=-l}^{l} \sqrt{\frac{(l-|m|)!}{(l+|m|)!}} P_l^{|m|}(\cos\Theta) e^{-im\Phi} D_m^{(l)}, \qquad (41.11)$$

where

$$D_m^{(l)} = \sum_a e_a r_a^l \sqrt{\frac{(l-|m|)!}{(l+|m|)!}} P_l^{|m|}(\cos\theta_a) e^{im\phi_a}. \qquad (41.12)$$

The set of $2l+1$ quantities $D^{(l)}$ constitutes the 2^l-pole moment of the system of charges.

Problem

Determine the quadrupole moment of a uniformly charged ellipsoid with respect to its center.

Solution: Replacing the summation in (41.3) by an integration over the volume of the ellipsoid, we have:

$$D_{xx} = \varrho \int\int\int (2x^2-y^2-z^2)\,dx\,dy\,dz, \quad \text{etc.}$$

Let us choose the coordinate axes along the axes of the ellipsoid with the origin at its center; from symmetry considerations it is obvious that these axes are the principal axes of the tensor $D_{\alpha\beta}$. By means of the transformation

$$x = x'a, \quad y = y'b, \quad z = z'c$$

the integration over the volume of the ellipsoid

$$\frac{x^2}{a^2}+\frac{y^2}{b^2}+\frac{z^2}{c^2}=1$$

is reduced to integration over the volume of the unit sphere

$$x'^2+y'^2+z'^2=1.$$

As a result we obtain:

$$D_{xx}=\frac{e}{5}(2a^2-b^2-c^2),\quad D_{yy}=\frac{e}{5}(2b^2-a^2-c^2),$$

$$D_{zz}=\frac{e}{5}(2c^2-a^2-b^2),$$

where $e=\frac{4\pi}{3}abc\varrho$ is the total charge of the ellipsoid.

§ 42. System of charges in an external field

We now consider a system of charges located in an external electric field. We designate the potential of this external field by $\phi(\mathbf{r})$. The potential energy of each of the charges is $e_a\phi(\mathbf{r}_a)$, and the total potential energy of the system is

$$U=\sum_a e_a\phi(\mathbf{r}_a). \tag{42.1}$$

We introduce another coordinate system with its origin anywhere within the system of charges; $\mathbf{r}_a$ is the radius vector of the charge e_a in these coordinates.

Let us assume that the external field changes slowly over the region of the system of charges, i.e., is quasiuniform with respect to the system. Then we can expand the energy U in powers of $\mathbf{r}_a$. In this expansion,

$$U=U^{(0)}+U^{(1)}+U^{(2)}+\cdots, \tag{42.2}$$

the first term is

$$U^{(0)}=\phi_0\sum e_a, \tag{42.3}$$

where ϕ_0 is the value of the potential at the origin. In this approximation, the energy of the system is the same as it would be if all the charges were located at one point (the origin).

The second term in the expansion is

$$U^{(1)}=\mathrm{grad}\,\phi_0\cdot\sum e_a\mathbf{r}_a,$$

where grad ϕ_0 is the value of the gradient of the potential at the origin; since grad $\phi=-\mathbf{E}$, it is just the field intensity $\mathbf{E}_0$ at the origin. Introducing the dipole moment $\mathbf{d}$ of the system, we have

$$U^{(1)}=-\mathbf{d}\cdot\mathbf{E}_0. \tag{42.4}$$

The total force acting on the system in the external quasiuniform field is, to the order we are considering,

$$\mathbf{F} = \mathbf{E}_0 \sum e_a + (\nabla \mathbf{d} \cdot \mathbf{E})_0.$$

If the total charge is zero, the first term vanishes, and

$$\mathbf{F} = (\mathbf{d} \cdot \nabla)\mathbf{E}, \tag{42.5}$$

i.e. the force is determined by the derivatives of the field intensity (taken at the origin). The first moment of the forces acting on the system is

$$\mathbf{K} = \sum (\mathbf{r}_a \times e_a \mathbf{E}_0) = \mathbf{d} \times \mathbf{E}_0, \tag{42.6}$$

i.e. it is determined by the field intensity itself.

Let us assume that there are two systems, each having total charge zero, and with dipole moments $\mathbf{d}_1$ and $\mathbf{d}_2$, respectively. Their mutual distance is assumed to be large in comparison with their internal dimensions. Let us determine their potential energy of interaction, U. To do this we regard one of the systems as being in the field of the other. Then

$$U = -\mathbf{d}_2 \cdot \mathbf{E}_1,$$

where $\mathbf{E}_1$ is the field of the first system. Substituting (40.8) for $\mathbf{E}_1$, we find:

$$U = \frac{(\mathbf{d}_1 \cdot \mathbf{d}_2)R^2 - 3(\mathbf{d}_1 \cdot \mathbf{R})(\mathbf{d}_2 \cdot \mathbf{R})}{R^5}, \tag{42.7}$$

where $\mathbf{R}$ is the vector separation between the two systems.

For the case where one of the systems has a total charge different from zero (and equal to e), we obtain similarly

$$U = e\frac{\mathbf{d} \cdot \mathbf{R}}{R^3}, \tag{42.8}$$

where $\mathbf{R}$ is the vector directed from the dipole to the charge.

The next term in the expansion (42.1) is

$$U^{(2)} = \frac{1}{2}\sum e x_\alpha x_\beta \frac{\partial^2 \phi_0}{\partial x_\alpha \partial x_\beta}.$$

Here, as in § 41, we omit the index numbering the charge; the value of the second derivative of the potential is taken at the origin; but the potential ϕ satisfies Laplace's equation,

$$\frac{\partial^2 \phi}{\partial x_\alpha^2} = \delta_{\alpha\beta}\frac{\partial^2 \phi}{\partial x_\alpha \partial x_\beta} = 0.$$

Therefore we can write

$$U^{(2)} = \frac{1}{2}\frac{\partial^2\phi_0}{\partial x_\alpha \partial x_\beta}\sum e\left(x_\alpha x_\beta - \frac{1}{3}\delta_{\alpha\beta}r^2\right)$$

or, finally,

$$U^{(2)} = \frac{D_{\alpha\beta}}{6}\frac{\partial^2\phi_0}{\partial x_\alpha \partial x_\beta}. \tag{42.9}$$

The general term in the series (42.2) can be expressed in terms of the 2^l-pole moments $D^{(l)}_m$ defined in the preceding section. To do this, we first expand the potential ϕ (**r**) in spherical harmonics; the general form of this expansion is

$$\phi(\mathbf{r}) = \sum_{l=0}^{\infty} r^l \sum_{m=-l}^{l} a_{lm} \sqrt{\frac{(l-|m|)!}{(l+|m|)!}}\, P_l^{|m|}(\cos\theta)\, e^{im\phi}, \tag{42.10}$$

where r, θ, ϕ are the spherical coordinates of a point. Forming the sum (42.1) and using the definition (41.12), we obtain:

$$U^{(l)} = \sum_{m=-l}^{l} a_{lm} D^{(l)}_m. \tag{42.11}$$

§ 43. Constant magnetic field

Let us consider the magnetic field produced by charges which perform a finite motion, in which the particles are always within a finite region of space and the momenta also always remain finite. Such a motion has a "stationary" character, and it is of interest to consider the time average magnetic field $\overline{\mathbf{H}}$, produced by the charges; this field will now be a function only of the coordinates and not of the time, that is, it will be constant.

In order to find equations for the average magnetic field $\overline{\mathbf{H}}$, we take the time average of the Maxwell equations

$$\operatorname{div}\mathbf{H} = 0, \operatorname{curl}\mathbf{H} = \frac{1}{c}\frac{\partial \mathbf{E}}{\partial t} + \frac{4\pi}{c}\mathbf{j}.$$

The first of these gives simply

$$\operatorname{div}\overline{\mathbf{H}} = 0. \tag{43.1}$$

In the second equation the average value of the derivative $\partial\mathbf{E}/\partial t$, like the derivative of any quantity which varies over a finite range, is zero (cf. the footnote on page 96). Therefore the second Maxwell equation becomes

$$\operatorname{curl}\overline{\mathbf{H}} = \frac{4\pi}{c}\overline{\mathbf{j}}. \tag{43.2}$$

These two equations determine the constant field $\overline{\mathbf{H}}$.

We introduce the average vector potential $\bar{\mathbf{A}}$ in accordance with

$$\operatorname{curl}\bar{\mathbf{A}} = \overline{\mathbf{H}}.$$

We substitute this in equation (43.2). We find

$$\text{grad div}\,\bar{\mathbf{A}}-\Delta\bar{\mathbf{A}}=\frac{4\pi}{c}\bar{\mathbf{j}}.$$

But we know that the vector potential of a field is not uniquely defined, and we can impose an arbitrary auxiliary condition on it. On this basis, we choose the potential $\bar{\mathbf{A}}$ so that

$$\text{div}\,\bar{\mathbf{A}}=0. \tag{43.3}$$

Then the equation defining the vector potential of the constant magnetic field becomes

$$\Delta\bar{\mathbf{A}}=-\frac{4\pi}{c}\bar{\mathbf{j}}. \tag{43.4}$$

It is easy to find the solution of this equation by noting that (43.4) is completely analogous to the Poisson equation (36.4) for the scalar potential of a constant electric field, where in place of the charge density ϱ we here have the current density $\bar{\mathbf{j}}/c$. By analogy with the solution (36.8) of the Poisson equation, we can write

$$\bar{\mathbf{A}}=\frac{1}{c}\int\frac{\bar{\mathbf{j}}}{R}\,dV, \tag{43.5}$$

where R is the distance from the field point to the volume element dV.

In formula (43.5) we can go over from the integral to a sum over the charges, by substituting in place of $\mathbf{j}$ the product $\varrho\mathbf{v}$, and recalling that all the charges are pointlike. In this we must keep in mind that in the integral (43.5), R is simply an integration variable, and is therefore not subject to the averaging process. If we write in place of the integral $\int\frac{\mathbf{j}}{R}\,dV$ the sum $\sum\frac{e_a\mathbf{v}_a}{R_a}$, then R_a here are the radius vectors of the various particles, which change during the motion of the charges. Therefore we must write

$$\bar{\mathbf{A}}=\frac{1}{c}\sum\overline{\frac{e_a\mathbf{v}_a}{R_a}}, \tag{43.6}$$

where we average the whole expression under the summation sign.

Knowing $\bar{\mathbf{A}}$, we can also find the magnetic field,

$$\bar{\mathbf{H}}=\text{curl}\,\bar{\mathbf{A}}=\text{curl}\,\frac{1}{c}\int\frac{\bar{\mathbf{j}}}{R}\,dV.$$

The curl operator refers to the coordinates of the field point. Therefore the curl can be brought under the integral sign and $\bar{\mathbf{j}}$ can be treated as constant in the differentiation. Applying the well known formula

$$\text{curl}\,f\mathbf{a}=f\,\text{curl}\,\mathbf{a}+\text{grad}\,f\times\mathbf{a},$$

where f and $\mathbf{a}$ are an arbitrary scalar and vector, to the product $\bar{\mathbf{j}}$. $1/R$, we get

$$\operatorname{curl}\frac{\bar{\mathbf{j}}}{R} = \operatorname{grad}\frac{1}{R}\times\bar{\mathbf{j}} = \frac{\bar{\mathbf{j}}\times\mathbf{R}}{R^3},$$

and consequently,

$$\overline{\mathbf{H}} = \frac{1}{c}\int\frac{\bar{\mathbf{j}}\times\mathbf{R}}{R^3}\,dV \tag{43.7}$$

(the radius vector $\mathbf{R}$ is directed from dV to the field point). This is the *law of Biot and Savart.*

§ 44. Magnetic moments

Let us consider the average magnetic field produced by a system of charges in stationary motion, at large distances from the system.

We introduce a coordinate system with its origin anywhere within the system of charges, just as we did in § 40. Again we denote the radius vectors of the various charges by $\mathbf{r}_a$, and the radius vector of the point at which we calculate the field by $\mathbf{R}_0$. Then $\mathbf{R}_0-\mathbf{r}_a$ is the radius vector from the charge e_a to the field point. According to (43.6), we have for the vector potential:

$$\bar{\mathbf{A}} = \frac{1}{c}\sum\overline{\frac{e_a\mathbf{v}_a}{|\mathbf{R}_0-\mathbf{r}_a|}}. \tag{44.1}$$

As in § 40, we expand this expression in powers of $\mathbf{r}_a$. To terms of first order (we omit the index a), we have

$$\bar{\mathbf{A}} = \frac{1}{cR_0}\sum e\bar{\mathbf{v}} - \frac{1}{c}\sum\overline{e\mathbf{v}\left(\mathbf{r}\cdot\nabla\frac{1}{R_0}\right)}.$$

In the first term we can write

$$\sum e\bar{\mathbf{v}} = \overline{\frac{d}{dt}\sum e\mathbf{r}}.$$

But the average value of the derivative of a quantity changing within a finite interval (like $\sum e\mathbf{r}$) is zero. Thus there remains for $\bar{\mathbf{A}}$ the expression

$$\bar{\mathbf{A}} = -\frac{1}{c}\sum\overline{e\mathbf{v}\left(\mathbf{r}\cdot\nabla\frac{1}{R_0}\right)} = \frac{1}{cR_0^3}\sum\overline{e\mathbf{v}(\mathbf{r}\cdot\mathbf{R}_0)}.$$

We transform this expression as follows. Noting that $\mathbf{v}=\dot{\mathbf{r}}$, we can write (remembering that $\mathbf{R}_0$ is a constant vector)

$$\sum e(\mathbf{R}_0\cdot\mathbf{r})\mathbf{v} = \frac{1}{2}\frac{d}{dt}\sum e\mathbf{r}(\mathbf{r}\cdot\mathbf{R}_0)+\frac{1}{2}\sum e[\mathbf{v}(\mathbf{r}\cdot\mathbf{R}_0)-\mathbf{r}(\mathbf{v}\cdot\mathbf{R}_0)].$$

Upon substitution of this expression in $\bar{\mathbf{A}}$, the average of the first term (containing the time derivative) again goes to zero, and we get

$$\bar{\mathbf{A}} = \frac{1}{2cR_0^3} \sum \overline{e[\mathbf{v}(\mathbf{r}\cdot\mathbf{R}_0) - \mathbf{r}(\mathbf{v}\cdot\mathbf{R}_0)]}.$$

We introduce the vector

$$\mathfrak{m} = \frac{1}{2c} \sum e\mathbf{r}\times\mathbf{v}, \tag{44.2}$$

which is called the *magnetic moment* of the system. Then we get for $\bar{\mathbf{A}}$:

$$\bar{\mathbf{A}} = \frac{\bar{\mathfrak{m}}\times\mathbf{R}_0}{R_0^3} = \nabla\frac{1}{R_0}\times\bar{\mathfrak{m}} \tag{44.3}$$

Knowing the vector potential, it is easy to find the magnetic field. With the aid of the formula

$$\operatorname{curl}(\mathbf{a}\times\mathbf{b}) = (\mathbf{b}\cdot\nabla)\mathbf{a} - (\mathbf{a}\cdot\nabla)\mathbf{b} + \mathbf{a}\operatorname{div}\mathbf{b} - \mathbf{b}\operatorname{div}\mathbf{a},$$

we find

$$\bar{\mathbf{H}} = \operatorname{curl}\bar{\mathbf{A}} = \operatorname{curl}\left(\frac{\bar{\mathfrak{m}}\times\mathbf{R}_0}{R_0^3}\right) = \bar{\mathfrak{m}}\operatorname{div}\frac{\mathbf{R}_0}{R_0^3} - (\bar{\mathfrak{m}}\cdot\nabla)\frac{\mathbf{R}_0}{R_0^3}.$$

Furthermore,

$$\operatorname{div}\frac{\mathbf{R}_0}{R_0^3} = \mathbf{R}_0\cdot\operatorname{grad}\frac{1}{R_0^3} + \frac{1}{R_0^3}\operatorname{div}\mathbf{R}_0 = 0$$

and

$$(\mathfrak{m}\cdot\nabla)\frac{\mathbf{R}_0}{R_0^3} = \frac{1}{R_0^3}(\mathfrak{m}\cdot\nabla)\mathbf{R}_0 + \mathbf{R}_0(\mathfrak{m}\cdot\nabla)\frac{1}{R_0^3} = \frac{\mathfrak{m}}{R_0^3} - \frac{3\mathbf{R}_0(\mathfrak{m}\cdot\mathbf{R}_0)}{R_0^5}.$$

Thus,

$$\bar{\mathbf{H}} = \frac{3\mathbf{n}(\bar{\mathfrak{m}}\cdot\mathbf{n}) - \bar{\mathfrak{m}}}{R_0^3}, \tag{44.4}$$

where $\mathbf{n}$ is again the unit vector along $\mathbf{R}_0$. We see that the magnetic field is expressed in terms of the magnetic moment by the same formula by which the electric field was expressed in terms of the dipole moment [see (40.8)].

If all the charges of the system have the same ratio of charge to mass, then we can write

$$\mathfrak{m} = \frac{1}{2c}\cdot\sum e\mathbf{r}\times\mathbf{v} = \frac{e}{2mc}\sum m\mathbf{r}\times\mathbf{v}.$$

If the velocities of all the charges $v \ll c$, then $m\mathbf{v}$ is the momentum $\mathbf{p}$ of the charge and we get

$$\mathfrak{m} = \frac{e}{2mc}\sum \mathbf{r}\times\mathbf{p} = \frac{e}{2mc}\mathbf{M}, \tag{44.5}$$

where $\mathbf{M} = \sum \mathbf{r}\times\mathbf{p}$ is the mechanical angular momentum of the system. Thus in this case, the ratio of magnetic moment to mechanical moment is constant and equal to $e/2mc$.

PROBLEM

Find the ratio of the magnetic to the mechanical moment for a system of two charges (velocities $v \ll c$).

Solution: Choosing the origin of coordinates as the center of mass of the two particles we have $m_1\mathbf{r}_1 + m_2\mathbf{r}_2 = 0$ and $\mathbf{p}_1 = -\mathbf{p}_2 = \mathbf{p}$, where $\mathbf{p}$ is the momentum of the relative motion With the aid of these relations, we find

$$\mathfrak{m} = \frac{1}{2c}\left(\frac{e_1}{m_1^2} + \frac{e_2}{m_2^2}\right)\frac{m_1 m_2}{m_1 + m_2}\mathbf{M}.$$

§ 45. Larmor's theorem

Let us consider a system of charges in an external constant uniform magnetic field.

The time average of the force acting on the system,

$$\overline{\mathbf{F}} = \sum \frac{e}{c}\overline{\mathbf{v}\times\mathbf{H}} = \overline{\frac{d}{dt}\sum \frac{e}{c}\mathbf{r}\times\mathbf{H}},$$

is zero, as is the time average of the time derivative of any quantity which varies over a finite range. The average value of the moment of the forces is

$$\overline{\mathbf{K}} = \sum \frac{e}{c}\overline{(\mathbf{r}\times(\mathbf{v}\times\mathbf{H}))}$$

and is different from zero. It can be expressed in terms of the magnetic moment of the system, by expanding the vector triple product:

$$\mathbf{K} = \sum \frac{e}{c}\{\mathbf{v}(\mathbf{r}\cdot\mathbf{H}) - \mathbf{H}(\mathbf{v}\cdot\mathbf{r})\} = \sum \frac{e}{c}\left\{\mathbf{v}(\mathbf{r}\cdot\mathbf{H}) - \frac{1}{2}\mathbf{H}\frac{d}{dt}\mathbf{r}^2\right\}.$$

The second term gives zero after averaging, so that

$$\overline{\mathbf{K}} = \sum \frac{e}{c}\overline{\mathbf{v}(\mathbf{r}\cdot\mathbf{H})} = \frac{1}{2c}\sum e\{\overline{\mathbf{v}(\mathbf{r}\cdot\mathbf{H})} - \overline{\mathbf{r}(\mathbf{v}\cdot\mathbf{H})}\}$$

[the last transformation is analogous to the one used in deriving (44.3)], or finally

$$\overline{\mathbf{K}} = \overline{\mathfrak{m}}\times\mathbf{H}. \tag{45.1}$$

We call attention to the analogy with formula (42.6) for the electrical case.

The Lagrangian for a system of charges in an external constant uniform magnetic field contains (compared with the Lagrangian for a closed system) the additional term

$$L_H = \sum \frac{e}{c}\mathbf{A}\cdot\mathbf{v} = \sum \frac{e}{2c}\mathbf{H}\times\mathbf{r}\cdot\mathbf{v} = \sum \frac{e}{2c}\mathbf{r}\times\mathbf{v}\cdot\mathbf{H}$$

[where we have used the expression (19.4) for the vector potential of a uniform field]. Introducing the magnetic moment of the system, we have:

$$L_H = \mathfrak{m}\cdot\mathbf{H}. \tag{45.2}$$

We call attention to the analogy with the electric field; in a uniform electric field, the Lagrangian of a system of charges with total charge zero contains the term

$$L_E = \mathbf{d} \cdot \mathbf{E},$$

which in that case is the negative of the potential energy of the charge system (see § 42).

We now consider a system of charges performing a finite motion (with velocities $v \ll c$) in the centrally symmetric electric field produced by a certain fixed charge. We transform from the laboratory coordinate system to a system rotating uniformly around an axis passing through the fixed particle. From the well-known formula, the velocity $\mathbf{v}$ of the particle in the new coordinate system is related to its velocity $\mathbf{v}'$ in the old system by the relation

$$\mathbf{v}' = \mathbf{v} + \boldsymbol{\Omega} \times \mathbf{r},$$

where $\mathbf{r}$ is the radius vector of the particle and $\boldsymbol{\Omega}$ is the angular velocity of the rotating coordinate system. In the fixed system the Lagrangian of the the system of charges is

$$L = \sum \frac{mv'^2}{2} - U,$$

where U is the potential energy of the charges in the external field plus the energy of their mutual interactions. The quantity U is a function of the distances of the charges from the fixed particle and of their mutual separations; when transformed to the rotating coordinate system it obviously remains unchanged. Therefore in the new system the Lagrangian is

$$L = \sum \frac{m}{2} (\mathbf{v} + \boldsymbol{\Omega} \times \mathbf{r})^2 - U.$$

Let us assume that all the charges have the same charge-to-mass ratio e/m, and set

$$\boldsymbol{\Omega} = \frac{e}{2mc} \mathbf{H}. \tag{45.3}$$

Then for sufficiently small H (when we can neglect terms in H^2) the Lagrangian becomes:

$$L = \sum \frac{mv^2}{2} + \frac{1}{2c} \sum e\mathbf{H} \times \mathbf{r} \cdot \mathbf{v} - U.$$

We see that it coincides with the Lagrangian which would have described the motion of the charges in the laboratory system of coordinates in the presence of a constant magnetic field (see (45.2)).

Thus we arrive at the result that, in the nonrelativistic case, the behavior of a system of charges all having the same e/m, performing a finite motion in a centrally symmetric electric field and in a weak uniform magnetic field

H, is equivalent to the behavior of the same system of charges in the same electric field in a coordinate system rotating uniformly with the angular velocity (45.3). This assertion is the content of the *Larmor theorem*, and the angular velocity $\Omega = eH/2mc$ is called the *Larmor frequency*.

We can approach this same problem from a different point of view. If the magnetic field is sufficiently weak, the Larmor frequency will be small compared to the frequencies of the finite motion of the system of charges. Then we may consider the averages, over times small compared to the period $2\pi/\Omega$, of quantities describing the system. These new quantities will vary slowly in time (with frequency Ω).

Let us consider the change in the average mechanical moment **M** of the system. According to a wellknown equation of mechanics, the derivative of **M** is equal to the moment **K** of the forces acting on the system. We therefore have, using (45.1):

$$\frac{d\overline{\mathbf{M}}}{dt} = \overline{\mathbf{K}} = \overline{\mathfrak{m}} \times \mathbf{H}.$$

If the e/m ratio is the same for all particles of the system, the mechanical and magnetic moments are proportional to one another, and we find by using formulas (44.5) and (45.3):

$$\frac{d\overline{\mathbf{M}}}{dt} = -\mathbf{\Omega} \times \overline{\mathbf{M}}. \tag{45.4}$$

This equation states that the vector $\overline{\mathbf{M}}$ (and with it the magnetic moment $\overline{\mathfrak{m}}$) rotates with angular velocity $-\mathbf{\Omega}$ around the direction of the field, while its absolute magnitude and the angle which it makes with this direction remain fixed. (This motion is called the *Larmor precession*.)

CHAPTER 6

ELECTROMAGNETIC WAVES

§ 46. The wave equation

The electromagnetic field in vacuum is determined by the Maxwell equations in which we must set $\varrho = 0$, $\mathbf{j} = 0$. We write them once more:

$$\operatorname{curl} \mathbf{E} = -\frac{1}{c}\frac{\partial \mathbf{H}}{\partial t}, \qquad \operatorname{div} \mathbf{H} = 0, \tag{46.1}$$

$$\operatorname{curl} \mathbf{H} = \frac{1}{c}\frac{\partial \mathbf{E}}{\partial t}, \qquad \operatorname{div} \mathbf{E} = 0. \tag{46.2}$$

These equations possess nonzero solutions. This means that an electromagnetic field can exist even in the absence of any charges.

Electromagnetic fields occurring in vacuum in the absence of charges are called *electromagnetic waves*. We now take up the study of the properties of such waves.

First of all we note that such fields must necessarily be time-varying. In fact, in the contrary case, $\partial\mathbf{H}/\partial t = \partial\mathbf{E}/\partial t = 0$ and the equations (46.1) and (46.2) go over into the equations (36.1), (36.2) and (43.1), (43.2) of a constant field in which, however, we now have $\varrho = 0$, $\mathbf{j} = 0$. But the solution of these equations which is given by formulas (36.8) and (43.5) becomes zero for $\varrho = 0$, $\mathbf{j} = 0$.

We derive the equations determining the potentials of electromagnetic waves.

As we already know, because of the ambiguity in the potentials we can always subject them to an auxiliary condition. For this reason, we choose the potentials of the electromagnetic wave so that the scalar potential is zero:

$$\phi = 0. \tag{46.3}$$

Then

$$\mathbf{E} = -\frac{1}{c}\frac{\partial \mathbf{A}}{\partial t}, \quad \mathbf{H} = \operatorname{curl} \mathbf{A}. \tag{46.4}$$

Substituting these two expressions in the first of equations (46.2), we get

$$\operatorname{curl}\operatorname{curl} \mathbf{A} = -\Delta\mathbf{A} + \operatorname{grad}\operatorname{div} \mathbf{A} = -\frac{1}{c^2}\frac{\partial^2 \mathbf{A}}{\partial t^2}. \tag{46.5}$$

Despite the fact that we have already imposed one auxiliary condition on the potentials, the potential $\mathbf{A}$ is still not completely unique. Namely, we can add to it the gradient of an arbitrary function which does not depend on the time (meantime leaving ϕ unchanged). In particular, we can choose the potentials of the electromagnetic wave so that

$$\operatorname{div} \mathbf{A} = 0. \tag{46.6}$$

In fact, substituting for $\mathbf{E}$ from (46.4) in $\operatorname{div} \mathbf{E} = 0$, we have

$$\operatorname{div} \frac{\partial \mathbf{A}}{\partial t} = \frac{\partial}{\partial t} \operatorname{div} \mathbf{A} = 0,$$

that is, $\operatorname{div} \mathbf{A}$ is a function only of the coordinates. This function can always be made zero by adding to $\mathbf{A}$ the gradient of a suitable time-independent function.

The equation (46.5) now becomes

$$\Delta \mathbf{A} - \frac{1}{c^2} \frac{\partial^2 \mathbf{A}}{\partial t^2} = 0. \tag{46.7}$$

This is the equation which determines the potentials of electromagnetic waves. It is called the *d'Alembert equation*, or the *wave equation*.

Applying to (46.7) the operators curl and $\partial/\partial t$, we can verify that the electric and magnetic fields $\mathbf{E}$ and $\mathbf{H}$ satisfy the same wave equation.

The operator $\Delta - \frac{1}{c^2} \frac{\partial^2}{\partial t^2}$ is called the *d'Alembertian* and is designated by the symbol $\Box$:

$$\Box = \Delta - \frac{1}{c^2} \frac{\partial^2}{\partial t^2}, \tag{46.8}$$

so that the wave equation can be written in the form

$$\Box f = 0, \tag{46.9}$$

where f is any one of the components of $\mathbf{A}$, $\mathbf{E}$, or $\mathbf{H}$. The d'Alembertian can be written in four-dimensional form as

$$\Box = \frac{\partial^2}{\partial x_i^2}. \tag{46.10}$$

§ 47. Plane waves

We consider the special case of electromagnetic waves in which the field depends only on one coordinate, say x (and on the time). Such waves are said to be *plane*. In this case the equation for the field becomes

$$\frac{\partial^2 f}{\partial t^2} - c^2 \frac{\partial^2 f}{\partial x^2} = 0, \tag{47.1}$$

where by f is understood any component of the vectors $\mathbf{E}$ or $\mathbf{H}$.

To solve this equation, we rewrite it in the form

$$\left(\frac{\partial}{\partial t}-c\frac{\partial}{\partial x}\right)\left(\frac{\partial}{\partial t}+c\frac{\partial}{\partial x}\right)f=0,$$

and introduce new variables

$$\xi=t-\frac{x}{c},\qquad \eta=t+\frac{x}{c}$$

so that $t=\frac{1}{2}(\eta+\xi)$, $x=\frac{c}{2}(\eta-\xi)$. Then

$$\frac{\partial}{\partial\xi}=\frac{1}{2}\left(\frac{\partial}{\partial t}-c\frac{\partial}{\partial x}\right),\qquad \frac{\partial}{\partial\eta}=\frac{1}{2}\left(\frac{\partial}{\partial t}+c\frac{\partial}{\partial x}\right),$$

so that the equation for f becomes

$$\frac{\partial^2 f}{\partial\xi\,\partial\eta}=0.$$

Integrating this equation with respect to ξ, we get

$$\frac{\partial f}{\partial\eta}=F(\eta),$$

where $F(\eta)$ is an arbitrary function. Integrating once more, we get $f=f_1(\xi)+f_2(\eta)$, where f_1 and f_2 are arbitrary functions. Thus

$$f=f_1\left(t-\frac{x}{c}\right)+f_2\left(t+\frac{x}{c}\right). \tag{47.2}$$

Suppose, for example, $f_2=0$, so that $f=f_1\left(t-\frac{x}{c}\right)$. Let us clarify the meaning of this solution. In each plane $x=$ const, the field changes with the time; at each given moment the field is different for different x. It is clear that the field has the same values for coordinates x and times t which satisfy the relation $t-\frac{x}{c}=$ const, that is,

$$x=\text{const}+ct.$$

This means that if, at some time $t=0$, the field at a certain point x in space had some definite value, then after an interval of time t the field has hat same value at a distance ct along the X axis from the original place. We can say that all the values of the electromagnetic field are propagated in space along the X axis with a velocity equal to the velocity of light, c.

Thus, $f_1\left(t-\frac{x}{c}\right)$ represents a plane wave moving in the positive direction along the X axis. It is easy to show that $f_2\left(t+\frac{x}{c}\right)$ represents a wave moving in the opposite, negative, direction along the X axis.

In § 46 we showed that the potentials of the electromagnetic wave can be chosen so that $\phi = 0$, and div $\mathbf{A} = 0$. We choose the potentials of the plane waves which we are now considering in this same way. The condition div $\mathbf{A} = 0$ gives in this case

$$\frac{\partial A_x}{\partial x} = 0,$$

since all quantities are independent of y and z. According to (47.1) we then have also $\partial^2 A_x/\partial t^2 = 0$, that is, $\partial A_x/\partial t = \text{const}$. But the derivative $\frac{\partial \mathbf{A}}{\partial t}$ determines the electric field, and we see that the nonzero component A_x represents in this case the presence of a constant longitudinal electric field. Since such a field has no relation to the electromagnetic wave, we can set $A_x = 0$.

Thus the vector potential of the plane wave can always be chosen perpendicular to the X axis, i.e., to the direction of propagation of that wave.

We consider a plane wave moving in the positive direction of the X axis; in this wave, all quantities, in particular also $\mathbf{A}$, are functions only of $t - \frac{x}{c}$. From the formulas

$$\mathbf{E} = -\frac{1}{c}\frac{\partial \mathbf{A}}{\partial t}, \qquad \mathbf{H} = \operatorname{curl} \mathbf{A},$$

we therefore obtain

$$\mathbf{E} = -\frac{1}{c}\,\mathbf{A}', \ \mathbf{H} = \nabla \times \mathbf{A} = \nabla\left(t - \frac{x}{c}\right) \times \mathbf{A}' = -\frac{1}{c}\,\mathbf{n} \times \mathbf{A}', \tag{47.3}$$

where the prime denotes differentiation with respect to $t - \frac{x}{c}$ and $\mathbf{n}$ is a unit vector along the direction of propagation of the wave. Substituting the first equation in the second, we obtain

$$\mathbf{H} = \mathbf{n} \times \mathbf{E}. \tag{47.4}$$

We see that the electric and magnetic fields $\mathbf{E}$ and $\mathbf{H}$ of a plane wave are directed perpendicular to the direction of propagation of the wave. For this reason, electromagnetic waves are said to be *transverse*. From (47.4) it is clear also that the electric and magnetic fields of the plane wave are perpendicular to each other and equal to each other in absolute value.

The energy flux in the plane wave, i.e., its Poynting vector is

$$\mathbf{S} = \frac{c}{4\pi}\,\mathbf{E} \times \mathbf{H} = \frac{c}{4\pi}\,\mathbf{E} \times (\mathbf{n} \times \mathbf{E}),$$

and since $\mathbf{E} \cdot \mathbf{n} = 0$,

$$\mathbf{S} = \frac{c}{4\pi} E^2 \mathbf{n} = \frac{c}{4\pi} H^2 \mathbf{n}.$$

Thus the energy flux is directed along the direction of propagation of the wave. Since $W = \frac{1}{8\pi}(E^2 + H^2) = \frac{E^2}{4\pi}$ is the energy density of the wave, we can write

$$\mathbf{S} = cW\mathbf{n}, \tag{47.5}$$

in accordance with the fact that the field propagates with the velocity of light.

The momentum per unit volume of the electromagnetic field is $\mathbf{S}/c^2$. For a plane wave this gives $(W/c)\mathbf{n}$. We call attention to the fact that the relation between energy W and momentum W/c for the electromagnetic wave is the same as for a particle moving with the velocity of light [see (9.9)].

The flux of momentum of the field is determined by the components $T_{\alpha\beta}$ of the energy-momentum tensor. Choosing the direction of propagation of the wave as the X axis, we find that the only nonzero component of $T_{\alpha\beta}$ is

$$T_{xx} = W. \tag{47.6}$$

As it must be, the flux of momentum is along the direction of propagation of the wave, and is equal in magnitude to the energy density.

Let us find the law of transformation of the energy density of a plane electromagnetic wave when we change from one inertial reference system to another. To do this we start from the formula

$$W = \frac{1}{1 - \frac{V^2}{c^2}} \left(W' + 2\frac{V}{c^2} S'_x + \frac{V^2}{c^2} T'_{xx} \right)$$

(see the problem in § 32) and substitute

$$S'_x = cW' \cos\alpha', \quad T'_{xx} = W' \cos^2\alpha',$$

where α' is the angle (in the K' system) between the X' axis (along which the velocity $\mathbf{V}$ is directed) and the direction of propagation of the wave. We find:

$$W = W' \frac{\left(1 + \frac{V}{c}\cos\alpha'\right)^2}{1 - \frac{V^2}{c^2}}. \tag{47.7}$$

Since $W = \frac{E^2}{4\pi} = \frac{H^2}{4\pi}$, the absolute values of the field intensities in the wave transform like $\sqrt{W}$.

Problems

1. Determine the force exerted on a wall from which an incident plane electromagnetic wave is reflected (with reflection coefficient R).

Solution: The force $\mathbf{f}$ acting on unit area of the wall is given by the flux of momentum through this area, i.e., it is the vector with components

$$f_\alpha = T_{\alpha\beta} N_\beta + T'_{\alpha\beta} N_\beta,$$

where $\mathbf{N}$ is the vector normal to the surface of the wall, and $T_{\alpha\beta}$ and $T'_{\alpha\beta}$ are the components of the energy-momentum tensors for the incident and reflected waves. Using (47.6), we obtain:

$$\mathbf{f} = W\mathbf{n}(\mathbf{N}\cdot\mathbf{n}) + W'\mathbf{n}'(\mathbf{N}\cdot\mathbf{n}').$$

From the definition of the reflection coefficient, we have: $W' = RW$. Also introducing the angle of incidence θ (which is equal to the reflection angle) and writing out components, we find the normal force ("light pressure")

$$f_N = W(1+R)\cos^2\theta$$

and the tangential force

$$f_t = W(1-R)\sin\theta\cos\theta.$$

2. Use the Hamilton-Jacobi method to find the motion in the field of a plane electromagnetic wave with vector potential $\mathbf{A}\left(t-\frac{x}{c}\right)$.

Solution: We write the Hamilton-Jacobi equation (16.11) in the form

$$\left(\frac{\partial S}{\partial x}\right)^2 + \left(\nabla S - \frac{e}{c}\mathbf{A}\right)^2 - \frac{1}{c^2}\left(\frac{\partial S}{\partial t}\right)^2 + m^2c^2 = 0;$$

throughout this problem all vectors (including ∇) are understood to be two-dimensional vectors in the y, z plane. We look for the action in the form

$$S = \mathbf{f}\cdot\mathbf{r} - \frac{c\gamma}{2}\left(t+\frac{x}{c}\right) + \phi\left(t-\frac{x}{c}\right),$$

where γ and $\mathbf{f}$ are constants and ϕ is an unknown function; the result is:

$$S = \mathbf{f}\cdot\mathbf{r} - \frac{c\gamma}{2}\left(t+\frac{x}{c}\right) - \frac{m^2c^3+cf^2}{2\gamma}\xi + \frac{e}{\gamma}\mathbf{f}\cdot\int \mathbf{A}\,d\xi - \frac{e^2}{2c\gamma}\int \mathbf{A}^2\,d\xi, \tag{1}$$

where $\xi = t - \frac{x}{c}$.

For the determination of the motion, we must, according to general principles†, equate the derivatives $\frac{\partial S}{\partial \mathbf{f}}$, $\frac{\partial S}{\partial \gamma}$ to some new constants, which can be made equal to zero by a suitable choice of the origin of coordinates and time. We thus obtain the parametric formulas (with parameter ξ):

$$\mathbf{r} = \frac{c}{\gamma}\mathbf{f}\xi - \frac{e}{\gamma}\int \mathbf{A}\,d\xi,$$

$$x = \frac{c}{2}\left(\frac{m^2c^2+f^2}{\gamma^2} - 1\right)\xi - \frac{e}{\gamma^2}\int \mathbf{f}\cdot\mathbf{A}(\xi)\,d\xi + \frac{e^2}{2c\gamma^2}\int \mathbf{A}^2(\xi)\,d\xi, \tag{2}$$

$$t = \xi + \frac{x}{c}.$$

---

† See *Mechanics*, § 47.

From general principles, the generalized momentum $\mathbf{P} = \mathbf{p}+\frac{e}{c}\mathbf{A}$ and the energy $\mathcal{E}$ are determined by differentiating the action with respect to the coordinates and with respect to $-t$; this gives

$$\mathbf{p} = \mathbf{f}-\frac{e}{c}\mathbf{A},$$

$$p_x = -\frac{\gamma}{2}+\frac{m^2c^2+f^2}{2\gamma}-\frac{e}{c\gamma}\mathbf{f}\cdot\mathbf{A}+\frac{e^2}{2\gamma c^2}\mathbf{A}^2, \tag{3}$$

$$\mathcal{E} = c(\gamma+p_x).$$

If we take the time average of these quantities, the terms in the first power of the periodic function $\mathbf{A}(\xi)$ go to zero. We can always choose a reference system in which the particle is at rest on the average, i.e., in which its average momentum is zero. Then, according to (3), $\mathbf{f} = 0$, and

$$\gamma^2 = m^2c^2+\frac{e^2}{c^2}\overline{\mathbf{A}^2}.$$

Thus the final formulas describing the motion have the form

$$\mathbf{r} = -\frac{e}{\gamma}\int \mathbf{A}\,d\xi, \quad x = \frac{e^2}{2c\gamma^2}\int (A^2-\overline{A^2})\,d\xi,$$

$$t = \xi+\frac{e^2}{2c^2\gamma^2}\int (A^2-\overline{A^2})\,d\xi, \tag{4}$$

$$\mathbf{p} = -\frac{e}{c}\mathbf{A}, \quad p_x = \frac{e^2}{2\gamma c^2}(A^2-\overline{A^2}), \tag{5}$$

$$\mathcal{E} = c\gamma+\frac{e^2}{2\gamma c}(A^2-\overline{A^2}).$$

§ 48. Monochromatic plane waves

A very important special case of electromagnetic waves is a wave in which the field is a simply periodic function of the time. Such a wave is said to be *monochromatic*. All quantities (potentials, field components) in a monochromatic wave depend on the time through a factor of the form $\cos(\omega t+\alpha)$. The quantity ω is called the *cyclic frequency* of the wave (we shall simply call it the *frequency*).

In the wave equation, the second derivative of the field with respect to the time is now $\partial^2 f/\partial t^2 = -\omega^2 f$, so that the distribution of the field in space is determined for a monochromatic wave by the equation

$$\nabla f+\frac{\omega^2}{c^2}f = 0. \tag{48.1}$$

In a plane wave (propagating along the x axis), the field is a function only of $t-\frac{x}{c}$. Therefore, if the plane wave is monochromatic, its field is a simply periodic function of $t-\frac{x}{c}$. The vector potential of such a wave is most conveniently written as the real part of a complex expression:

$$\mathbf{A} = \mathrm{Re}\left\{\mathbf{A}_0\, e^{-i\omega\left(t-\frac{x}{c}\right)}\right\} \tag{48.2}$$

Here $\mathbf{A}_0$ is a certain constant complex vector. Obviously, the fields **E** and **H** of such a wave have analogous forms with the same frequency ω. The quantity

$$\lambda = \frac{2\pi c}{\omega} \tag{48.3}$$

is called the *wavelength*; it is the period of variation of the field with the coordinate x at a fixed time t.

The vector

$$\mathbf{k} = \frac{\omega}{c}\mathbf{n} \tag{48.4}$$

(where **n** is a unit vector along the direction of propagation of the wave) is called the *wave vector*. In terms of it we can write (48.2) in the form

$$\mathbf{A} = \mathrm{Re}\left\{\mathbf{A}_0\, e^{i(\mathbf{k}\cdot\mathbf{r}-\omega t)}\right\}, \tag{48.5}$$

which is independent of the choice of coordinate axes. The quantity which appears multiplied by i in the exponent is called the *phase* of the wave.

So long as we perform only linear operations, we can omit the sign Re for taking the real part, and operate with complex quantities as such.† Thus, substituting

$$\mathbf{A} = \mathbf{A}_0\, e^{i(\mathbf{k}\cdot\mathbf{r}-\omega t)}$$

in (47.3), we find the relation between the intensities and the vector potential of a plane monochromatic wave in the form

$$\mathbf{E} = ik\mathbf{A}, \qquad \mathbf{H} = i\mathbf{k}\times\mathbf{A}. \tag{48.6}$$

---

† If two quantities $\mathbf{A}(t)$ and $\mathbf{B}(t)$ are written in complex form

$$\mathbf{A}(t) = \mathbf{A}_0\, e^{-i\omega t}, \qquad \mathbf{B}(t) = \mathbf{B}_0\, e^{-i\omega t},$$

then in forming their product we must first, of course, separate out the real part. But if, as it frequently happens, we are interested only in the time average of this product, it can be computed as

$$\tfrac{1}{2}\,\mathrm{Re}\,\{\mathbf{A}\cdot\mathbf{B}^*\}.$$

In fact, we have:

$$\mathrm{Re}\,\mathbf{A}\cdot\mathrm{Re}\,\mathbf{B} = \tfrac{1}{4}(\mathbf{A}_0\, e^{-i\omega t}+\mathbf{A}_0^*\, e^{i\omega t})\cdot(B_0\, e^{-i\omega t}+B_0^*\, e^{i\omega t}).$$

When we average, the terms containing factors $e^{\pm 2i\omega t}$ vanish, so that we are left with

$$\overline{\mathrm{Re}\,\mathbf{A}\cdot\mathrm{Re}\,\mathbf{B}} = \tfrac{1}{4}(\mathbf{A}_0\cdot\mathbf{B}_0^*+\mathbf{A}_0^*\cdot\mathbf{B}_0) = \tfrac{1}{2}\,\mathrm{Re}(\mathbf{A}\cdot\mathbf{B}^*).$$

We now treat in more detail the direction of the field of a monochromatic wave. To be specific, we shall talk of the electric field

$$\mathbf{E} = \text{Re}\{\mathbf{E}_0\, e^{i(\mathbf{k}\cdot\mathbf{r}-\omega t)}\}$$

(everything stated below applies equally well, of course, to the magnetic field). The quantity $\mathbf{E}_0$ is a certain complex vector. Its square $\mathbf{E}_0^2$ is (in general) a complex number. If the argument of this number is -2α (i.e. $\mathbf{E}_0^2 = |\mathbf{E}_0^2|e^{-2i\alpha}$), the vector $\mathbf{b}$ defined by

$$\mathbf{E}_0 = \mathbf{b}\, e^{-i\alpha} \tag{48.7}$$

will have its square real, $\mathbf{b}^2 = |\mathbf{E}_0|^2$. With this definition, we write:

$$\mathbf{E} = \text{Re}\{\mathbf{b}\, e^{i(\mathbf{k}\cdot\mathbf{r}-\omega t-\alpha)}\}. \tag{48.8}$$

We write $\mathbf{b}$ in the form

$$\mathbf{b} = \mathbf{b}_1 + i\,\mathbf{b}_2,$$

where $\mathbf{b}_1$ and $\mathbf{b}_2$ are real vectors. Since $\mathbf{b}^2 = \mathbf{b}_1^2 - \mathbf{b}_2^2 + 2i\,\mathbf{b}_1\cdot\mathbf{b}_2$ must be a real quantity, $\mathbf{b}_1\cdot\mathbf{b}_2 = 0$, i.e. the vectors $\mathbf{b}_1$ and $\mathbf{b}_2$ are mutually perpendicular. We choose the direction of $\mathbf{b}_1$ as the y axis (and the x axis along the direction of propagation of the wave). We then have from (48.8):

$$\begin{aligned} E_y &= b_1 \cos(\omega t - \mathbf{k}\cdot\mathbf{r}+\alpha),\\ E_z &= \pm b_2 \sin(\omega t - \mathbf{k}\cdot\mathbf{r}+\alpha), \end{aligned} \tag{48.9}$$

where we use the plus (minus) sign if $\mathbf{b}_2$ is along the positive (negative) z axis. From (48.9) it follows that

$$\frac{E_y^2}{b_1^2} + \frac{E_z^2}{b_2^2} = 1. \tag{48.10}$$

Thus we see that, at each point in space, the electric field vector rotates in a plane perpendicular to the direction of propagation of the wave, while its endpoint describes the ellipse (48.10). Such a wave is said to be *elliptically polarized.* The rotation occurs in the direction of (opposite to) a right-hand screw rotating along the x axis, if we have the plus (minus) sign in (48.10).

If $b_1 = b_2$, the ellipse (48.10) reduces to a circle, i.e. the vector $\mathbf{E}$ rotates while remaining constant in magnitude. In this case we say that the wave is *circularly polarized.* The choice of the directions of the y and z axes is now obviously arbitrary. We note that in such a wave the ratio of the y and z components of the complex amplitude is

$$\frac{E_{0z}}{E_{0y}} = \pm i \tag{48.11}$$

for rotation in the same (opposite) direction as that of a right-hand screw.

Finally, if b_1 or b_2 equals zero, the field of the wave is everywhere and always parallel (or antiparallel) to one and the same direction. In this case the wave is said to be *linearly polarized*, or plane polarized. An elliptically polarized wave can clearly be treated as the superposition of two plane polarized waves.

Now let us turn to the definition of the wave vector and introduce the four-dimensional wave vector with components

$$k_{1,2,3} = k_{x,y,z}, \quad k_4 = \frac{i\omega}{c}. \tag{48.12}$$

That these quantities actually form a four-vector is obvious from the fact that we get a scalar (the phase of the wave) when we multiply by x_i:

$$k_i x_i = \mathbf{k}\cdot\mathbf{r} - \omega t. \tag{48.13}$$

From the definitions (48.5) and (48.13) we see that the square of the wave four-vector is zero:

$$k_i^2 = 0. \tag{48.14}$$

This relation also follows directly from the fact that the expression

$$\mathbf{A} = \mathbf{A}_0 e^{ik_i x_i}$$

must be a solution of the wave equation $\dfrac{\partial^2 \mathbf{A}}{\partial x_i^2} = 0.$

As is the case for every plane wave, in a monochromatic wave propagating along the x axis only the following components of the energy-momentum tensor are different from zero (see § 47):

$$T_{11} = W, \quad T_{14} = iW, \quad T_{44} = -W.$$

By means of the wave four-vector, these equations can be written in tensor form as

$$T_{ik} = \frac{Wc^2}{\omega^2} k_i k_k. \tag{48.15}$$

Finally, by using the law of transformation of the wave four-vector we can easily treat the so-called *Doppler effect* — the change in frequency ω of the wave emitted by a source moving with respect to the observer, as compared to the "true" frequency ω_0 of the same source in the reference system (K_0) in which it is at rest.

Let V be the velocity of the source, i.e. the velocity of the K_0 system relative to K. According to the general formula for transformation of four-vectors, we have:

$$k_4^{(0)} = \frac{k_4 - i\dfrac{V}{c}k_1}{\sqrt{1-\dfrac{V^2}{c^2}}}$$

(the velocity of the K system relative to K_0 is $-V$). Substituting $k_4 = i\omega/c$, $k_1 = k\cos\alpha = \frac{\omega}{c}\cos\alpha$, where α is the angle (in the K system) between the direction of emission of the wave and the direction of motion of the source, and expressing ω in terms of ω_0, we obtain:

$$\omega = \omega_0 \frac{\sqrt{1-\frac{V^2}{c^2}}}{1-\frac{V}{c}\cos\alpha}. \tag{48.16}$$

This is the required formula. For $V \ll c$, and if the angle α is not too close to $\pi/2$, it gives:

$$\omega \cong \omega_0\left(1+\frac{V}{c}\cos\alpha\right). \tag{48.17}$$

For $\alpha = \pi/2$, we have:

$$\omega = \omega_0\sqrt{1-\frac{V^2}{c^2}} \cong \omega_0\left(1-\frac{V^2}{2c^2}\right); \tag{48.18}$$

in this case the relative change in frequency is proportional to the square of the ratio V/c.

Problems

1. Determine the direction and magnitude of the axes of the polarization ellipse in terms of the complex amplitude $\mathbf{E}_0$.

Solution: The problem consists in determining the vector $\mathbf{b} = \mathbf{b}_1 + i\mathbf{b}_2$, whose square is real. We have from (48.7):

$$\mathbf{E}_0 \cdot \mathbf{E}_0^* = b_1^2 + b_2^2, \qquad \mathbf{E}_0 \times \mathbf{E}_0^* = -2i\,\mathbf{b}_1 \times \mathbf{b}_2, \tag{1}$$

or

$$b_1^2 + b_2^2 = A^2 + B^2, \qquad b_1 b_2 = AB\sin\delta,$$

where we have introduced the notation

$$|E_{0y}| = A, \quad |E_{0z}| = B, \quad \frac{E_{0z}}{B} = \frac{E_{0y}}{A} e^{i\delta}$$

for the absolute values of E_{0y} and E_{0z} and for the phase difference δ between them. Then

$$b_{1,2} = \sqrt{A^2+B^2+2AB\sin\delta} \pm \sqrt{A^2+B^2-2AB\sin\delta}, \tag{2}$$

from which we get the magnitudes of the semiaxes of the polarization ellipse.

To determine their directions (relative to the arbitrary initial axes y and z) we start from the equality

$$\operatorname{Re}\{(\mathbf{E}_0 \cdot \mathbf{b}_1)(\mathbf{E}_0^* \cdot \mathbf{b}_2)\} = 0,$$

which is easily verified by substituting $\mathbf{E}_0 = (\mathbf{b}_1 + i\mathbf{b}_2)e^{-i\alpha}$. Writing out this equality in the y, z coordinates, we get for the angle θ between the direction of $\mathbf{b}_1$ and the y axis:

$$\tan 2\theta = \frac{2AB\cos\delta}{A^2-B^2}. \tag{3}$$

The direction of rotation of the field is determined by the sign of the x component of the vector $\mathbf{b}_1\times\mathbf{b}_2$. Taking its expression from (1)

$$2i(\mathbf{b}_1\times\mathbf{b}_2)_x = E_{0z}E_{0y}^* - E_{0z}^*E_{0y} = |E_{0y}|^2\left\{\left(\frac{E_{0z}}{E_{0y}}\right)-\left(\frac{E_{0z}}{E_{0y}}\right)^*\right\},$$

we see that the direction of $\mathbf{b}_1\times\mathbf{b}_2$ (whether it is along or opposite to the positive direction of the x axis), and the sign of the rotation (whether in the same direction, or opposite to the direction of a right-hand screw along the x axis) are given by the sign of the imaginary part of the ratio E_{0z}/E_{0y} (plus for the first case and minus for the second). This is a generalization of the rule (48.11) for the case of circular polarization.

2. Determine the motion of a charge in the field of a plane monochromatic linearly polarized wave.

Solution: Choosing the direction of the field $\mathbf{E}$ of the wave as the y axis, we write:

$$E_y = E = E_0\cos\omega\xi, \qquad A_y = A = -\frac{cE_0}{\omega}\sin\omega\xi$$

($\xi = t - x/c$). From formulas (4) and (5) of problem 2, § 47, we find (in the reference system in which the particle is at rest on the average) the following representation of the motion in terms of the parameter $\eta = \omega\xi$):

$$x = -\frac{e^2E_0^2c}{8\gamma^2\omega^3}\sin 2\eta, \qquad y = -\frac{eE_0c}{\gamma\omega^2}\cos\eta, \qquad z = 0,$$

$$t = \frac{\eta}{\omega} - \frac{e^2E_0^2}{8\gamma^2\omega^3}\sin 2\eta, \qquad \gamma^2 = m^2c^2 + \frac{e^2E_0^2}{2\omega^2};$$

$$p_x = -\frac{e^2E_0^2}{4\gamma\omega^2}\cos 2\eta, \qquad p_y = \frac{eE_0}{\omega}\sin\eta, \qquad p_z = 0.$$

The charge moves moves in the x, y plane in a symmetric figure-8 curve with its longitudinal axis along the y axis.

3. Determine the motion of a charge in the field of a circularly polarized wave.

Solution: For the field of the wave we have:

$$E_y = E_0\cos\omega\xi, \qquad E_z = E_0\sin\omega\xi,$$

$$A_y = -\frac{cE_0}{\omega}\sin\omega\xi, \qquad A_z = \frac{cE_0}{\omega}\cos\omega\xi.$$

The motion is given by the formulas:

$$x = 0, \qquad y = -\frac{ecE_0}{\gamma\omega^2}\cos\omega t, \qquad z = -\frac{ecE_0}{\gamma\omega^2}\sin\omega t,$$

$$p_x = 0, \qquad p_y = \frac{eE_0}{\omega}\sin\omega t, \qquad p_z = -\frac{eE_0}{\omega}\cos\omega t,$$

$$\gamma^2 = m^2c^2 + \frac{c^2E_0^2}{\omega^2}.$$

Thus the charge moves in the y, z plane along a circle of radius $ecE_0/\gamma\omega^2$ with a momentum having the constant magnitude $p = eE_0/\omega$; at each instant the direction of the momentum $\mathbf{p}$ coincides with the direction of the magnetic field $\mathbf{H}$ of the wave.

§ 49. Spectral resolution

Every wave can be subjected to the process of spectral resolution, i.e. can be represented as a superposition of monochromatic waves with various frequencies. The character of this expansion varies according to the character of the time dependence of the field.

One category consists of those cases where the expansion contains frequencies forming a discrete sequence of values. The simplest case of this type arises in the resolution of a purely periodic (though not monochromatic) field. This is the usual expansion in Fourier series; it contains the frequencies which are integral multiples of the "fundamental" frequency $\omega_0 = 2\pi/T$, where T is the period of the field. We write it in the form

$$f = \mathrm{Re}\left\{\sum_{n=1}^{\infty} f_n e^{-i\omega_0 nt}\right\} \tag{49.1}$$

(where f is any of the quantities describing the field). The quantities f_n are defined in terms of the function f by the integrals

$$f_n = \frac{2}{T}\int_0^T f(t)\, e^{in\omega_0 t}\, dt. \tag{49.2}$$

In more complicated cases, the expansion may contain integral multiples (and sums of integral multiples) of several different incommensurable fundamental frequencies.

When the sum (49.1) is squared and averaged over the time, the products of terms with different frequencies give zero because they contain oscillating factors. Thus the average of the square of the field, i.e. the average intensity of the wave, is the sum of the intensities of its monochromatic components. Each of these gives the value $|f_n|^2/2$ (see the footnote on p. 130), so that

$$\overline{f^2} = \tfrac{1}{2}\sum_{n=1}^{\infty} |f_n|^2. \tag{49.3}$$

Another category consists of fields which are expandable in a Fourier integral containing a continuous sequence of different frequencies. For this to be possible, the function $f(t)$ must satisfy certain definite conditions; usually we consider functions which vanish for $t \to \pm\infty$. Such an expansion has the form

$$f(t) = \int_{-\infty}^{\infty} f_\omega e^{-i\omega t} d\omega, \tag{49.4}$$

where the Fourier components are given in terms of the function $f(t)$ by the integrals

$$f_\omega = \frac{1}{2\pi}\int_{-\infty}^{\infty} f(t)\, e^{i\omega t}\, dt. \tag{49.5}$$

Components which differ in the sign of ω, are related by the equation

$$f_{-\omega} = f_\omega^*, \tag{49.6}$$

which is obvious from (49.5), since the function $f(t)$ is real.

Let us express the total intensity of the wave (49.4), i.e. the integral of f^2 over all time, in terms of the intensity of the Fourier components. Using (49.4) and (49.5), we have:

$$\int_{-\infty}^{\infty} f^2\,dt = \int_{-\infty}^{\infty}\Big\{f\int_{-\infty}^{\infty} f_\omega e^{-i\omega t}\,d\omega\Big\}\,dt = \int_{-\infty}^{\infty}\Big\{f_\omega\int_{-\infty}^{\infty} f e^{-i\omega t}\;dt\Big\}\,d\omega = 2\pi\int_{-\infty}^{\infty} f_\omega f_{-\omega}\,d\omega,$$

or, using (49.6),

$$\int_{-\infty}^{\infty} f^2\,dt = 2\pi\int_{-\infty}^{\infty}|f_\omega|^2\,d\omega = 4\pi\int_{0}^{\infty}|f_\omega|^2\,d\omega. \tag{49.7}$$

§ 50. Partially polarized light

Every monochromatic wave is, by definition, necessarily polarized. However we usually have to deal with waves which are only approximately monochromatic, and which contain frequencies in a small interval $\Delta\omega$. We consider such a wave, and let ω be some average frequency for it. Then its field (to be specific we shall consider the electric field $\mathbf{E}$) at a fixed point in space can be written in the form

$$\mathbf{E}_0(t)e^{-i\omega t},$$

where the complex amplitude $\mathbf{E}_0(t)$ is some slowly varying function of the time (for a strictly monochromatic wave $\mathbf{E}_0$ would be constant). Since $\mathbf{E}_0$ determines the polarization of the wave, this means that at each point of the wave, its polarization changes with time; such a wave is said to be *partially polarized.*

The polarization properties of electromagnetic waves, and of light in particular, are observed experimentally by passing the light to be investigated through various bodies† and then observing the intensity of the transmitted light. From the mathematical point of view this means that we draw conclusions concerning the polarization properties of the light from the values of certain quadratic functions of its field. Here of course we are considering the time averages of such functions.

Quadratic functions of the field are made up of terms proportional to the products $E_\alpha E_\beta$, $E_\alpha^* E_\beta^*$ or $E_\alpha E_\beta^*$. Products of the form

$$E_\alpha E_\beta = E_{0\alpha}E_{0\beta}e^{-2i\omega t}, \qquad E_\alpha^* E_\beta^* = E_{0\alpha}^* E_{0\beta}^* e^{2i\omega t},$$

which contain the rapidly oscillating factors $e^{\pm 2i\omega t}$ give zero when the time average is taken. The products $E_\alpha E_\beta^* = E_{0\alpha}E_{0\beta}^*$ do not contain such factors, and so their averages are not zero. Thus we see that the polarization properties of the light are completely characterized by the tensor

$$J_{\alpha\beta} = \overline{E_{0\alpha}E_{0\beta}^*}. \tag{50.1}$$

† For example, through a Nicol prism.

Since the vector $\mathbf{E}_0$ always lies in a plane perpendicular to the direction of the wave, the tensor $J_{\alpha\beta}$ has altogether four components (in this section the indices α, β are understood to take on only two values: $\alpha, \beta = y, z$). From the definition of $J_{\alpha\beta}$ it is clear that among the components of this tensor there exists the relation

$$J_{\alpha\beta} = J^*_{\beta\alpha} \tag{50.2}$$

(i.e. the tensor is Hermitian).

The sum of the diagonal components of the tensor $J_{\alpha\beta}$ is the average value of the square modulus of the vector $\mathbf{E}$:

$$J_{\alpha\alpha} = |\mathbf{E}_0|^2.$$

This quantity (which we denote by J) determines the intensity of the wave (as measured by the energy flux density).

The tensor $J_{\alpha\beta}$ can always be decomposed into two parts — a symmetric and an antisymmetric part. Of these, the first,

$$S_{\alpha\beta} = \tfrac{1}{2}(J_{\alpha\beta}+J_{\beta\alpha}), \tag{50.3}$$

is a purely real tensor, because of the Hermiticity of $J_{\alpha\beta}$. The antisymmetric part, on the other hand, is pure imaginary; like every antisymmetric tensor whose rank is equal to the number of dimensions of the space, it reduces to a scalar (more precisely, a pseudoscalar)

$$\tfrac{1}{2}(J_{\alpha\beta}-J_{\beta\alpha}) = i e_{\alpha\beta} A, \tag{50.4}$$

where A is a real scalar and $e_{\alpha\beta}$ is the unit antisymmetric tensor of the second rank (with components $e_{12} = -e_{21} = 1$). Thus, in general, the polarization properties of the light are characterized by one symmetric real tensor of rank two, and by one scalar.

Let us examine the conditions which the tensor $J_{\alpha\beta}$ must satisfy in order for the light to be completely polarized. In this case, $\mathbf{E}_0 = \text{const}$, so we have simply:

$$J_{\alpha\beta} = E_{0\alpha} E^*_{0\beta} \tag{50.5}$$

(without averaging), i.e. the components of the tensor can be written as products of components of a certain constant vector. The necessary and sufficient condition for this is that the determinant be zero:†

$$|J_{\alpha\beta}| = J_{yy}J_{zz}-J_{yz}J_{zy} = 0. \tag{50.6}$$

The opposite case is that of unpolarized or *natural* (ordinary) light. Complete absence of polarization means that all directions (in the plane perpen-

† In general, for an arbitrary tensor of the form (50.1), the determinant satisfies $|J_{\alpha\beta}| \geqslant 0$. This is easily shown by considering, for simplicity, the averaging as a summation over a set of different discrete values, and applying the wellknown algebraic inequality

$$\Big|\sum_{a,b} x_a y_b\Big|^2 \leqslant \sum_a |x_a|^2 \sum_b |y_b|^2.$$

dicular to the direction of propagation) are completely equivalent. This means that the tensor $J_{\alpha\beta}$ must reduce to a scalar, i.e. it must have the form

$$J_{\alpha\beta} = J_{\beta\alpha} = \tfrac{1}{2} J\delta_{\alpha\beta}. \tag{50.7}$$

If the tensor $J_{\alpha\beta}$ is purely real ($J_{\alpha\beta} = S_{\alpha\beta}$), but does not have the form (50.7), it can, like every symmetric tensor, be brought to principal axes, with two different principal values, which we denote by λ_1 and λ_2. The directions of the principal axes are perpendicular to one another; denoting the unit vectors in these directions by $\mathbf{n}^{(1)}$ and $\mathbf{n}^{(2)}$, we can write $J_{\alpha\beta}$ in the form

$$J_{\alpha\beta} = \lambda_1 n_\alpha^{(1)} n_\beta^{(1)} + \lambda_2 n_\alpha^{(2)} n_\beta^{(2)}. \tag{50.8}$$

Each of the two terms in (50.8) has the form of a simple product of the two components of a constant real vector ($\sqrt{\lambda_1}\,\mathbf{n}^{(1)}$ or $\sqrt{\lambda_2}\,\mathbf{n}^{(2)}$). In other words, each of these terms corresponds to linearly polarized light. Furthermore we see that there is no term in (50.8) containing the product of components of these two waves. This means that the two parts can be treated as physically independent of one another, or, as it is usually called, *incoherent*. Actually, if two waves are independent of one another, the average value of the product $\overline{E_\alpha^{(1)} E_\beta^{(2)*}}$ is equal to the product of the average values $\overline{E_\alpha^{(1)}}\,\overline{E_\beta^{(2)*}}$, and since each of the latter is equal to zero, $\overline{E_\alpha^{(1)} E_\beta^{(2)*}} = 0$.

Thus we arrive at the result that in the present case (real $J_{\alpha\beta}$) a partially polarized wave can be represented as the superposition of two incoherent waves which are linearly polarized along mutually perpendicular directions.† The total intensity of the light is proportional to the sum $J = \lambda_1 + \lambda_2$. The ratio

$$\varrho = \frac{\lambda_2}{\lambda_1} \tag{50.9}$$

of the smaller of the two quantities λ_1, λ_2 to the larger is called the *degree of depolarization* of the light. If the light is completely polarized, then one of the quantities λ_1, λ_2 is equal to zero, so that $\varrho = 0$. For ordinary light, $\lambda_1 = \lambda_2$, so that $\varrho = 1$.

Finally we show how light having arbitrary partial polarization can be resolved into "ordinary" and "polarized" parts. For the tensor $J_{\alpha\beta}$, such a decomposition means that it is written in the form

$$J_{\alpha\beta} = \tfrac{1}{2} J^{(o)} \delta_{\alpha\beta} + E_{0\alpha}^{(p)} E_{0\beta}^{(p)*}; \tag{50.10}$$

the first term corresponds to the ordinary and the second to the polarized part of the light. The latter is, in general, an elliptically polarized wave; the

†In the general case of a complex tensor $J_{\alpha\beta}$, it can be shown (though we shall not do this here) that the light can be represented as a superposition of two incoherent elliptically polarized waves, whose polarization ellipses are similar and mutually perpendicular.

directions of the axes of the polarization ellipse are easily shown to coincide with the directions of the principal axes of the symmetric real part $S_{\alpha\beta}$ of the tensor $J_{\alpha\beta}$.

To determine the intensities of these parts, we note that the determinant

$$|J_{\alpha\beta}-\tfrac{1}{2}J^{(o)}\delta_{\alpha\beta}| = |E_{0\alpha}^{(p)}E_{0\beta}^{(p)*}| = 0.$$

Thus the intensity of the "natural" part of the light is given by twice the root of the equation

$$|J_{\alpha\beta}-\lambda\,\delta_{\alpha\beta}| = 0 \tag{50.11}$$

where, of the two roots

$$\lambda_{1,2} = \tfrac{1}{2}(J_{yy}+J_{zz})\pm\sqrt{\tfrac{1}{4}(J_{yy}-J_{zz})^2+|J_{yz}|^2} \tag{50.12}$$

we should take the smaller:

$$J^{(o)} = J_{yy}+J_{zz}-\sqrt{(J_{yy}-J_{zz})^2+4|J_{yz}|^2} \tag{50.13}$$

(since $J^{(0)}$ must obviously be smaller than the total intensity $J = J_{yy}+J_{zz}$). The intensity of the "polarized" part is given by the difference

$$J^{(p)} = |\mathbf{E}_0^{(p)}|^2 = J-J^{(0)},$$

or

$$J^{(p)} = \sqrt{(J_{yy}-J_{zz})^2+4|J_{yz}|^2}. \tag{50.14}$$

PROBLEM

Determine the direction of the axes of polarization of the polarized part of the light.

Solution: Applying formula (1) of problem 1, § 48, to the vector $\mathbf{E}_0^{(p)}$, and using (50.10), we obtain:

$$b_1^2+b_2^2 = \sqrt{(J_{yy}-J_{zz})^2+4|J_{yz}|^2},$$
$$2b_1b_2 = i(J_{yz}-J_{zy}).$$

From these two equations, we can determine the values of b_1 and b_2. The direction of the polarization axes (the angle θ between $\mathbf{b}_1$ and the y axis) is given by the formula

$$\tan 2\theta = \frac{E_{0y}^{(p)}E_{0z}^{(p)*}+E_{0y}^{(p)*}E_{0z}^{(p)}}{|E_{0y}^{(p)}|^2-|E_{0z}^{(p)}|^2}$$

[see formula (3), problem 1, § 48], or

$$\tan 2\theta = \frac{J_{yz}+J_{zy}}{J_{yy}-J_{zz}} = \frac{2S_{yz}}{S_{yy}-S_{zz}}.$$

This formula, naturally, coincides with the well known formula for the directions of the principal axes of the symmetric tensor $S_{\alpha\beta}$.

§ 51. The Fourier resolution of the electrostatic field

The field produced by charges can also be formally expanded in plane waves (in a Fourier integral). This expansion, however, is essentially different from the expansion of electromagnetic waves in vacuum, for the field produced by charges does not satisfy the homogeneous wave equation, and therefore each term of this expansion does not satisfy the equation. From this it follows that for the plane waves into which the field of charges can be expanded, the relation $k^2 = \omega^2/c^2$, which holds for plane monochromatic electromagnetic waves, is not fulfilled.

In particular, if we formally represent the electrostatic field as a superposition of plane waves, then the "frequency" of these waves is clearly zero, since the field under consideration does not depend on the time. The wave vectors themselves are, of course, different from zero.

We consider the field produced by a point charge e, located at the origin of coordinates. The potential ϕ of this field is determined by the equation (see § 36)

$$\Delta\phi = -4\pi e\,\delta(\mathbf{r}). \tag{51.1}$$

We expand ϕ in a Fourier integral, i.e., we represent it in the form

$$\phi = \int_{-\infty}^{+\infty} e^{i\mathbf{k}\cdot\mathbf{r}}\phi_{\mathbf{k}}\,d^3k \tag{51.2}$$

where d^3k denotes $dk_x\,dk_y\,dk_z$. Applying the Laplace operator to both sides of this equation, we obtain

$$\Delta\phi = -\int_{-\infty}^{+\infty} k^2 e^{i\mathbf{k}\cdot\mathbf{r}}\phi_{\mathbf{k}}\,d^3k,$$

so that the Fourier component of the expression $\Delta\phi$ is

$$(\Delta\phi)_{\mathbf{k}} = -k^2\phi_{\mathbf{k}}.$$

On the other hand, we can find $(\Delta\phi)_{\mathbf{k}}$ by taking Fourier components of both sides of equation (51.1),

$$(\Delta\phi)_{\mathbf{k}} = -\frac{1}{(2\pi)^3}\int_{-\infty}^{+\infty} 4\pi e\,\delta(\mathbf{r})\,e^{-i\mathbf{k}\cdot\mathbf{r}}\,dV = -\frac{e}{2\pi^2}.$$

Equating the two expressions obtained for $(\Delta\phi)_{\mathbf{k}}$, we find

$$\phi_{\mathbf{k}} = \frac{e}{2\pi^2}\frac{1}{k^2}. \tag{51.3}$$

This formula solves our problem.

Just as for the potential ϕ, we can expand the field

$$\mathbf{E} = \int_{-\infty}^{+\infty} \mathbf{E}_{\mathbf{k}} e^{i\mathbf{k}\cdot\mathbf{r}}\,d^3k. \tag{51.4}$$

With the aid of (51.2), we have

$$\mathbf{E} = -\operatorname{grad}\int_{-\infty}^{+\infty} \phi_{\mathbf{k}} e^{i\mathbf{k}\cdot\mathbf{r}}\,d^3k = -\int i\mathbf{k}\phi_{\mathbf{k}} e^{i\mathbf{k}\cdot\mathbf{r}}\,d^3k.$$

Comparing with (51.4), we obtain

$$\mathbf{E}_{\mathbf{k}} = -i\mathbf{k}\phi_{\mathbf{k}} = -\frac{i\mathbf{k}}{k^2}\frac{e}{2\pi^2}. \tag{51.5}$$

From this we see that the field of the waves, into which we have resolved the Coulomb field, is directed along the wave vector. Therefore these waves can be said to be *longitudinal.*

§ 52. Characteristic vibrations of the field

We consider an electromagnetic field in some finite volume of space.† To simplify further calculations we assume that this volume has the form of a rectangular parallelepiped with sides A, B, C, respectively. Then we can expand all quantities characterizing the field in this parallelepiped in a triple Fourier series (for the three coordinates). This expansion can be written (e.g., for the vector potential) in the form:

$$\mathbf{A} = \sum_{\mathbf{k}} \mathbf{A}_{\mathbf{k}} e^{i\mathbf{k}\cdot\mathbf{r}}. \tag{52.1}$$

The summation extends here over all possible values of the vector $\mathbf{k}$ whose components run through the values

$$k_x = \frac{2\pi n_x}{A}, \qquad k_y = \frac{2\pi n_y}{B}, \qquad k_z = \frac{2\pi n_z}{C}, \tag{52.2}$$

where n_x, n_y, n_z are positive and negative integers. The coefficients $\mathbf{A}_{\mathbf{k}}$ must satisfy the relations $\mathbf{A}_{-\mathbf{k}} = \mathbf{A}_{\mathbf{k}}^*$, since $\mathbf{A}$ must be real. From the equation $\operatorname{div} \mathbf{A} = 0$ it follows that for each $\mathbf{k}$,

$$\mathbf{k}\cdot\mathbf{A}_{\mathbf{k}} = 0, \tag{52.3}$$

i.e., the complex vectors $\mathbf{A}_{\mathbf{k}}$ are "perpendicular" to the corresponding wave vectors $\mathbf{k}$. The vectors $\mathbf{A}_{\mathbf{k}}$ are, of course, functions of the time; they satisfy the equation

$$\ddot{\mathbf{A}}_{\mathbf{k}} + c^2k^2\mathbf{A}_{\mathbf{k}} = 0. \tag{52.4}$$

If the dimensions A, B, C of the volume are sufficiently large, then neighboring values of k_x, k_y, k_z (for which n_x, n_y, n_z differ by unity) are very close to one another. In this case we may speak of the number of possible values of k_x, k_y, k_z in the small intervals Δk_x, Δk_y, Δk_z.

Since to neighboring values of, say, k_x, there correspond values of n_x differing by unity, the number Δn_x of possible values of k_x in the interval Δk_x is equal simply to the number of values of n_x in the corresponding interval. Thus, we obtain

$$\Delta n_x = \frac{A}{2\pi}\Delta k_x, \qquad \Delta n_y = \frac{B}{2\pi}\Delta k_y, \qquad \Delta n_z = \frac{C}{2\pi}\Delta k_z.$$

† We deal here with a field in the absence of charges ("free radiation").

The total number Δn of possible values of the vector $\mathbf{k}$ with components in the intervals Δk_x, Δk_y, Δk_z is equal to the product $\Delta n_x \Delta n_y \Delta n_z$, that is,

$$\Delta n = \frac{V}{(2\pi)^3} \Delta k_x \Delta k_y \Delta k_z, \tag{52.5}$$

where $V = ABC$ is the volume of the field.

It is easy to determine from this the number of possible values of the wave vector having absolute values in the interval Δk, and directed into the element of solid angle Δo. To get this we need only transform to polar coordinates in the "k space" and write in place of $\Delta k_x \Delta k_y \Delta k_z$ the element of volume in these coordinates. Thus

$$\Delta n = \frac{V}{(2\pi)^3} k^2 \Delta k \Delta o. \tag{52.6}$$

Finally, the number of possible values of the wave vector with absolute value k in the interval Δk and pointing in all directions is (we write 4π in place of Δo)

$$\Delta n = \frac{V}{2\pi^2} k^2 \Delta k. \tag{52.7}$$

The vectors $\mathbf{A}_\mathbf{k}$ as functions of the time behave like simply periodic functions with periods $\omega_k = ck$ (see 52.4). We present the expansion of the field in such a form that it appears as an expansion in propagating plane waves. To do this, we write the series (52.1), regrouping its terms, in the form

$$\mathbf{A} = \sum_\mathbf{k} (\mathbf{a}_\mathbf{k} e^{i\mathbf{k}\cdot\mathbf{r}} + \mathbf{a}_\mathbf{k}^* e^{-i\mathbf{k}\cdot\mathbf{r}}) \tag{52.8}$$

(this form clearly shows the reality of $\mathbf{A}$) and assume that each of the $\mathbf{a}_\mathbf{k}$ depends on the time through the factor $e^{-i\omega_k t}$:

$$\mathbf{a}_\mathbf{k} \sim e^{-i\omega_k t}, \qquad \omega_k = ck. \tag{52.9}$$

Then each individual term in the sum (52.8) is a function only of the difference $\mathbf{k}\cdot\mathbf{r} - \omega_k t$ which corresponds to a wave propagating in the direction of the vector $\mathbf{k}$.

We calculate the total energy

$$\mathcal{E} = \frac{1}{8\pi} \int (E^2 + H^2)\, dV$$

of the field in the volume V, expressing it in terms of the quantities $\mathbf{a}_\mathbf{k}$. For the electric field we have

$$\mathbf{E} = -\frac{1}{c}\dot{\mathbf{A}} = -\frac{1}{c} \sum_\mathbf{k} (\dot{\mathbf{a}}_\mathbf{k} e^{i\mathbf{k}\cdot\mathbf{r}} + \dot{\mathbf{a}}_k^* e^{-i\mathbf{k}\cdot\mathbf{r}}),$$

or, keeping in mind (52.9),

$$\mathbf{E} = i \sum_\mathbf{k} k (\mathbf{a}_\mathbf{k} e^{i\mathbf{k}\cdot\mathbf{r}} - \mathbf{a}_\mathbf{k}^* e^{-i\mathbf{k}\cdot\mathbf{r}}). \tag{52.10}$$

For the magnetic field $\mathbf{H} = \text{curl}\,\mathbf{A}$, we obtain

$$\mathbf{H} = i\sum_{\mathbf{k}} (\mathbf{k}\times\mathbf{a}_{\mathbf{k}}e^{+i\mathbf{k}\cdot\mathbf{r}} - \mathbf{k}\times\mathbf{a}_{\mathbf{k}}^{*}e^{-i\mathbf{k}\cdot\mathbf{r}}). \qquad (52.11)$$

When calculating the squares of these sums, we must keep in mind that all products of terms with wave vectors $\mathbf{k} \neq \mathbf{k}'$ give zero on integration over the whole volume. In fact, such terms contain factors of the form $e^{\pm i\mathbf{q}\cdot\mathbf{r}}$, $\mathbf{q} = \mathbf{k}\pm\mathbf{k}'$, and the integral, e.g., of

$$\int_0^A e^{i\frac{2\pi}{A}n_x x}\,dx,$$

with integer n_x different from zero, gives zero. For the same reason, products containing the factors $e^{\pm 2i\mathbf{k}\cdot\mathbf{r}}$ vanish. In those terms from which the exponentials drop out, integration over dV gives just the volume V.

As a result, we obtain

$$\mathcal{E} = \frac{V}{4\pi}\sum_{\mathbf{k}}\{k^2\mathbf{a}_{\mathbf{k}}\cdot\mathbf{a}_{\mathbf{k}}^{*} + (\mathbf{k}\times\mathbf{a}_{\mathbf{k}})\cdot(\mathbf{k}\times\mathbf{a}_{\mathbf{k}}^{*})\}.$$

Since $\mathbf{a}_{\mathbf{k}}\cdot\mathbf{k} = 0$, we have

$$(\mathbf{k}\times\mathbf{a}_{\mathbf{k}})\cdot(\mathbf{k}\times\mathbf{a}_{\mathbf{k}}^{*}) = k^2\mathbf{a}_{\mathbf{k}}\cdot\mathbf{a}_{\mathbf{k}}^{*},$$

and we obtain finally

$$\mathcal{E} = \sum_{\mathbf{k}}\mathcal{E}_{\mathbf{k}}, \qquad \mathcal{E}_{\mathbf{k}} = \frac{k^2V}{2\pi}\mathbf{a}_{\mathbf{k}}\cdot\mathbf{a}_{\mathbf{k}}^{*}. \qquad (52.12)$$

Thus the total energy of the field is expressed as a sum of the energies $\mathcal{E}_{\mathbf{k}}$, associated with each of the plane waves individually.

In a completely analogous fashion, we can calculate the total momentum of the field,

$$\frac{1}{c^2}\int \mathbf{S}\,dV = \frac{1}{4\pi c}\int \mathbf{E}\times\mathbf{H}\,dV,$$

for which we obtain

$$\sum_{\mathbf{k}}\frac{\mathbf{k}}{k}\frac{\mathcal{E}_{\mathbf{k}}}{c}. \qquad (52.13)$$

This result could have been anticipated in view of the relation between the energy and momentum of a plane wave (see § 47).

The expansions we have derived (52.8 or 52.1) succeed in expressing the field in terms of a series of discrete parameters (the vectors $\mathbf{a}_{\mathbf{k}}$), in place of the description in terms of a continuous series of parameters, which is essentially what is done when we give the potential $\mathbf{A}(x, y, z, t)$ at all points of space. We now make a transformation of the variables $\mathbf{a}_{\mathbf{k}}$, which has the result that the equations of the field take on a form similar to the canonical equations (Hamilton equations) of mechanics.

We introduce the real "canonical variables" $\mathbf{Q_k}$ and $\mathbf{P_k}$ according to the relations

$$\mathbf{Q_k} = \alpha(\mathbf{a_k}+\mathbf{a_k^*}), \tag{52.14}$$
$$\mathbf{P_k} = -i\omega_k\alpha(\mathbf{a_k}-\mathbf{a_k^*}) = \dot{\mathbf{Q}}_\mathbf{k}.$$

Here α is some real constant, which we determine later so that the relation $\mathbf{P_k} = \dot{\mathbf{Q}}_\mathbf{k}$ between the "generalized momenta" and "coordinates" actually is a consequence of the equations of motion.

The Hamiltonian of the field is obtained by replacing the quantities $\mathbf{a_k}$ in the energy (52.12) by their expressions in terms of $\mathbf{P_k}$ and $\mathbf{Q_k}$:

$$\mathcal{H} = \sum_\mathbf{k} \mathcal{H}_\mathbf{k} = \sum_\mathbf{k} \frac{V}{8\pi c^2\alpha^2}(\mathbf{P_k^2}+\omega_k^2\mathbf{Q_k^2}).$$

In order that the Hamilton equation $\partial\mathcal{H}/\partial\mathbf{P_k} = \dot{\mathbf{Q}}_\mathbf{k}$ shall coincide with $\mathbf{P_k} = \dot{\mathbf{Q}}_\mathbf{k}$, we must set $V/8\pi c^2\alpha^2 = \frac{1}{2}$, that is,

$$\alpha = \sqrt{\frac{V}{4\pi c^2}}. \tag{52.15}$$

Then the Hamiltonian takes the form

$$\mathcal{H} = \sum_\mathbf{k} \tfrac{1}{2}(\mathbf{P_k^2}+\omega_k^2\mathbf{Q_k^2}) = \sum_\mathbf{k} \mathcal{H}_\mathbf{k}. \tag{52.16}$$

The "equations of motion,"

$$\frac{\partial\mathcal{H}}{\partial\mathbf{Q_k}} = -\dot{\mathbf{P}}_\mathbf{k}, \quad \frac{\partial\mathcal{H}}{\partial\mathbf{P_k}} = \dot{\mathbf{Q}}_\mathbf{k},$$

become the equations

$$\ddot{\mathbf{Q}}_\mathbf{k}+\omega_k^2\mathbf{Q_k} = 0, \tag{52.17}$$

that is, they are identical with the equations of the field.

Each of the vectors $\mathbf{Q_k}$ and $\mathbf{P_k}$ is perpendicular to the wave vector $\mathbf{k}$, i.e. has two independent components. The direction of these vectors determines the direction of polarization of the corresponding traveling wave. Denoting the two components of the vector $\mathbf{Q_k}$ (in the plane perpendicular to $\mathbf{k}$) by $Q_{\mathbf{k}j}$, $j = 1, 2$, we have $\mathbf{Q_k^2} = \sum_j Q_{\mathbf{k}j}^2$, and similarly for $\mathbf{P_k}$. Then

$$\mathcal{H} = \sum_{\mathbf{k}j} \mathcal{H}_{\mathbf{k}j}, \quad \mathcal{H}_{\mathbf{k}j} = \tfrac{1}{2}(P_{\mathbf{k}j}^2+\omega_k^2 Q_{\mathbf{k}j}^2). \tag{52.18}$$

We see that the Hamiltonian splits into a sum of independent terms $\mathcal{H}_{\mathbf{k}j}$, each of which contains only one pair of the quantities $Q_{\mathbf{k}j}$, $P_{\mathbf{k}j}$. Each such term corresponds to a traveling wave with a definite wave vector and polarization. The quantity $\mathcal{H}_{\mathbf{k}j}$ has the form of the Hamiltonian of a one-dimensional oscillator, performing a simple harmonic vibration. For this reason, one sometimes refers to this result as the expansion of the field in terms of oscillators.

We give the formulas which express the field explicitly in terms of the variables $\mathbf{P_k}$, $\mathbf{Q_k}$. From (52.14) and (52.15), we have

$$\mathbf{a_k} = \frac{i}{k}\sqrt{\frac{\pi}{V}}(\mathbf{P_k} - i\omega_k \mathbf{Q_k}), \quad \mathbf{a_k^*} = -\frac{i}{k}\sqrt{\frac{\pi}{V}}(\mathbf{P_k} + i\omega_k \mathbf{Q_k}). \tag{52.19}$$

Substituting these expressions in (52.8), we obtain for the vector potential of the field:

$$\mathbf{A} = 2\sqrt{\frac{\pi}{V}}\sum_{\mathbf{k}}\frac{1}{k}(ck\mathbf{Q_k}\cos\mathbf{k}\cdot\mathbf{r} - \mathbf{P_k}\sin\mathbf{k}\cdot\mathbf{r}). \tag{52.20}$$

For the electric and magnetic fields, we find

$$\begin{aligned}\mathbf{E} &= -2\sqrt{\frac{\pi}{V}}\sum_{\mathbf{k}}(ck\mathbf{Q_k}\sin\mathbf{k}\cdot\mathbf{r} + \mathbf{P_k}\cos\mathbf{k}\cdot\mathbf{r}),\\ \mathbf{H} &= -2\sqrt{\frac{\pi}{V}}\sum_{\mathbf{k}}\frac{1}{k}\{ck(\mathbf{k}\times\mathbf{Q_k})\sin\mathbf{k}\cdot\mathbf{r} + (\mathbf{k}\times\mathbf{P_k})\cos\mathbf{k}\cdot\mathbf{r}\}.\end{aligned} \tag{52.21}$$

CHAPTER 7

THE PROPAGATION OF LIGHT

§ 53. Geometrical optics

A plane wave is characterized by the property that its direction of propagation and amplitude are the same everywhere. Arbitrary electromagnetic waves, of course, do not have this property. Nevertheless, a great many electromagnetic waves, which are not plane, have the property that within each small region of space they can be considered to be plane. For this, it is clearly necessary that the amplitude and direction of the wave remain practically constant over distances of the order of the wavelength. If this condition is satisfied, we can introduce the so-called *wave surface*, i.e., a surface at all of whose points the phase of the wave is the same (at a given time). (The wave surfaces of a plane wave are obviously planes perpendicular to the direction of propagation of the wave.) In each small region of space we can speak of a direction of propagation of the wave, normal to the wave surface. In this way we can introduce the concept of *rays* — curves whose tangents at each point coincide with the direction of propagation of the wave.

The study of the laws of propagation of waves in this case constitutes the domain of *geometrical optics*. Consequently, geometrical optics considers the propagation of waves, in particular of light, as the propagation of rays, completely divorced from their wave properties. In other words, geometrical optics corresponds to the limiting case of small wavelength, $\lambda \rightarrow 0$.

We now take up the derivation of the fundamental equation of geometrical optics — the equation determining the direction of the rays. Let f be any quantity describing the field of the wave (any component of **E** or **H**). For a plane monochromatic wave, f has the form

$$f = ae^{i(\mathbf{k}\cdot\mathbf{r}-\omega t+\alpha)} = ae^{i(k_i x^i+\alpha)} \tag{53.1}$$

(we omit the Re; it is understood that we take the real part of all expressions).

We write the expression for the field in the form

$$f = ae^{i\psi}. \tag{53.2}$$

In case the wave is not plane, but geometrical optics is applicable, the amplitude a is, generally speaking, a function of the coordinates and time, and the phase ψ, which is called the *eikonal*, does not have a simple form, as in (53.1). It is essential, however, that ψ be a large quantity. This is clear immediately from the fact that it changes by 2π when we move through one wavelength, and geometrical optics corresponds to the limit $\lambda \to 0$.

Over small space regions and time intervals the eikonal ψ can be expanded in series; to terms of first order, we have

$$\psi = \psi_0 + \mathbf{r} \cdot \frac{\partial \psi}{\partial \mathbf{r}} + t \frac{\partial \psi}{\partial t}$$

(the origin for coordinates and time has been chosen within the space region and time interval under consideration; the derivatives are evaluated at the origin). Comparing this expression with (53.1), we can write

$$\mathbf{k} = \frac{\partial \psi}{\partial \mathbf{r}} = \text{grad}\, \psi, \quad \omega = -\frac{\partial \psi}{\partial t}, \tag{53.3}$$

which corresponds to the fact that in each small region of space (and each small interval of time) the wave can be considered as plane. In four-dimensional form, the relation (53.3) is expressed as

$$k_i = \frac{\partial \psi}{\partial x_i}, \tag{53.4}$$

where k_i is the wave four-vector.

We saw in § 48 that the components of the four-vector k_i are related by $k_i^2 = 0$. Substituting (53.4), we obtain the equation

$$\left(\frac{\partial \psi}{\partial x_i}\right)^2 = 0. \tag{53.5}$$

This equation, the *eikonal equation*, is the fundamental equation of geometrical optics.

The eikonal equation can also be derived by direct transition to the limit $\lambda \to 0$ in the wave equation. The field f satisfies the wave equation

$$\frac{\partial^2 f}{\partial x_i^2} = 0.$$

Substituting $f = a e^{i\psi}$, we obtain

$$\frac{\partial^2 a}{\partial x_i^2} e^{i\psi} + 2i \frac{\partial a}{\partial x_i} \frac{\partial \psi}{\partial x_i} e^{i\psi} + if \frac{\partial^2 \psi}{\partial x_i^2} - \left(\frac{\partial \psi}{\partial x_i}\right)^2 f = 0. \tag{53.6}$$

But the eikonal ψ, as we pointed out above, is a large quantity; therefore we can neglect the first three terms compared with the fourth, and we arrive once more at equation (53.5).

We shall give certain relations which, in their application to the propagation of light in vacuum, lead only to completely obvious results. Nevertheless, they are important because, in their general form, these derivations apply also to the propagation of light in material media.

From the form of the eikonal equation there results a remarkable analogy between geometrical optics and the mechanics of material particles. The motion of a material particle is determined by the Hamilton-Jacobi equation (23.12):

$$\left(\frac{\partial S}{\partial x_i}-\frac{e}{c}A_i\right)^2+m^2c^2=0.$$

This equation, like the eikonal equation, is an equation in the first partial derivatives and is of second degree. As we know, the action S is related to the momentum $\mathbf{p}$ and the Hamiltonian $\mathcal{H}$ of the particle by the relations

$$\mathbf{p}=\frac{\partial S}{\partial \mathbf{r}},\quad \mathcal{H}=-\frac{\partial S}{\partial t}.$$

Comparing these formulas with the formulas (53.3), we see that the wave vector plays the same role in geometrical optics as the momentum of the particle in mechanics, while the frequency plays the role of the Hamiltonian, i.e., the energy of the particle. The absolute magnitude k of the wave vector is related to the frequency by the formula $k=\omega/c$. This relation is analogous to the relation $p=\mathcal{E}/c$ between the momentum and energy of a particle with zero mass, and velocity equal to the velocity of light.

For a particle, we have the Hamilton equations

$$\dot{\mathbf{p}}=-\frac{\partial \mathcal{H}}{\partial \mathbf{r}},\quad \mathbf{v}=\dot{\mathbf{r}}=\frac{\partial \mathcal{H}}{\partial \mathbf{p}}.$$

In view of the analogy we have pointed out, we can immediately write the corresponding equations for rays:

$$\dot{\mathbf{k}}=-\frac{\partial \omega}{\partial \mathbf{r}},\quad \dot{\mathbf{r}}=\frac{\partial \omega}{\partial \mathbf{k}}. \tag{53.7}$$

In vacuum, $\omega=ck$, so that $\dot{\mathbf{k}}=0$, $\mathbf{v}=c\mathbf{n}$ ($\mathbf{n}$ is a unit vector along the direction of propagation); in other words, as it must be, in vacuum the rays are straight lines, along which the light travels with velocity c.

The analogy between the wave vector of a wave and the momentum of a particle is made especially clear by the following consideration. Let us consider a wave which is a superposition of monochromatic waves with frequencies in a certain small interval and occupying some finite region in space (this is called a *wave packet*). We calculate the four-momentum of the field of this wave, using formula (32.6) with the energy-momentum tensor (48.15) (for each monochromatic component). Replacing k_i in this formula by some average value, we obtain an expression of the form

$$P_i=Ak_i, \tag{53.8}$$

where the coefficient of proportionality A between the two four-vectors P_i and k_i is some scalar. In three-dimensional form this relation gives:

$$\mathbf{P}=A\mathbf{k},\quad \mathcal{E}=A\omega. \tag{53.9}$$

Thus we see that the momentum and energy of a wave packet transform, when we go from one reference system to another, like the wave vector and the frequency.

Pursuing the analogy, we can establish for geometrical optics a principle analogous to the principle of least action in mechanics. However, it cannot be written in Hamiltonian form as $\delta\int L\,dt = 0$, since it turns out to be impossible to introduce, for rays, a function analogous to the Lagrangian of a particle. Since the Lagrangian of a particle is related so the Hamiltonian by the equation $L = \mathbf{p}\cdot\partial\mathcal{H}/\partial\mathbf{p}-\mathcal{H}$, replacing the Hamiltonian $\mathcal{H}$ by the frequency ω and the momentum by the wave vector $\mathbf{k}$, we should have to write for the Lagrangian in optics $\mathbf{k}\cdot\partial\omega/\partial\mathbf{k}-\omega$. But this expression is equal to zero, since $\omega = ck$. The impossibility of introducing a Lagrangian for rays is also clear directly from the consideration mentioned earlier that the propagation of rays is analogous to the motion of particles with zero mass.

If the wave has a definite constant frequency ω, then the time dependence of its field is given by a factor of the form $e^{-i\omega t}$. Therefore for the eikonal of such a wave we can write

$$\psi = -\omega t+\psi_0(x, y, z), \tag{53.10}$$

where ψ_0 is a function only of the coordinates. The eikonal equation (53.5) now takes the form

$$(\operatorname{grad}\psi_0)^2 = \frac{\omega^2}{c^2}. \tag{53.11}$$

The wave surfaces are the surfaces of constant eikonal, i.e., the family of surfaces of the form $\psi_0(x, y, z) = \text{const}$. The rays themselves are at each point normal to the corresponding wave surface; their direction is determined by the gradient $\nabla\psi_0$.

As is well known, in the case where the energy is constant, the principle of least action for particles can also be written in the form of the so-called *principle of Maupertuis*:

$$\delta S = \delta\int \mathbf{p}\cdot d\mathbf{l} = 0,$$

where the integration extends over the trajectory of the particle between two of its points. In this expression the momentum is assumed to be a function of the energy and the coordinate differentials. The analogous principle for rays is called *Fermat's principle*. In this case, we can write by analogy:

$$\delta\psi = \delta\int \mathbf{k}\cdot d\mathbf{l} = 0. \tag{53.12}$$

In vacuum, $\mathbf{k} = \frac{\omega}{c}\mathbf{n}$, and we obtain ($d\mathbf{l}\cdot\mathbf{n} = dl$):

$$\delta\int dl = 0, \tag{53.13}$$

which corresponds to rectilinear propagation of the rays.

§ 54. Intensity

In geometrical optics, the light wave can be considered as a bundle of rays. The rays themselves, however, determine only the direction of propagation of the light at each point; there remains the question of the distribution of the light intensity in space.

On some wave surface of the bundle of rays under consideration, we isolate an infinitesimal surface element. From differential geometry it is known that every surface has, at each of its points, two (generally different) principal radii of curvature. Let *ac* and *bd* (Fig. 7) be elements of the principal

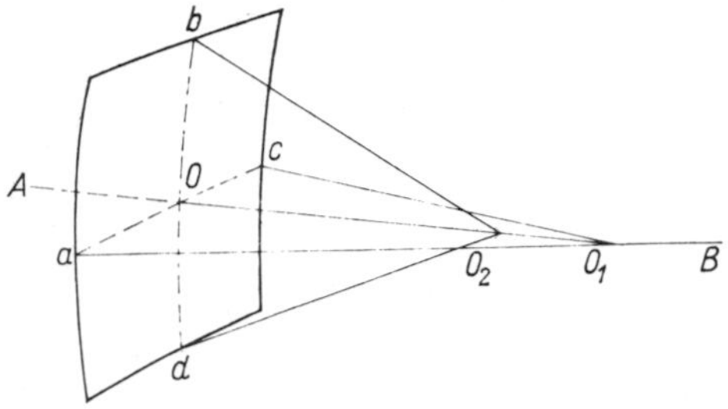

FIG. 7.

circles of curvature, constructed at a given element of the wave surface. Then the rays passing through *a* and *c* meet at the corresponding center of curvature O_1, while the rays passing through *b* and *d* meet at the other center of curvature O_2.

For fixed angular openings of the beams starting from O_1 and O_2, the lengths of the arcs *ac* and *bd* are, clearly, proportional to the corresponding radii of curvature R_1 and R_2 (i.e., to the lengths O_1a and O_2b). The area of the surface element is proportional to the product of the lengths *ac* and *bd*, i.e., proportional to R_1R_2. In other words, if we consider the element of the wave surface bounded by a definite set of rays, then as we move along them the area of the element will change proportionally to R_1R_2.

On the other hand, the intensity, i.e., the energy flux density, is inversely proportional to the surface area through which a given amount of light energy passes. Thus we arrive at the result that the intensity is

$$I = \frac{\text{const}}{R_1 R_2}. \tag{54.1}$$

This formula must be understood as follows. On each ray (*AB* in Fig. 7) there are definite points O_1 and O_2, which are the centers of curvature (at their points of intersection with the ray) of all the wave surfaces intersecting the given ray. The distances OO_1 and OO_2 from the point O where the wave surface intersects the ray, to the points O_1 and O_2, are the radii of curvature

R_1 and R_2 of the wave surface at the point O. Thus formula (54.1) determines the change in intensity of the light along a given ray as a function of the distances from definite points on this ray. We emphasize that this formula cannot be used to compare intensities at different points on a single wave surface.

Since the intensity is determined by the square modulus of the field, we can write for the change of the field itself along the ray

$$f = \frac{\text{const}}{\sqrt{R_1 R_2}} e^{ikR}, \tag{54.2}$$

where in the phase factor e^{ikR} we can write either e^{ikR_1} or e^{ikR_2}. The quantities e^{ikR_1} and e^{ikR_2} (for a given ray) differ from each other only by a constant factor, since the difference $R_1 - R_2$, the distance between the two centers of curvature, is a constant.

If the two radii of curvature of the wave surface coincide, then (54.1) and (54.2) have the form:

$$I = \frac{\text{const}}{R^2}, \quad f = \frac{\text{const}}{R} e^{ikR}. \tag{54.3}$$

This happens always when the light is emitted from a point source (the wave surfaces are then concentric spheres and R is the distance from the light source).

From (54.1) we see that the intensity becomes infinite at the points $R_1 = 0$, $R_2 = 0$, i.e., at the centers of curvature of the wave surface. Applying this to all the rays in a bundle, we find that the intensity of the light in the given bundle becomes infinite, generally, on two surfaces — the geometrical loci of all the centers of curvature of the wave surfaces. These surfaces are called *caustics*. In the special case of a beam of rays with spherical wave surfaces, the two caustics fuse into a single point (*focus*).

We note from well-known results of differential geometry concerning the properties of the loci of centers of curvature of a family of surfaces, that the rays are tangent to the caustic.

It is necessary to keep in mind that (for convex wave surfaces) the centers of curvature of the wave surfaces can turn out to lie not on the rays themselves, but on their extensions beyond the optical system from which they emerge. In such cases we speak of *imaginary caustics* (or foci). In this case the intensity of the light does not become infinite anywhere.

As for the increase of intensity to infinity, in actuality we must understand that the intensity does become large at points on the caustic, but it remains finite (see the problem in § 59). The formal increase to infinity means that the approximation of geometrical optics is never applicable in the neighborhood of the caustic. To this is related the fact that the change in phase along the ray can be determined from formula (54.2) only over sections of the ray which do not include its point of tangency to the caustic. Later (in § 59), we shall show that actually in passing through the caustic the phase of the field decreases by $\pi/2$. This means that if, on the section of the ray before its first intersection with the caustic, the field is proportional to the factor e^{ikx} (x is the coordinate along the ray), then after passage through the caustic the field will be proportional to $e^{i\left(kx-\frac{\pi}{2}\right)}$. The same thing occurs in the neighborhood of the point of tangency to the second caustic, and beyond that point the field is proportional to $e^{i(kx-\pi)}$.†

§ 55. The angular eikonal

A light ray traveling in vacuum and impinging on a transparent body will, on its emergence from this body, generally have a direction different from its initial direction. This change in direction will, of course, depend on the specific properties of the body and on its form. However, it turns out that one can derive general laws relating to the change in direction of a light ray on passage through an arbitrary material body. In this it is assumed only that geometrical optics is applicable to rays propagating in the interior of the body under consideration. As is customary, we shall call such transparent bodies, through which rays of light propagate, *optical systems.*

Because of the analogy mentioned in § 53, between the propagation of rays and the motion of particles, the same general laws are valid as for the change in direction of motion of a particle, initially moving in a straight line in vacuum, then passing through some electromagnetic field, and once more emerging into vacuum. For definiteness, we shall, however, always speak later of the propagation of light rays.

We saw in a previous section that the eikonal equation, describing the propagation of the rays, can be written in the form (53.11) (for light of a definite frequency). From now on we shall, for convenience, designate by ψ the eikonal ψ_0 divided by the constant ω/c. Then the basic equation of geometrical optics has the form:

$$(\nabla\psi)^2 = 1. \tag{55.1}$$

Each solution of this equation describes a definite beam of rays, in which the direction of the rays passing through a given point in space is determined by the gradient of ψ at that point. However, for our purposes this description is insufficient, since we are seeking general relations determining the passage through an optical system not of a single definite bundle of rays, but of arbitrary rays. Therefore we must use an eikonal expressed in such

†Although formula (54.2) itself is not valid near the caustic, the change in phase of the field corresponds formally to a change in sign (i.e. multiplication by $e^{i\pi}$) of R_1 or R_2 in this formula.

a form that it describes all the generally possible rays of light, i.e., rays passing through any pair of points in space. In its usual form the eikonal $\psi(\mathbf{r})$ is the phase of the rays in a certain bundle passing through the point $\mathbf{r}$. Now we must introduce the eikonal as a function $\psi(\mathbf{r}, \mathbf{r}')$ of the coordinates of two points ($\mathbf{r}, \mathbf{r}'$ are the radius vectors of the initial and end points of the ray). A ray can pass through each pair of points $\mathbf{r}, \mathbf{r}'$, and $\psi(\mathbf{r}, \mathbf{r}')$ is the phase difference (or, as it is called, the *optical path length*) of this ray between the points $\mathbf{r}$ and $\mathbf{r}'$. From now on we shall always understand by $\mathbf{r}$ and $\mathbf{r}'$ the radius vectors to points on the ray before and after its passage through the optical system.

If in $\psi(\mathbf{r}, \mathbf{r}')$ one of the radius vectors, say $\mathbf{r}'$, is fixed, then ψ as a function of $\mathbf{r}$ describes a definite bundle of rays, namely, the bundle of rays passing through the point $\mathbf{r}'$. Then ψ must satisfy equation (55.1), where the differentiations are applied to the components of $\mathbf{r}$. Similarly, if $\mathbf{r}$ is assumed fixed, we again obtain an equation for $\psi(\mathbf{r}, \mathbf{r}')$, so that

$$(\nabla_{\mathbf{r}}\psi)^2 = 1, \quad (\nabla_{\mathbf{r}'}\psi)^2 = 1. \tag{55.2}$$

The direction of the ray is determined by the gradient of its phase. Since $\psi(\mathbf{r}, \mathbf{r}')$ is the difference in phase at the points $\mathbf{r}$ and $\mathbf{r}'$, the direction of the ray at the point $\mathbf{r}'$ is given by the vector $\mathbf{n}' = \partial\psi/\partial\mathbf{r}'$, and at the point $\mathbf{r}$ by the vector $\mathbf{n} = -\partial\psi/\partial\mathbf{r}$. From (55.2) it is clear that $\mathbf{n}$ and $\mathbf{n}'$ are unit vectors:

$$\mathbf{n}^2 = \mathbf{n}'^2 = 1. \tag{55.3}$$

The four vectors $\mathbf{r}, \mathbf{r}', \mathbf{n}, \mathbf{n}'$ are interrelated, since two of them ($\mathbf{n}, \mathbf{n}'$) are derivatives of a certain function ψ with respect to the other two ($\mathbf{r}, \mathbf{r}'$). The function ψ itself satisfies the auxiliary conditions (55.2)

To obtain the relation between $\mathbf{n}, \mathbf{n}', \mathbf{r}, \mathbf{r}'$, it is convenient to introduce, in place of ψ, another quantity, on which no auxiliary condition is imposed (i.e., is not required to satisfy any differential equations). This can be done as follows. In the function ψ the independent variables are $\mathbf{r}$ and $\mathbf{r}'$, so that for the differential $d\psi$ we have

$$d\psi = \frac{\partial\psi}{\partial\mathbf{r}}\cdot d\mathbf{r} + \frac{\partial\psi}{\partial\mathbf{r}'}\cdot d\mathbf{r}' = -\mathbf{n}\cdot d\mathbf{r} + \mathbf{n}'\cdot d\mathbf{r}'.$$

We now make a Legendre transformation from $\mathbf{r}, \mathbf{r}'$ to the new independent variables $\mathbf{n}, \mathbf{n}'$, that is, we write

$$d\psi = -d(\mathbf{n}\cdot\mathbf{r}) + \mathbf{r}\cdot d\mathbf{n} + d(\mathbf{n}'\cdot\mathbf{r}') - \mathbf{r}'\cdot d\mathbf{n}',$$

from which, introducing the function

$$\chi = \mathbf{n}'\cdot\mathbf{r}' - \mathbf{n}\cdot\mathbf{r} - \psi, \tag{55.4}$$

we have

$$d\chi = -\mathbf{r}\cdot d\mathbf{n} + \mathbf{r}'\cdot d\mathbf{n}'. \tag{55.5}$$

The function χ is called the *angular eikonal*; as we see from (55.5), the independent variables in it are **n** and **n**′. No auxiliary conditions are imposed on χ. In fact, equation (55.3) now states only a condition referring to the independent variables: of the three components n_x, n_y, n_z, of the vector **n** (and similarly for **n**′), only two are independent. As independent variables we shall use n_y, n_z, n'_y, n'_z; then

$$n_x = \sqrt{1-n_y^2-n_z^2},\quad n'_x = \sqrt{1-n_y'^2-n_z'^2}.$$

Substituting these expressions in

$$d\chi = -x\,dn_x - y\,dn_y - z\,dn_z + x'\,dn'_x + y'\,dn'_y + z'\,dn'_z,$$

we obtain for the differential $d\chi$:

$$d\chi = -\left(y-\frac{n_y}{n_x}x\right)dn_y - \left(z-\frac{n_z}{n_x}x\right)dn_z + \left(y'-\frac{n'_y}{n'_x}x'\right)dn'_y + \left(z'-\frac{n'_z}{n'_x}x'\right)dn'_z.$$

From this we obtain, finally, the following equations:

$$\begin{aligned} y-\frac{n_y}{n_x}x &= -\frac{\partial\chi}{\partial n_y}, & z-\frac{n_z}{n_x}x &= -\frac{\partial\chi}{\partial n_z}, \\ y'-\frac{n'_y}{n'_x}x' &= \frac{\partial\chi}{\partial n'_y}, & z'-\frac{n'_z}{n'_x}x' &= \frac{\partial\chi}{\partial n'_z}, \end{aligned} \tag{55.6}$$

which is the relation sought between **n**, **n**′, **r**, **r**′. The function χ characterizes the special properties of the body through which the rays pass (or the properties of the field, in the case of the motion of a charged particle).

For fixed values of **n**, **n**′, each of the two pairs of equations (55.6) represent a straight line. These lines are precisely the rays before and after passage through the optical system. Thus the equation (55.6) directly determines the path of the ray on the two sides of the optical system.

§ 56. Narrow bundles of rays

In studying the passage of beams of rays through optical systems, special interest attaches to bundles whose rays all pass through one point (such bundles are said to be *homocentric*).

After passage through an optical system, homocentric bundles in general cease to be homocentric, i.e., after passing through a body the rays no longer come together in any one point. Only in exceptional cases will the rays starting from a luminous point come together after passage through an optical system and all meet at one point (the image of the luminous point).†

One can show (see § 57) that the only case for which all homocentric bundles remain strictly homocentric after passage through the optical system

† The point of intersection can lie either on the rays themselves or on their continuations; depending on this, the image is said to be *real* or *virtual*.

is the case of identical imaging, i.e., the case where the optical system gives for any object an image identical with it in form and dimensions (in other words, the image differs from the object only in its position or orientation, or is mirror inverted).

Thus no optical system can give a completely sharp image of an object (having finite dimensions) except in the trivial case of identical imaging.† Only approximate, but not completely sharp images can be produced of an extended body, in any case other than for identical imaging.

The most important case where there is approximate transition of homocentric bundles into homocentric bundles is that of sufficiently narrow beams (i.e. beams with a small opening angle) passing close to a particular line (for the given optical system). This line is called the *optic axis* of the system.

Nevertheless, we must note that even infinitely narrow bundles of rays (in the three-dimensional case) are in general not homocentric; we have seen (Fig. 7) that even in such a bundle different rays intersect at different points (this phenomenon is called *astigmatism*). Exceptions are those points of the wave surface at which the two principal radii of curvature are equal — a small region of the surface in the neighborhood of such points can be considered as spherical, and the corresponding narrow bundle of rays is homocentric.

We consider an optical system having axial symmetry.‡ The axis of symmetry of the system is also its optical axis. The wave surface of a bundle of rays traveling along this axis also has axial symmetry; as we know, surfaces of rotation have equal radii of curvature at their points of intersection with the symmetry axis. Therefore a narrow bundle moving in this direction remains homocentric.

To obtain completely quantitative relations, determining image formation with the aid of narrow bundles, passing through an axially-symmetric optical system, we use the general equations (55.6) after determining first of all the form of the function χ in the case under consideration.

Since the bundles of rays are narrow and move in the neigborhood of the optical axis, the vectors **n**, **n**$'$ for each bundle are directed almost along this axis. If we choose the optical axis as the X axis, then the components n_y, n_z, n'_y, n'_z will be small compared with unity. As for the components n_x, n'_x; $n_x \approx 1$ and n'_x can be approximately equal to either $+1$ or -1. In the first case the rays continue to travel almost in their original direction, emerging into the space on the other side of the optical system, which in this case

† Such imaging can be produced with a plane mirror.

‡ It can be shown that the problem of image formation with the aid of narrow bundles, moving in the neighborhood of the optical axis in a nonaxially-symmetric system, can be reduced to image formation in an axially-symmetric system plus a subsequent rotation of the image thus obtained, relative to the object.

is called a *lens*. In the second the rays change their direction to almost the reverse; such an optical system is called a *mirror*.

Making use of the smallness of n_y, n_z, n'_y, n'_z, we expand the angular eikonal $\chi(n_y, n_z, n'_y, n'_z)$ in series and stop at the first terms. Because of the axial symmetry of the whole system, χ must be invariant with respect to rotations of the coordinate system around the optical axis. From this it is clear that in the expansion of χ there can be no terms of first order, proportional to the first powers of the y- and z-components of the vectors $\mathbf{n}$ and $\mathbf{n}'$; such terms would not have the required invariance. The terms of second order which have the required property are the squares $\mathbf{n}^2$ and $\mathbf{n}'^2$ and the scalar product $\mathbf{n}\cdot\mathbf{n}'$. Thus, to terms of second order, the angular eikonal of an axially-symmetric optical system has the form

$$\chi = \text{const} + \frac{g}{2}(n_y^2+n_z^2) + f(n_y n'_y + n_z n'_z) + \frac{h}{2}(n'^2_y + n'^2_z), \tag{56.1}$$

where f, g, h are constants.

For definiteness, we now consider a lens, so that we set $n'_x \approx 1$; for a mirror, as we shall show later, all the formulas have a similar appearance. Now substituting the expression (56.1) in the general equations (55.6), we obtain:

$$\begin{aligned} n_y(x-g) - fn'_y &= y, \quad & fn_y + n'_y(x'+h) &= y', \\ n_z(x-g) - fn'_z &= z, \quad & fn_z + n'_z(x'+h) &= z'. \end{aligned} \tag{56.2}$$

We consider a homocentric bundle emanating from the point x, y, z; let the point x', y', z' be the point in which all the rays of the bundle intersect after passing through the lens. If the first and second pairs of equations (56.2) were independent, then these four equations, for given x, y, z, x', y', z', would determine one definite set of values n_y, n_z, n'_y, n'_z, that is, there would be just *one* ray starting from the point x, y, z, which would pass through the point x', y', z'. In order that all rays starting from x, y, z shall pass through x', y', z', it is consequently necessary that the equations (56.2) not be independent, that is, one pair of these equations must be a consequence of the other. The necessary condition for this dependence is that the coefficients in the one pair of equations be proportional to the coefficients of the other pair. Thus we must have

$$\frac{x-g}{f} = -\frac{f}{x'+h} = \frac{y}{y'} = \frac{z}{z'}. \tag{56.3}$$

In particular,

$$(x-g)(x'+h) = -f^2. \tag{56.4}$$

The equations we have obtained give the required connection between the coordinates of the image and object for image formation using narrow bundles.

The points $x = g$ and $x = -h$ on the optical axis are called the *principal foci* of the optical system. Let us consider bundles of rays parallel to the optical axis. The source point of such rays is, clearly, located at infinity on the optical axis, that is, $x = \infty$. From (56.3) we see that in this case, $x' = -h$. Thus a parallel bundle of rays, after passage through the optical system, intersects at the principal focus. Conversely, a bundle of rays emerging from the principal focus becomes parallel after passage through the system.

In the equation (56.3) the coordinates x and x' are measured from the same origin of coordinates, lying on the optical axis. It is, however, more convenient to measure the coordinates of object and image from different origins, choosing them at the corresponding principal foci. As positive direction of the coordinates we choose the direction from the corresponding focus toward the side to which the light travels. Designating the new coordinates of object and image by capital letters, we have

$$X = x-g,\ X' = x'+h,\ Y = y,\ Y' = y',\ Z = z,\ Z' = z'.$$

The equations of image formation (56.3) and (56.4) in the new coordinates take the form

$$XX' = -f^2, \tag{56.5}$$

$$\frac{Y'}{Y} = \frac{Z'}{Z} = \frac{f}{X} = -\frac{X'}{f}. \tag{56.6}$$

The quantity f is called the *principal focal length* of the system.

The ratio Y'/Y is called the *lateral magnification*. As for the *longitudinal magnification*, since the coordinates are not simply proportional to each other, it must be written in differential form, comparing the length of an element of the object (along the direction of the axis) with the length of the corresponding element in the image. From (56.5) we get for the "longitudinal magnification"

$$\left|\frac{dX'}{dX}\right| = \frac{f^2}{X^2} = \left(\frac{Y'}{Y}\right)^2. \tag{56.7}$$

We see from this that even for an infinitely small object, it is impossible to obtain a geometrically similar image. The longitudinal magnification is never equal to the transverse (except in the trivial case of identical imaging).

A bundle passing through the point $X = f$ on the optical axis intersects once more at the point $X' = -f$ on the axis; these two points are called *principal points*. From equation (56.2) ($n_y X - fn'_y = Y$, $n_z X - fn'_z = Z$) it is clear that in this case ($X = f$, $Y = Z = 0$), we have the equations $n_y = n'_y$, $n_z = n'_z$. Thus every ray starting from a principal point crosses the optical axis again at the other principal point in a direction parallel to its original direction.

If the coordinates of object and image are measured from the principal points (and not from the principal foci), then for these coordinates ξ and ξ', we have

$$\xi' = X'+f,\ \xi = X-f.$$

Substituting in (56.5) it is easy to obtain the equations of image formation in the form

$$\frac{1}{\xi}-\frac{1}{\xi'} = -\frac{1}{f}. \tag{56.8}$$

One can show that for an optical system with small thickness (for example, a mirror or a thin lens), the two principal points almost coincide. In this case the equation (56.8) is particularly convenient, since in it ξ and ξ' are then measured practically from one and the same point.

If the focal distance is positive, then objects located in front of the focus ($X > 0$) are imaged erect ($Y'/Y > 0$); such optical systems are said to be *converging*. If $f < 0$, then for $X > 0$ we have $Y'/Y < 0$, that is, the object is imaged in inverted form; such systems are said to be *diverging*.

There is one limiting case of image formation which is not contained in the formulas (56.8); this is the case where all three coefficients f, g, h are infinite (i.e., the optical system has an infinite focal distance and its principal foci are located at infinity). Going to the limit of infinite f, g, h in (56.4) we obtain

$$x' = \frac{h}{g}x+\frac{f^2-gh}{g}.$$

Since we are interested only in the case where the object and its image are located at finite distances from the optical system, f, g, h must approach infinity in such fashion that the ratios h/g, $(f^2-gh)/g$ are finite. Denoting them, respectively, by α^2 and β, we have

$$x' = \alpha^2 x+\beta.$$

For the other two coordinates we now have from the general equation (56.7):

$$\frac{y'}{y} = \frac{z'}{z} = \alpha.$$

Finally, again measuring the coordinates x and x' from different origins, namely from some arbitrary point on the axis and from the image of this point, respectively, we finally obtain the equations of image formation in the simple form

$$X' = \alpha^2 X,\ Y' = \pm\alpha Y,\ Z' = \pm\alpha Z. \tag{56.9}$$

Thus the longitudinal and transverse magnifications are constants (but not equal to each other). This case of image formation is called *telescopic*.

All the equations (56.5) through (56.9), derived by us for lenses, apply equally to mirrors, and even to an optical system without axial symmetry, if only the image formation occurs by means of narrow bundles of rays traveling near the optical axis. In this, the reference points for the x coordinates of object and image must always be chosen along the optical axis from corresponding points (principal foci or principal points) in the direction of propagation of the ray. In doing this, we must keep in mind that for an optical system not possessing axial symmetry, the directions of the optical axis in front of and beyond the system do not lie in the same plane.

PROBLEM

1. Find the focal distance for image formation with the aid of two axially-symmetric optical systems whose optical axes coincide.

Solution: Let f_1 and f_2 be the focal lengths of the two systems. For each system separately, we have

$$X_1X_1' = -f_1^2, \quad X_2X_2' = -f_2^2.$$

Since the image produced by the first system acts as the object for the second, then denoting by l the distance between the rear principal focus of the first system and the front focus of the second, we have $X_2 = X_1' - l$; expressing X_2' in terms of X_1, we obtain

$$X_2' = \frac{X_1f_2^2}{f_1^2+lX_1}$$

or

$$\left(X_1+\frac{f_1^2}{l}\right)\left(X_2'-\frac{f_2^2}{l}\right) = -\left(\frac{f_1f_2}{l}\right)^2,$$

from which it is clear that the principal foci of the composite system are located at the points $X_1 = -f_1^2/l, X_2' = f_2^2/l$ and the focal length is

$$f = -\frac{f_1f_2}{l}$$

(to choose the sign of this expression, we must write the corresponding equation for the transverse magnification).

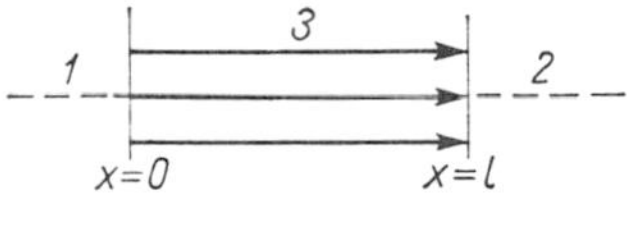

FIG. 8.

In case $l = 0$, the focal length $f = \infty$, that is, the composite system gives telescopic image formation. In this case we have $X_2' = X_1(f_2/f_1)^2$, that is, the parameter α in the general formula (56.9) is $\alpha = f_2/f_1$.

2. Find the focal length for charged particles of a "magnetic lens" in the form of a longitudinal homogeneous field in the section of length l (Fig. 8).†

---

† This might be the field inside a long solenoid, when we neglect the disturbance of the homogeneity of the field near the ends of the solenoid.

Solution: The kinetic energy of the particle is conserved during its motion in a magnetic field; therefore the Hamilton-Jacobi equation for the reduced action S_0 (**r**) (where the total action is $S = -\mathcal{E}t+S_0$) is

$$\left(\nabla S_0-\frac{e}{c}\mathbf{A}\right)^2 = p^2,$$

where

$$p^2 = \frac{\mathcal{E}^2}{c^2}-m^2c^2 = \text{const.}$$

Using formula (19.4) for the vector potential of the homogeneous magnetic field, choosing the x axis along the field direction and considering this axis as the optical axis of an axially-symmetric optical system, we get the Hamilton-Jacobi equation in the form:

$$\left(\frac{\partial S_0}{\partial x}\right)^2+\left(\frac{\partial S_0}{\partial r}\right)^2+\frac{e^2}{4c^2}H^2r^2 = p^2, \tag{1}$$

where r is the distance from the x axis, and S_0 is a function of x and r.

For narrow beams of particles propagating close to the optical axis, the coordinate r is small, so that accordingly we try to find S_0 as a power series in r. The first two terms of this series are

$$S_0 = px+\tfrac{1}{2}\sigma(x)r^2, \tag{2}$$

where σ (x) satisfies the equation

$$p\sigma'(x)+\sigma^2+\frac{e^2}{4c^2}H^2 = 0. \tag{3}$$

In region 1 in front of the lens, we have:

$$\sigma^{(1)} = \frac{p}{x-x_1},$$

where $x_1 < 0$ is a constant. This solution corresponds to a free beam of particles, emerging along straight line rays from the point $x = x_1$ on the optical axis in region 1. In fact, the action function for the free motion of a particle with a momentum p in a direction out from the point $x = x_1$ is

$$S_0 = p\sqrt{r^2+(x-x_1)^2}\simeq p(x-x_1)+\frac{pr^2}{2(x-x_1)}.$$

Similarly, in region 2 behind the lens we write:

$$\sigma^{(2)} = \frac{p}{x-x_2},$$

where the constant x_2 is the coordinate of the image of the point x_1.

In region 3 inside the lens, equation (3) is solved by separation of variables, and gives:

$$\sigma^{(3)} = \frac{eH}{2c}\cot\left(\frac{eH}{2cp}x+C\right),$$

where C is an arbitrary constant.

The constant C and x_2 (for given x_1) are determined by the requirements of continuity of $\sigma(x)$ for $x = 0$ and $x = l$:

$$-\frac{p}{x_1} = \frac{eH}{2c}\cot C, \qquad \frac{p}{l-x_2} = \frac{eH}{2c}\cot\left(\frac{eH}{2cp}l+C\right).$$

Eliminating the constant C from these equations, we find:

$$(x_1-g)(x_2+h) = -f^2,$$

where†

$$g = \frac{2cp}{eH}\cot\frac{eHl}{2cp}, \qquad h = g-l,$$

$$f = \frac{2cp}{eH\sin\dfrac{eHl}{2cp}}.$$

§ 57. Image formation with broad bundles of rays

The formation of images with the aid of narrow bundles of rays, which was considered in the previous section, is approximate; it is the more exact (i.e., the sharper) the narrower the bundles. We now go over to the question of image formation with bundles of rays of arbitrary breadth.

In contrast to the formation of an image of an object by narrow beams, which can be achieved for any optical system having axial symmetry, image formation with broad beams is possible only for specially constituted optical systems. Even with this limitation, as already pointed out in § 56, image formation is not possible for all points in space.

The later derivations are based on the following essential remark. Suppose that all rays, starting from a certain point O and traveling through the optical system, intersect again at some other point O'. It is easy to see that the optical path length ψ is the same for all these rays. In the neighborhood of each of the points O, O', the wave surfaces for the rays intersecting in them are spheres with centers at O and O', respectively, and, in the limit as we approach O and O', degenerate to these points. But the wave surfaces are the surfaces of constant phase, and therefore the change in phase along different rays, between their points of intersection with two given wave surfaces, is the same. From what has been said, it follows that the total change in phase between the points O and O' is the same (for the different rays).

Let us consider the conditions which must be fulfilled in order to have formation of an image of a small line segment using broad beams; the image is then also a small line segment. We choose the directions of these segments as the directions of the ξ and ξ' axes, with origins at any two corresponding points O and O' of the object and image. Let ψ be the optical path length for the rays starting from O and reaching O'. For the rays starting from a point infinitely near to O with coordinate $d\xi$, and arriving at a point of the image with coordinate $d\xi'$, the optical path length is $\psi+d\psi$, where

$$d\psi = \frac{\partial\psi}{\partial\xi}d\xi+\frac{\partial\psi}{\partial\xi'}d\xi'.$$

† The value of f is given with the correct sign. However, to show this requires additional investigation.

We introduce the "magnification"

$$\alpha_\xi = \frac{d\xi}{d\xi'}$$

as the ratio of the length $d\xi'$ of the element of the image to the length $d\xi$ of the imaged element. Because of the smallness of the line segment which is being imaged, the quantity α can be considered constant along the line segment. Writing, as usual, $\partial\psi/\partial\xi = -n_\xi$, $\partial\psi/\partial\xi' = n'_\xi$ (n_ξ, n'_ξ are the cosines of the angles between the directions of the ray and the corresponding axes ξ and ξ'), we obtain

$$d\psi = (\alpha_\xi n'_\xi - n_\xi)\, d\xi.$$

As for every pair of corresponding points of object and image, the optical path length $\psi + d\psi$ must be the same for all rays starting from the point $d\xi$ and arriving at the point $d\xi'$. From this we obtain the condition:

$$\alpha_\xi n'_\xi - n_\xi = \text{const.} \tag{57.1}$$

This is the condition we have been seeking, which the paths of the rays in the optical system must satisfy in order to have image formation for a small line segment using broad beams. The relation (57.1) must be fulfilled for all rays starting from the point O.

Let us apply this condition to image formation by means of an axially-symmetric optical system. We start with the image of a line segment coinciding with the optical axis (x axis); clearly the image also coincides with the axis. A ray moving along the optical axis ($n_x = 1$), because of the axial symmetry of the system, does not change its direction after passing through it, that is, n'_x is also 1. From this it follows that const in (57.1) is equal in this case to $\alpha_x - 1$, and we can rewrite (57.1) in the form

$$\frac{1-n_x}{1-n'_x} = \alpha_x.$$

Denoting by θ and θ' the angles subtended by the rays with the optical axis at points of the object and image, we have

$$1-n_x = 1-\cos\theta = 2\sin^2\frac{\theta}{2}, \quad 1-n'_x = 1-\cos\theta' = 2\sin^2\frac{\theta'}{2}.$$

Thus we obtain the condition for image formation in the form

$$\frac{\sin\frac{\theta}{2}}{\sin\frac{\theta'}{2}} = \text{const} = \sqrt{\alpha_x}. \tag{57.2}$$

Next, let us consider the imaging of a small portion of a plane perpendicular to the optical axis of an axially symmetric system; the image will obviously also be perpendicular to this axis. Applying (57.1) to an arbitrary segment lying in the plane which is to be imaged, we get:

$$\alpha_r \sin\theta' - \sin\theta = \text{const},$$

where θ and θ' are again the angles made by the beam with the optical axis. For rays emerging from the point of intersection of the object plane with the optical axis, and directed along this axis ($\theta = 0$), we must have $\theta' = 0$, because of symmetry. Therefore const is zero, and we obtain the condition for imaging in the form

$$\frac{\sin\theta}{\sin\theta'} = \text{const} = \alpha_r. \tag{57.3}$$

As for the formation of an image of a three-dimensional object using broad beams, it is easy to see that this is impossible even for a small volume, since the conditions (57.2) and (57.3) are incompatible.

§ 58. The limits of geometrical optics

From the definition of a monochromatic plane wave, its amplitude is the same everywhere and at all times. Such a wave is infinite in extent in all directions in space, and exists over the whole range of time from $-\infty$ to $+\infty$. Any wave whose amplitude is not constant everywhere at all times can only be more or less monochromatic. We now take up the question of the "degree of non-monochromaticity" of a wave.

Let us consider an electromagnetic wave whose amplitude at each point is a function of the time. Let ω_0 be some average frequency of the wave. Then the field of the wave, for example the electric field, at a given point has the form $\mathbf{E}_0(t)e^{i\omega_0 t}$. This field, although it is of course not monochromatic, can be expanded in monochromatic waves, that is, in a Fourier integral. The amplitude of the component in this expansion, with frequency ω, is proportional to the integral

$$\int_{-\infty}^{+\infty} \mathbf{E}_0(t)e^{i(\omega-\omega_0)t}\,dt.$$

The factor $e^{i(\omega-\omega_0)t}$ is a periodic function whose average value is zero. If E_0 were exactly constant, then the integral would be exactly zero, for $\omega \neq \omega_0$. If, however, $\mathbf{E}_0(t)$ is variable, but hardly changes over a time interval of order $1/(\omega-\omega_0)$, then the integral is almost equal to zero, the more exactly the slower the variation of $\mathbf{E}_0$. In order for the integral to be significantly different from zero, it is necessary that $\mathbf{E}_0(t)$ vary significantly over a time interval of the order of $1/(\omega-\omega_0)$.

We denote by Δt the order of magnitude of the time interval during which the amplitude of the wave at a given point in space changes significantly. From these considerations, it now follows that the frequencies deviating most from ω_0, which appear with reasonable intensity in the spectral resolution of this wave, are determined by the condition $1/(\omega-\omega_0) \sim \Delta t$. If we denote by $\Delta\omega$ the frequency interval (around the average frequency ω_0) which enters in the spectral resolution of the wave, then we have the relation

$$\Delta\omega\,\Delta t \sim 1. \tag{58.1}$$

We see that a wave is the more monochromatic (i.e., the smaller $\Delta\omega$) the larger Δt, i.e., the slower the variation of the amplitude at a given point in space.

Relations similar to (58.1) are easily derived for the wave vector. Let Δx, Δy, Δz be the orders of magnitude of distances along the X, Y, Z axes, in which the wave amplitude changes significantly. At a given time, the field of the wave as a function of the coordinates has the form

$$\mathbf{E}_0(\mathbf{r})\,e^{i\mathbf{k}_0\cdot\mathbf{r}},$$

where $\mathbf{k}_0$ is some average value of the wave vector. By a completely analogous derivation to that for (58.1) we can obtain the interval $\Delta\mathbf{k}$ of values contained in the expansion of the wave into a Fourier integral:

$$\Delta k_x\,\Delta x \sim 1, \quad \Delta k_y\,\Delta y \sim 1, \quad \Delta k_z\,\Delta z \sim 1. \tag{58.2}$$

Let us consider, in particular, a wave which is radiated during a finite time interval. We denote by Δt the order of magnitude of this interval. The amplitude at a given point in space changes significantly during the time Δt in the course of which the wave travels completely past the point. Because of the relations (58.1) we can now say that the "lack of monochromaticity" of such a wave, $\Delta\omega$, cannot be smaller than $1/\Delta t$ (it can of course be larger):

$$\Delta\omega \gtrsim \frac{1}{\Delta t}. \tag{58.3}$$

Similarly, if Δx, Δy, Δz are the orders of magnitude of the extension of the wave in space, then for the spread in the values of components of the wave vector, entering in the resolution of the wave, we obtain

$$\Delta k_x \gtrsim \frac{1}{\Delta x}, \quad \Delta k_y \gtrsim \frac{1}{\Delta y}, \quad \Delta k_z \gtrsim \frac{1}{\Delta z}. \tag{58.4}$$

From these formulas it follows that if we have a beam of light of finite width, then the direction of propagation of the light in such a beam cannot be strictly constant. Taking the X axis along the (average) direction of light in the beam, we obtain

$$\theta_y \gtrsim \frac{1}{k\,\Delta y} \sim \frac{\lambda}{\Delta y}, \tag{58.5}$$

where θ_y is the order of magnitude of the deviation of the beam from its average direction in the XY plane and λ is the wavelength.

On the other hand, the formula (58.5) answers the question of the limit of sharpness of optical image formation. A beam of light whose rays, according to geometrical optics, would all intersect in a point, actually gives an image not in the form of a point but in the form of a spot. For the width Δ of this spot, we obtain, according to (58.5),

$$\Delta \sim \frac{1}{k\theta} \sim \frac{\lambda}{\theta}, \tag{58.6}$$

where θ is the opening angle of the beam. This formula can be applied not only to the image but also to the object. Namely, we can state that in observing a beam of light emerging from a luminous point, this point cannot be distinguished from a body of dimensions λ/θ. In this way formula (58.6) determines the limiting *resolving power* of a microscope. The minimum value of Δ, which is reached for $\theta \sim 1$, is λ, in complete agreement with the fact that the limit of geometrical optics is determined by the wavelength of the light.

Problem

Determine the order of magnitude of the smallest width of a light beam produced from a parallel beam at a distance l from a diaphragm.

Solution: Denoting the size of the aperture in the diaphragm by d, we have from (58.5) for the angle of deflection of the beam (the "diffraction angle"), λ/d, so that the width of the beam is of order $d+\frac{\lambda}{d}l$. The smallest value of this quantity is $2\sqrt{\lambda l}$.

§ 59. Diffraction

The laws of geometrical optics are strictly correct only in the ideal case when the wavelength can be considered to be infinitely small. The more poorly this condition is fulfilled, the greater are the deviations from geometrical optics. Phenomena which are the consequence of such deviations are called *diffraction phenomena*.

Diffraction phenomena can be observed, for example, if along the path of propagation of the light † there is an obstacle — an opaque body (we call it a *screen*) of arbitrary form or, for example, if the light passes through holes in opaque screens. If the laws of geometrical optics were strictly satisfied, there would be beyond the screen regions of "shadow" sharply delineated from regions where light falls. The diffraction has the consequence that, instead of a sharp boundary between light and shadow, there is a quite complex distribution of the intensity of the light. These diffraction phenomena appear the more strongly the smaller the dimensions of the screens and the apertures in them, or the greater the wavelength.

† In what follows, in discussing diffraction we shall talk of the diffraction of light; all these same considerations also apply, of course, to any electromagnetic wave.

The problem of the theory of diffraction consists in determining, for given positions and shapes of the objects (and locations of the light sources), the distribution of the light, that is, the electromagnetic field over all space. The exact solution of this problem is possible only through solution of the wave equation with suitable boundary conditions at the surface of the body, these conditions being determined also by the optical properties of the material. Such a solution usually presents great mathematical difficulties.

However, there is an approximate method which for many cases is a satisfactory solution of the problem of the distribution of light near the boundary between light and shadow. This method is applicable to cases of small deviation from geometrical optics, i.e., when firstly, the dimensions of all bodies are large compared with the wavelength (this requirement applies both to the dimensions of screens and apertures and also to the distances from the bodies to the points of emission and observation of the light); and secondly when there are only small deviations of the light from the directions of the rays given by geometrical optics.

Let us consider a screen with an aperture through which the light passes from given sources. Figure 9 shows the screen in profile (the heavy line); the light travels from left to right. We denote by u some one of the components of **E** or **H**. Here we shall understand u to mean a function only of the coordinates, i.e., without the factor $e^{-i\omega t}$ determining the time dependence.

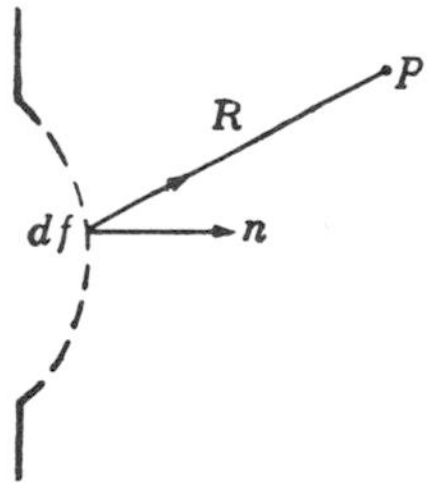

FIG. 9.

Our problem is to determine the light intensity, that is, the field u, at any point of observation P beyond the screen. For an approximate solution of this problem in cases where the deviations from geometrical optics are small, we may assume that at the points of the aperture the field is the same as it would have been in the absence of the screen. In other words, the values of the field here are those which follow directly from geometrical optics. At all points immediately behind the screen, the field can be set equal to zero. In this the properties of the screen (i.e., of the screen material) obviously play no part. It is also obvious that in the cases we are considering, what is important for the diffraction is only the shape of the edge of the aperture, while the shape of the opaque screen is unimportant.

We introduce some surface which covers the aperture in the screen and is bounded by its edges (a profile of such a surface is shown in Fig. 9 as a dashed line). We break up this surface into sections with area df, whose dimensions are small compared with the size of the aperture, but large compared with the wavelength of the light. We can then consider each of these sections through which the light passes as if it were itself a source of light waves spreading out on all sides from this section. We shall consider the field at the point P to be the result of superposition of the fields produced by all the sections df of the surface covering the aperture. (This is called *Huygens' principle.*)

The field produced at the point P by the section df is obviously proportional to the value u of the field at the section df itself (we recall that the field at df is assumed to be the same as it would have been in the absence of the screen). In addition, it is proportional to the projection df_n of the area df on the plane perpendicular to the direction n of the ray coming from the light source at df. This follows from the fact that no matter what shape the element df has, the same rays will pass through it provided its projection df_n remains fixed, and therefore its effect on the field at P will be the same.

Thus the field produced at the point P by the section df is proportional to $u\,df_n$. Furthermore, we must still take into account the change in the amplitude and phase of the wave during its propagation from df to P. The law of this change is determined by formula (54.3). Therefore $u\,df_n$ must be multiplied by $\frac{1}{R}e^{ikR}$ (where R is the distance from df to P, and k is the absolute value of the wave vector of the light), and we find that the required field is

$$au\frac{e^{ikR}}{R}df_n,$$

where a is an as yet unknown constant. The field at the point P, being the result of the addition of the fields produced by all the elements df, is consequently equal to

$$u_P = a\int u\frac{e^{ikR}}{R}df_n, \tag{59.1}$$

where the integral extends over the surface bounded by the edge of the aperture. In the approximation we are considering, this integral cannot, of course, depend on the form of this surface. Formula (59.1) is, obviously, applicable not only to diffraction by an aperture in a screen, but also to diffraction by a screen around which the light passes freely. In that case the surface of integration in (59.1) extends on all sides from the edge of the screen.

To determine the constant a, we consider a plane wave propagating along the X axis; the wave surfaces are parallel to the plane YZ. Let u be the value of the field in the YZ plane. Then at the point P, which we choose on the X axis, the field is equal to $u_p = ue^{ikx}$. On the other hand, the field at the point P can be determined starting from formula (59.1), choosing as surface of integration, for example, the YZ plane. In doing this, because of the smallness of the angle of diffraction, only those points of the YZ plane are important in the integral which lie close to the origin, i.e., the points for which $y, z \ll x$ (x is the coordinate of the point P). Then

$$R = \sqrt{x^2+y^2+z^2} \approx x + \frac{y^2+z^2}{2x},$$

and (59.1)

$$u_p = \frac{a}{x} \int\int_{-\infty}^{+\infty} ue^{ik\left(x+\frac{y^2+z^2}{2x}\right)} dy\, dz.$$

Here u is a constant (the field in the YZ plane); in the factor $1/R$, we can put $R \simeq x = \text{const}$. Thus,

$$u_p = au\frac{e^{ikx}}{x} \int_{-\infty}^{+\infty} dy\, e^{ik\frac{y^2}{2x}} \int_{-\infty}^{+\infty} dz\, e^{ik\frac{z^2}{2x}}.$$

By the substitution $y = \xi\sqrt{2x/k}$ these two integrals can be transformed to the integral

$$\int_{-\infty}^{+\infty} e^{i\xi^2}\, d\xi = \int_{-\infty}^{+\infty} \cos \xi^2\, d\xi + i \int_{-\infty}^{+\infty} \sin^2 \xi\, d\xi = \sqrt{\frac{\pi}{2}}(1+i),$$

and we get

$$u_p = aue^{ikx}\frac{2i\pi}{k}.$$

On the other hand, $u_p = ue^{ikx}$, and consequently

$$a = \frac{k}{2\pi i}.$$

Substituting in (59.1), we obtain the solution to our problem in the form

$$u_p = \int \frac{ku}{2\pi i R} e^{ikR}\, df_n. \tag{59.2}$$

In deriving formula (59.2), the light source was assumed to be essentially a point, and the light was assumed to be strictly monochromatic. The case of a real, extended source, which emits non-monochromatic light, does not, however, require special treatment. Because of the complete independence (incoherence) of the light emitted by different points of the source, and the incoherence of the different spectral components of the emitted light, the total diffraction pattern is simply the sum of the intensity distributions obtained from the diffraction of the independent components of the light.

Let us apply formula (59.2) to the solution of the problem of the change in phase of a ray on passing through its point of tangency to the caustic (see the end of § 54). We choose as our surface of integration in (59.2) any wave surface, and determine the field u_p at a point P, lying on some given ray at a distance x from its point of intersection with the wave surface we have chosen (we choose this point as coordinate origin O, and as YZ plane the plane tangent to the wave surface at the point O). In the integration of (59.2) only a small area of the wave surface in the neighborhood of O is important. If the XY and XZ planes are chosen to coincide with the principal planes of curvature of the wave surface at the point O, then near this point the equation of the surface is

$$X = \frac{y^2}{2R_1} + \frac{z^2}{2R_2},$$

where R_1 and R_2 are the radii of curvature. The distance R from the point on the wave surface with coordinates X, y, z, to the point P with coordinates x, 0, 0, is

$$R = \sqrt{(x-X)^2+y^2+z^2} \simeq x + \frac{y^2}{2}\left(\frac{1}{x}-\frac{1}{R_1}\right) + \frac{z^2}{2}\left(\frac{1}{x}-\frac{1}{R_2}\right).$$

On the wave surface, the field u can be considered constant; the same applies to the factor $1/R$. Since we are interested only in changes in the phase of the wave, we drop coefficients and write simply

$$u_p \sim \frac{1}{i}\int e^{ikR}\,df_n \simeq \frac{e^{ikx}}{i}\int_{-\infty}^{+\infty} dy\, e^{ik\frac{y^2}{2}\left(\frac{1}{x}-\frac{1}{R_1}\right)} \int_{-\infty}^{+\infty} dz\, e^{ik\frac{z^2}{2}\left(\frac{1}{x}-\frac{1}{R_2}\right)}. \tag{59.3}$$

The centers of curvature of the wave surface lie on the ray we are considering, at the points $x = R_1$ and $x = R_2$; these are the points where the ray is tangent to the caustic. Suppose $R_2 < R_1$. For $x < R_2$, the coefficients of i in the exponentials appearing in the two integrands are positive, and each of these integrals is proportional to $(1+i)$. Therefore on the part of the ray before its first tangency to the caustic, we have $u_p \sim e^{ikx}$. For $R_2 < x < R_1$, that is, on the segment of the ray between its two points of tangency, the integral over y is proportional to $1+i$, but the integral over z is proportional to $1-i$, so that their product does not contain i. Thus we have here $u_p \sim -ie^{ikx} = e^{i\left(kx-\frac{\pi}{2}\right)}$, that is, as the ray passes in the neighborhood of the first caustic, its phase undergoes an additional change of $-\pi/2$. Finally, for $x > R_1$, we have $u_p \sim -e^{ikx} = e^{i(kx-\pi)}$, that is, on passing in the neighborhood of the second caustic, the phase once more changes by $-\pi/2$.

Problem

Determine the distribution of the light intensity in the neighborhood of the point where the ray is tangent to the caustic.

Solution: To solve the problem, we use formula (59.2), taking the integral in it over any wave surface which is sufficiently far from the point of tangency of the ray to the caustic. In Fig. 10, *ab* is a section of this wave surface, and *a′b′* is a section of the caustic; *a′b′* is the

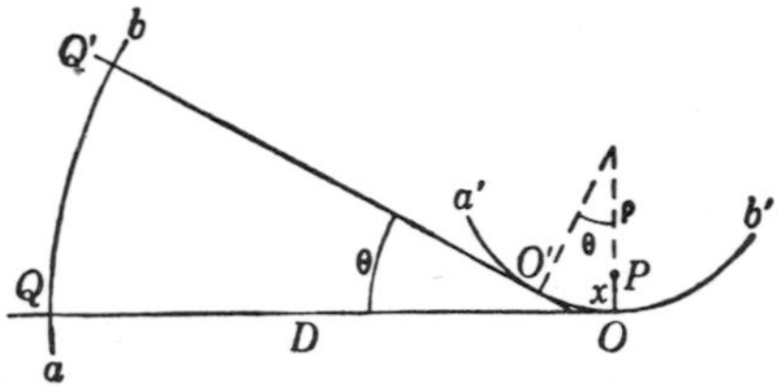

Fig. 10.

evolute of the curve *ab*. We are interested in the intensity distribution in the neighborhood of the point O where the ray QO is tangent to the caustic; we assume the length D of the segment QO of the ray to be large. We denote by x the distance from the point O along the normal to the caustic, and assume positive values x for points on the normal in the direction of the center of curvature.

The integrand in (59.2) is a function of the distance R from the arbitrary point Q' on the wave surface to the point P. From a well-known property of the evolute, the sum of the length of the segment $Q'O'$ of the tangent at the point O' and the length of the arc OO' is equal to the length QO of the tangent at the point O. For points O and O' which are near to each other we have $OO' = \theta\varrho$ (ϱ is the radius of curvature of the caustic at the point O). Therefore the length $Q'O' = D-\theta\varrho$. The distance $Q'O$ (along a straight line) is approximately (the angle θ is assumed to be small)†

$$Q'O \cong Q'O'+\varrho\sin\theta = D-\theta\varrho+\varrho\sin\theta \cong D-\varrho\frac{\theta^3}{6}.$$

Finally, the distance $R = Q'P$† is equal to $R = Q'O - x\sin\theta \cong Q'O - x\theta$, that is,

$$R \cong D - x\theta - \tfrac{1}{6}\varrho\theta^3.$$

Substituting this expression in (59.2), we obtain

$$u_P \sim \int_{-\infty}^{+\infty} e^{-ikx\theta - i\frac{k\rho}{6}\theta^3}\, d\theta = 2\int_0^{\infty} \cos\left(kx\theta+\frac{k\varrho}{6}\theta^3\right) d\theta$$

(the slowly varying factor $1/R$ in the integrand is unimportant compared with the exponential

---

† We here use an approximate formula for the absolute value of the sum of two vectors, one of which is large in absolute value compared with the other:

$$|\mathbf{A}+\mathbf{a}| \simeq A + a_A$$

($A \gg a$; a_A is the projection of the vector $\mathbf{a}$ on the direction of the vector $\mathbf{A}$).

factor, so we assume it constant). Introducing the new integration variable $\xi = \left(\frac{k\varrho}{2}\right)^{\frac{1}{3}}\theta$, we get

$$u_p \sim \Phi\left(x\sqrt[3]{\frac{2k^2}{\varrho}}\right),$$

where $\Phi(t)$ is the Airy function.†

For the intensity $I \sim |u_p|^2$, we write:

$$I = 2A\left(\frac{2k^2}{\varrho}\right)^{\frac{1}{6}}\Phi^2\left(x\sqrt[3]{\frac{2k^2}{\varrho}}\right)$$

(concerning the choice of the constant factor, cf. below).

For large positive values of x, we have from this the asymptotic formula

$$I \approx \frac{A}{2\sqrt{x}}\exp\left\{-\frac{4x^{\frac{3}{2}}}{3}\sqrt{\frac{2k^2}{\varrho}}\right\},$$

that is, the intensity drops exponentially (shadow region). For large negative values of x we have

$$I \approx \frac{2A}{\sqrt{-x}}\sin^2\left\{\frac{2(-x)^{\frac{3}{2}}}{3}\sqrt{\frac{2k^2}{\varrho}}+\frac{\pi}{4}\right\},$$

that is, the intensity oscillates rapidly; its average value over these oscillations is

$$\bar{I} = \frac{A}{\sqrt{-x}}.$$

From this the meaning of the constant A is clear — it is the intensity far from the caustic which would be obtained from geometrical optics neglecting diffraction effects.

---

† Following V. A. Fock (*Tables of the Airy Function*, Moscow, 1946), we define the Airy function $\Phi(t)$ as

$$\Phi(t) = \frac{1}{\sqrt{\pi}}\int_0^\infty \cos\left(\frac{\xi^3}{3}+\xi t\right)d\xi.$$

For large positive values of the argument, the asymptotic expression for $\Phi(t)$ is

$$\Phi(t) \approx \frac{1}{2t^{\frac{1}{4}}}e^{-\frac{2}{3}t^{3/2}},$$

that is, $\Phi(t)$ goes exponentially to zero. For large negative values of t, we have the formula

$$\Phi(t) \approx \frac{1}{(-t)^{\frac{1}{4}}}\sin\left(\frac{2}{3}(-t)^{\frac{3}{2}}+\frac{\pi}{4}\right),$$

that is $\Phi(t)$ oscillates with an amplitude which is inversely proportional to $(-t)^{\frac{1}{4}}$.

The function $\Phi(t)$ satisfies the differential equation

$$\Phi'' - t\Phi = 0$$

and is that combination of the two independent solutions which remains finite for all t (including $t \to \infty$).

The function $\Phi(t)$ attains its largest value, 0.949, for $t = -1.02$; correspondingly, the maximum intensity is reached at $x(2k^2/\varrho)^{\frac{1}{3}} = -1.02$, where

$$I = 2.03\, Ak^{\frac{1}{3}}\varrho^{-\frac{1}{6}}.$$

At the point where the ray is tangent to the caustic ($x = 0$), we have $I = 0.89Ak^{+\frac{1}{3}}\varrho^{-\frac{1}{6}}$ [since $\Phi(0) = 0.629$].

Thus at points of the caustic the intensity is proportional to $k^{\frac{1}{3}}$, that is, to $\lambda^{-\frac{1}{3}}$ (λ is the wavelength). For $\lambda \to 0$, the intensity goes to infinity, as it should (see § 54).

§ 60. Fresnel diffraction

If the light source and the point P at which we determine the intensity of the light are located at finite distances from the screen, then in determining the intensity at the point P, only those points are important which lie in a small region of the wave surface over which we integrate in (59.2) — the region which lies on the line joining the source and the point P. In fact, since the deviations from geometrical optics are small, the intensity of the light arriving at P from various points of the wave surface decreases very rapidly as we move away from this line. Diffraction phenomena in which only a small portion of the wave surface plays a role are called *Fresnel diffraction* phenomena.

Let us consider the Fresnel diffraction by a screen. From what we have just said, only a small region at the edge of the screen is important for this diffraction. But over sufficiently small regions, the edge of the screen can be considered to be a straight line. We shall therefore, from now on, understand the edge of the screen to mean just such a small straight line segment.

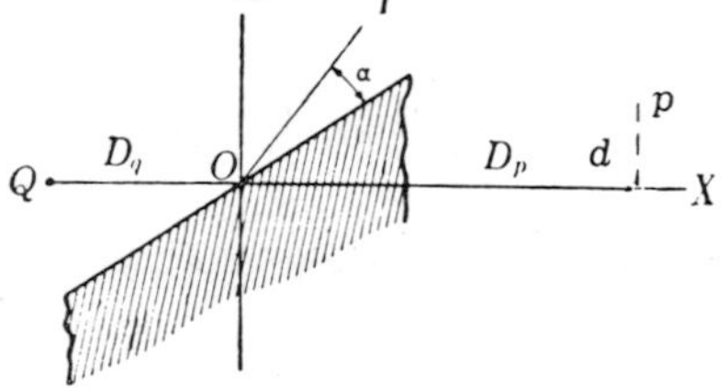

FIG. 11.

We choose as the XY plane a plane passing through the light source Q (Fig. 11) and through the line of the edge of the screen. Perpendicular to this, we choose the plane XZ so that it passes through the point Q and the point of observation P, at which we try to determine the light intensity. Finally, we choose the origin of coordinates O on the line of the edge of the screen, after which the positions of all three axes are completely determined.

Let the distance from the light source Q to the origin be D_q. We denote the x-coordinate of the point of observation P by D_p, and its z-coordinate, i.e., its distance from the XY plane, by d. According to geometrical optics, the light should pass only through points lying above the XY plane; the region below the XY plane is the region which according to geometrical optics should be in shadow (region of geometrical shadow).

We now determine the distribution of light intensity on the screen near the edge of the geometrical shadow, i.e., for values of d small compared with D_p and D_q. A negative d means that the point P is located within the geometrical shadow.

As the surface of integration in (59.2) we choose the half-plane passing through the line of the edge of the screen and perpendicular to the XY plane. The coordinates x and y of points on this surface are related by the equation $x = y \tan\alpha$ (α is the angle between the line of the edge of the screen and the Y axis), and the z coordinate is positive. The field of the wave produced by the source Q, at the distance R_q from it, is proportional to the factor e^{ikR_q}. Therefore the field u on the surface of integration is proportional to

$$u \sim \exp\{ik\sqrt{y^2+z^2+(D_q+y\tan\alpha)^2}\}.$$

In the integral (59.2) we must now substitute for R,

$$R = \sqrt{y^2+(z-d)^2+(D_p-y\tan\alpha)^2}.$$

The slowly varying factors in the integrand are unimportant compared with the exponential. Therefore we may consider $1/R$ constant, and write $dy\,dz$ in place of df_n. We then find that the field at the point P is

$$u_p \sim \int_{-\infty}^{+\infty}\int_{0}^{\infty} \exp\{ik(\sqrt{(D_q+y\tan\alpha)^2+y^2+z^2} + \sqrt{(D_p-y\tan\alpha)^2+(z-d)^2+y^2})\}\,dy\,dz. \quad (60.1)$$

As we have already said, the light passing through the point P comes mainly from points of the plane of integration which are in the neighborhood of O. Therefore in the integral (60.1) only values of y and z which are small (compared with D_q and D_p) are important. For this reason we can write

$$\sqrt{(D_q+y\tan\alpha)^2+y^2+z^2} \simeq D+\frac{y^2\sec^2\alpha+z^2}{2D_q}+y\tan\alpha,$$

$$\sqrt{(D_p-y\tan\alpha)^2+(z-d)^2+y^2} \simeq D_p+\frac{(z-d)^2+y^2\sec^2\alpha}{2D_p}-y\tan\alpha.$$

We substitute this in (60.1). Since we are interested only in the field as a function of the distance d, the constant factor $\exp\{ik(D_p+D_q)\}$ can be omitted;

the integral over y also gives an expression not containing d, so we omit it also. We then find

$$u_p \sim \int_0^\infty \exp\left\{ik\left(\frac{1}{2D_q}z^2+\frac{1}{2D_p}(z-d)^2\right)\right\}dz.$$

This expression can also be written in the form

$$u_p \sim \exp\left\{ik\frac{d^2}{2(D_p+D_q)}\right\}\int_0^\infty \exp\left\{ik\frac{\frac{1}{2}\left[\left(\frac{1}{D_p}+\frac{1}{D_q}\right)z-\frac{d}{D_p}\right]^2}{\frac{1}{D_p}+\frac{1}{D_q}}\right\}dz. \quad (60.2)$$

The light intensity is determined by the square of the field, that is, by the square modulus $|u_p|^2$. Therefore, when calculating the intensity, the factor standing in front of the integral disappears, since when multiplied by the complex conjugate expression it gives unity.

An obvious substitution reduces the integral to

$$u_p \sim \int_{-w}^{\infty} e^{i\eta^2}\,d\eta, \quad (60.3)$$

where

$$w = d\sqrt{\frac{kD_q}{2D_p(D_q+D_p)}}. \quad (60.4)$$

Thus, the intensity I at the point P is:

$$I=\frac{I_0}{2}\left|\sqrt{\frac{2}{\pi}}\int_{-w}^{\infty} e^{i\eta^2}\,d\eta\right|^2 = \frac{I_0}{2}\left\{\left(C(w)+\frac{1}{2}\right)^2+\left(S(w)+\frac{1}{2}\right)^2\right\}, \quad (60.5)$$

where

$$C(w)=\sqrt{\frac{2}{\pi}}\int_0^w \cos\eta^2\,d\eta,\quad S(w)=\sqrt{\frac{2}{\pi}}\int_0^w \sin\eta^2\,d\eta$$

are called the *Fresnel integrals*. Formula (60.5) solves our problem of determining the light intensity as a function of d. The quantity I_0 is the intensity in the illuminated region at points not too near the edge of the shadow; more precisely, at those points with $w \gg 1$ ($C(\infty)=S(\infty)=\frac{1}{2}$ in the limit $w\to\infty$).

The region of geometrical shadow corresponds to negative w. It is easy to find the asymptotic form of the function $I(w)$ for large negative values of w. To do this we proceed as follows. Integrating by parts, we have

$$\int_{|w|}^{\infty} e^{i\eta^2}\,d\eta = -\frac{1}{2i|w|}e^{iw^2}+\frac{1}{2i}\int_{|w|}^{\infty} e^{i\eta^2}\frac{d\eta}{\eta^2}.$$

Integrating by parts once more on the right side of the equation and repeating this process, we obtain an expansion in powers of $1/|w|$:

$$\int_{|w|}^{\infty} e^{i\eta^2}\, d\eta = e^{iw^2}\left[-\frac{1}{2i\,|w|}+\frac{1}{4\,|w|^3}-\ldots\right]. \qquad (60.6)$$

Although an infinite series of this type does not converge, nevertheless, because the successive terms decrease very rapidly for large values of $|w|$, the first term already gives a good representation of the function on the left for sufficiently large $|w|$ (such a series is said to be *asymptotic*). Thus, for the intensity $I(w)$, (60.5), we obtain the following asymptotic formula, valid for large negative values of w:

$$I = \frac{I_0}{4\pi w^2}. \qquad (60.7)$$

We see that in the region of geometric shadow, far from its edge, the intensity goes to zero as the inverse square of the distance from the edge of the shadow.

We now consider positive values of w, that is, the region above the XY plane. We write

$$\int_{-w}^{\infty} e^{i\eta^2}\, d\eta = \int_{-\infty}^{+\infty} e^{i\eta^2}\, d\eta - \int_{-\infty}^{-w} e^{i\eta^2}\, d\eta = (1+i)\sqrt{\frac{\pi}{2}} - \int_{w}^{\infty} e^{i\eta^2}\, d\eta.$$

For sufficiently large w, we can use an asymptotic representation for the integral standing on the right side of the equation, and we have

$$\int_{-w}^{\infty} e^{i\eta^2}\, d\eta \cong (1+i)\sqrt{\frac{\pi}{2}} + \frac{1}{2iw}\, e^{iw^2}. \qquad (60.8)$$

Substituting this expression in (60.5), we obtain

$$I = I_0\left(1+\sqrt{\frac{1}{\pi}}\,\frac{\sin\left(w^2-\frac{\pi}{4}\right)}{w}\right). \qquad (60.9)$$

Thus in the illuminated region, far from the edge of the shadow, the intensity has an infinite sequence of maxima and minima, so that the ratio I/I_0 oscillates on both sides of unity. With increasing w, the amplitude of these oscillations decreases inversely with the distance from the edge of the geometric shadow, and the positions of the maxima and minima steadily approach one another.

For small w, the function $I(w)$ has qualitatively this same character (Fig. 12). In the region of the geometric shadow, the intensity decreases monotonically as we move away from the boundary of the shadow. (On the boundary itself, $I/I_0 = \frac{1}{4}$.) For positive w, the intensity has alternating maxima and minima. At the first (largest) maximum, $I/I_0 = 1.37$.

§ 61. Fraunhofer diffraction

Of special interest for physical applications are those diffraction phenomena which occur when a plane parallel bundle of rays is incident on a screen. As a result of the diffraction, the beam ceases to be parallel, and there is light propagation along directions other than the initial one. Let us consider the problem of determining the distribution over direction of the intensity of the diffracted light at large distances beyond the screen (this formulation of the problem corresponds to *Fraunhofer diffraction*). Here we shall again restrict ourselves to the case of small deviations from geometrical optics, i.e. we shall assume that the angles of deviation of the rays from the initial direction (the diffraction angles) are small.

This problem can be solved by starting from the general formula (59.2) and passing to the limit where the light source and the point of observation are at infinite distances from the screen. A characteristic feature of the case we are considering is that, in the integral which determines the intensity of

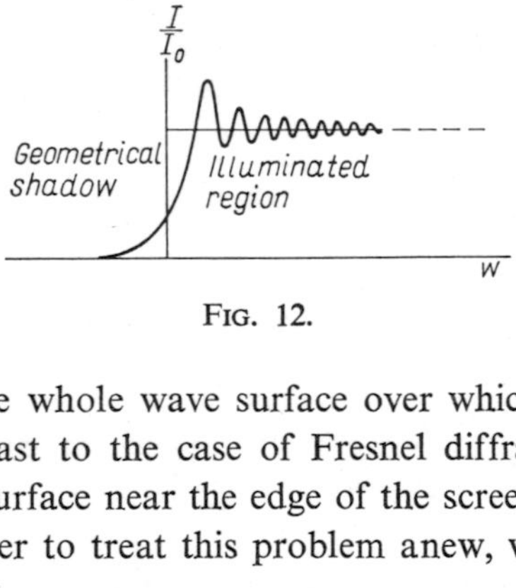

FIG. 12.

the diffracted light, the whole wave surface over which the integral is taken is important (in contrast to the case of Fresnel diffraction, where only the portions of the wave surface near the edge of the screens are important).†

However, it is simpler to treat this problem anew, without recourse to the general formula (59.2).

Let us denote by u_0 the field which would exist beyond the screens if geometrical optics were rigorously valid. This field is a plane wave, but its cross section has certain regions (corresponding to the "shadows" of opaque screens)

† The criteria for Fresnel and Fraunhofer diffraction are easily found by returning to formula (60.2) and applying it, for example, to a slit of width a (instead of to the edge of an isolated screen). The integrat on over z in (60.2) should then be taken between the limits from 0 to a. Fresnel diffraction corresponds to the case when the term containing z^2 in the exponent of the integrand is important, and the upper limit of the integral can be replaced by ∞. For this to be the case, we must have

$$ka^2\left(\frac{1}{D_p}+\frac{1}{D_q}\right) \gg 1 .$$

On the other hand, if this inequality is reversed, the term in z^2 can be dropped; this corresponds to the case of Fraunhofer diffraction.

in which the field is zero. We denote by S the part of the plane cross section on which the field u_0 is different from zero; since each such plane is a wave surface of the plane wave, u_0 = const over the whole surface S.

Actually, however, a wave with a limited cross sectional area cannot be strictly plane (see § 58). In its spatial Fourier expansion there appear components with wave vectors having different directions, and this is precisely the origin of the diffraction.

Let us expand the field u_0 into a two-dimensional Fourier integral with respect to the coordinates y, z in the plane of the transverse cross section of the wave. For the Fourier components, we have:

$$u_{\mathbf{q}} = \frac{1}{(2\pi)^2} \iint_S u_0 e^{-i\mathbf{q}\cdot\mathbf{r}} dy\, dz, \tag{61.1}$$

where the vectors $\mathbf{q}$ are constant vectors in the y, z plane; the integration actually extends only over that portion S of the y, z plane on which u_0 is different from zero. If $\mathbf{k}$ is the wave vector of the incident wave, the field component $u_{\mathbf{q}} e^{i\mathbf{q}\cdot\mathbf{r}}$ gives the wave vector $\mathbf{k}' = \mathbf{k}+\mathbf{q}$. Thus the vector $\mathbf{q} = \mathbf{k}'-\mathbf{k}$ determines the change in the wave vector of the light in the diffraction. Since the absolute values $k = k' = \omega/c$, the small diffraction angles θ_y, θ_z in the xy- and xz-planes are related to the components of the vector q by the equations

$$q_y = \frac{\omega}{c}\theta_y, \qquad q_z = \frac{\omega}{c}\theta_z. \tag{61.2}$$

For small deviations from geometrical optics, the components in the expansion of the field u_0 can be assumed to be identical with the components of the actual field of the diffracted light, so that formula (61.1) solves our problem.

The intensity distribution of the diffracted light is given by the square $|u_{\mathbf{q}}|^2$ as a function of the vector $\mathbf{q}$. The quanititative connection with the intensity of the incident light is established by the formula

$$\iint u_0^2\, dy\, dz = (2\pi)^2 \iint |u_{\mathbf{q}}|^2\, dq_y\, dq_z \tag{61.3}$$

[compare (49.7); the coefficient $(2\pi)^2$ appears here in place of the 2π in (49.7) because this is a two-dimensional expansion]. From this we see that the relative intensity diffracted into the solid angle $do = d\theta_y\, d\theta_z$ is given by

$$\frac{4\pi^2 |u_{\mathbf{q}}|^2}{u_0^2} dq_y\, dq_z = \left(\frac{2\pi\omega}{c}\right)^2 \left|\frac{u_{\mathbf{q}}}{u_0}\right|^2 do. \tag{61.4}$$

Let us consider the Fraunhofer diffraction from two screens which are "complementary": the first screen has holes where the second is opaque and conversely. We denote by $u^{(1)}$ and $u^{(2)}$ the field of the light diffracted by these screens (when the same light is incident in both cases). Since $u_{\mathbf{q}}^{(1)}$ and

$u_{\mathbf{q}}^{(2)}$ are expressed by integrals (61.1) taken over the surfaces of the apertures in the screens, and since the apertures in the two screens complement one another to give the whole plane, the sum $u_{\mathbf{q}}^{(1)}+u_{\mathbf{q}}^{(2)}$ is the Fourier component of the field obtained in the absence of the screens, i.e. it is simply the incident light. But the incident light is a rigorously plane wave with definite direction of propagation, so that $u_{\mathbf{q}}^{(1)}+u_{\mathbf{q}}^{(2)} = 0$ for all nonzero values of $\mathbf{q}$. Thus we have $u_{\mathbf{q}}^{(1)} = -u_{\mathbf{q}}^{(2)}$, or for the corresponding intensities,

$$|u_{\mathbf{q}}^{(1)}|^2 = |u_{\mathbf{q}}^{(2)}|^2 \text{ for } \mathbf{q} \neq 0. \tag{61.5}$$

This means that complementary screens give the same distribution of intensity of the diffracted light (this is called *Babinet's principle*).

We call attention here to one interesting consequence of the Babinet principle. Let us consider a blackbody, i.e., one which absorbs completely all the light falling on it. According to geometrical optics, when such a body is illuminated, there is produced behind it a region of geometrical shadow, whose cross-sectional area is equal to the area of the body in the direction perpendicular to the direction of incidence of the light. However, the presence of diffraction causes the light passing by the body to be partially deflected from its initial direction. As a result, at large distances behind the body there wil not be complete shadow but, in addition to the light propagating in the original direction, there will also be a certain amount of light propagating at small angles to the original direction. It is easy to determine the intensity of this scattered light. To do this, we point out that according to Babinet's principle, the amount of light deviated because of diffraction by the body under consideration is equal to the amount of light which would be deviated by diffraction from an aperture cut in an opaque screen, the shape and size of the aperture being the same as that of the transverse section of the body But in Fraunhofer diffraction from an aperture *all* the light passing through the aperture is deflected. From this it follows that the total amount of light scattered by a blackbody is equal to the amount of light falling on its surface and absorbed by it.

Problems

1. Calculate the Fraunhofer diffraction of a plane wave normally incident on an infinite slit (of width $2a$) with parallel sides cut in an opaque screen.

Solution: We choose the plane of the slit as the $y\,z$ plane, with the z axis along the slit (Fig. 13 shows a section of the screen). For normally incident light, the plane of the slit is one of the wave surfaces, and we choose it as the surface of integration in (61.1). Since the slit is infinitely long, the light is deflected only in the xy plane [since the integral (61.1) becomes zero for $q_z \neq 0$].

Therefore the field should be expanded only in the y coordinate:

$$u_q = \frac{u_0}{2\pi} \int_{-a}^{a} e^{-iqy}\, dy = \frac{u_0}{\pi q} \sin qa.$$

The intensity of the diffracted light in the angular range $d\theta$ is

$$dI = \frac{I_0}{2a} 2\pi \left| \frac{u_q}{u_0} \right|^2 dq = \frac{I_0}{\pi ak} \frac{\sin^2 ka\theta}{\theta^2} d\theta,$$

where $k = \omega/c$, and I_0 is the total intensity of the light incident on the slit.

$dI/d\theta$ as a function of diffraction angle has the form shown in Fig. 14. As θ increases toward either side from $\theta = 0$, the intensity goes through a series of maxima with rapidly decreasing height. The successive maxima are separated by minima at the points $\theta = n\pi/ka$ (where n is an integer); at the minima, the intensity falls to zero.

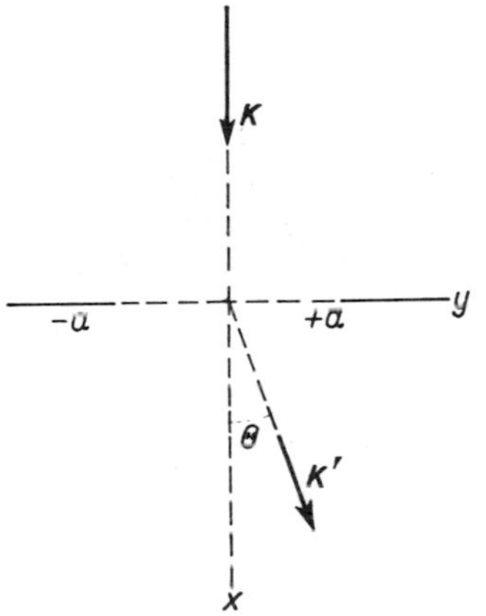

FIG. 13.

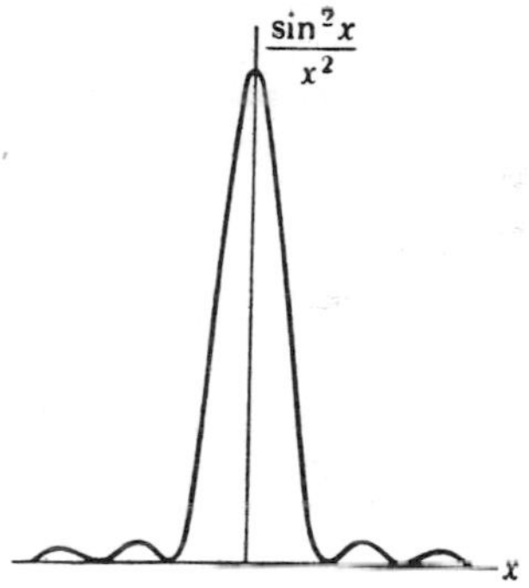

FIG. 14.

2. Calculate the Fraunhofer diffraction by a diffraction grating — a plane screen in which are cut a series of identical parallel slits (the width of the slits is $2a$, the width of opaque screen between neighboring slits is $2b$, and the number of slits is N).

Solution: We choose the plane of the grating as the yz plane, with the z axis parallel o the slits. Diffraction occurs only in the xy plane, and integration of (61.1) gives:

$$u_q = u'_q \sum_{n=0}^{N-1} e^{-2inqd} = u'_q \frac{1-e^{-2iNqd}}{1-e^{-2iqd}},$$

where $d = a+b$, and u'_q is the result of the integration over a single slit. Using the results of problem 1, we get:

$$dI = \frac{I_0 a}{N\pi} \left(\frac{\sin Nqd}{\sin qd}\right)^2 \left(\frac{\sin qa}{qa}\right)^2 dq = \frac{I_0}{N\pi ak} \left(\frac{\sin Nk\theta d}{\sin k\theta d}\right)^2 \frac{\sin^2 ka\theta}{\theta^2} d\theta$$

(I_0 is the total intensity of the light passing through all the slits).

For the case of a large number of slits ($N \to \infty$), this formula can be written in another form. For values $q = \pi n/d$, where n is an integer, dI/dq has a maximum; near such a maximum (i.e. for $qd = n\pi + \epsilon$, with ϵ small)

$$dI = I_0 a \left(\frac{\sin qa}{qa}\right)^2 \frac{\sin^2 N\epsilon}{\pi N\epsilon^2} dq.$$

But for $N \to \infty$, we have the formula†

$$\lim_{N\to\infty} \frac{\sin^2 Nx}{\pi N x^2} = \delta(x).$$

We therefore have, in the neighborhood of each maximum:

$$dI = I_0 \frac{a}{d} \left(\frac{\sin qa}{qa}\right)^2 \delta(\epsilon)\, d\epsilon,$$

i.e., in the limit the widths of the maxima are infinitely narrow and the total light intensity in the n'th maximum is

$$I^{(n)} = I_0 \frac{d}{\pi^2 a} \frac{\sin^2 (n\pi a/d)}{n^2}.$$

3. Find the distribution of intensity over direction for the diffraction of light which is incident normal to the plane of a circular aperture of radius a.

Solution: We introduce cylindrical coordinates $z, r\,\phi$, with the z axis passing through the center of the aperture and perpendicular to its plane. It is obvious that the diffraction is symmetric about the z axis, so that the vector q has only a radial component $q_r = q = k\theta$. Measuring the angle ϕ from the direction q, and integrating in (61.1) over the plane of the aperture, we find:

$$u_q = \frac{u_0}{(2\pi)^2} \int_0^a \int_0^{2\pi} e^{-iqr\cos\phi}\, r\, d\phi\, dr = \frac{u_0}{2\pi} \int_0^a J_0(qr) r\, dr,$$

where J_0 is the zero'th order Bessel function. Using the well-known formula

$$\int_0^a J_0(qr) r\, dr = \frac{a}{q} J_1(aq),$$

we then have

$$u_q = \frac{u_0 a}{2\pi q} J_1(aq),$$

and according to (61.4) we obtain for the intensity of the light diffracted into the element of solid angle do:

$$dI = I_0 \frac{J_1^2(ak\theta)}{\pi\theta^2} do,$$

where I_0 is the total intensity of the light incident on the aperture.

---

† For $x = 0$ the function on the left side of the equation is zero, while according to a well-known formula of the theory of Fourier series,

$$\lim_{N\to\infty} \left(\frac{1}{\pi} \int_{-a}^{a} f(x) \frac{\sin^2 Nx}{Nx^2} dx\right) = f(0).$$

From this we see that the properties of this function actually coincide with those of the δ-function (see the footnote on p. 78).

CHAPTER 8

THE FIELD OF MOVING CHARGES

§ 62. The retarded potentials

In Chapter 5 we studied the constant field, produced by charges at rest, and in Chapter 6, the variable field in the absence of charges. Now we take up the study of varying fields in the presence of arbitrarily moving charges.

We derive equations determining the potentials for a arbitrary electromagnetic field. This derivation is most conveniently done in four-dimensional form. For this, we write the second pair of Maxwell equations in the form (30.2)

$$\frac{\partial F_{ik}}{\partial x_k} = \frac{4\pi}{c} j_i.$$

Substituting for F_{ik} its expression in terms of the potentials,

$$F_{ik} = \frac{\partial A_k}{\partial x_i} - \frac{\partial A_i}{\partial x_k},$$

we obtain

$$\frac{\partial^2 A_k}{\partial x_i\, \partial x_k} - \frac{\partial^2 A}{\partial x_k^2} = \frac{4\pi}{c} j_i, \tag{62.1}$$

Now we impose on the potentials A_i the auxiliary condition (*Lorentz condition*)

$$\frac{\partial A_i}{\partial x_i} = 0. \tag{62.2}$$

Written in three-dimensional form, it states

$$\operatorname{div} \mathbf{A} + \frac{1}{c}\frac{\partial \phi}{\partial t} = 0. \tag{62.3}$$

This condition is a generalization of the conditions which we imposed on the potentials in the cases considered earlier. Thus for the constant field, (62.3) reduces to div $\mathbf{A} = 0$, that is, to the same condition as (43.3). For an electromagnetic field in vacuum (§ 46), we chose the potentials so that $\Phi = 0$ and div $\mathbf{A} = 0$; these potentials clearly also satisfy the condition (62.3).†

† It should be pointed out that despite the auxiliary condition (62.3) on the potentials ϕ and $\mathbf{A}$, they are still not completely unique. Namely, we can add grad f to $\mathbf{A}$, and subtract $\frac{1}{c}\frac{\partial f}{\partial t}$ from ϕ, where however, the function f is now no longer arbitrary but, as can easily be verified, must satisfy the equation

$$\Delta f - \frac{1}{c^2}\frac{\partial^2 f}{\partial t^2} = 0.$$

The equation (62.1) now reduces to

$$\frac{\partial^2 A_i}{\partial x_k^2} = -\frac{4\pi}{c} j_i. \tag{62.4}$$

This is the equation which determines the potentials of an arbitrary electromagnetic field. In three-dimensional form it is written as two equations, for **A** and for ϕ:

$$\Delta \mathbf{A} - \frac{1}{c^2}\frac{\partial^2 \mathbf{A}}{\partial t^2} = -\frac{4\pi}{c}\mathbf{j}, \tag{62.5}$$

$$\Delta \phi - \frac{1}{c^2}\frac{\partial^2 \phi}{\partial t^2} = -4\pi\varrho. \tag{62.6}$$

For constant fields, these reduce to the already familiar equations (36.4) and (43.4), and for variable fields without charges, to the homogeneous wave equation.

As we know, the solution of the inhomogeneous linear equations (62.5) and (62.6) can be represented as the sum of the solution of these equations without the right-hand side, and a particular integral of these equations with the right-hand side. To find the particular solution, we divide the whole space into infinitely small regions and determine the field produced by the charges located in one of these volume elements. Because of the linearity of the field equations, the actual field will be the sum of the fields produced by all such elements.

The charge de in a given volume element is, generally speaking, a function of the time. If we choose the origin of coordinates in the volume element under consideration, then the charge density is $\varrho = de(t)\ \delta(\mathbf{R})$, where **R** is the distance from the origin. Thus we must solve the equation

$$\Delta\phi - \frac{1}{c^2}\frac{\partial^2 \phi}{\partial t^2} = -4\pi\, de(t)\ \delta(\mathbf{R}). \tag{62.7}$$

Everywhere, except at the origin, $\delta(\mathbf{R}) = 0$, and we have the equation

$$\Delta \phi - \frac{1}{c^2}\frac{\partial^2 \phi}{\partial t^2} = 0. \tag{62.8}$$

It is clear that in the case we are considering ϕ has central symmetry, i.e., ϕ is a function only of R. Therefore if we write the Laplace operator in spherical coordinates, (62.8) reduces to

$$\frac{1}{R^2}\frac{\partial}{\partial R}\left(R^2 \frac{\partial \phi}{\partial R}\right) - \frac{1}{c^2}\frac{\partial^2 \phi}{\partial t^2} = 0.$$

To solve this equation, we make the substitution $\phi = \chi(R, t)/R$. Then, we find for χ

$$\frac{\partial^2 \chi}{\partial R^2} - \frac{1}{c^2}\frac{\partial^2 \chi}{\partial t^2} = 0.$$

But this is the equation of plane waves, whose solution has the form (see § 47):

$$\chi = f_1\left(t-\frac{R}{c}\right)+f_2\left(t+\frac{R}{c}\right).$$

Since we only want a particular solution of the equation, it is sufficient to choose only one of the functions f_1 and f_2. Usually it turns out to be convenient to take $f_2 = 0$ (concerning this, see below). Then, everywhere except at the origin, ϕ has the form

$$\phi = \frac{\chi\left(t-\frac{R}{c}\right)}{R}. \tag{62.9}$$

So far the function χ is arbitrary; we now choose it so that we also obtain the correct value for the potential at the origin. In other words, we must select χ so that at the origin equation (62.7) is satisfied. This is easily done noting that as $R \to 0$, the potential increases to infinity, and therefore its derivatives with respect to the coordinates increase more rapidly than its time derivative. Consequently as $R \to 0$, we can, in equation (62.7), neglect the term $\frac{1}{c^2}\frac{\partial^2\phi}{\partial t^2}$ compared with $\Delta\phi$. Then (62.7) goes over into the familiar equation (36.9) leading to the Coulomb law. Thus, near the origin, (62.9) must go over into the Coulomb law, from which it follows that $\chi(t) = de(t)$, that is,

$$\phi = \frac{de\left(t-\frac{R}{c}\right)}{R}. \tag{62.10}$$

From this it is easy to get to the solution of equation (62.6) for an arbitrary distribution of charges $\varrho(x, y, z, t)$. To do this, it is sufficient to write in (62.10), $de = \varrho\, dV$ (dV is the volume element) and integrate over the whole space. To this solution of the inhomogeneous equation (62.6) we can still add the solution ϕ_0 of the same equation without the right-hand side. Thus, the general solution has the form:

$$\phi(x, y, z, t) = \int \frac{1}{R}\varrho\left(x', y', z', t-\frac{R}{c}\right) dV' + \phi_0,$$

$$R^2 = (x-x')^2+(y-y')^2+(z-z')^2, \quad dV' = dx'\, dy'\, dz'$$

(R is the distance from the volume element dV to the "field point" at which we determine the potential). We shall write this expression briefly as

$$\phi = \int \frac{\varrho_{t-(R/c)}}{R}\, dV + \phi_0, \tag{62.11}$$

where the subscribt $t-\frac{R}{c}$ means that the quantity ϱ is to be taken at the time $t-\frac{R}{c}$, and the prime on dV has been omitted.

Similarly we have for the vector potential:

$$\mathbf{A}=\frac{1}{c}\int\frac{\mathbf{j}_{t-(R/c)}}{R}\,dV+\mathbf{A}_0, \tag{62.12}$$

where $\mathbf{A}_0$ is the solution of equation (62.5) without the right-hand term.

The potentials (62.11) and (62.12) (without ϕ_0 and $\mathbf{A}_0$) are called the retarded potentials.

In case the charges are at rest (i.e., density ϱ independent of the time), formula (62.11) goes over into the well-known formula (36.8) for the electrostatic field; for the case of stationary motion of the charges, formula (62.12), after averaging, goes over into formula (43.5) for the vector potential of a constant magnetic field.

The quantities $\mathbf{A}_0$ and ϕ_0 in (62.11) and (62.12) are to be determined so that the conditions of the problem are fulfilled. To do this it is clearly sufficient to impose initial conditions, that is, to fix the values of the field at the initial time. However we do not usually have to deal with such initial conditions. Instead we are usually given conditions at large distances from the system of charges throughout all of time. Thus, we may be told that radiation is incident on the system from outside. Corresponding to this, the field which is developed as a result of the interaction of this radiation with the system can differ from the external field only by the radiation originating from the system. This radiation emitted by the system must, at large distances, have the form of waves spreading out from the system, that is, in the direction of increasing R. But precisely this condition is satisfied by the retarded potentials. Thus these solutions represent the field produced by the system, while ϕ_0 and $\mathbf{A}_0$ must be set equal to the external field acting on the system.

§ 63. The Lienard-Wiechert potentials

Let us apply (62.11) and (62.12) to the field produced by a single charge moving arbitrarily. In this case the integrands in the retarded potentials can be different from zero only at various isolated points. For it is easy to see that at each given moment of time they differ from zero only at one point in space. To see this, we choose the field point P with coordinates x, y, z, and the time of observation t as origin O of the four-dimensional coordinate system, and construct the "light cone" (see p. 9) with axis along the time axis. The surface of the lower half of this cone, surrounding the region of "absolute past" (with respect to the event O), is the geometrical locus of points from which light signals can reach the world point O. The points in which this surface intersects the world line of the moving charge are, clearly, those world points in which the integrands in (62.11) and (62.12) are different from zero. But since the velocity of the particle is always smaller than the velocity of light, the world line of its motion has everywhere a smaller "slope" relative to the time axis than the "slope" of the surface of the light cone. Therefore it is clear that the world line of the particle can intersect the lower half of the light cone in only one point. The time t' corresponding to this point is determined by the equation

$$t' + \frac{R(t')}{c} = t, \tag{63.1}$$

where t is the moment of observation, and $R(t')$ is the distance from the charge to the point of observation, which is a given function of the time.

In order to calculate the potential, we must assume that the charge has finite dimensions and, later, let its dimensions go to zero. In this we can clearly take the factor $1/R$ in the integrands of (62.11) and (62.12) out from under the integral sign. However it is not possible in (62.11) for example, to replace the integral of ϱ simply by the value of the charge e, since different points of the volume of integration correspond to different times $t - \frac{R}{c}$.

This can only be done if the particle is at rest at the time t' determined by (63.1). In other words, in a system of reference in which the particle is at rest at time t', the potentials at the point of observation at time t are:

$$\phi = \frac{e}{R}, \qquad \mathbf{A} = 0, \tag{63.2}$$

where R is the distance from the charge to the point of observation at the time t', in this reference system.

The expressions for the potentials in an arbitrary reference system can be found directly by finding a four-vector which for $\mathbf{v} = 0$ coincides with the expressions just given for ϕ and $\mathbf{A}$. Noting that ϕ in (63.2) can also be written in the form

$$\phi = \frac{e}{c\,(t-t')}$$

(using 63.1), we find that the required four-vector is:

$$A_i = -e\frac{u_i}{R_k u_k}, \tag{63.3}$$

where u_i is the four-velocity of the charge, R_k is the four-vector with components $(x-x')$, $(y-y')$, $(z-z')$, $ic(t-t')$, where x', y', z', t' are related by the equation (63.1), which in four-dimensional form is

$$R_i^2 = 0. \tag{63.4}$$

Now once more transforming to three-dimensional notation, we obtain, for the potentials of the field produced by an arbitrarily moving point charge, the following expressions:

$$\phi = \frac{e}{\left(R - \frac{\mathbf{v}\cdot\mathbf{R}}{c}\right)}, \quad \mathbf{A} = \frac{e\mathbf{v}}{c\left(R - \frac{\mathbf{v}\cdot\mathbf{R}}{c}\right)}, \tag{63.5}$$

where $\mathbf{R}$ is the radius vector, taken from the point where the charge is located to the point of observation P, and all the quantities on the right sides of the equations must be evaluated at the time t', determined from (63.1). The potentials of the field, in the form (63.5), are called the *Lienard-Wiechert potentials.*

To calculate the intensities of the electric and magnetic fields from the formulas

$$\mathbf{E} = -\frac{1}{c}\frac{\partial \mathbf{A}}{\partial t} - \operatorname{grad}\phi, \quad \mathbf{H} = \operatorname{curl}\mathbf{A},$$

we must differentiate ϕ and $\mathbf{A}$ with respect to the coordinates x, y, z of the point, and the time t of observation. But the formulas (63.5) express the potentials as functions of t', and only through the relation (63.1) as implicit functions of x, y, z, t. Therefore to calculate the required derivatives we must first calculate the derivatives of t'. Differentiating the relation $R(t') = c(t-t')$ with respect to t, we get

$$\frac{\partial R}{\partial t} = \frac{\partial R}{\partial t'}\frac{\partial t'}{\partial t} = -\frac{\mathbf{R}\cdot\mathbf{v}}{R}\frac{\partial t'}{\partial t} = c\left(1 - \frac{\partial t'}{\partial t}\right).$$

(The value of $\partial R/\partial t'$ is obtained by differentiating the identity $R^2 = \mathbf{R}^2$ and substituting $\partial\mathbf{R}(t')/\partial t' = -\mathbf{v}(t')$. The minus sign is present because $\mathbf{R}$ is the radius vector from the charge e to the point P, and not the reverse.) Thus,

$$\frac{\partial t'}{\partial t} = \frac{1}{1 - \frac{\mathbf{v}\cdot\mathbf{R}}{Rc}}. \tag{63.6}$$

Similarly, differentiating the same relation with respect to the coordinates, we find

$$\operatorname{grad} t' = -\frac{1}{c}\operatorname{grad} R(t') = -\frac{1}{c}\left(\frac{\partial R}{\partial t'}\operatorname{grad} t' + \frac{\mathbf{R}}{R}\right),$$

so that

$$\operatorname{grad} t' = -\frac{\mathbf{R}}{c\left(R - \frac{\mathbf{R}\cdot\mathbf{v}}{c}\right)}. \tag{63.7}$$

With the aid of these formulas, there is no difficulty in carrying out the calculation of the fields **E** and **H**. Omitting the intermediate calculations, we give the final results:

$$\mathbf{E} = e\frac{1-\frac{v^2}{c^2}}{\left(R-\frac{\mathbf{R}\cdot\mathbf{v}}{c}\right)^3}\left(\mathbf{R}-\frac{\mathbf{v}}{c}R\right)+\frac{e}{c^2\left(R-\frac{\mathbf{R}\cdot\mathbf{v}}{c}\right)^3}\mathbf{R}\times\left\{\left(\mathbf{R}-\frac{\mathbf{v}}{c}R\right)\times\dot{\mathbf{v}}\right\}, \qquad (63.8)$$

$$\mathbf{H} = \frac{1}{R}\mathbf{R}\times\mathbf{E}. \qquad (63.9)$$

Here, $\dot{\mathbf{v}} = \partial\mathbf{v}/\partial t'$; all quantities on the right sides of the equations refer to the time t'. It is interesting to note that the magnetic field turns out to be everywhere perpendicular to the electric.

The electric field (63.8) consists of two parts of different type. The first term depends only on the velocity of the particle (and not on its acceleration) and varies at large distances like $1/R^2$. The second term depends on the acceleration, and for large R it varies like $1/R$. Later (§ 66) we shall see that this latter term is related to the electromagnetic waves radiated by the particle.

As for the first term, since it is independent of the acceleration it must correspond to the field produced by a uniformly moving charge. In fact, for constant velocity the difference

$$\mathbf{R}_{t'}-\frac{\mathbf{v}}{c}R_{t'} = \mathbf{R}_{t'}-\mathbf{v}(t-t')$$

is the distance $\mathbf{R}_t$ from the charge to the point of observation at precisely the moment of observation. It is also easy to show directly that

$$R_{t'}-\frac{1}{c}\mathbf{R}_{t'}\cdot\mathbf{v} = \sqrt{R_t^2-\frac{1}{c^2}(\mathbf{v}\times\mathbf{R}_t)^2} = R_t\sqrt{1-\frac{v^2}{c^2}\sin^2\theta_t},$$

where θ_t is the angle between $\mathbf{R}_t$ and $\mathbf{v}$. Consequently the first term in (63.8) is identical with the expression (38.8).

§ 64. Spectral resolution of the retarded potentials

The field produced by moving charges can be expanded into monochromatic waves. The potentials of the different monochromatic components of the field have the form $\phi_\omega e^{-i\omega t}$, $\mathbf{A}_\omega e^{-i\omega t}$. The charge density and current of the system of charges producing the field can also be expanded in a Fourier series or integral. It is clear that each Fourier component of ϱ and $\mathbf{j}$ is responsible for the creation of the corresponding monochromatic component of the field.

In order to express the Fourier components of the field in terms of the Fourier components of the charge density and current, we substitute in (62.11) for ϕ and ϱ respectively, $\phi_\omega e^{-i\omega t}$ and $\varrho_\omega e^{-i\omega t}$. We then obtain

$$\phi_\omega e^{-i\omega t} = \int \varrho_\omega \frac{e^{-i\omega\left(t-\frac{R}{c}\right)}}{R} dV.$$

Factoring $e^{-i\omega t}$ and introducing the absolute value of the wave vector $k = \omega/c$, we have:

$$\phi_\omega = \int \varrho_\omega \frac{e^{ikR}}{R} dV. \tag{64.1}$$

Similarly, for $\mathbf{A}_\omega$ we get

$$\mathbf{A}_\omega = \int \mathbf{j}_\omega \frac{e^{ikR}}{cR} dV. \tag{64.2}$$

We note that formula (64.1) represents a generalization of the solution of the Poisson equation to a more general equation of the form

$$\Delta\phi_\omega + k^2\phi_\omega = -4\pi\varrho_\omega \tag{64.3}$$

(obtained from equations (62.6) for ϱ, ϕ depending on the time through the factor $e^{-i\omega t}$).

If we were dealing with expansion into a Fourier integral, then the Fourier components of the charge density would be

$$\varrho_\omega = \frac{1}{2\pi} \int_{-\infty}^{+\infty} \varrho e^{i\omega t} dt.$$

Substituting this expression in (64.1), we get

$$\phi_\omega = \frac{1}{2\pi} \int\int_{-\infty}^{+\infty} \frac{\varrho}{R} e^{i(\omega t + kR)} dV dt. \tag{64.4}$$

We must still go over from the continuous distribution of charge density to the point charges which we are actually considering. Thus, if there is just one point charge, we set

$$\varrho = e\,\delta[\mathbf{r} - \mathbf{r}_0(t)],$$

where $\mathbf{r}_0(t)$ is the radius vector of the charge, and is a given function of the time. Substituting this expression in (64.4) and carrying out the space integration [which reduces to replacing $\mathbf{r}$ by $\mathbf{r}_0(t)$], we get:

$$\phi_\omega = \frac{e}{2\pi} \int_{-\infty}^{\infty} \frac{1}{R(t)} e^{i\omega[t+R(t)/c]} dt, \tag{64.5}$$

where now $R(t)$ is the distance from the moving particle to the point of observation. Similarly we find for the vector potential:

$$\mathbf{A}_\omega = \frac{e}{2\pi c}\int_{-\infty}^{\infty} \frac{\mathbf{v}(t)}{R(t)} e^{i\omega[t+R(t)/c]}\,dt, \tag{64.6}$$

where $\mathbf{v} = \dot{\mathbf{r}}_0(t)$ is the velocity of the particle.

Formulas analogous to (64.5), (64.6) can also be written for the case where the spectral resolution of the charge and current densities contains a discrete series of frequencies. Thus, for a periodic motion of a point charge (with period $T = 2\pi/\omega_0$) the spectral resolution of the field contains only frequencies of the form $n\omega_0$, and the corresponding components of the vector potential are

$$\mathbf{A}_n = \frac{2e}{T}\int_0^T \frac{\mathbf{v}(t)}{R(t)} e^{in\omega_0[t+R(t)/c]}\,dt \tag{64.7}$$

(and similarly for ϕ_n). The difference in the coefficients in (64.6) and (64.7) is related to the difference in the definitions of the Fourier components for the two cases (see § 49).

Problem

Find the expansion in plane waves of the field of a charge in uniform rectilinear motion.

Solution: We proceed in similar fashion to that used in § 51. We write the charge density in the form $\varrho = e\,\delta(\mathbf{r}-\mathbf{v}t)$, where $\mathbf{v}$ is the velocity of the particle. Taking Fourier components of the equation $\Box\phi = -4\pi e\,\delta(\mathbf{r}-\mathbf{v}t)$, we find $(\Box\phi)_\mathbf{k} = -\frac{e}{2\pi^2} e^{-i(\mathbf{v}\cdot\mathbf{k})t}$.

On the other hand, from

$$\phi = \int e^{i\mathbf{k}\cdot\mathbf{r}}\phi_\mathbf{k}\,d^3k$$

we have

$$(\Box\phi)_\mathbf{k} = -k^2\phi_\mathbf{k} - \frac{1}{c^2}\frac{\partial^2\phi_\mathbf{k}}{\partial t^2}.$$

Thus,

$$\frac{1}{c^2}\frac{\partial^2\phi_\mathbf{k}}{\partial t^2} + k^2\phi_\mathbf{k} = \frac{e}{2\pi^2}e^{-i(\mathbf{k}\cdot\mathbf{v})t},$$

from which, finally

$$\phi_\mathbf{k} = \frac{e}{2\pi^2}\frac{e^{-i(\mathbf{k}\cdot\mathbf{v})t}}{k^2-\left(\frac{\mathbf{k}\cdot\mathbf{v}}{c}\right)^2}.$$

From this it follows that the wave with wave vector $\mathbf{k}$ has the frequency $\omega = \mathbf{k}\cdot\mathbf{v}$. Similarly, we obtain for the vector potential,

$$\mathbf{A}_\mathbf{k} = \frac{e}{2\pi^2 c}\frac{\mathbf{v}e^{-i(\mathbf{k}\cdot\mathbf{v})t}}{k^2-\left(\frac{\mathbf{k}\cdot\mathbf{v}}{c}\right)^2}.$$

Finally, we have for the fields,

$$\mathbf{E}_{\mathbf{k}} = -i\mathbf{k}\phi_{\mathbf{k}} + i\frac{\mathbf{k}\cdot\mathbf{v}}{c}\mathbf{A}_{\mathbf{k}} = \frac{e}{2\pi^2}i\frac{-\mathbf{k}+\dfrac{(\mathbf{k}\cdot\mathbf{v})}{c^2}\mathbf{v}}{k^2-\left(\dfrac{\mathbf{k}\cdot\mathbf{v}}{c}\right)^2}e^{-i(\mathbf{k}\cdot\mathbf{v})t},$$

$$\mathbf{H}_{\mathbf{k}} = i\mathbf{k}\times\mathbf{A}_{\mathbf{k}} = \frac{e}{2\pi^2}i\frac{\mathbf{k}\times\dfrac{\mathbf{v}}{c}}{k^2-\left(\dfrac{\mathbf{k}\cdot\mathbf{v}}{c}\right)^2}e^{-i(\mathbf{k}\cdot\mathbf{v})t}.$$

§ 65. The Lagrangian to terms of second order

In ordinary classical mechanics, we can describe a system of particles interacting with each other with the aid of a Lagrangian which depends only on the coordinates and velocities of these particles (at one and the same time). The possibility of doing this is, in the last analysis, dependent on the fact that in mechanics the velocity of propagation of interactions is assumed to be infinite.

We already know that because of the finite velocity of propagation, the field must be considered as an independent system with its own "degrees of freedom". From this it follows that if we have a system of interacting particles (charges), then to describe it we must consider the system consisting of these particles and the field. Therefore, when we take into account the finite velocity of propagation of interactions, it is impossible to describe the system of interacting particles rigorously with the aid of a Lagrangian, depending only on the coordinates and velocities of the particles and containing no quantities related to the internal "degrees of freedom" of thet field.

However, if the velocity v of all the particles is small compared with the velocity of light, then the system can be described by a certain approximate Lagrangian. It turns out to be possible to introduce a Lagrangian describing the system, not only when all powers of v/c are neglected (classical Lagrangian), but also to terms of second order, v^2/c^2. This last remark is related to the fact that the radiation of electromagnetic waves by moving charges (and consequently, the appearance of a "self"-field) occurs only in the third approximation in v/c (see later, in § 67).†

As a preliminary, we note that in zero'th approximation, that is, when we completely neglect the retardation of the potentials, the Lagrangian for a system of charges has the form

$$L^{(0)} = \sum_a \tfrac{1}{2}m_a\mathbf{v}_a^2 - \sum_{a>b}\frac{e_a e_b}{R_{ab}} \tag{65.1}$$

† In special cases the appearance of the radiation terms can even be put off until the fifth approximation in v/c; in this case a Lagrangian even exists up to terms of order $(v/c)^4$. (See problem 2 of § 75.)

(the summation extends over the charges which make up the system). The second term is the potential energy of interaction as it would be for charges at rest.

To get the next approximation, we proceed in the following fashion. The Lagrangian for a charge e_a in an external field is [see (16.4)]

$$L_a = -mc^2\sqrt{1-\frac{v_a^2}{c^2}} - e_a\phi + \frac{e_a}{c}\mathbf{A}\cdot\mathbf{v}_a. \tag{65.2}$$

Choosing any one of the charges of the system, we determine the potentials of the field produced by all the other charges at the position of the first, and express them in terms of the coordinates and velocities of the charges which produce this field (this can be done only approximately — for ϕ, to terms of order v^2/c^2, and for $\mathbf{A}$, to terms in v/c). Substituting the expressions for the potentials, obtained in this way, in the expression for L_a given above, we get the Lagrangian for one of the charges of the system (for a given motion of the other charges). From this, one can then easily find the Lagrangian for the whole system.

We start from the expressions for the retarded potentials

$$\phi = \int \frac{\varrho_{t-\frac{R}{c}}}{R}\,dV, \qquad \mathbf{A} = \frac{1}{c}\int \frac{\mathbf{j}_{t-\frac{R}{c}}}{R}\,dV.$$

If the velocities of all the charges are small compared with the velocity of light, then the charge distribution does not change significantly during the time R/c. Therefore we can expand $\varrho_{t-\frac{R}{c}}$ and $\mathbf{j}_{t-\frac{R}{c}}$ in series of powers of R/c. For the scalar potential we thus find, to terms of second order:

$$\phi = \int \frac{\varrho\,dV}{R} - \frac{1}{c}\frac{\partial}{\partial t}\int \varrho\,dV + \frac{1}{2c^2}\frac{\partial^2}{\partial t^2}\int R\varrho\,dV$$

(ϱ without indices is the value of ϱ at time t; the time differentiations can clearly be taken out from under the integral sign). But $\int \varrho\,dV$ is the constant total charge of the system. Therefore the second term in our expression is zero, so that

$$\phi = \int \frac{\varrho\,dV}{R} + \frac{1}{2c^2}\frac{\partial^2}{\partial t^2}\int R\varrho\,dV. \tag{65.3}$$

We can proceed similarly with $\mathbf{A}$. But the expression for the vector potential in terms of the current density already contains $1/c$, and when substituted in the Lagrangian is multiplied once more by $1/c$. Since we are looking for a Lagrangian which is correct only to terms of second order, we can limit ourselves to the first term in the expansion of $\mathbf{A}$, that is,

$$\mathbf{A} = \frac{1}{c}\int \frac{\varrho\mathbf{v}}{R}\,dV \tag{65.4}$$

(we have substituted $\mathbf{j} = \varrho\mathbf{v}$).

Let us first assume that there is only a single point charge e. Then we obtain, from (65.3) and (65.4),

$$\phi = \frac{e}{R} + \frac{e}{2c^2}\frac{\partial^2 R}{\partial t^2}, \qquad \mathbf{A} = \frac{e\mathbf{v}}{cR}, \tag{65.5}$$

where R is the distance from the charge.

We choose in place of ϕ and $\mathbf{A}$ other potentials ϕ' and $\mathbf{A}'$, making the transformation (see § 18):

$$\phi' = \phi - \frac{1}{c}\frac{\partial f}{\partial t}, \qquad \mathbf{A}' = \mathbf{A} + \operatorname{grad} f,$$

in which we choose for f the function

$$f = \frac{e}{2c}\frac{\partial R}{\partial t}.$$

Then we get†

$$\phi' = \frac{e}{R}, \qquad \mathbf{A}' = \frac{e\mathbf{v}}{cR} + \frac{e}{2c}\nabla\frac{\partial R}{\partial t}.$$

To calculate $\mathbf{A}'$ we note first of all that $\nabla\frac{\partial R}{dt} = \frac{\partial}{\partial t}\nabla R$. The grad operator here means differentiation with respect to the coordinates of the field point at which we seek the value of $\mathbf{A}'$. Therefore ∇R is the unit vector $\mathbf{n}$, directed from the charge e to the field point, so that

$$\mathbf{A}' = \frac{e\mathbf{v}}{cR} + \frac{e}{2c}\dot{\mathbf{n}}.$$

We also write:

$$\dot{\mathbf{n}} = \frac{\partial}{\partial t}\left(\frac{\mathbf{R}}{R}\right) = \frac{\dot{\mathbf{R}}}{R} - \frac{\mathbf{R}\dot{R}}{R^2}.$$

But the derivative $\dot{\mathbf{R}}$ for a given field point is minus the velocity $\mathbf{v}$ of the charge, and the derivative $\dot{R}$ is easily determined by differentiating $R^2 = \mathbf{R}^2$, that is, by writing

$$R\dot{R} = \mathbf{R}\cdot\dot{\mathbf{R}} = -\mathbf{R}\cdot\mathbf{v}.$$

Thus,

$$\dot{\mathbf{n}} = \frac{-\mathbf{v} + \mathbf{n}(\mathbf{n}\cdot\mathbf{v})}{R}.$$

Substituting this in the expression for $\mathbf{A}'$, we get finally:

$$\phi' = \frac{e}{R}, \qquad \mathbf{A}' = \frac{e[\mathbf{v} + (\mathbf{v}\cdot\mathbf{n})\mathbf{n}]}{2cR}. \tag{65.6}$$

If there are several charges then we must, clearly, sum these expressions over all the charges.

† These potentials no longer satisfy (62.5) and (62.6), since they do not satisfy the condition (62.3).

Substituting these expressions in (65.2), we obtain the Lagrangian L_a for the charge e_a (for a fixed motion of the other charges). In doing this we must also expand the first term in (65.2) in powers of v_a/c, retaining terms up to the second order. Thus we get the following expression for L_a:

$$L_a = \frac{m_a v_a^2}{2} + \frac{1}{8}\frac{m_a v_a^4}{c^2} - e_a \sum_b \frac{e_b}{R_{ab}} + \frac{e_a}{2c^2}\sum_b \frac{e_b}{R_{ab}}[\mathbf{v}_a \cdot \mathbf{v}_b + (\mathbf{v}_a \cdot \mathbf{n}_{ab})(\mathbf{v}_b \cdot \mathbf{n}_{ab})]$$

(the summation goes over all the charges except e_a; $\mathbf{n}_{ab}$ is the unit vector from e_b to e_a).

From this, it is no longer difficult to get the Lagrangian for the whole system. It is easy to convince oneself that this function is not the sum of the L_a for all the charges, but has the form

$$L = \sum_a \frac{m_a v_a^2}{2} + \sum_a \frac{m_a v_a^4}{8c^2} - \sum_{a>b} \frac{e_a e_b}{R_{ab}} + \sum_{a>b} \frac{e_a e_b}{2c^2 R_{ab}}[\mathbf{v}_a \cdot \mathbf{v}_b + (\mathbf{v}_a \cdot \mathbf{n}_{ab})(\mathbf{v}_b \cdot \mathbf{n}_{ab})]. \quad (65.7)$$

Actually, for each of the charges under a given motion of all the others, this function L goes over into L_a as given above. The expression (65.7) determines the Lagrangian of a system of charges correctly to terms of second order. (It was first obtained by Darwin, 1922.)

Finally we find the Hamiltonian of a system of charges in this same approximation. This could be done by the general rule for calculating $\mathcal{H}$ from L; however it is simpler to proceed as follows. The second and fourth terms in (65.7) are small corrections to $L^{(0)}$ (65.1). On the other hand, we know from mechanics that for small changes of L and $\mathcal{H}$, the additions to them are equal in magnitude and opposite in sign (here the variations of L are considered for constant coordinates and velocities, while the changes in $\mathcal{H}$ refer to constant coordinates and momenta).†

Therefore we can at once write $\mathcal{H}$, subtracting from

$$\mathcal{H}_0 = \sum_a \frac{p_a^2}{2m_a c^2} + \sum_{a>b} \frac{e_a e_b}{R_{ab}}$$

the second and fourth terms of (65.7), replacing the velocities in them by the first approximation $\mathbf{v}_a = \mathbf{p}_a/m_a$. Thus,

$$\mathcal{H} = \sum_a \frac{p_a^2}{2m_a} - \sum_a \frac{p_a^4}{8c^2 m_a^3} + \sum_{a>b} \frac{e_a e_b}{R_{ab}} - \sum_{a>b} \frac{e_a e_b}{2c^2 m_a m_b R_{ab}}[\mathbf{p}_a \cdot \mathbf{p}_b + (\mathbf{p}_a \cdot \mathbf{n}_{ab})(\mathbf{p}_b \cdot \mathbf{n}_{ab})] \quad (65.8)$$

† See *Mechanics*, § 40.

Problems

1. Determine (correctly to terms of second order) the center of inertia of a system of interacting particles.

Solution: The problem is solved most simply by using the formula

$$\mathbf{R} = \frac{\sum_a \mathcal{E}_a \mathbf{r}_a + \int W \mathbf{r}\, dV}{\sum_a \mathcal{E}_a + \int W\, dV}$$

[see (14.8)], where $\mathcal{E}_a$ is the kinetic energy of the particle (including its rest energy), and W is the energy density of the field produced by the particles. Since the $\mathcal{E}_a$ contain the large quantities $m_a c^2$, it is sufficient, in obtaining the next approximation, to consider only those terms in $\mathcal{E}_a$ and W which do not contain c, i.e. we need consider only the nonrelativistic kinetic energy of the particles and the energy of the electrostatic field. We then have:

$$\int W \mathbf{r}\, dV = \frac{1}{8\pi}\int E^2 \mathbf{r}\, dV = \frac{1}{8\pi}\int (\nabla\varphi)^2 \mathbf{r}\, dV$$

$$= \frac{1}{8\pi}\int \left(d\mathbf{f}\cdot\nabla\frac{\varphi^2}{2}\right)\mathbf{r} - \frac{1}{8\pi}\int \nabla\frac{\varphi^2}{2} dV - \frac{1}{8\pi}\int \varphi\Delta\varphi\cdot\mathbf{r}\, dV;$$

the integral over the infinitely distant surface vanishes; the second integral also is transformed into a surface integral and vanishes, while we substitute $\Delta\varphi = -4\pi\varrho$ in the third integral and obtain:

$$\int W \mathbf{r}\, dV = \frac{1}{2}\int \varrho\varphi \mathbf{r}\, dV = \frac{1}{2}\sum_a e_a \varphi_a \mathbf{r}_a,$$

where φ_a is the potential produced at the point $\mathbf{r}_a$ by all the charges other than e_a.†

Finally, we get:

$$\mathbf{R} = \frac{1}{\mathcal{E}}\sum_a \mathbf{r}_a \left(m_a c^2 + \frac{p_a^2}{2m_a} + \frac{e_a}{2}\sum_b \frac{e_b}{R_{ab}}\right)$$

(with a summation over all b except $b = a$), where

$$\mathcal{E} = \sum_a \left(m_a c^2 + \frac{p_a^2}{2m_a} + \sum_{a>b} \frac{e_a e_b}{R_{ab}}\right)$$

is the total energy of the system. Thus in this approximation the coordinates of the center of inertia can actually be expressed in terms of quantities referring only to the particles.

2. Write the Hamiltonian in second approximation for a system of two particles, omitting the motion of the system as a whole.

Solution. We choose a system of reference in which the total momentum of the two particles is zero. Expressing the momenta as derivatives of the action, we have

$$\mathbf{p}_1 + \mathbf{p}_2 = \partial S/\partial \mathbf{r}_1 + \partial S/\partial \mathbf{r}_2 = 0.$$

From this it is clear that in the reference system chosen the action is a function of $\mathbf{r} = \mathbf{r}_2 - \mathbf{r}_1$, the difference of the radius vector of the two particles. Therefore we have $\mathbf{p}_2 = -\mathbf{p}_1 = \mathbf{p}$, where $\mathbf{p} = \partial S/\partial \mathbf{r}$ is the momentum of relative motion of the particles. The Hamiltonian is

$$\mathcal{H} = \frac{1}{2}\left(\frac{1}{m_1} + \frac{1}{m_2}\right)p^2 - \frac{1}{8c^2}\left(\frac{1}{m_1^3} + \frac{1}{m_2^3}\right)p^4 + \frac{e_1 e_2}{r} + \frac{e_1 e_2}{2m_1 m_2 c^2 r}[p^2 + (\mathbf{p}\cdot\mathbf{n})^2].$$

† The elimination of the self-field of the particles corresponds to the mass "renormalization" mentioned in the footnote on p. 102).

CHAPTER 9

RADIATION OF ELECTROMAGNETIC WAVES

§ 66. The field of a system of charges at large distances

We consider the field produced by a system of moving charges at distances large compared with the dimensions of the system.

We choose the origin of coordinates O anywhere in the interior of the system of charges. The radius vector from O to the point P, where we determine the field, we denote by $\mathbf{R}_0$, and the unit vector in this direction by $\mathbf{n}$. Let the radius vector of the charge element $de = \varrho\, dV$ be $\mathbf{r}$, and the radius vector from de to the point P be $\mathbf{R}$. Obviously $\mathbf{R} = \mathbf{R}_0 - \mathbf{r}$.

At large distances from the system of charges, $\mathbf{R}_0 \gg \mathbf{r}$, and we have approximately,

$$R = |\mathbf{R}_0 - \mathbf{r}| = R_0 - \mathbf{r}\cdot\mathbf{n}.$$

We substitute this in formulas (62.11), (62.12) for the retarded potentials. In the denominator of the integrands we can neglect $\mathbf{r}\cdot\mathbf{n}$ compared with R_0. In $t - \frac{R}{c}$, however, this is generally not possible; whether it is possible to neglect these terms is determined not by the relative values of R_0/c and $\mathbf{r}\cdot\frac{\mathbf{n}}{c}$, but by how much the quantities ϱ and $\mathbf{j}$ change during the time $\mathbf{r}\cdot\frac{\mathbf{n}}{c}$. Since R_0 is constant in the integration and can be taken out from under the integral sign, we get for the potentials of the field at large distances from the system of charges the expressions:

$$\phi = \frac{1}{R_0}\int \varrho_{t-\frac{R_0}{c}+\mathbf{r}\cdot\frac{\mathbf{n}}{c}}\, dV, \tag{66.1}$$

$$\mathbf{A} = \frac{1}{cR_0}\int \mathbf{j}_{t-\frac{R_0}{c}+\mathbf{r}\cdot\frac{\mathbf{n}}{c}}\, dV. \tag{66.2}$$

At sufficiently large distances from the system of charges, the field over small regions of space can be considered to be a plane wave. For this it is necessary that the distance be large compared not only with the dimensions of the system, but also with the wavelength of the electromagnetic waves radiated by the system. We refer to this region of space as the *wave zone* of the radiation.

In a plane wave, the fields $\mathbf{E}$ and $\mathbf{H}$ are related to each other by (47.4), $\mathbf{E} = \mathbf{H}\times\mathbf{n}$. Since $\mathbf{H} = \text{curl}\ \mathbf{A}$, it is sufficient for a complete determination of the field in the wave zone to calculate only the vector potential. In a plane wave we have $\mathbf{H} = \frac{1}{c}\dot{\mathbf{A}}\times\mathbf{n}$ [see (47.3)], where the dot indicates differentiation with respect to time.* Thus, knowing **A**, we find **H** and **E** from the formulas:†

$$\mathbf{H} = \frac{1}{c}\dot{\mathbf{A}}\times\mathbf{n}, \qquad \mathbf{E} = \frac{1}{c}(\dot{\mathbf{A}}\times\mathbf{n})\times\mathbf{n}. \tag{66.3}$$

We note that the field at large distances is inversely proportional to the first power of the distance R_0 from the radiating system. We also note that the time t enters into the expressions (66.1) to (66.3) always in the combination $t - \frac{R_0}{c}$.

For the radiation produced by a single arbitrarily moving point charge, it turns out to be convenient to use the Lienard-Wiechert potentials. At large distances, we can replace the radius vector R in formula (63.5) by the constant vector R_0, and in the condition (63.1) determining t', we must set $R = R_0 - \mathbf{r}_0\cdot\mathbf{n}$ ($\mathbf{r}_0(t)$ is the radius vector of the charge). Thus,§

$$\mathbf{A} = \frac{e\mathbf{v}(t')}{cR_0\left(1 - \frac{\mathbf{n}\cdot\mathbf{v}(t')}{c}\right)}, \tag{66.4}$$

where t' is determined from the equality

$$t' - \frac{\mathbf{r}_0(t')}{c}\cdot\mathbf{n} = t - \frac{R_0}{c}. \tag{66.5}$$

The radiated electromagnetic waves carry off energy. The energy flux is given by the Poynting vector which, for a plane wave, is

$$\mathbf{S} = c\frac{H^2}{4\pi}\mathbf{n}.$$

The intensity dI of radiation into the element of solid angle do is defined as the amount of energy passing in unit time through the element $df = R_0^2\,do$ of the spherical surface with center at the origin and radius R_0. This quantity is clearly equal to the energy flux density S multiplied by df, i.e.,

$$dI = c\frac{H^2}{4\pi}R_0^2\,do. \tag{66.6}$$

---

* In the present case, this formula is easily verified also by direct computation of the curl of the expression (66.2), and dropping terms in $1/R_0^2$ in comparison with terms $\sim 1/R_0$.

† The formula $\mathbf{E} = -\frac{1}{c}\dot{\mathbf{A}}$ [see (47.3)] is here not applicable to the potentials ϕ, **A**, since they do not satisfy the same auxiliary condition as was imposed on them in § 47.

§ In formula (63.8) for the electric field, the present approximation corresponds to dropping the first term in comparison with the second.

Since the field H is inversely proportional to R_0, we see that the amount of energy radiated by the system in unit time into the element of solid angle do is the same for all distances (if the values of $t-\frac{R_0}{c}$ are the same for them). This is, of course, as it should be, since the energy radiated from the system spreads out with velocity c into the surrounding space, not accumulating or disappearing anywhere.

We derive the formulas for the spectral resolution of the field of the waves radiated by the system. These formulas can be obtained directly from those in § 64. Substituting in (64.2) $R = R_0 - \mathbf{r}\cdot\mathbf{n}$ (in which we can set $R = R_0$ in the denominator of the integrand), we get for the Fourier components of the vector potential:

$$\mathbf{A}_\omega = \frac{e^{ikR_0}}{cR_0}\int \mathbf{j}_\omega e^{-i\mathbf{k}\cdot\mathbf{r}}\,dV \tag{66.7}$$

(where $\mathbf{k} = k\mathbf{n}$). The components $\mathbf{H}_\omega$ and $\mathbf{E}_\omega$ are determined using formula (66.3). Substituting in it for **H**, **E**, **A**, respectively, $\mathbf{H}_\omega e^{-i\omega t}$, $\mathbf{E}_\omega e^{-i\omega t}$, $\mathbf{A}_\omega e^{-i\omega t}$, and then dividing by $e^{-i\omega t}$, we find

$$\mathbf{H}_\omega = i\mathbf{k}\times\mathbf{A}_\omega, \qquad \mathbf{E}_\omega = \frac{ic}{\omega}(\mathbf{k}\times\mathbf{A}_\omega)\times\mathbf{k}. \tag{66.8}$$

When speaking of the spectral distribution of the intensity of radiation, we must distinguish between expansions in Fourier series and Fourier integrals. We deal with the expansion into a Fourier integral in the case of the radiation accompanying the collision of charged particles. In this case the quantity of interest is the total amount of energy radiated during the time of the collision (and correspondingly lost by the colliding particles). Suppose $d\mathcal{E}_{\mathbf{n}\omega}$ is the energy radiated into the element of solid angle do in the form of waves with frequencies in the interval $d\omega$. According to the general formula (49.7), the part of the total radiation lying in the frequency interval $d\omega$ is obtained from the usual formula for the intensity by replacing the square of the field by the square modulus of its Fourier component and multiplying by 4π. Therefore we have in place of (66.6):

$$d\mathcal{E}_{\mathbf{n}\omega} = c\,|\mathbf{H}_\omega|^2 R_0^2\,do\,d\omega. \tag{66.9}$$

If the charges carry out a periodic motion, then the radiation field must be expanded in a Fourier series. According to the general formula (49.3) the intensities of the various components of the Fourier resolutoin are obtained from the usual formula for the intensity by replacing the field by the Fourier components and then multiplying by two. Thus the intensity of the radiation into the element of solid angle do, with frequency $\omega = n\omega_0$ equals

$$dI_n = \frac{c}{2\pi}\,|\mathbf{H}_n|^2 R_0^2\,do. \tag{66.10}$$

Finally, we give the formulas for determining the Fourier components of the radiation field directly from the given motion of the radiating charges. For the Fourier integral expansion, we have:

$$\mathbf{j}_\omega = \frac{1}{2\pi} \int_{-\infty}^{\infty} \mathbf{j} e^{i\omega t}\, dt.$$

Substituting this in (66.7) and changing from the continuous distribution of currents to a point charge moving along a trajectory $\mathbf{r}_0 = \mathbf{r}_0$ (t) (see § 64), we obtain:

$$\mathbf{A}_\omega = \frac{e^{ikR_0}}{2\pi c R_0} \int_{-\infty}^{+\infty} e\mathbf{v}(t) e^{i[\omega t - \mathbf{k}\cdot\mathbf{r}_0(t)]}\, dt, \tag{66.11}$$

Since $\mathbf{v} = d\mathbf{r}_0/dt$, $\mathbf{v}\, dt = d\mathbf{r}_0$ and this formula can also be written in the form of a line integral taken along the trajectory of the charge:

$$\mathbf{A}_\omega = e\frac{e^{ikR_0}}{2\pi c R_0} \int e^{i(\omega t - \mathbf{k}\cdot\mathbf{r}_0)} d\mathbf{r}_0. \tag{66.12}$$

According to (66.8), the Fourier components of the magnetic field have the form:

$$\mathbf{H}_\omega = e\frac{i\omega e^{ikR_0}}{2\pi c^2 R_0} \int e^{i(\omega t - \mathbf{k}\cdot\mathbf{r}_0)}\, \mathbf{n}\times d\mathbf{r}_0. \tag{66.13}$$

If the charge carries out a periodic motion in a closed trajectory, then the field must be expanded in a Fourier series. The components of the Fourier series expansion are obtained by replacing the factor $1/2\pi$ in formulas (66.11) to (66.13) by $1/T$, while the integration now goes over the period T of the motion (see § 49). For the Fourier component of the magnetic field with frequency $\omega = n\omega_0 = n\dfrac{2\pi}{T}$, we have

$$\mathbf{H}_n = e\frac{4\pi i n e^{ikR_0}}{c^2 T^2 R_0} \int_0^T e^{i[n\omega_0 t - \mathbf{k}\cdot\mathbf{r}_0(t)]}\, \mathbf{n}\times \mathbf{v}(t)\, dt$$

$$= e\frac{4\pi i n e^{ikR_0}}{c^2 T^2 R_0} \oint e^{i(n\omega_0 t - \mathbf{k}\cdot\mathbf{r}_0)}\, \mathbf{n}\times d\mathbf{r}_0. \tag{66.14}$$

In the second integral, the integration goes over the closed orbit of the particle.

Problem

Find the four-dimensional expression for the spectral resolution of the four-momentum radiated by a charge moving along a given trajectory.

Solution: Substituting (66.8) in (66.9), and using the fact that, because of the condition (62.3), $k\phi_\omega = \mathbf{k}\cdot\mathbf{A}_\omega$, we find:

$$d\mathcal{E}_{n\omega} = c(k^2 |\mathbf{A}_\omega|^2 - |\mathbf{k}\cdot\mathbf{A}_\omega|^2) R_0^2\, do\, d\omega =$$

$$= ck^2 (|A_\omega|^2 - |\phi_\omega|^2) R_0^2\, do\, d\omega = ck^2 A_{i\omega} A^*_{i\omega} R_0^2\, do\, d\omega.$$

Representing the four-potential $A_{i\omega}$ in a form analogous to (66.12), we get:

$$d\mathcal{E}_{\mathbf{n}\omega} = \frac{k^2 e^2}{4\pi^2} \left| \int e^{ik_l x_l} dx_i \right|^2 do\, dk,$$

where the integration is performed along the world line of the trajectory of the particle. Finally, changing to four-dimensional notation [including the four-dimensional "volume element" in k-space, as in (10.1a)], we find for the radiated four-momentum:

$$dP_i = \frac{e^2 k_i}{2\pi^2 ic} \left| \int e^{ik_l x_l} dx_k \right|^2 \delta(k_m^2) d^4k.$$

§ 67. Dipole radiation

The time $\mathbf{r}\cdot\frac{\mathbf{n}}{c}$ in the integrands of the expressions (66.1) and (66.2) for the retarded potentials can be neglected in cases where the distribution of charge changes little during this time. It is easy to find the conditions for satisfying this requirement. Let T denote the order of magnitude of the time during which the distribution of the charges in the system changes significantly. The radiation of the system will obviously contain periods of order T (i.e., frequencies of order $1/T$). We further denote by a the order of magnitude of the dimensions of the system. Then the time $\mathbf{r}\cdot\frac{\mathbf{n}}{c}$ is of order a/c. In order that the distribution of the charges in the system shall not undergo a significant change during this time, it is necessary that $a/c \ll T$. But cT is just the wavelength λ of the radiation. Thus the condition $a \ll cT$ can be written in the form

$$a \ll \lambda, \tag{67.1}$$

that is, the dimensions of the system must be small compared with the radiated wavelength.

We note that this same condition (67.1) can also be obtained from (66.7). In the integrand, $\mathbf{r}$ goes through values in an interval of the order of the dimensions of the system, since outside the system $\mathbf{j}$ is zero. Therefore the exponent $i\mathbf{k}\cdot\mathbf{r}$ is small, and can be neglected for those waves in which $ka \ll 1$, which is equivalent to (67.1).

This condition can be written in still another form by noting that $T \sim a/v$, so that $\lambda \sim ca/v$, if v is of the order of magnitude of the velocities of the charges. From $a \ll \lambda$, we then find

$$v \ll c, \tag{67.2}$$

that is, the velocities of the charges must be small compared with the velocity of light.

We shall assume that this condition is fulfilled, and take up the study of the radiation at distances from the radiating system large compared with the wavelength (and consequently, in any case, large compared with the dimensions of the system). As was pointed out in § 66, at such distances, the field can be considered as a plane wave, and therefore in determining the field it is sufficient to calculate only the vector potential.

The vector potential (66.2) of the field now has the form

$$\mathbf{A} = \frac{1}{cR_0}\int \mathbf{j}_{t'}\,dV, \tag{67.3}$$

where the time $t' = t - \frac{R_0}{c}$ now no longer depends on the variable of integration. Substituting $\mathbf{j} = \varrho\mathbf{v}$, we rewrite (67.3) in the form

$$\mathbf{A} = \frac{1}{cR_0}\left(\sum e\mathbf{v}\right)$$

(the summation goes over all the charges of the system; for brevity, we omit the index t' — all quantities on the right side of the equation refer to time t'). But

$$\sum e\mathbf{v} = \frac{d}{dt}\sum e\mathbf{r} = \dot{\mathbf{d}},$$

where $\mathbf{d}$ is the dipole moment of the system. Thus,

$$\mathbf{A} = \frac{1}{cR_0}\dot{\mathbf{d}}. \tag{67.4}$$

With the aid of formula (66.3) we find that the magnetic field is equal to

$$\mathbf{H} = \frac{1}{c^2R_0}\ddot{\mathbf{d}}\times\mathbf{n}, \tag{67.5}$$

and the electric field to

$$\mathbf{E} = \frac{1}{c^2R_0}(\ddot{\mathbf{d}}\times\mathbf{n})\times\mathbf{n}. \tag{67.6}$$

We note that in the approximation considered here, the radiation is determined by the second derivative of the dipole moment of the system. Radiation of this kind is called *dipole radiation.*

Since $\mathbf{d} = \sum e\mathbf{r}$, $\ddot{\mathbf{d}} = \sum e\dot{\mathbf{v}}$. Thus the charges can radiate only if they move with acceleration. Charges in uniform motion do not radiate. This also follows directly from the principle of relativity, since a charge in uniform motion can be considered in the inertial system in which it is at rest, and a charge at rest does not radiate.

Substituting (67.5) in (66.6), we get the intensity of the dipole radiation:

$$dI = \frac{1}{4\pi c^3}(\ddot{\mathbf{d}}\times\mathbf{n})^2\,do = \frac{\ddot{\mathbf{d}}^2}{4\pi c^3}\sin^2\theta\,do, \tag{67.7}$$

where θ is the angle between $\mathbf{d}$ and $\mathbf{n}$. This is the amount of energy radiated by the system in unit time into the element of solid angle do. We note that the angular distribution of the radiation is given by the factor $\sin^2\theta$.

Substituting $do = 2\pi \sin\theta\, d\theta$ and integrating over θ from 0 to π, we find for the total radiation

$$I = \frac{2}{3c^3}\ddot{\mathbf{d}}^2. \tag{67.8}$$

If we have just one charge moving in the external field, then $\mathbf{d} = e\mathbf{r}$ and $\ddot{\mathbf{d}} = e\mathbf{w}$, where $\mathbf{w}$ is the acceleration of the charge. Thus the total radiation of the moving charge is

$$I = \frac{2e^2w^2}{3c^3}. \tag{67.9}$$

We note that a closed system of particles, for all of which the ratio of charge to mass is the same, cannot radiate (by dipole radiation). In fact, for such a system, the dipole moment

$$\mathbf{d} = \sum e\mathbf{r} = \sum \frac{e}{m} m\mathbf{r} = \text{const} \sum m\mathbf{r},$$

where const is the charge-to-mass ratio common to all the charges. But $\sum m\mathbf{r} = \mathbf{R}\sum m$, where $\mathbf{R}$ is the radius vector of the center of inertia of the system (remember that all of the velocities are small, $v \ll c$, so that non-relativistic mechanics is applicable). Therefore $\ddot{\mathbf{d}}$ is proportional to the acceleration of the center of inertia, which is zero, since the center of inertia moves uniformly.

Finally, we give the formula for the spectral resolution of the intensity of dipole radiation. For radiation accompanying a collision, we introduce the quantity $d\mathcal{E}_\omega$ of energy radiated throughout the time of the collision in the form of waves with frequencies in the interval $d\omega$ (see § 66). It is obtained by replacing the vector $\ddot{\mathbf{d}}$ in (67.8) by its Fourier component $\ddot{\mathbf{d}}_\omega$ and multiplying by 4π:

$$d\mathcal{E}_\omega = \frac{8\pi}{3c^3}(\ddot{\mathbf{d}}_\omega)^2\, d\omega.$$

For determining the Fourier components, we have

$$\ddot{\mathbf{d}}_\omega e^{-i\omega t} = \frac{d^2}{dt^2}(\mathbf{d}_\omega e^{-i\omega t}) = -\omega^2 \mathbf{d}_\omega e^{-i\omega t},$$

from which $\ddot{\mathbf{d}}_\omega = -\omega^2 \mathbf{d}_\omega$. Thus, we get

$$d\mathcal{E}_\omega = \frac{8\pi\omega^4}{3c^3}|\mathbf{d}_\omega|^2\, d\omega. \tag{67.10}$$

For periodic motion of the particles, we obtain in similar fashion the intensity of radiation with frequency $\omega = n\omega_0$ in the form

$$I_n = \frac{\omega_0^4 n^4}{3c^3}|\mathbf{d}_n|^2. \tag{67.11}$$

PROBLEMS

1. Find the radiation from a dipole $\mathbf{d}$, rotating in a plane with constant angular velocity Ω.†

Solution: Choosing the plane of the rotation as the x, y plane, we have:

$$d_x = d_0 \cos \Omega t, \qquad d_y = d_0 \sin \Omega t.$$

Since these functions are monochromatic, the radiation is also monochromatic, with frequency $\omega = \Omega$. From formula (67.7) we find for the angular distribution of the radiation (averaged over the period of the rotation):

$$\overline{dI} = \frac{d_0^2 \Omega^4}{8\pi c^3}(1 + \cos^2\theta)\, do,$$

where θ is the angle between the direction $\mathbf{n}$ of the radiation and the z axis. The total radiation is

$$\overline{I} = \frac{2d_0^2\Omega^4}{3c^3}.$$

The polarization of the radiation is along the vector $\ddot{\mathbf{d}} \times \mathbf{n} = \omega^2 \mathbf{n} \times \mathbf{d}$. Resolving it into components in the $\mathbf{n}$, z plane and perpendicular to it, we find that the radiation is elliptically polarized, and that the ratio of the axes of the ellipse is equal to $n_z = \cos\theta$; in particular, the radiation along the z axis is circularly polarized.

2. Determine the angular distribution of the radiation from a system of charges, moving as a whole (with velocity $\mathbf{v}$), if the distribution of the radiation is known in the reference system in which the system is at rest as a whole.

Solution: Let

$$dI' = f(\cos\theta', \phi')\, do', \qquad do' = d(\cos\theta')\, d\phi'$$

be the intensity of the radiation in the K' frame which is attached to the moving charge system (θ', ϕ' are the polar coordinates; the polar axis is along the direction of motion of the system). The energy $d\mathcal{E}$ radiated during a time interval dt in the fixed (laboratory) reference frame K, is related to the energy $d\mathcal{E}'$ radiated in the K' system by the transformation formula

$$d\mathcal{E}' = \frac{d\mathcal{E} - \mathbf{V}\cdot d\mathbf{P}}{\sqrt{1 - \frac{V^2}{c^2}}} = d\mathcal{E}\frac{1 - \frac{V}{c}\cos\theta}{\sqrt{1 - \frac{V^2}{c^2}}}$$

(the momentum of radiation propagating in a given direction is related to its energy by the equation $|d\mathbf{P}| = d\mathcal{E}/c$). The polar angles θ, θ' of the direction of the radiation in the K and K' frames are related by formulas (5.6), and the azimuths ϕ and ϕ' are equal. Finally, the time interval dt' in the K' system corresponds to the time $dt = \dfrac{dt'}{\sqrt{1 - \frac{V^2}{c^2}}}$ in the K system.

As a result, we find for the intensity $dI = \dfrac{d\mathcal{E}}{dt}$ in the K system:

$$dI = \frac{\left(1 - \frac{V^2}{c^2}\right)^2}{\left(1 - \frac{V}{c}\cos\theta\right)^3} f\left(\frac{\cos\theta - \frac{V}{c}}{1 - \frac{V}{c}\cos\theta}, \phi\right) do.$$

† The radiation from a rotator or a symmetric top which has a dipole moment is of this type. In the first case, $\mathbf{d}$ is the total dipole moment of the rotator; in the second case $\mathbf{d}$ is the projection of the dipole moment of the top on a plane perpendicular to its axis of precession (i.e. the direction of the total angular momentum).

Thus, for a dipole moving along the direction of its own axis, $f = \text{const}\cdot\sin^2\theta'$, and by using the formula just obtained, we find:

$$dI = \text{const}\,\frac{\left(1-\frac{V^2}{c^2}\right)^3 \sin^2\theta}{\left(1-\frac{V}{c}\cos\theta\right)^5}\,do.$$

§ 68. Dipole radiation during collisions

In problems of radiation during collisions, one is seldom interested in the radiation accompanying the collision of two particles moving along definite trajectories. Usually we have to consider the scattering of a whole current of particles moving parallel to each other, and the problem consists in determining the total radiation per unit current density of particles.

If the current density is unity, i.e., if one particle passes per unit time across unit area of the cross section of the beam, then the number of particles in the flux which have "impact parameters"† between ϱ and $\varrho+d\varrho$, is $2\pi\varrho\, d\varrho$ (the area of the ring bounded by the circles of radius ϱ and $\varrho+d\varrho$). Therefore the required total radiation is gotten by multiplying the total radiation $\Delta\mathcal{E}$ from a single particle (with given impact parameter) by $2\pi\varrho\, d\varrho$ and integrating over ϱ from 0 to ∞. The quantity determined in this way has the dimensions of energy times area. We call it the *effective radiation* (in analogy to the effective cross section for scattering) and denote it by χ:

$$\varkappa = \int_0^\infty \Delta\mathcal{E}\cdot 2\pi\varrho\, d\varrho. \tag{68.1}$$

We can determine in completely analogous manner the effective radiation in a given solid angle element do, in a given frequency interval $d\omega$, etc.‡

We derive the general formula for the angular distribution of radiation emitted in the scattering of a beam of particles by a centrally symmetric field, assuming dipole radiation.

The intensity of the radation (at a given time) from each of the particles of the beam under consideration is determined by formula (67.7), in which $\mathbf{d}$ is the dipole moment of the particle relative to the scattering center.§ First of all we average this expression over all directions of the vectors $\ddot{\mathbf{d}}$ in the plane perpendicular to the beam direction. Since $(\ddot{\mathbf{d}}\times\mathbf{n})^2 = \ddot{\mathbf{d}}^2-(\mathbf{n}\cdot\ddot{\mathbf{d}})^2$,

† By *impact parameter* we mean the distance at which the colliding particles would have passed each other if they moved in straight lines.

‡ If the expression to be integrated depends on the angle of orientation of the projection of the dipole moment of the particle on the plane transverse to the beam, then we must first average over all directions in this plane and only then multiply by $2\pi\varrho\, d\varrho$ and integrate.

§ Actually one usually deals with the dipole moment of two particles — the scatterer and the scattered particle — relative to their common center of interia.

the averaging affects only $(\mathbf{n}\cdot\ddot{\mathbf{d}})^2$. Because the scattering field is centrally symmetric and the incident beam is parallel, the scattering, and also the radiation, has axial symmetry around an axis passing through the center. We choose this axis as x axis. From symmetry, it is obvious that the first powers $\ddot{d}_y$, $\ddot{d}_z$ give zero on averaging, and since $\ddot{d}_x$ is not subjected to the averaging process,

$$\overline{\ddot{d}_x\ddot{d}_y} = \overline{\ddot{d}_x\ddot{d}_z} = 0.$$

The average values of $\ddot{d}_y^2$ and $\ddot{d}_z^2$ are equal to each other, so that

$$\overline{\ddot{d}_y^2} = \overline{\ddot{d}_z^2} = \tfrac{1}{2}[(\ddot{\mathbf{d}})^2-\ddot{d}_x^2].$$

Keeping all this in mind, we find without difficulty:

$$\overline{(\ddot{\mathbf{d}}\times\mathbf{n})^2} = \tfrac{1}{2}(\ddot{\mathbf{d}}^2+\ddot{d}_x^2)+\tfrac{1}{2}(\ddot{\mathbf{d}}^2-3\ddot{d}_x^2)\cos^2\theta,$$

where θ is the angle between the direction $\mathbf{n}$ of the radiation and the x axis.

Integrating the intensity over the time and over all impact parameters, we obtain the following final expression giving the effective radiation as a function of the direction of radiation:

$$d\varkappa_{\mathbf{n}} = \frac{do}{4\pi c^3}\left[A+B\frac{3\cos^2\theta-1}{2}\right], \tag{68.2}$$

where

$$A = \frac{2}{3}\int_0^{\infty}\int_{-\infty}^{+\infty}\ddot{\mathbf{d}}^2\,dt\,2\pi\varrho\,d\varrho, \quad B = \frac{1}{3}\int_0^{\infty}\int_{-\infty}^{+\infty}(\ddot{\mathbf{d}}^2-3\ddot{d}_x^2)\,dt\,2\pi\varrho\,d\varrho. \tag{68.3}$$

The second term in (68.2) is written in such a form that it gives zero when averaged over all directions, so that the total effective radiation is $\chi = A/c^3$. We call attention to the fact that the angular distribution of the radiation is symmetric with respect to the plane passing through the scattering center and perpendicular to the beam, since the expression (68.2) is unchanged if we replace θ by $\pi-\theta$. This property is specific to dipole radiation, and is no longer true for higher approximations in v/c.

The intensity of the radiation accompanying the scattering can be separated into two parts — radiation polarized in the plane passing through the x axis and the direction $\mathbf{n}$ (we choose this plane as the xy plane), and radiation polarized in a plane perpendicular to this one.

The vector of the electric field has the direction of the vector

$$(\ddot{\mathbf{d}}\times\mathbf{n})\times\mathbf{n} = \mathbf{n}(\mathbf{n}\cdot\ddot{\mathbf{d}})-\ddot{\mathbf{d}}$$

[see (67.6)]. The component of this vector in the direction perpendicular to the xy plane is $-\ddot{d}_z$, and its projection on the xy plane is $\sin\theta\ddot{d}_x-\cos\theta\ddot{d}_y$. This latter quantity is most conveniently determined from the z-component of the magnetic field which is equal to it and has the direction $\ddot{\mathbf{d}}\times\mathbf{n}$.

Squaring **E** and averaging over all directions of the vector $\ddot{\mathbf{d}}$ in the yz plane, we see first of all that the product of the projections of the field on the xy plane and perpendicular to it, vanishes. This means that the intensity can actually be represented as the sum of two independent parts — the intensities of the radiation polarized in the two mutually perpendicular planes.

The intensity of the radiation with its electric vector perpendicular to the xy plane is determined by the mean square $\overline{\ddot{d}_z^2} = \frac{1}{2}(\ddot{\mathbf{d}}^2 - \ddot{d}_x^2)$. For the corresponding part of the effective radiation, we obtain the expression

$$d\varkappa_{\mathbf{n}}^{\perp} = \frac{do}{4\pi c^3} \frac{1}{2} \int_0^{\infty} \int_{-\infty}^{+\infty} (\ddot{\mathbf{d}}^2 - \ddot{d}_x^2)\, dt\, 2\pi\varrho\, d\varrho. \tag{68.4}$$

We note that this part of the radiation is isotropic. It is unnecessary to give the expression for the effective radiation with electric vector in the xy plane since it is clear that

$$d\varkappa_{\mathbf{n}}^{\parallel} + d\varkappa_{\mathbf{n}}^{\perp} = d\varkappa_{\mathbf{n}}.$$

In a similar way we can get the expression for the angular distribution of the effective radiation in a given frequency interval $d\omega$. Without repeating all the discussion, which is completely analogous to that given above, we present the final expression:

$$d\varkappa_{\mathbf{n},\omega} = \frac{do\, d\omega}{c^3} \left[A(\omega) + B(\omega) \frac{3\cos^2\theta - 1}{2} \right], \tag{68.5}$$

where

$$A(\omega) = \frac{2\omega^4}{3} \int_0^{\infty} \mathbf{d}_\omega^2\, 2\pi\varrho\, d\varrho, \quad B(\omega) = \frac{\omega^4}{3} \int_0^{\infty} (\mathbf{d}_\omega^2 - 3\, d_{x\omega}^2)\, 2\pi\varrho\, d\varrho. \tag{68.6}$$

§ 69. Radiation of low frequency in collisions

In the spectral distribution of the radiation accompanying a collision, the main part of the intensity is contained in frequencies $\omega \sim 1/\tau$, where τ is the order of magnitude of the duration of the collision. However, we shall here not consider this region of the spectrum (for which one cannot obtain any general formulas) but rather the "tail" of the distribution at low frequencies, satisfying the condition

$$\omega\tau \ll 1. \tag{69.1}$$

We shall not assume that the velocities of the colliding particles are small compared to the velocity of light, as we did in the preceding section; the formulas which follow will be valid for arbitrary velocities.

In the integral

$$\mathbf{H}_\omega = \frac{1}{2\pi}\int_{-\infty}^{\infty} \mathbf{H}e^{i\omega t}\,dt,$$

the field **H** of the radiation is significantly different from zero only during a time interval of the order of τ. Therefore, in accord with condition (69.1), we can assume that $\omega\tau \ll 1$ in the integral, so that we can replace $e^{i\omega t}$ by unity; then

$$\mathbf{H}_\omega = \frac{1}{2\pi}\int_{-\infty}^{\infty} \mathbf{H}\,dt.$$

Substituting $\mathbf{H} = \dot{\mathbf{A}}\times\mathbf{n}/c$ and carrying out the time integration, we get:

$$\mathbf{H}_\omega = \frac{1}{2\pi c}(\mathbf{A}_2-\mathbf{A}_1)\times\mathbf{n}, \tag{69.2}$$

where $\mathbf{A}_2-\mathbf{A}_1$ is the change in the vector potential produced by the colliding particles during the time of the collision.

The total radiation (with frequency ω) during the time of the collision is found by substituting (69.2) in (66.9):

$$d\mathcal{E}_{\mathbf{n}\omega} = \frac{R_0^2}{4c\pi^2}[(\mathbf{A}_2-\mathbf{A}_1)\times\mathbf{n}]^2\,do\,d\omega. \tag{69.3}$$

We can use the Lienard-Wiechert expression (66.4) for the vector potential, and obtain:

$$d\mathcal{E}_{\mathbf{n}\omega} = \frac{1}{4\pi^2c^3}\left\{\sum e\left(\frac{\mathbf{v}_2\times\mathbf{n}}{1-\frac{1}{c}\mathbf{n}\cdot\mathbf{v}_2} - \frac{\mathbf{v}_1\times\mathbf{n}}{1-\frac{1}{c}\mathbf{n}\cdot\mathbf{v}_1}\right)\right\}^2 do\,d\omega, \tag{69.4}$$

where $\mathbf{v}_1$ and $\mathbf{v}_2$ are the velocities of the particle before and after the collision, and the sum is taken over the two colliding particles. We note that the coefficient of $d\omega$ is independent of frequency. In other words, at low frequencies [condition (69.1)], the spectral distribution is independent of frequency, i.e. $d\mathcal{E}_{\mathbf{n}\omega}/d\omega$ tends toward a constant limit as $\omega\to 0$.†

If the velocities of the colliding particles are small compared with the velocity of light, then (69.4) becomes

$$d\mathcal{E}_{\mathbf{n}\omega} = \frac{1}{4\pi^2c^3}[\sum e(\mathbf{v}_2-\mathbf{v}_1)\times\mathbf{n}]^2\,do\,d\omega. \tag{69.5}$$

---

† By integrating over the impact parameters, we can obtain an analogous result for the effective radiation in the scattering of a beam of particles. However it must be remembered that this result is not valid for the effective radiation when there is a Coulomb interaction of the colliding particles, because then the integral over ϱ is divergent (logarithmically) for large ϱ. We shall see in the next section that in this case the effective radiation at low frequencies depends logarithmically on frequency and does not remain constant.

This expression corresponds to the case of dipole radiation, with the vector potential given by formula (67.4).

An interesting application of these formulas is to the radiation produced in the emission of a new charged particle (e.g. the emergence of a β-particle from a nucleus). This process is to be treated as an instantaneous change in the velocity of the particle from zero to its actual value. [Because of the symmetry of formula (69.5) with respect to interchange of $\mathbf{v}_1$ and $\mathbf{v}_2$, the radiation originating in this process is identical with the radiation which would be produced in the inverse process — the instantaneous stopping of the particle.] The essential point is that, since the "time" for the process is $\tau \to 0$, condition (69.1) is actually satisfied for all frequencies.†

PROBLEM

Find the spectral distribution of the total radiation produced when a charged particle is emitted which moves with velocity v.

Solution: According to formula (69.4) (in which we set $\mathbf{v}_2 = \mathbf{v}$, $\mathbf{v}_1 = 0$), we have:

$$d\mathcal{E}_\omega = d\omega \frac{e^2 v^2}{4\pi^2 c^3} \int_0^\pi \frac{\sin^2\theta}{\left(1 - \frac{v}{c}\cos\theta\right)^2} 2\pi \sin\theta \, d\theta.$$

Evaluation of the integral gives:‡

$$d\mathcal{E}_\omega = \frac{e^2}{\pi c}\left(\frac{c}{v}\ln\frac{c+v}{c-v} - 2\right) d\omega. \tag{1}$$

For $v \ll c$, this formula goes over into

$$d\mathcal{E}_\omega = \frac{2e^2 v^2}{3\pi c^3} d\omega,$$

which can also be obtained directly from (69.5).

§ 70 Radiation in the case of Coulomb interaction

In this section we present, for reference purposes, a series of formulas relating to the dipole radiation of a system of two charged particles; it is assumed that the velocities of the particles are small compared with the velocity of light.

Uniform motion of the system as a whole, i.e., motion of its center of mass, is not of interest, since it does not lead to radiation, therefore we need

† However, the applicability of these formulas is limited by the quantum condition that $\hbar\omega$ be small compared with the total kinetic energy of the particle.

‡ Even though, as we have already pointed out, condition (69.1) is satisfied for all frequencies, because the process is "instantaneous", we cannot find the total radiated energy by integrating (1) over ω — the integral diverges at high frequencies. We mention that, aside from the violation of the conditions for classical behavior at high frequencies, in the present case the cause of the divergence lies in the incorrect formulation of the classical problem, in which the particle has an infinite acceleration at the initial time.

only consider the relative motion of the particles. We choose the origin of coordinates at the center of mass. Then the dipole moment of the system $\mathbf{d} = e_1\mathbf{r}_1 + e_2\mathbf{r}_2$ has the form

$$\mathbf{d} = \frac{e_1 m_2 - e_2 m_1}{m_1 + m_2}\mathbf{r} = \mu\left(\frac{e_1}{m_1} - \frac{e_2}{m_2}\right) r \tag{70.1}$$

where the indices 1 and 2 refer to the two particles, and $\mathbf{r} = \mathbf{r}_1 - \mathbf{r}_2$ is the radius vector between them, and $\mu = \dfrac{m_1 m_2}{m_1 + m_2}$ is the reduced mass.

We start with the radiation accompanying the elliptical motion of two particles attracting each other according to the Coulomb law. As we know from mechanics†, this motion can be expressed as the motion of a particle with mass μ in the ellipse whose equation in polar coordinates is

$$1 + \epsilon \cos\phi = \frac{a(1-\epsilon^2)}{r}, \tag{70.2}$$

where the semimajor axis a and the eccentricity ϵ are

$$a = \frac{\alpha}{2|\mathcal{E}|}, \quad \epsilon = \sqrt{1 - \frac{2|\mathcal{E}|M^2}{\mu\alpha^2}}. \tag{70.3}$$

Here $\mathcal{E}$ is the total energy of the particles (omitting their rest energy!) and is negative for a finite motion; $M = \mu r^2 \dot{\phi}$ is the angular momentum, and α is the constant in the Coulomb law

$$\alpha = |e_1 e_2|.$$

The time dependence of the coordinates can be expressed in terms of the parametric equations

$$r = a(1 - \epsilon\cos\xi), \quad t = \sqrt{\frac{\mu a^3}{\alpha}}\,(\xi - \epsilon\sin\xi). \tag{70.4}$$

One full revolution in the ellipse corresponds to a change of the parameter ξ from 0 to 2π; the period of the motion is

$$T = 2\pi\sqrt{\frac{\mu a^3}{\alpha}}.$$

We calculate the Fourier components of the dipole moment. Since the motion is periodic we are dealing with an expansion in Fourier series. Since the dipole moment is proportional to the radius vector $\mathbf{r}$, the problem reduces to the calculation of the Fourier components of the coordinates $x = r\cos\phi$, $y = r\sin\phi$. The time dependence of x and y is given by the parametric equations

$$x = a(\cos\xi - \epsilon), \quad y = a\sqrt{1-\epsilon^2}\sin\xi,$$
$$\omega_0 t = \xi - \epsilon\sin\xi. \tag{70.5}$$

† See *Mechanics*, § 15.

Here we have introduced the frequency

$$\omega_0 = 2\pi/T = \sqrt{\alpha/\mu a^3} = \frac{(2|\mathcal{E}|)^{3/2}}{\alpha\mu^{1/2}}.$$

Instead of the Fourier components of the coordinates, it is more convenient to calculate the Fourier components of the velocities, using the fact that $\dot{x}_n = -i\omega_0 n x_n$; $\dot{y}_n = -i\omega_0 n y_n$. We have

$$x_n = \frac{\dot{x}_n}{-i\omega_0 n} = \frac{i}{\omega_0 n}\frac{2}{T}\int_0^T e^{i\omega_0 nt}\dot{x}\,dt.$$

But $\dot{x}\,dt = dx = -a\sin\xi\,d\xi$; transforming from an integral over t to one over ξ, we have

$$x_n = \frac{ia}{\pi n}\int_0^{2\pi} e^{in(\xi-\epsilon\sin\xi)}\sin\xi\,d\xi.$$

Similarly, we find

$$y_n = \frac{ia\sqrt{1-\epsilon^2}}{\pi n}\int_0^{2\pi} e^{in(\xi-\epsilon\sin\xi)}\cos\xi\,d\xi = \frac{ia\sqrt{1-\epsilon^2}}{\pi n\epsilon}\int_0^{2\pi} e^{in(\xi-\epsilon\sin\xi)}\,d\xi$$

(in going from the first to the second integral, we write the integrand as $\cos\xi \equiv (\cos\xi - 1/\epsilon) + 1/\epsilon$; then the integral with $\cos\xi - 1/\epsilon$ can be done, and gives identically zero). Finally, we use a formula of the theory of Bessel functions,

$$\frac{1}{2\pi}\int_0^{2\pi} e^{i(n\xi - x\sin\xi)}\,d\xi = \frac{1}{\pi}\int_0^{\pi}\cos(n\xi - x\sin\xi)\,d\xi = J_n(x), \qquad (70.6)$$

where $J_n(x)$ is the Bessel function of integral order n. As a final result, we obtain the following expression for the required Fourier components:

$$x_n = \frac{2a}{n}J_n'(n\epsilon), \quad y_n = \frac{2ia\sqrt{1-\epsilon^2}}{n\epsilon}J_n(n\epsilon) \qquad (70.7)$$

(the prime on the Bessel function means differentiation with respect to its argument).

The expression for the intensity of the monochromatic components of the radiation is obtained by substituting x_ω and y_ω into the formula

$$I_n = \frac{\omega_0^4 n^4}{3c^3}\mu^2\left(\frac{e_1}{m_1} - \frac{e_2}{m_2}\right)^2 (|x_\omega|^2 + |y_\omega|^2)$$

[see (67.11)]. Expressing a and ω_0 in terms of the characteristics of the particles, we obtain finally:

$$I_n = \frac{64 n^2 \mathcal{E}^4}{3c^3\alpha^2}\left(\frac{e_1}{m_1} - \frac{e_2}{m_2}\right)^2\left[J_n'^2(n\epsilon) + \frac{1-\epsilon^2}{\epsilon^2}J_n^2(n\epsilon)\right]. \qquad (70.8)$$

In particular, we shall give the asymptotic formula for the intensity of very high harmonics (large n) for motion in an orbit which is close to a parabola (ϵ close to 1). For this purpose, we use the formula

$$J_n(n\epsilon) \cong \frac{1}{\sqrt{\pi}}\left(\frac{2}{n}\right)^{\frac{1}{3}} \Phi\left[\left(\frac{n}{2}\right)^{\frac{2}{3}}(1-\epsilon^2)\right] \tag{70.9}$$

(Φ is the Airy function; see the footnote on p. 171) which is valid for†

$$n \gg 1, \ 1-\epsilon \ll 1.$$

Substituting in (70.8) gives:

$$I_n = \frac{64 \cdot 2^{2/3}}{3\pi} \frac{n^{4/3}\mathcal{E}^4}{c^3\alpha^2}\left(\frac{e_1}{m_1}-\frac{e_2}{m_2}\right)^2 \left\{(1-\epsilon^2)\Phi^2\left[\left(\frac{n}{2}\right)^{2/3}(1-\epsilon^2)\right] + \right.$$
$$\left. + \left(\frac{2}{n}\right)^{2/3}\Phi'^2\left[\left(\frac{n}{2}\right)^{2/3}(1-\epsilon^2)\right]\right\}. \tag{70.10}$$

Next, we consider the collision of two attracting charged particles. Their relative motion is described as the motion of a particle with mass μ in the hyperbola

$$1+\epsilon\cos\phi = \frac{a(\epsilon^2-1)}{r}, \tag{70.11}$$

where

$$a = \frac{\alpha}{2\mathcal{E}}, \qquad \epsilon = \sqrt{1+\frac{2\mathcal{E}M^2}{\mu\alpha^2}} \tag{70.12}$$

(now $\mathcal{E} > 0$). The time dependence of r is given by the parametric equations

$$r = a(\epsilon\cosh\xi - 1), \qquad t = \sqrt{\frac{\mu a^3}{\alpha}}(\epsilon\sinh\xi - \xi), \tag{70.13}$$

where the parameter ξ runs through values from $-\infty$ to $+\infty$. For the coordinates x, y, we have

$$x = a(\epsilon - \cosh\xi), \quad y = a\sqrt{\epsilon^2-1}\sinh\xi. \tag{70.14}$$

---

† For $n \gg 1$, the main contributions to the integral

$$J_n(n\epsilon) = \frac{1}{\pi}\int_0^\pi \cos[n(\xi - \epsilon\sin\xi)]\,d\xi$$

come from small values of ξ (for larger values of ξ, the integrand oscillates rapidly). In accordance with this, we expand the argument of the cosine in powers of ξ:

$$J_n(n\epsilon) = \frac{1}{\pi}\int_0^\infty \cos\left[n\left(\frac{1-\epsilon^2}{2}\xi + \frac{\xi^3}{6}\right)\right] d\xi;$$

because of the rapid convergence of the integral, the upper limit has been replaced by ∞; the term in ξ^3 must be kept because the first order term contains the small coefficient $1-\epsilon \cong \frac{1-\epsilon^2}{2}$. The integral above is reduced to the form (70.10) by an obvious substitution.

The calculation of the Fourier components (we are now dealing with expansion in a Fourier integral) proceeds in complete analogy to the preceding case. We find the result:

$$x_\omega = \frac{a}{2\omega} H_{i\nu}^{(1)\prime}(i\nu\epsilon), \quad y_\omega = -\frac{a\sqrt{\epsilon^2-1}}{2\omega\epsilon} H_{i\nu}^{(1)}(i\nu\epsilon). \tag{70.15}$$

where $H_{i\nu}^{(1)}$ is the Hankel function of the first kind, of order $i\nu$, and we have introduced the notation

$$\nu = \frac{\omega}{\sqrt{\dfrac{\alpha}{\mu a^3}}} = \frac{\omega}{\mu v_0^3} \tag{70.16}$$

(v_0 is the relative velocity of the particles at infinity; the energy is $\mathcal{E} = \mu v_0^2/2$). In the calculation we have used the formula from the theory of Bessel functions:†

$$\int_{-\infty}^{+\infty} e^{p\xi - ix\sinh\xi}\, d\xi = i\pi H_p^{(1)}(ix). \tag{70.17}$$

Substituting (70.15) in the formula

$$d\mathcal{E}_\omega = \frac{8\pi\omega^4\mu^2}{3c^3}\left(\frac{e_1}{m_1}-\frac{e_2}{m_2}\right)^2 (|x_\omega|^2+|y_\omega|^2)\, d\omega$$

[see (67.10)], we get:

$$d\mathcal{E}_\omega = \frac{\pi\mu^2 a^2\omega^2}{6c^3\mathcal{E}^2}\left(\frac{e_1}{m_1}-\frac{e_2}{m_2}\right)^2 \left\{[H_{i\nu}^{(1)\prime}(i\nu\epsilon)]^2 - \frac{\epsilon^2-1}{\epsilon^2}[H_{i\nu}^{(1)}(i\nu\epsilon)]^2\right\} d\omega. \tag{70.18}$$

A quantity of great interest is the "effective radiation" during the scattering of a parallel beam of particles (see § 68). To calculate it, we multiply $d\mathcal{E}_\omega$ by $2\pi\varrho\, d\varrho$ and integrate over all ϱ from zero to infinity. We transform from an integral over ϱ to one over ϵ (between the limits 1 and ∞) using the fact that $2\pi\varrho\, d\varrho = 2\pi a^2\epsilon\, d\epsilon$; this relation follows from the definition (70.12), in which the angular momentum M and the energy $\mathcal{E}$ are related to the impact parameter ϱ and the velocity v_0 by

$$M = \mu\varrho v_0, \quad \mathcal{E} = \mu\frac{v_0^2}{2}.$$

The resultant integral can be directly integrated with the aid of the formula

$$z\left[Z_p'^2 + \left(\frac{p^2}{z^2}-1\right)Z_p^2\right] = \frac{d}{dz}(zZ_pZ_p'),$$

where $Z_p(z)$ is an arbitrary solution of the Bessel equation of order p.‡ Keep-

† Note that the function $H_{i\nu}^{(1)}(i\nu\epsilon)$ is purely imaginary, while its derivative $H_{i\nu}^{(1)\prime}(i\nu\epsilon)$ is real.

‡ This formula is a direct consequence of the Bessel equation

$$Z'' + \frac{1}{z}Z' + \left(1-\frac{p^2}{z^2}\right)Z = 0.$$

ing in mind that for $\epsilon \to \infty$, the Hankel function $H_{i\nu}^{(1)}(i\nu\epsilon)$ goes to zero, we get as our result the following formula:

$$d\varkappa_\omega = \frac{4\pi^2 a^3 \omega}{3c^3 \mu v_0^5} \left(\frac{e_1}{m_1} - \frac{e_2}{m_2} \right)^2 |H_{i\nu}^{(1)}(i\nu)| H_{i\nu}^{(1)\prime}(i\nu)\, d\omega. \tag{70.19}$$

Let us consider the limiting cases of low and high frequencies. In the integral

$$\int_{-\infty}^{+\infty} e^{i\nu(\xi - \sinh \xi)}\, d\xi = i\pi H_{i\nu}^{(1)}(i\nu) \tag{70.20}$$

defining the Hankel function, the only important range of the integration parameter ξ is that in which the exponent is of order unity. For low frequencies ($\nu \ll 1$), only the region of large ξ is important. But for large ξ we have $\sinh \xi \gg \xi$. Thus, approximately,

$$H_{i\nu}^{(1)}(i\nu) \cong -\frac{i}{\pi} \int_{-\infty}^{+\infty} e^{-i\nu \sinh \xi}\, d\xi = H_0^{(1)}(i\nu).$$

Similarly, we find that

$$H_{i\nu}^{(1)\prime}(i\nu) \cong H_0^{(1)\prime}(i\nu).$$

Using the approximate expression (for small x) from the theory of Bessel functions:

$$iH_0^{(1)}(ix) \cong \frac{2}{\pi} \ln \frac{2}{\gamma x}$$

($\gamma = e^C$, where C is the Euler constant; $\gamma = 1.781\ldots$), we get the following expression for the effective radiation at low frequencies:

$$d\varkappa_\omega = \frac{16 a^2}{3 v_0^2 c^3} \left(\frac{e_1}{m_1} - \frac{e_2}{m_2} \right)^2 \ln \left(\frac{2\mu v_0^3}{\gamma \omega a} \right) d\omega \quad \text{for } \omega \ll \frac{\mu v_0^3}{a}. \tag{70.21}$$

It depends logarithmically on the frequency.

For high frequencies ($\nu \gg 1$), on the other hand, the region of small ξ is important in the integral (70.20). In accordance with this, we expand the exponent of the integrand in powers of ξ and get, approximately,

$$H_{i\nu}^{(1)}(i\nu) \cong -\frac{i}{\pi} \int_{-\infty}^{+\infty} e^{-\frac{i\nu\xi^3}{6}}\, d\xi = -\frac{2i}{\pi} \operatorname{Re} \left(\int_0^{\infty} e^{-\frac{i\nu\xi^3}{6}}\, d\xi \right).$$

By the substitution $\dfrac{i\nu\xi^3}{6} = \eta$, the integral goes over into the Γ-function, and we obtain the result:

$$H_{i\nu}^{(1)}(i\nu) \cong -\frac{i}{\pi\sqrt{3}} \left(\frac{6}{\nu} \right)^{1/3} \Gamma\left(\frac{1}{3} \right).$$

Similarly, we find

$$H_{i\nu}^{(1)\prime}(i\nu) = \frac{1}{\pi\sqrt{3}}\left(\frac{6}{\nu}\right)^{2/3}\Gamma\left(\frac{2}{3}\right)$$

Next, using the formula of the theory of the Γ-function,

$$\Gamma(x)\Gamma(1-x) = \frac{\pi}{\sin \pi x},$$

we obtain for the effective radiation at high frequencies:

$$d\varkappa_\omega = \frac{16\pi\alpha^2}{3^{3/2}v_0^2c^3}\left(\frac{e_1}{m_1}-\frac{e_2}{m_2}\right)^2 d\omega, \text{ for } \omega \gg \frac{\mu v_0^3}{\alpha}, \tag{70.22}$$

that is, an expression which is independent of the frequency.

We now proceed to the radiation accompanying the collision of two particles repelling each other according to the Coulomb law $U = \frac{\alpha}{r}$ $(\alpha > 0)$. The motion occurs in a hyperbola,

$$-1+\epsilon\cos\phi = \frac{a(\epsilon^2-1)}{r}. \tag{70.23}$$

The time dependence is given by the parametric equations

$$x = a(\epsilon+\cosh\xi), \quad y = a\sqrt{\epsilon^2-1}\sinh\xi,$$

$$t = \sqrt{\frac{\mu a^3}{\alpha}}(\epsilon\sinh\xi+\xi) \tag{70.24}$$

[a and ϵ as in (70.12)]. All the calculations for this case reduce immediately to those given above, so it is not necessary to present them. Namely, the integral

$$x_\omega = \frac{ia}{2\pi\omega}\int_{-\infty}^{+\infty} e^{i\nu(\epsilon\sinh\xi+\xi)}\sinh\xi\, d\xi$$

for the Fourier component of the coordinate x reduces, by making the substitution $\xi \to i\pi-\xi$, to the integral for the case of attraction, multiplied by $e^{-\pi\nu}$; the same holds for y_ω.

Thus the expressions for the Fourier components x_ω, y_ω in the case of repulsion differ from the corresponding expressions for the case of attraction by the factor $e^{-\pi\nu}$. So the only change in the formulas for the radiation is an additional factor $e^{-2\pi\nu}$. In particular, for low frequencies we get the previous formula (70.21) (since for $\nu \ll 1$, $e^{-2\pi\nu} \cong 1$). For high frequencies, the effective radiation has the form

$$d\varkappa_\omega = \frac{16\pi\alpha^2}{3^{3/2}v_0^2c^3}\left(\frac{e_1}{m_1}-\frac{e_2}{m_2}\right)^2 \exp\left(-\frac{2\pi\omega\alpha}{\mu v_0^3}\right) d\omega, \quad \text{for } \omega \gg \frac{\mu v_0^3}{\alpha}. \tag{70.25}$$

It drops exponentially with increasing frequency.

Problems

1. Calculate the average total intensity of the radiation for elliptical motion of two attracting charges.

Solution: From the expression (70.1) for the dipole moment, we have for the total intensity of the radiation:

$$I = \frac{2\mu^2}{3c^3}\left(\frac{e_1}{m_1}-\frac{e_2}{m_2}\right)^2 \ddot{\mathbf{r}}^2 = \frac{2\alpha^2}{3c^3}\left(\frac{e_1}{m_1}-\frac{e_2}{m_2}\right)^2 \frac{1}{r^4},$$

where we have used the equation of motion $\mu\ddot{\mathbf{r}} = -\alpha\mathbf{r}/r^3$. We express the coordinate r in terms of ϕ from the orbit equation (70.2) and, by using the equation $dt = \mu r^2\, d\phi/M$, we replace the time integration by an integration over the angle ϕ (from 0 to 2π). As a result, we find for the average intensity:

$$\bar{I} = \frac{1}{T}\int_0^T I\,dt = \frac{2^{3/2}}{3c^3}\left(\frac{e_1}{m_1}-\frac{e_2}{m_2}\right)^2 \frac{\mu^{5/2}\alpha^3|\mathcal{E}|^{3/2}}{M^5}\left(3-\frac{2|\mathcal{E}|M^2}{\mu\alpha^2}\right).$$

2. Calculate the total radiation $\Delta\mathcal{E}$ for the collision of two charged particles.

Solution. In the case of attraction the trajectory is the hyperbola (70.11) and in the case of repulsion, (70.12). The angle between the asymptotes of the hyperbola and its axis is ϕ_0, determined from $\pm\cos\phi_0 = 1/\epsilon$, and the angle of deflection of the particles (in the system of coordinates in which the center of mass is at rest) is $\chi = |\pi-2\phi_0|$. The calculation proceeds the same as in Problem 1 (the integral over ϕ is taken between the limits $-\phi_0$ and $+\phi_0$). The result for the case of attraction is

$$\Delta\mathcal{E} = \frac{\mu^3 v_0^5}{3c^3|\alpha|}\tan^3\frac{\chi}{2}\left\{(\pi+\chi)\left(1+3\tan^2\frac{\chi}{2}\right)+6\tan\frac{\chi}{2}\right\}\left(\frac{e_1}{m_1}-\frac{e_2}{m_2}\right)^2,$$

and for the case of repulsion:

$$\Delta\mathcal{E} = \frac{\mu^3 v_0^5}{3c^3\alpha}\tan^3\frac{\chi}{2}\left\{(\pi-\chi)\left(1+3\tan^2\frac{\chi}{2}\right)-6\tan\frac{\chi}{2}\right\}\left(\frac{e_1}{m_1}-\frac{e_2}{m_2}\right)^2.$$

In both, χ is understood to be a positive angle, determined from the relation

$$\cot\frac{\chi}{2} = \frac{\mu v_0^2\varrho}{\alpha}.$$

Thus for a head-on collision ($\varrho\to 0, \chi\to\pi$) of charges repelling each other:

$$\Delta\mathcal{E} = \frac{8\mu^3 v_0^5}{45c^3\alpha}\left(\frac{e_1}{m_1}-\frac{e_2}{m_2}\right)^2.$$

3. Calculate the total effective radiation in the scattering of a beam of particles in a repulsive Coulomb field.

Solution: The required quantity is

$$\varkappa = \int_0^\infty\int_{-\infty}^{+\infty} I\,dt\,2\pi\varrho\,d\varrho = \frac{2\alpha^2}{3c^3}\left(\frac{e_1}{m_1}-\frac{e_2}{m_2}\right)^2 2\pi\int_0^\infty\int_{-\infty}^{+\infty}\frac{1}{r^4}\,dt\varrho\,d\varrho.$$

We replace the time integration by integration over r along the trajectory of the charge, writing $dt = dr/v_r$, where the radial velocity $v_r \equiv \dot{r}$ is expressed in terms of r by the formula

$$v_r = \sqrt{\frac{2}{\mu}\left[\mathcal{E}-\frac{M^2}{2\mu r^2}-U(r)\right]} = \sqrt{v_0^2-\frac{\varrho^2 v_0^2}{r^2}-\frac{2\alpha}{\mu r}}.$$

The integration over r goes between the limits from ∞ to the distance of closest approach $r_0 = r_0(\varrho)$ (the point at which $v_r = 0$), and then from r_0 once again to infinity; this reduces to twice the integral from r_0 to ∞. the calculation of the double integral is conveniently done by changing the order of integration – integrating first over ϱ and then over r. The result of the calculation is:

$$\varkappa = \frac{8\pi}{9c^3} a\mu v_0 \left(\frac{e_1}{m_1} - \frac{e_2}{m_2}\right)^2.$$

4. Calculate the angular distribution of the total radiation emitted when one charge passes by another, if the velocity is so large (though still small compared with the velocity of light) that the deviation from straight-line motion can be considered small.

Solution: The angle of deflection is small if the kinetic energy $\mu v^2/2$ is large compared to the potential energy, which is of order a/ϱ ($\mu v^2 \gg a/\varrho$). We choose the plane of the motion as the x, y plane, with the origin at the center of inertia and the x axis along the direction of the velocity. In first approximation, the trajectory is the straight line $x = vt$, $y = \varrho$. In the next approximation, the equations of motion give

$$\mu\ddot{x} = \frac{a}{r^2}\frac{x}{r} \cong \frac{avt}{r^3}, \qquad \mu\ddot{y} = \frac{a}{r^2}\frac{y}{r} \cong \frac{a\varrho}{r^3},$$

with

$$r = \sqrt{x^2+y^2} \cong \sqrt{\varrho^2+v^2t^2}.$$

Using formula (67.7), we have:

$$d\mathcal{E}_{\mathbf{n}} = do\frac{\mu^2}{4\pi c^3}\left(\frac{e_1}{m_1} - \frac{e_2}{m_2}\right)^2 \int_{-\infty}^{\infty} [\ddot{x}^2+\ddot{y}^2-(\ddot{x}n_x+\ddot{y}n_y)^2]\,dt,$$

where $\mathbf{n}$ is the unit vector in the direction of do. Expressing the integrand in terms of t and performing the integration, we get:

$$d\mathcal{E}_{\mathbf{n}} = \frac{a^2}{32vc^3\varrho^3}\left(\frac{e_1}{m_1} - \frac{e_2}{m_2}\right)^2 (4-n_x^2-3n_y^2)\,do.$$

§ 71. Quadrupole and magnetic dipole radiation

We now consider the radiation associated with the succeeding terms in the expansion of the vector potential in powers of the ratio a/λ of the dimensions of the system to the wave length. Since a/λ is assumed to be small, these terms are generally small compared with the first (dipole) term, but they are important in those cases where the dipole moment of the system is zero, so that dipole radiation does not occur.

Expanding the integrand in (66.2),

$$\mathbf{A} = \frac{1}{cR_0}\int \mathbf{j}_{t'+\frac{\mathbf{r}\cdot\mathbf{n}}{c}}\,dV,$$

in powers of $\mathbf{r}\cdot\mathbf{n}/c$, we find, correct to terms of first order:

$$\mathbf{A} = \frac{1}{cR_0}\int \mathbf{j}_{t'}\,dV + \frac{1}{c^2R_0}\frac{\partial}{\partial t'}\int (\mathbf{r}\cdot\mathbf{n})\mathbf{j}_{t'}\,dV.$$

Substituting $\mathbf{j} = \varrho\mathbf{v}$ and changing to point charges, we obtain:

$$\mathbf{A} = \frac{\sum e\mathbf{v}}{cR_0} + \frac{1}{c^2R_0}\frac{\partial}{\partial t}\sum e\mathbf{v}(\mathbf{r}\cdot\mathbf{n}). \tag{71.1}$$

(From now on, as in § 67, we drop the index t' in all quantities).

In the second term we write

$$\mathbf{v}(\mathbf{r}\cdot\mathbf{n}) = \frac{1}{2}\frac{\partial}{\partial t}\mathbf{r}(\mathbf{n}\cdot\mathbf{r}) + \frac{1}{2}\mathbf{v}(\mathbf{n}\cdot\mathbf{r}) - \frac{1}{2}\mathbf{r}(\mathbf{n}\cdot\mathbf{v})$$

$$= \frac{1}{2}\frac{\partial}{\partial t}\mathbf{r}(\mathbf{n}\cdot\mathbf{r}) + \frac{1}{2}(\mathbf{r}\times\mathbf{v})\times\mathbf{n}.$$

We then find for $\mathbf{A}$ the expression

$$\mathbf{A} = \frac{\dot{\mathbf{d}}}{cR_0} + \frac{1}{2c^2R_0}\frac{\partial^2}{\partial t^2}\sum e\mathbf{r}(\mathbf{n}\cdot\mathbf{r}) + \frac{1}{cR_0}(\dot{\mathfrak{m}}\times\mathbf{n}), \tag{71.2}$$

where $\mathbf{d}$ is the dipole moment of the system, and $\mathfrak{m} = \frac{1}{2c}\sum e\mathbf{r}\times\mathbf{v}$ is its magnetic moment. For further transformation, we note that we can, without changing the field, add to $\mathbf{A}$ any vector proportional to $\mathbf{n}$, since according to formula (66.3), $\mathbf{H}$ and $\mathbf{E}$ are unchanged by this. For this reason we can replace (71.2) by

$$\mathbf{A} = \frac{\dot{\mathbf{d}}}{cR_0} + \frac{1}{6c^2R_0}\frac{\partial^2}{\partial t^2}\sum e[3\mathbf{r}(\mathbf{n}\cdot\mathbf{r}) - \mathbf{n}r^2] + \frac{1}{cR_0}\dot{\mathfrak{m}}\times\mathbf{n}.$$

But the expression under the summation sign is just the product $n_\beta D_{\alpha\beta}$ of the vector $\mathbf{n}$ and the quadrupole moment tensor $D_{\alpha\beta} = \sum e(3x_\alpha x_\beta - \delta_{\alpha\beta}r^2)$ (see § 41). We introduce the vector $\mathbf{D}$ with components $D_\alpha = D_{\alpha\beta}n_\beta$, and get the final expression for the vector potential:

$$\mathbf{A} = \frac{\dot{\mathbf{d}}}{cR_0} + \frac{1}{6c^2R_0}\ddot{\mathbf{D}} + \frac{1}{cR_0}\dot{\mathfrak{m}}\times\mathbf{n}. \tag{71.3}$$

Knowing $\mathbf{A}$, we can now determine the fields $\mathbf{H}$ and $\mathbf{E}$ of the radiation, using the general formula (66.3):

$$\mathbf{H} = \frac{1}{c^2R_0}\left\{\ddot{\mathbf{d}}\times\mathbf{n} + \frac{1}{6c}\dddot{\mathbf{D}}\times\mathbf{n} + (\ddot{\mathfrak{m}}\times\mathbf{n})\times\mathbf{n}\right\},$$

$$\mathbf{E} = \frac{1}{c^2R_0}\left\{(\ddot{\mathbf{d}}\times\mathbf{n})\times\mathbf{n} + \frac{1}{6c}(\dddot{\mathbf{D}}\times\mathbf{n})\times\mathbf{n} + \mathbf{n}\times\ddot{\mathfrak{m}}\right\}. \tag{71.4}$$

The intensity dI of the radiation in the solid angle do is given by the general formula (66.6). We calculate here the total radiation, i.e., the energy radiated by the system in unit time in all directions. To do this, we average dI over all directions of $\mathbf{n}$; the total radiation is equal to this average multiplied by 4π. In averaging the square of the magnetic field, all the cross-products of the three terms in **H** vanish, so that there remain only the mean squares of the three. A simple calculation† gives the following result for I:

$$I = \frac{2}{3c^3}\ddot{\mathbf{d}}^2 + \frac{1}{180c^5}\dddot{D}^2_{\alpha\beta} + \frac{2}{3c^3}\ddot{\mathfrak{m}}^2. \tag{71.5}$$

Thus the total radiation consists of three independent parts; they are called, respectively, *dipole*, *quadrupole*, and *magnetic dipole* radiation.

We not that the magnetic dipole radiation is actually not present for many systems. Thus it is not present for a system in which the charge-to-mass ratio is the same for all the moving charges (in this case the dipole radiation also vanishes, as already shown in § 67). Namely, for such a system the magnetic moment is proportional to the angular momentum (see § 44) and therefore, since the latter is conserved, $\dot{\mathfrak{m}} = 0$. For the same reason, magnetic dipole radiation does not occur for a system consisting of just two particles (cf. the problem in § 44. In this case we cannot draw any conclusion concerning the dipole radiation).

PROBLEM

Calculate the total effective radiation in the scattering of a beam of charged particles by particles identical with them.

Solution. In the collision of identical particles, dipole radiation (and also magnetic dipole radiation) does not occur, so that we must calculate the quadrupole radiation. The quadrupole moment tensor of a system of two identical particles (relative to their center of mass) is

$$D_{\alpha\beta} = \frac{e}{2}(3x_\alpha x_\beta - r^2\delta_{\alpha\beta}),$$

where x_α are the components of the radius vector **r** between the particles. After threefold differentiation of $D_{\alpha\beta}$, we express the first, second, and third derivatives with respect to time of x_α in terms of the relative velocity of the particles v_α as:

$$\dot{x}_\alpha = v, \quad \mu\ddot{x}_\alpha = \frac{m}{2}\ddot{x}_\alpha = \frac{e^2 x_\alpha}{r^3}, \quad \frac{m}{2}\dddot{x}_\alpha = e^2\frac{v_\alpha r - 3x_\alpha v_r}{r^4},$$

where $v_r = \mathbf{v}\cdot\mathbf{r}/r$ is the radial component of the velocity (the second equality is the equation of motion of the charge, and the third is obtained by differentiating the second). The calculation leads to the following expression for the intensity:

$$I = \frac{\dddot{D}^2_{\alpha\beta}}{180c^5} = \frac{2e^6}{15m^2c^5}\frac{1}{r^4}(v^2 + 11v_\phi^2)$$

† We present a convenient method for averaging the products of components of a unit vector. Since **n** is a unit vector, $\overline{n_\alpha n_\beta}$, being a symmetric tensor, can be expressed in terms of the unit tensor $\delta_{\alpha\beta}$, that is, $\overline{n_\alpha n_\beta} = a\delta_{\alpha\beta}$. Contracting on the pair of indices α, β, and remembering that $n_\alpha^2 = 1$, we find that $a = \frac{1}{3}$.

For the average value of the product of four components we write, similarly,

$$\overline{n_\alpha n_\beta n_\gamma n_\delta} = a(\delta_{\alpha\beta}\delta_{\gamma\delta} + \delta_{\alpha\gamma}\delta_{\beta\delta} + \delta_{\alpha\delta}\delta_{\beta\gamma})$$

(keeping in mind the symmetry of $n_\alpha n_\beta n_\gamma n_\delta$ in all four indices). Contracting on the pairs of indices α, β and γ, δ, we find $a = \frac{1}{15}$.

($v^2 = v_r^2 + v_\phi^2$); v and v_ϕ are expressible in terms of r by using the equalities

$$v^2 = v_0^2 - \frac{4e^2}{mr}, \qquad v_\phi = \frac{\varrho v_0}{r}.$$

We replace the time integration by an integration over r in the same way as was done in Problem 3 of § 70, namely, we write

$$dt = \frac{dr}{v_r} = \frac{dr}{\sqrt{v_0^2 - \dfrac{\varrho^2 v_0^2}{r^2} - \dfrac{4e^2}{mr}}}.$$

In the double integral (over ϱ and r), we first carry out the integration over ϱ and then over r. The result of the calculation is:

$$\varkappa = \frac{4\pi}{9} \frac{e^4 v_0^3}{mc^5}.$$

§ 72. The field of the radiation at near distances

The formulas for the dipole radiation were derived by us for the field at distances large compared with the wavelength (and, all the more, large compared with the dimensions of the radiating system). In this section we shall assume, as before, that the wavelength is large compared with the dimensions of the system, but shall consider the field at distances which are not large compared with, but *of the same order, as* the wavelength.

The formula (67.4) for the vector potential

$$\mathbf{A} = \frac{1}{cR_0}\dot{\mathbf{d}} \tag{72.1}$$

is still valid, since in deriving it we used only the fact that R_0 was large compared with the dimensions of the system. However, now the field cannot be considered to be a plane wave even over small regions. Therefore the formulas (67.5) and (67.6) for the electric and magnetic fields are no longer applicable, so that to calculate them, we must first determine both $\mathbf{A}$ and ϕ.

The formula for the scalar potential can be derived directly from that for the vector potential, using the general condition (62.3),

$$\operatorname{div}\mathbf{A} + \frac{1}{c}\frac{\partial \phi}{\partial t} = 0,$$

imposed on the potentials. Substituting (72.1) in this, and integrating over the time, we get

$$\phi = -\operatorname{div}\frac{\mathbf{d}}{R_0}. \tag{72.2}$$

The integration constant (an arbitrary function of the coordinates) is omitted, since we are interested only in the variable part of the potential. We recall that in the formula (72.2) as well as in (72.1) the value of **d** must be taken at the time $t' = t - \frac{R_0}{c}$.†

Now it is no longer difficult to calculate the electric and magnetic field. From the usual formulas, relating **E** and **H** to the potentials,

$$\mathbf{H} = \frac{1}{c}\,\mathrm{curl}\,\frac{\dot{\mathbf{d}}}{R_0}, \tag{72.3}$$

$$\mathbf{E} = \mathrm{grad}\,\mathrm{div}\,\frac{\mathbf{d}}{R_0} - \frac{1}{c^2}\frac{\ddot{\mathbf{d}}}{R_0}. \tag{72.4}$$

The expression for **E** can be rewritten in another form, noting that $\mathbf{d}_{t'}/R_0$ $\left[\text{just as any function of coordinates and time of the form } \frac{1}{R_0} f\left(t - \frac{R_0}{c}\right)\right]$ satisfies the wave equation:

$$\frac{1}{c^2}\frac{\partial^2}{\partial t^2}\left(\frac{\mathbf{d}}{R_0}\right) = \Delta\left(\frac{\mathbf{d}}{R_0}\right).$$

Also using the formula

$$\mathrm{curl}\,\mathrm{curl}\,\mathbf{a} = \mathrm{grad}\,\mathrm{div}\,\mathbf{a} - \Delta\mathbf{a},$$

we find that

$$\mathbf{E} = \mathrm{curl}\,\mathrm{curl}\,\frac{\mathbf{d}}{R_0}. \tag{72.5}$$

The results obtained determine the field at distances of the order of the wavelength. It is understood that in all these formulas it is not permissible to take $1/R_0$ out from under the differentiation sign, since the ratio of terms containing $1/R_0^2$ to terms with $1/R_0$ is just of the same order as λ/R_0.

Finally, we give the formulas for the Fourier components of the field. To determine $\mathbf{H}_\omega$ we substitute in (72.3) for **H** and **d** their monochromatic components $\mathbf{H}_\omega e^{-i\omega t}$ and $\mathbf{d}_\omega e^{-i\omega t}$, respectively. However, we must remember that the quantities on the right sides of equations (72.1) to (72.5) refer to the time $t' = t - \frac{R_0}{c}$. Therefore we must substitute in place of **d** the expression

$$\mathbf{d}_\omega e^{-i\omega\left(t - \frac{R_0}{c}\right)} = \mathbf{d}_\omega e^{-i\omega t + ikR_0}.$$

† Sometimes one introduces the so-called Hertz vector, defined by

$$\mathbf{Z} = -\frac{1}{R_0}\,\mathbf{d}\left(t - \frac{R_0}{c}\right).$$

Then

$$\mathbf{A} = -\frac{1}{c}\dot{\mathbf{Z}}, \qquad \phi = \mathrm{div}\,\mathbf{Z}.$$

Making the substitution and dividing by $e^{-i\omega t}$, we get

$$\mathbf{H}_\omega = -ik \operatorname{curl}\left(\mathbf{d}_\omega \frac{e^{ikR_0}}{R_0}\right) = ik\mathbf{d}_\omega \times \nabla \frac{e^{ikR_0}}{R_0}.$$

or, performing the differentiation,

$$\mathbf{H}_\omega = ik\mathbf{d}_\omega \times \mathbf{n}\left(\frac{ik}{R_0} - \frac{1}{R_0^2}\right) e^{ikR_0}, \tag{72.6}$$

where $\mathbf{n}$ is a unit vector along $\mathbf{R}_0$.

In similar fashion, we find from (72.4):

$$\mathbf{E}_\omega = k^2 \mathbf{d}_\omega \frac{e^{ikR_0}}{R_0} + (\mathbf{d}_\omega \cdot \nabla)\nabla \frac{e^{ikR_0}}{R_0},$$

and differentiation gives

$$\mathbf{E}_\omega = \mathbf{d}_\omega\left(\frac{k^2}{R_0} + \frac{ik}{R_0^2} - \frac{1}{R_0^3}\right) e^{ikR_0} + \mathbf{n}(\mathbf{n}\cdot\mathbf{d}_\omega)\left(-\frac{k^2}{R_0} - \frac{3ik}{R_0^2} + \frac{3}{R_0^3}\right) e^{ikR_0}. \tag{72.7}$$

At distances large compared to the wave length ($kR_0 \gg 1$), we can neglect the terms in $1/R_0^2$ and $1/R_0^3$ in formulas (72.5) and (72.6), and we arrive at the field in the "wave zone",

$$\mathbf{E}_\omega = \frac{k^2}{R_0}\mathbf{n}\times(\mathbf{d}_\omega \times \mathbf{n})\, e^{ikR_0}, \qquad \mathbf{H}_\omega = -\frac{k^2}{R_0}\mathbf{d}_\omega \times \mathbf{n}\, e^{ikR_0}.$$

At distances which are small compared to the wave length ($kR_0 \ll 1$), we neglect the terms in $1/R_0$ and $1/R_0^2$ and set $e^{ikR_0} \cong 1$; then

$$\mathbf{E}_\omega = \frac{1}{R_0^3}\{3\mathbf{n}(\mathbf{d}_\omega \cdot \mathbf{n}) - \mathbf{d}_\omega\},$$

which corresponds to the static field of an electric dipole (§ 40); in this approximation, the magnetic field vanishes.

Problem

Calculate the quadrupole and magnetic dipole radiation field at near distances.

Solution: Assuming, for brevity, that dipole radiation is not present, we have (see the calculation carried out in § 71)

$$\mathbf{A} = \frac{1}{c}\int \mathbf{j}_{t-\frac{R}{c}} \frac{dV}{R} \cong -\frac{1}{c}\int (\mathbf{r}\cdot\nabla) \frac{\mathbf{j}_{t-\frac{R_0}{c}}}{R_0}\, dV$$

(we have expanded in powers of $\mathbf{r} = \mathbf{R}_0 - \mathbf{R}$). In contrast to what was done in § 71, the factor $1/R_0$ cannot here be taken out from under the differentiation sign. We take the differential operator out of the integral and rewrite the integral in tensor notation:

$$A_\alpha = -\frac{1}{c}\frac{\partial}{\partial X_\beta}\int \frac{x_\beta j_\alpha}{R_0}\, dV$$

(X_β are the components of the radius vector $\mathbf{R}_0$). Transforming from the integral to a sum over the charges, we find

$$A_\alpha = -\frac{1}{c}\frac{\partial}{\partial X_\beta}\frac{\left(\sum e v_\alpha x_\beta\right)_t}{R_0}.$$

In the same way as in § 71, this expression breaks up into a quadrupole part and a magnetic dipole part. The corresponding scalar potentials are calculated from the vector potentials in the same way as in the text. As a result, we obtain for the quadrupole radiation:

$$A_\alpha = -\frac{1}{6c}\frac{\partial}{\partial X_\beta}\frac{\dot{D}_{\alpha\beta}}{R_0}, \qquad \phi = \frac{1}{6}\frac{\partial^2}{\partial X_\alpha \partial X_\beta}\frac{D_{\alpha\beta}}{R_0},$$

and for the magnetic dipole radiation:

$$\mathbf{A} = \operatorname{curl}\frac{\mathfrak{m}}{R_0}, \qquad \phi = 0$$

(all quantities on the right sides of the equations refer as usual to the time $t' = t - \frac{R_0}{c}$).

The field intensities for magnetic dipole radiation are:

$$\mathbf{E} = -\frac{1}{c}\operatorname{curl}\frac{\dot{\mathfrak{m}}}{R_0}, \qquad \mathbf{H} = \operatorname{curl}\operatorname{curl}\frac{\mathfrak{m}}{R_0}.$$

Comparing with (72.3), (72.4), we see that in the magnetic dipole case, **E** and **H** are expressed in terms of $\mathfrak{m}$ in the same way as $-$**H** and **E** are expressed in terms of **d** for the electric dipole case.

The spectral components of the potentials of the quadrupole radiation are:

$$A_\alpha^{(\omega)} = \frac{ik}{6} D_{\alpha\beta}^{(\omega)} \frac{\partial}{\partial X_\beta}\frac{e^{ikR_0}}{R_0}, \qquad \phi^{(\omega)} = \frac{1}{6} D_{\alpha\beta}^{(\omega)} \frac{\partial^2}{\partial X_\alpha \partial X_\beta}\frac{e^{ikR_0}}{R_0}.$$

Because of their complexity, we shall not give the expressions for the field.

§ 73. Radiation from a rapidly moving charge

Now we consider a charged particle moving with a velocity which is not small compared with the velocity of light.

The formulas of § 67, derived under the assumption that $v \ll c$, are not immediately applicable to this case. We can, however, consider the particle in that system of reference in which the particle is at rest at a given moment; in this system of reference the formulas referred to are of course valid (we call attention to the fact that this can be done only for the case of a *single* moving particle; for a system of several particles there is generally no system of reference in which all the particles are at rest simultaneously).

Thus in this particular system of reference, the particle radiates in time dt, the energy

$$d\mathcal{E} = \frac{2e^2}{3c^3} w_0^2\, dt \tag{73.1}$$

[in accordance with formula (67.9)], where w_0 is the acceleration of the particle in this system of reference. In this system of reference, the "radiated" momentum is zero:

$$d\mathbf{P} = 0. \tag{73.2}$$

In fact, the radiated momentum is given by the integral of the momentum flux density in the radiation field over a closed surface surrounding the particle.

But because of the symmetry of the dipole radiation, the momenta carried off in opposite directions are equal in magnitude and opposite in direction; therefore the integral is identically zero.

For the transformation to an arbitrary reference system, we rewrite formulas (73.1) and (73.2) in four-dimensional form. It is easy to see that the "radiated four-momentum" dP_i must be written as

$$dP_i = \frac{2e^2}{3c}\left(\frac{du_k}{ds}\right)^2 dx_i = \frac{2e^2}{3c}\left(\frac{du_k}{ds}\right)^2 u_i\, ds. \qquad (73.3)$$

In fact, in the reference frame in which the particle is at rest, the space components of the four-velocity u_i are equal to zero, and $\left(\frac{du_k}{ds}\right)^2 = \frac{w_0^2}{c^4}$; therefore the space components of dP_i become zero and the time component gives equation (73.1).

The total four-momentum radiated during the time of passage of the particle through a given electromagnetic field is equal to the integral of (73.3), that is,

$$\Delta P_i = \frac{2e^2}{3c}\int\left(\frac{du_k}{ds}\right)^2 dx_i. \qquad (73.4)$$

We rewrite this formula in another form, expressing the four-acceleration du_i/ds in terms of the electromagnetic field tensor, using the equation of motion (23.5):

$$mc\frac{du_k}{ds} = \frac{e}{c}F_{kl}u_l.$$

We then obtain

$$\Delta P_i = \frac{2e^4}{3m^2c^5}\int (F_{kl}u_l)^2\, dx_i. \qquad (73.5)$$

The time component of (73.4) or (73.5) gives the total radiated energy $\Delta\mathcal{E}$. Substituting for all the four-dimensional quantities their expressions in terms of three-dimensional quantities, we find

$$\Delta\mathcal{E} = \frac{2e^2}{3c^3}\int_{-\infty}^{\infty}\frac{w^2 - \dfrac{(\mathbf{v}\times\mathbf{w})^2}{c^2}}{\left(1-\dfrac{v^2}{c^2}\right)^3}\,dt \qquad (73.6)$$

($\mathbf{w} = \dot{\mathbf{v}}$ is the acceleration of the particle), or, in terms of the external electric and magnetic fields:

$$\Delta\mathcal{E} = \frac{2e^4}{3m^2c^3}\int_{-\infty}^{\infty}\frac{\left\{\mathbf{E}+\dfrac{1}{c}\mathbf{v}\times\mathbf{H}\right\}^2 - \dfrac{1}{c^2}(\mathbf{E}\cdot\mathbf{v})^2}{1-\dfrac{v^2}{c^2}}\,dt. \qquad (73.7)$$

The expressions for the total radiated momentum differ by having an extra factor **v** in the integrand.

It is clear from formula (73.7) that for velocities close to the velocity of light, the total energy radiated per unit time varies with the velocity essentially like $\left(1-\frac{v^2}{c^2}\right)^{-1}$, that is, proportionally to the square of the energy of the moving particle. The only exception is motion in an electric field, along the direction of the field. In this case the factor $\left(1-\frac{v^2}{c^2}\right)$ standing in the denominator is cancelled by an identical factor in the numerator, and the radiation does not depend on the energy of the particle.

Finally there is the question of the angular distribution of the radiation from a rapidly moving charge. To solve this problem, it is convenient to use the Lienard-Wiechert expressions for the fields, (63.8) and (63.9). At large distances we must retain only the term of lowest order in $1/R$ [the second term in (63.8)]. Introducing the unit vector **n** in the direction of the radiation ($\mathbf{R}=\mathbf{n}R$), we thus get for the field produced by the charge the formulas

$$\mathbf{E}=\frac{e}{c^2R}\frac{\mathbf{n}\times\left\{\left(\mathbf{n}-\frac{\mathbf{v}}{c}\right)\times\mathbf{w}\right\}}{\left(1-\frac{\mathbf{n}\cdot\mathbf{v}}{c}\right)^3},\qquad \mathbf{H}=\mathbf{n}\times\mathbf{E}, \tag{73.8}$$

where all the quantities on the right sides of the equations refer to the retarded time $t'=t-\frac{R}{c}$.

The intensity radiated into the solid angle do is $dI=\frac{c}{4\pi}E^2R^2\,do$. Expanding E^2, we get

$$dI=\frac{e^2}{4\pi c^3}\left\{\frac{2(\mathbf{n}\cdot\mathbf{w})(\mathbf{v}\cdot\mathbf{w})}{c\left(1-\frac{\mathbf{v}\cdot\mathbf{n}}{c}\right)^5}+\frac{\mathbf{w}^2}{\left(1-\frac{\mathbf{v}\cdot\mathbf{n}}{c}\right)^4}-\frac{\left(1-\frac{v^2}{c^2}\right)(\mathbf{n}\cdot\mathbf{w})^2}{\left(1-\frac{\mathbf{v}\cdot\mathbf{n}}{c}\right)^6}\right\}do. \tag{73.9}$$

If we want to determine the angular distribution of the total radiation throughout the whole motion of the particle, we must integrate the intensity over the time. In doing this, it is important to remember that the integrand is a function of t'; therefore we must write

$$dt=\frac{\partial t}{\partial t'}dt'=\left(1-\frac{\mathbf{n}\cdot\mathbf{v}}{c}\right)dt' \tag{73.10}$$

[see (63.6)], after which the integration over t' is immediately done. Thus we have the following expression for the total radiation into the solid angle do:

$$d\mathcal{E}_{\mathbf{n}} = \frac{e^2}{4\pi c^3} do \int \left\{ \frac{2(\mathbf{n}\cdot\mathbf{w})(\mathbf{v}\cdot\mathbf{w})}{c\left(1-\frac{\mathbf{v}\cdot\mathbf{n}}{c}\right)^4} + \frac{\mathbf{w}^2}{\left(1-\frac{\mathbf{v}\cdot\mathbf{n}}{c}\right)^3} - \frac{\left(1-\frac{v^2}{c^2}\right)(\mathbf{n}\cdot\mathbf{w})^2}{\left(1-\frac{\mathbf{n}\cdot\mathbf{v}}{c}\right)^5} \right\} dt'. \tag{73.11}$$

As we see from (73.9), in the general case the angular distribution of the radiation is quite complicated. In the ultrarelativistic case, $\left(1-\frac{v}{c} \ll 1\right)$ it has a characteristic appearance, which is related to the presence of high powers of the difference $1-\frac{\mathbf{v}\cdot\mathbf{n}}{c}$ in the denominators of the various terms in this expression. Thus, the intensity is large within the narrow range of angles in which the difference $1-\frac{\mathbf{v}\cdot\mathbf{n}}{c}$ is small. Denoting by θ the small angle between $\mathbf{n}$ and $\mathbf{v}$, we have:

$$1-\frac{v}{c}\cos\theta \cong 1-\frac{v}{c}+\frac{\theta^2}{2};$$

this difference is small $\left(\sim 1-\frac{v}{c}\right)$ for $\theta \sim \sqrt{1-\frac{v}{c}}$, i.e. for

$$\theta \sim \sqrt{1-\frac{v^2}{c^2}}. \tag{73.12}$$

Thus an ultrarelativistic particle radiates mainly along the direction of its own motion, within the small range (73.12) of angles around the direction of its velocity.

We also point out that, for arbitrary velocity and acceleration of the particle, there are always two directions for which the radiated intensity is zero. These are the directions for which the vector $\mathbf{n}-\frac{\mathbf{v}}{c}$ is parallel to the vector $\mathbf{w}$, so that the field (73.9) becomes zero. (See also problem 2 of this section.)

If the velocity and acceleration of the particle are parallel,

$$\mathbf{H} = \frac{e}{c^2 R} \frac{\mathbf{w}\times\mathbf{n}}{\left(1-\frac{\mathbf{n}\cdot\mathbf{v}}{c}\right)^3},$$

and the intensity is

$$dI = \frac{e^2}{4\pi c^3} \frac{w^2 \sin^2\theta}{\left(1-\frac{v}{c}\cos\theta\right)^6} do. \tag{73.13}$$

It is naturally, symmetric around the common direction of **v** and **w**, and vanishes along ($\theta = 0$) and opposite to ($\theta = \pi$) the direction of the velocity. In the ultrarelativistic case, the intensity as a function of θ has a sharp double maximum in the region (73.12), with a "pass" which drops to zero for $\theta = 0$.

If the velocity and acceleration are perpendicular to one another, we have from (73.9):

$$dI = \frac{e^2 w^2}{4\pi c^3}\left[\frac{1}{\left(1-\frac{v}{c}\cos\theta\right)^4} - \frac{\left(1-\frac{v^2}{c^2}\right)\sin^2\theta\cos^2\phi}{\left(1-\frac{v}{c}\cos\theta\right)^6}\right] do, \qquad (73.14)$$

where θ is again the angle between **n** and **v**, and ϕ is the azimuthal angle of the vector **n** relative to the plane passing through **v** and **w**. This intensity is symmetric only with respect to the plane of **v** and **w**, and vanishes along the two directions in this plane which form the angle $\theta = \cos^{-1}(v/c)$ with the velocity.

Problems

1. Find the total radiation from a relativistic particle with charge e_1, which passes with impact parameter ϱ through the Coulomb field of a fixed center (with potential $\phi = e_2/r$).

Solution: In passing through the field, the relativistic particle is hardly deflected at all.† We may therefore regard the velocity **v** in (73.7) as constant, so that the field at the position of the particle is

$$\mathbf{E} = \frac{e_2\mathbf{r}}{r^3} \cong \frac{e_2\mathbf{r}}{(\varrho^2 + v^2 t^2)^{\frac{3}{2}}},$$

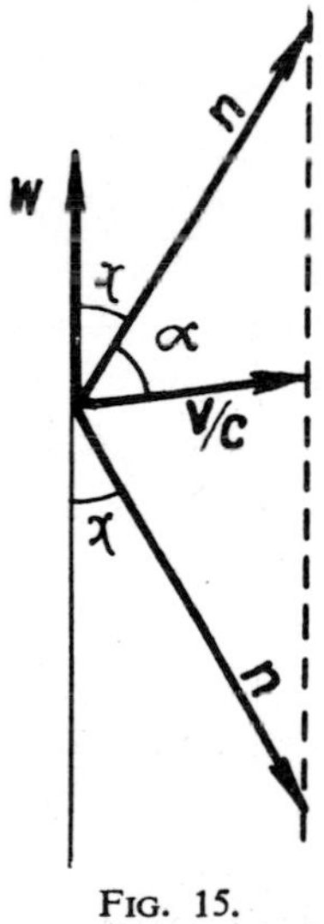

Fig. 15.

† For $v \sim c$, deviations through sizable angles can occur only for impact parameters $\varrho \sim e^2/mc^2$, which cannot in general be treated classically.

with $x = vt$, $y = \varrho$. Performing the time integration in (73.7), we obtain:

$$\Delta\mathcal{E} = \frac{\pi e_1^4 e_2^4}{12m^2c^3\varrho^3 v}\,\frac{4c^2-v^2}{c^2-v^2}.$$

2. Find the directions along which the intensity of the radiation from a moving particle vanishes.

Solution: From the geometrical construction (Fig. 15) we find that the required directions **n** lie in the plane passing through **v** and **w**, and form an angle χ with the direction of **w**, where

$$\sin\chi = \frac{v}{c}\sin\alpha,$$

and α is the angle between **v** and **w**.

§ 74. Radiation from a charge moving uniformly in a circle

We consider in detail the radiation from a charge moving with arbitrary velocity in a circle in a uniform constant magnetic field. The radius of the orbit r and the cyclic frequency of the motion ω_0 are expressible in terms of the field intensity H and the velocity of the particle v, by the formulas (see § 21):

$$r = \frac{mcv}{eH\sqrt{1-\frac{v^2}{c^2}}}, \quad \omega_0 = \frac{v}{r} = \frac{eH}{mc}\sqrt{1-\frac{v^2}{c^2}}. \tag{74.1}$$

The total intensity of the radiation over all directions is given directly by (73.7), omitting the time integration, in which we must set $\mathbf{E} = 0$ and $\mathbf{H} \perp \mathbf{v}$:

$$I = \frac{2e^4H^2v^2}{3m^2c^5\left(1-\frac{v^2}{c^2}\right)}. \tag{74.2}$$

We see that the total intensity is proportional to the square of the momentum of the particle.

If we are interested in the angular distribution of the radiation, then we must use formula (73.11). One quantity of interest is the average intensity during a period of the motion. For this we integrate (73.11) over the time of revolution of the particle in the circle and divide the result by the period $T = 2\pi/\omega_0$.

We choose the plane of the orbit as the XY plane (the origin is at the center of the circle), and we draw the XY plane to pass through the direction **n** of the radiation (Fig. 16). The magnetic field is along the Z axis. Further, let θ be the angle between the direction **n** of the radiation and the Z axis, and $\phi = \omega_0 t$ be the angle between the radius vector of the particle and the X axis. Then the cosine of the angle between **n** and the velocity **v** is $\cos(\mathbf{n}, \mathbf{v}) = \sin\theta\cos\phi$ (the vector **v** lies in the XY plane, and at each moment is perpendicular to the radius vector of the particle). We express the acceleration **w** of the particle in terms of the field **H** and the velocity **v** by means of the equation of motion [see (21.1)]:

$$\mathbf{w} = \frac{e}{mc}\sqrt{1-\frac{v^2}{c^2}}\,\mathbf{v}\times\mathbf{H}.$$

After a simple calculation, we get:

$$\overline{dI} = do\,\frac{e^4 H^2 v^2}{8\pi^2 m^2 c^5}\left(1-\frac{v^2}{c^2}\right)\int\limits_0^{2\pi}\frac{\left(1-\frac{v^2}{c^2}\right)\cos^2\theta+\left(\frac{v}{c}-\sin\theta\cos\phi\right)^2}{\left(1-\frac{v}{c}\sin\theta\cos\phi\right)^5}\,d\phi \quad (74.3)$$

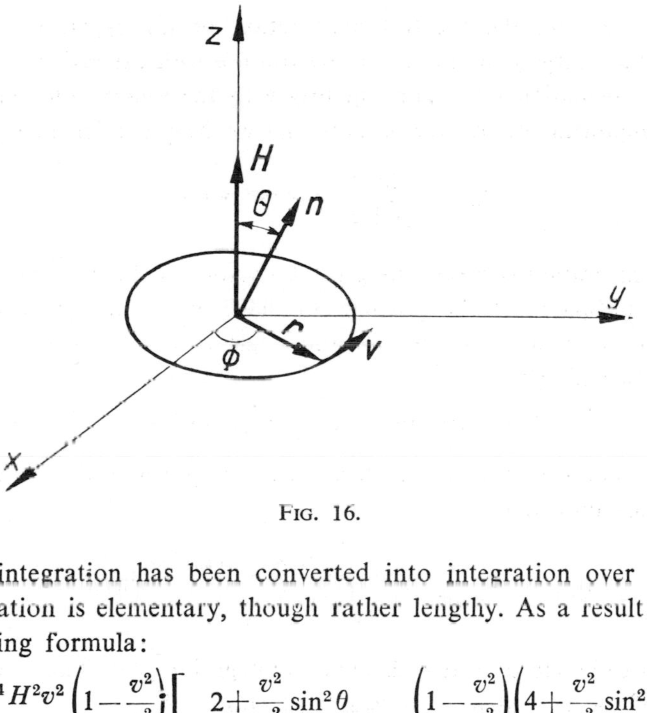

FIG. 16.

(the time integration has been converted into integration over $\phi = \omega_0 t$). The integration is elementary, though rather lengthy. As a result one finds the following formula:

$$\overline{dI} = do\,\frac{e^4 H^2 v^2\left(1-\frac{v^2}{c^2}\right)}{8\pi m^2 c^5}\left[\frac{2+\frac{v^2}{c^2}\sin^2\theta}{\left(1-\frac{v^2}{c^2}\sin^2\theta\right)^{\frac{5}{2}}}-\frac{\left(1-\frac{v^2}{c^2}\right)\left(4+\frac{v^2}{c^2}\sin^2\theta\right)\sin^2\theta}{4\left(1-\frac{v^2}{c^2}\sin^2\theta\right)^{\frac{7}{2}}}\right]. \quad (74.4)$$

The ratio of the intensity of radiation for $\theta = 0$ (perpendicular to the plane of the orbit) to the intensity for $\theta = \pi/2$ (in the plane of the orbit) is

$$\frac{\left(\frac{dI}{do}\right)_{\frac{\pi}{2}}}{\left(\frac{dI}{do}\right)_0} = \frac{4+3\frac{v^2}{c^2}}{8\left(1-\frac{v^2}{c^2}\right)^{\frac{5}{2}}}.$$

As $v \to 0$, this ratio approaches $\frac{1}{2}$, but for velocities close to the velocity of light, it becomes very large. In other words, for a motion with high velocity, the radiation is concentrated mainly in the plane of the orbit. The "width" $\Delta\theta$ of the angular range within which most of the radiation is included is easily evaluated from the condition $1 - \frac{v^2}{c^2}\sin^2\theta \sim 1 - \frac{v^2}{c^2}$, writing $\theta = \frac{\pi}{2} \pm \Delta\theta$, $\sin\theta \cong 1 - \frac{(\Delta\theta)^2}{2}$. It is clear that†

$$\Delta\theta \sim \sqrt{1 - \frac{v^2}{c^2}}. \tag{74.5}$$

Next we consider the spectral distribution of the radiation. Since the motion of the charge is periodic, we are dealing with expansion in a Fourier series. The calculation starts conveniently with the vector potential. For the Fourier components of the vector potential we have the formula (see § 66):

$$\mathbf{A}_n = e \frac{2e^{ikR_0}}{cR_0 T} \oint e^{i(\omega_0 nt - \mathbf{k}\cdot\mathbf{r})}\, d\mathbf{r},$$

where the integration is taken along the trajectory of the particle (the circle). For the coordinates of the particle we have $x = r\cos\omega_0 t$, $y = r\sin\omega_0 t$. As integration variable we choose the angle $\phi = \omega_0 t$. Noting that $dx = -r\sin\phi\, d\phi$ and that

$$\mathbf{k}\cdot\mathbf{r} = kr\ \sin\theta\ \sin\phi = nv/c\ \sin\theta\ \sin\phi$$

($k = n\omega_0/c = nv/cr$), we find for the Fourier components of the x-component of the vector potential:

$$A_{xn} = -\frac{ev}{\pi c R_0} e^{ikR_0} \int_0^{2\pi} e^{in\left(\phi - \frac{v}{c}\sin\theta\sin\phi\right)} \sin\phi\, d\phi.$$

We have already had to deal with such an integral in § 70. It can be expressed in terms of the derivative of a Bessel function:

$$A_{xn} = -\frac{2iev}{cR_0} e^{ikR_0} J_n'\left(\frac{nv}{c}\sin\theta\right). \tag{74.6}$$

Similarly, one calculates A_{yn}:

$$A_{yn} = \frac{2e}{R_0 \sin\theta} e^{ikR_0} J_n\left(\frac{nv}{c}\sin\theta\right). \tag{74.7}$$

The component along the Z axis obviously vanishes.

---

† This result is, of course, in agreement with the angular distribution of the instantaneous intensity which we found in the preceding section [see (73.12)]; however, the reader should not confuse the angle θ of this section with the angle θ between $\mathbf{n}$ and $\mathbf{v}$ in § 73!

From the formulas of § 66 we have for the intensity of radiation with frequency $\omega = n\omega_0$, in the element of solid angle do:

$$dI_n = \frac{c}{8\pi} |\mathbf{H}_n|^2 R_0^2\, do = \frac{c}{8\pi} |\mathbf{k}\times\mathbf{A}_n|^2 R_0^2 do.$$

Noting that

$$|\mathbf{A}\times\mathbf{k}|^2 = A_x^2 k^2 + A_y^2 k^2 \cos^2\theta,$$

and substituting (74.6) and (74.7), we get for the intensity of radiation the following formula (Schott, 1912):

$$dI_n = \frac{n^2 e^4 H^2}{2\pi c^3 m^2}\left(1-\frac{v^2}{c^2}\right)\left[\cot^2\theta \cdot J_n^2\left(\frac{nv^2}{c}\sin\theta\right) + \frac{v^2}{c^2} J_n'^2\left(\frac{nv}{c}\sin\theta\right)\right] do. \tag{74.8}$$

To determine the total intensity over all directions of the radiation with frequency $\omega = n\omega_0$, this expression must be integrated over all angles. However, the integration cannot be carried out in finite form. By a series of transformations, making use of certain relations from the theory of Bessel functions, the required integral can be written in the following form:†

$$I_n = \frac{2e^4 H^2\left(1-\frac{v^2}{c^2}\right)}{m^2 c^2 v}\left[\frac{nv^2}{c^2} J'_{2n}\left(\frac{2nv}{c}\right) - n^2\left(1-\frac{v^2}{c^2}\right)\int_0^{\frac{v}{c}} J_{2n}(2n\xi)\, d\xi\right]. \tag{74.9}$$

We consider in more detail the spectral distribution of the radiation in the ultrarelativistic case where the velocity of motion of the particle is close to the velocity of light (L. Arzimovich and I. Pomeranchuk, 1945). We shall see below that in this case the main role in the radiation is played by frequencies with large n. We can therefore use the asymptotic formula (70.9), according to which:

$$J_{2n}(2n\xi) \simeq \frac{1}{\sqrt{\pi}\, n^{\frac{1}{3}}} \Phi[n^{\frac{2}{3}}(1-\xi^2)]. \tag{74.10}$$

Substituting in (74.9), we get the following formula for the spectral distribution of the radiation for large values of n:‡

$$I_n = -\frac{2e^4 H^2 \left(1-\frac{v^2}{c^2}\right)^{\frac{1}{2}} u^{\frac{1}{2}}}{\sqrt{\pi}\, m^2 c^3}\left\{\Phi'(u) + \frac{u}{2}\int_u^{\infty} \Phi(u)\, du\right\}, \tag{74.11}$$

$$u = n^{\frac{2}{3}}\left(1-\frac{v^2}{c^2}\right).$$

---

† The computations can be found in the book by G.A. Schott, *Electromagnetic Radiation*, 84, Cambridge, 1912.

‡ In making the substitution, the limit $n^{\frac{2}{3}}$ of the integral can be changed to infinity, to within the required accuracy; we have also set $v = c$ wherever possible. Even though values of ξ close to 1 are important in the integral (74.9), the use of formula (74.10) is still permissible, since the integral converges rapidly at the lower limit.

For $u \to 0$ the function in the curly brackets approaches the constant limit $\Phi'(0) = -0.4587\ldots$† Therefore for $u \ll 1$, we have

$$I_n = 0.52\frac{e^4H^2}{m^2c^3}\left(1-\frac{v^2}{c^2}\right)n^{\frac{1}{3}}, \qquad 1 \ll n \ll \left(1-\frac{v^2}{c^2}\right)^{-\frac{3}{2}}, \tag{74.12}$$

that is, the intensity of the nth harmonic is proportional to $n^{\frac{1}{3}}$.

For $u \gg 1$, we can use the asymptotic expression for the Airy function (see the footnote on p. 171, and obtain:

$$I_n = \frac{e^4H^2\left(1-\frac{v^2}{c^2}\right)^{\frac{5}{4}} n^{\frac{1}{2}}}{2\sqrt{\pi}\,m^2c^3}\exp\left\{-\frac{2}{3}n\left(1-\frac{v^2}{c^2}\right)^{\frac{3}{2}}\right\}, \qquad n \gg \left(1-\frac{v^2}{c^2}\right)^{-\frac{3}{2}} \tag{74.13}$$

that is, the intensity drops exponentially for large n. Consequently the spectrum has a maximum for $n \sim \left(1-\frac{v^2}{c^2}\right)^{-\frac{3}{2}}$, and the main part of the radiation is concentrated in the region of frequencies for which

$$\omega \sim \omega_0\left(1-\frac{v^2}{c^2}\right)^{-\frac{3}{2}} = \frac{eH}{mc}\left(1-\frac{v^2}{c^2}\right)^{-1}. \tag{74.14}$$

Since these values of ω are very large, and the distance between neighboring frequencies is ω_0 (which is comparatively small), we may say that the spectrum has a "quasicontinuous" character, consisting of a large number of closely spaced lines.

Problems

1. Find the law of variation of energy with time for a particle moving in a circular orbit in a constant uniform magnetic field, and losing energy by radiation.

Solution: According to (74.2), we have for the energy loss per unit time:

$$-\frac{d\mathcal{E}}{dt} = \frac{2e^4H^2}{3m^4c^7}(\mathcal{E}^2 - m^2c^4)$$

($\mathcal{E}$ is the energy of the particle). From this we find:

$$\frac{\mathcal{E}}{mc^2} = \coth\left(\frac{2e^4H^2}{3m^3c^5}t + \text{const}\right).$$

As t increases, the energy decreases monotonically, approaching the value $\mathcal{E} = mc^2$ (for complete stopping of the particle) asymptotically as $t \to \infty$.

---

† From the definition of the Airy function, we have:

$$\Phi'(0) = -\frac{1}{\sqrt{\pi}}\int_0^\infty \xi\sin\frac{\xi^3}{3}\,d\xi = -\frac{1}{\sqrt{\pi}\cdot 3^{\frac{1}{3}}}\int_0^\infty x^{-\frac{1}{3}}\sin x\,dx = -\frac{3^{\frac{1}{6}}\Gamma(\frac{2}{3})}{2\sqrt{\pi}}.$$

2. Find the asymptotic formula for the spectral distribution of the radiation at large values of n for a particle moving in a circle with a velocity which is not close to the velocity of light.

Solution. We use the well known asymptotic formula of the theory of Bessel functions

$$J_n(n\epsilon) = \frac{1}{\sqrt{2\pi n}\,(1-\epsilon^2)^{1/4}}\left[\frac{\epsilon}{1+\sqrt{1-\epsilon^2}}\,e^{\sqrt{1-\epsilon^2}}\right]^n,$$

which is valid for $n(1-\epsilon^2)^{3/2} \gg 1$. Using this formula, we find from (74.9):

$$I_n = \frac{e^4 H^2 n^{1/2}}{2\sqrt{\pi}\, m^2 c^3}\left(1-\frac{v^2}{c^2}\right)^{3/4}\left[\frac{\frac{v}{c}}{1+\sqrt{1-\frac{v^2}{c^2}}}\,e^{\sqrt{1-\frac{v^2}{c^2}}}\right]^{2n}.$$

This formula is applicable for $n\left(1-\frac{v^2}{c^2}\right)^{3/2} \gg 1$; if in addition $1-v^2/c^2$ is small, the formula goes over into (74.13).

§ 75. Radiation damping

In § 65 we showed that the expansion of the potentials of the field of a system of charges in a series of powers of v/c leads in the second approximation to a Lagrangian completely describing (in this approximation) the motion of the charges. We now continue the expansion of the field to terms of higher order and discuss the effects to which these terms lead.

In the expansion of the scalar potential

$$\phi = \int \frac{1}{R}\varrho_{t-\frac{R}{c}}\, dV,$$

the term of third order in $1/c$ is

$$\phi^{(3)} = -\frac{1}{6c^3}\frac{\partial^3}{\partial t^3}\int R^2 \varrho\, dV. \tag{75.1}$$

For the same reason as in the derivation following (65.3), in the expansion of the vector potential we need only take the term of second order in $1/c$, that is,

$$\mathbf{A}^{(2)} = -\frac{1}{c^2}\frac{\partial}{\partial t}\int \mathbf{j}\, dV. \tag{75.2}$$

We make a transformation of the potentials:

$$\phi' = \phi - \frac{1}{c}\frac{\partial f}{\partial t}, \quad \mathbf{A}' = \mathbf{A} + \operatorname{grad} f,$$

choosing the function f so that the scalar potential $\phi^{(3)}$ becomes zero. To do this, it is clearly necessary that

$$f = -\frac{1}{6c^2}\frac{\partial^2}{\partial t^2}\int R^2 \varrho\, dV.$$

Then the new vector potential is equal to

$$\mathbf{A}'^{(2)} = -\frac{1}{c^2}\frac{\partial}{\partial t}\int \mathbf{j}\, dV - \frac{1}{6c^2}\frac{\partial^2}{\partial t^2}\nabla\int R^2\varrho\, dV$$

$$= -\frac{1}{c^2}\frac{\partial}{\partial t}\int \mathbf{j}\, dV - \frac{1}{3c^2}\frac{\partial^2}{\partial t^2}\int \mathbf{R}\varrho\, dV.$$

Making the transition from the integral to a sum over individual charges, we get for the first term on the right the expression $-\frac{1}{c^2}\sum e\dot{\mathbf{v}}$. In the second term, we write $\mathbf{R} = \mathbf{R}_0 - \mathbf{r}$, where $\mathbf{R}_0$ and $\mathbf{r}$ have their usual meaning (see § 66); then $\dot{\mathbf{R}} = -\dot{\mathbf{r}} = -\mathbf{v}$ and the second term takes the form $\frac{1}{3c^2}\sum e\dot{\mathbf{v}}$. Thus,

$$\mathbf{A}'^{(2)} = -\frac{2}{3c^2}\sum e\dot{\mathbf{v}}. \tag{75.3}$$

The magnetic field corresponding to this potential is zero ($\mathbf{H} = \text{curl}\ \mathbf{A}'^{(2)} = 0$), since $\mathbf{A}'^{(2)}$ does not contain the coordinates explicitly. The electric field $\mathbf{E} = -\frac{1}{c}\dot{\mathbf{A}}'^{(2)}$ is

$$\mathbf{E} = \frac{2}{3c^3}\dddot{\mathbf{d}}, \tag{75.4}$$

where $\mathbf{d}$ is the dipole moment of the system.

Thus the third order terms in the expansion of the field lead to certain additional forces acting on the charges, not contained in the Lagrangian (65.7); these forces depend on the time derivatives of the accelerations of the charges.

Let us consider a system of charges carrying out a stationary motion† and calculate the average work done by the field (75.4) per unit time. The force acting on each charge e is $\mathbf{f} = e\mathbf{E}$, that is,

$$\mathbf{f} = \frac{2e}{3c^3}\dddot{\mathbf{d}}. \tag{75.5}$$

The work done by this force in unit time is $\mathbf{f}\cdot\mathbf{v}$, so that the total work performed on all the charges is equal to the sum, taken over all the charges:

$$\sum \mathbf{f}\cdot\mathbf{v} = \frac{2}{3c^3}\dddot{\mathbf{d}}\cdot\sum e\mathbf{v} = \frac{2}{3c^3}\dddot{\mathbf{d}}\cdot\dot{\mathbf{d}} = \frac{2}{3c^3}\frac{d}{dt}(\dot{\mathbf{d}}\cdot\ddot{\mathbf{d}}) - \frac{2}{3c^3}(\ddot{\mathbf{d}})^2.$$

When we average over the time, the first term vanishes, so that the average work is equal to

$$\overline{\sum \mathbf{f}\cdot\mathbf{v}} = -\overline{\frac{2}{3c^3}\ddot{\mathbf{d}}^2}. \tag{75.6}$$

† More precisely, a motion which, although it would have been stationary if radiation were neglected, proceeds with continual slowing down.

The expression standing on the right is (except for a sign reversal) just the average energy radiated by the system in unit time [see (67.8)]. Thus, the forces (75.5) appearing in third approximation, describe the reaction of the radiation on the charges. These forces are called *radiation damping* or *Lorentz frictional forces.*

Simultaneously with the energy loss from a radiating system of charges, there also occurs a certain loss of angular momentum. The decrease in angular momentum per unit time, $d\mathbf{M}/dt$, is easily calculated with the aid of the expression for the damping forces. Taking the time derivative of the angular momentum $\mathbf{M} = \sum \mathbf{r}\times\mathbf{p}$, we have $\dot{\mathbf{M}} = \sum \mathbf{r}\times\dot{\mathbf{p}}$, since $\sum \dot{\mathbf{r}}\times\mathbf{p} = \sum m(\mathbf{v}\times\mathbf{v}) = 0$. We replace the time derivative of the momentum of the particle by the friction force (75.5) acting on it, and find

$$\dot{\mathbf{M}} = \sum \mathbf{r}\times\mathbf{f} = \frac{2}{3c^3}\sum e\mathbf{r}\times\dddot{\mathbf{d}} = \frac{2}{3c^3}\mathbf{d}\times\dddot{\mathbf{d}}.$$

We are interested in the time average of the loss of angular momentum for a stationary motion, just as before, we considered the time average of the energy loss. Writing

$$\mathbf{d}\times\dddot{\mathbf{d}} = \frac{d}{dt}(\mathbf{d}\times\ddot{\mathbf{d}}) - \dot{\mathbf{d}}\times\ddot{\mathbf{d}}$$

and noting that the time derivative (first term) vanishes on averaging, we finally obtain the following expression for the average loss of angular momentum of a radiating system:

$$\frac{\overline{d\mathbf{M}}}{dt} = -\frac{2}{3c^3}\overline{\dot{\mathbf{d}}\times\ddot{\mathbf{d}}}. \tag{75.7}$$

Radiation damping occurs also for a single charge moving in an external field. It is equal to

$$\mathbf{f} = \frac{2e^2}{3c^3}\ddot{\mathbf{v}}. \tag{75.8}$$

For a single charge, we can always choose such a system of reference that the charge at the given moment is at rest in it. If, in this reference frame, we calculate the higher terms in the expansion of the field produced by the charge, it turns out that they have the following property. As the radius vector R from the charge to the field point approaches zero, all these terms become zero. Thus in the case of a single charge, formula (75.8) is in a certain sense an exact formula for the reaction of the radiation, in the system of reference in which the charge is at rest.

Nevertheless, we must keep in mind that the description of the action of the charge "on itself" with the aid of the damping force is unsatisfactory in general, and contains contradictions. The equation of motion of a charge, in the absence of an external field, on which only the force (75.8) acts, has the form

$$m\dot{\mathbf{v}} = \frac{2e^2}{3c^3}\ddot{\mathbf{v}}.$$

This equation has, in addition to the trivial solution $\mathbf{v} = \text{const}$, another solution in which the acceleration $\dot{\mathbf{v}}$ is proportional to $\exp(3mc^3t/2e^2)$, that is, increases indefinitely with the time. This means, for example, that a charge passing through any field, upon emergence from the field, would have to be infinitely "self-accelerated". The absurdity of this result is evidence for the limited applicability of formula (75.8).

One can raise the question of how electrodynamics, which satisfies the law of conservation of energy, can lead to the absurd result that a free charge increases its energy without limit. Actually the root of this difficulty lies in the earlier remarks (§ 37) concerning the infinite electromagnetic "intrinsic mass" of elementary particles. When in the equation of motion we write a finite mass for the charge, then in doing this we essentially assign to it formally an infinite negative "intrinsic mass" of nonelectromagnetic origin, which together with the electromagnetic mass should result in a finite mass for the particle. Since, however, the subtraction of one infinity from another is not an entirely correct mathematical operation, this leads to a series of further difficulties, among which is the one mentioned here.

In a system of coordinates in which the velocity of the particle is small, the equation of motion when we include the radiation damping has the form

$$m\dot{\mathbf{v}} = e\mathbf{E} + \frac{e}{c}\mathbf{v}\times\mathbf{H} + \frac{2}{3}\frac{e^2}{c^3}\ddot{\mathbf{v}}. \tag{75.9}$$

From our discussion, this equation is applicable only to the extent that the damping force is small compared with the force exerted on the charge by the external field.

To clarify the physical meaning of this condition, we proceed as follows. In the system of reference in which the charge is at rest at a given moment, the second time derivative of the velocity is equal, neglecting the damping force, to

$$\ddot{\mathbf{v}} = \frac{e}{m}\dot{\mathbf{E}} + \frac{e}{mc}\dot{\mathbf{v}}\times\mathbf{H}.$$

In the second term we substitute (to the same order of accuracy) $\dot{\mathbf{v}} = \frac{e}{m}\mathbf{E}$, and obtain

$$\ddot{\mathbf{v}} = \frac{e}{m}\dot{\mathbf{E}} + \frac{e^2}{m^2c}\mathbf{E}\times\mathbf{H}.$$

Corresponding to this, the damping force consists of two terms:

$$\mathbf{f} = \frac{2e^3}{3mc^3}\dot{\mathbf{E}} + \frac{2e^4}{3m^2c^4}\mathbf{E}\times\mathbf{H}. \tag{75.10}$$

If ω is the frequency of the motion, then $\dot{\mathbf{E}}$ is proportional to $\omega\mathbf{E}$ and, consequently, the first term is of order $\frac{e^3\omega}{mc^3}\mathbf{E}$; the second is of order $\frac{e^4}{m^2c^4}EH$. Therefore the condition for the damping force to be small compared with the force eE exerted by the external field on the charge gives, first of all,

$$\frac{e^2}{mc^3}\omega \ll 1,$$

or, introducing the wavelength $\lambda \sim c/\omega$,

$$\lambda \gg \frac{e^2}{mc^2}. \tag{75.11}$$

Thus formula (75.8) for the radiation damping is applicable only if the wavelength of the radiation incident on the charge is large compared with the "*radius*" of the charge c^2/mc^2. We see that once more a distance of order e^2/mc^2 appears as the limit at which electrodynamics leads to internal contradictions (see § 37).

Secondly, comparing the second term in the damping force to the force eE, we find the condition

$$H \ll \frac{m^2c^4}{e^3}. \tag{75.12}$$

Thus it is also necessary that the field itself be not too large. A field of order m^2c^4/e^3 also represents a limit at which classical electrodynamics leads to internal contradictions. Also we must remember here that actually, because of quantum effects, electrodynamics is already not applicable for considerably smaller fields.†

To avoid misunderstanding, we remind the reader that the wavelength in (75.11) and the field value in (75.12) refer to the system of reference in which the particle is at rest at the given moment.

Problems

1. Calculate the time in which two attracting charges, performing an elliptic motion (with velocity small compared with the velocity of light) and losing energy due to radiation, "fall in" toward each other.

Solution: Assuming that the relative energy loss in one revolution is small, we can equate the time derivative of the energy to the average intensity of the radiation (which was determined in problem 1 of § 70):

$$\frac{d|\mathcal{E}|}{dt} = \frac{(2|\mathcal{E}|)^{\frac{3}{2}}\mu^{\frac{5}{2}}\alpha^3}{3c^3M^5}\left(\frac{e_1}{m_1} - \frac{e_2}{m_2}\right)^2\left(3 - \frac{2|\mathcal{E}|M^2}{\mu\alpha^2}\right), \tag{1}$$

† For fields of order m^2c^3/he, where h is Planck's constant.

where $a = |e_1 e_2|$. Together with the energy, the particles lose angular momentum. The loss of angular momentum per unit time is given by formula (75.7); substituting the expression (70.1) for **d**, and noting that $\mu\ddot{\mathbf{r}} = -a\mathbf{r}/r^3$ and $\mathbf{M} = \mu\mathbf{r}\times\mathbf{v}$, we find:

$$\frac{d\mathbf{M}}{dt} = -\frac{2a}{3c^3}\left(\frac{e_1}{m_1} - \frac{e_2}{m_2}\right)^2 \frac{\mathbf{M}}{r^3}.$$

We average this expression over a period of the motion. Because of the slowness of the changes in **M**, it is sufficient to average on the right only over r^{-3}; this average value is computed in precisely the same way as the average of r^{-4} was found in problem 1 of § 70. As a result we find for the average loss of angular momentum per unit time the following expression:

$$\frac{d\mathbf{M}}{dt} = -\frac{2a(2\mu|\mathcal{E}|)^{\frac{3}{2}}}{3c^3}\left(\frac{e_1}{m_1} - \frac{e_2}{m_2}\right)^2 \qquad (2)$$

[as in equation (1), we omit the average sign]. Dividing (1) by (2), we get the differential equation

$$\frac{d|\mathcal{E}|}{dM} = -\frac{\mu a^2}{2M^3}\left(3 - 2\frac{|\mathcal{E}|M^2}{\mu a^2}\right),$$

which, on integration, gives:

$$|\mathcal{E}| = \frac{\mu a^2}{2M^2}\left(1 - \frac{M^3}{M_0^3}\right) + \frac{|\mathcal{E}_0|}{M_0}M. \qquad (3)$$

The constant of integration is chosen so that for $M = M_0$, we have $\mathcal{E} = \mathcal{E}_0$, where M_0 and $\mathcal{E}_0$ are the initial angular momentum and energy of the particles.

The "falling in" of the particles toward one another corresponds to $M \to 0$. From (3) we see that then $\mathcal{E} \to -\infty$.

We note that the product $|\mathcal{E}|M^2$ tends toward $\mu a^2/2$, and from formula (70.3) it is clear that the eccentricity $\epsilon \to 0$, i.e., as the particles approach one another, the orbit approaches a circle. Substituting (3) in (2), we determine the derivative dt/dM expressed as a function of M, after which integration with respect to M between the limits M_0 and 0 gives the time of fall:

$$t_{\text{fall}} = \frac{c^3 M_0^5}{a\sqrt{2|\mathcal{E}_0|\mu^3}}\left(\frac{e_1}{m_1} - \frac{e_2}{m_2}\right)^{-2}(\sqrt{\mu a^2} + \sqrt{2M_0^2|\mathcal{E}_0|})^{-2}.$$

2. Find the Lagrangian for a system of two identical charged particles, correct to terms of fourth order† (Ya. A. Smorodinskii and V. N. Golubenkov, 1956).

Solution: The computation is conveniently done by a scheme which is somewhat different from the one used in § 65. We start from the expression for the Lagrangian of the particles and the field produced by them,

$$L = \int\left\{\frac{1}{8\pi}(\mathbf{E}^2 - \mathbf{H}^2) + \frac{1}{c}\mathbf{j}\cdot\mathbf{A} - \varrho\phi\right\}dV - \sum_a m_a c^2\sqrt{1 - \frac{v_a^2}{c^2}}.$$

Writing

$$\mathbf{E}^2 - \mathbf{H}^2 = \mathbf{E}\cdot\left(-\frac{1}{c}\frac{\partial\mathbf{A}}{\partial t} - \nabla\phi\right) - \mathbf{H}\cdot\operatorname{curl}\mathbf{A},$$

and carrying out the integration over the particles, we get:

$$\frac{1}{8\pi}\int(\mathbf{E}^2 - \mathbf{H}^2)\,dV = -\frac{1}{8\pi}\oint\{\mathbf{E}\phi + \mathbf{A}\times\mathbf{H}\}\cdot d\mathbf{f} - \frac{1}{8\pi c}\frac{d}{dt}\int\mathbf{E}\cdot\mathbf{A}\,dV -$$

$$-\frac{1}{2}\int\left(\frac{1}{c}\mathbf{j}\cdot\mathbf{A} - \varrho\phi\right)dV.$$

---

† See the footnote on p. 190. The third order terms in the Lagrangian drop out automatically: the terms of this order in the field produced by the particles are determined by the time derivative of the dipole moment [see (75.3)], which is conserved in the present case.

For a system which does not emit dipole radiation, the integral over the infinitely distant surface gives no contribution to the terms of order $1/c^4$. The term with the total time derivative can be dropped from the Lagrangian. Thus the required fourth order terms in the Lagrangian are contained in the expression

$$L' = \frac{1}{2}\int\left(\frac{1}{c}\mathbf{j}\cdot\mathbf{A}-\varrho\phi\right)dV - \sum_a m_a c^2\sqrt{1-\frac{v_a^2}{c^2}}.$$

Continuing the expansion which was done in § 65, we find the terms of fourth order in the potentials (ϕ and $\mathbf{A}/c$) of the field produced by charge 1 at the position of charge 2:

$$\phi_1(2) = \frac{e}{24c^4}\frac{\partial^4 R^3}{\partial t^4}, \qquad \frac{1}{c}\mathbf{A}_1(2) = \frac{e}{2c^4}\frac{\partial^2}{\partial t^2}(R\mathbf{v}_1).$$

By the transformation (18.2) with the appropriate function f, we can bring these potentials to the equivalent form

$$\phi_1(2) = 0, \qquad \frac{1}{c}\mathbf{A}_1(2) = \frac{e}{2c^4}\left[\frac{\partial^2}{\partial t^2}(R\mathbf{v}_1)+\frac{1}{12}\frac{\partial^3}{\partial t^3}(\nabla R^3)\right] \tag{1}$$

(the differentiation $\partial/\partial t$ is done for a fixed position of the field point, i.e. of charge 2; the differentiation ∇ is with respect to the coordinates of the field point).

The second order terms in the Lagrangian now give the expression†:

$$L^{(4)} = \frac{e}{2c}[\mathbf{A}_1(2)\cdot\mathbf{v}_2+\mathbf{A}_2(1)\cdot\mathbf{v}_1)+\frac{m}{16c^4}(v_1^6+v_2^6). \tag{2}$$

After performing some of the differentiations in (1), we can represent $\mathbf{A}_1(2)$ as

$$\frac{1}{c}\mathbf{A}_1(2) = \frac{e}{8c^4}\frac{\partial \mathbf{F}_1}{\partial t}, \qquad \mathbf{F}_1 = \frac{\partial}{\partial t}[3R\mathbf{v}_1 - R\mathbf{n}(\mathbf{n}\cdot\mathbf{v}_1)]$$

(where $\mathbf{n}$ is a unit vector in the direction from point 1 to point 2). Before making any further calculations, it is convenient to eliminate from $L^{(4)}$ those terms which contain time derivatives of the velocity which are higher than first order; for this purpose we note that

$$\frac{1}{c}\mathbf{A}_1(2)\cdot\mathbf{v}_2 = \frac{e}{8c^4}\mathbf{v}_2\cdot\frac{\partial\mathbf{F}_1}{\partial t} = \frac{e}{8c^4}\left\{\frac{d}{dt}(\mathbf{v}_2\cdot\mathbf{F})-(\mathbf{v}_2\cdot\nabla)(\mathbf{v}_2\cdot\mathbf{F})-\mathbf{F}\cdot\dot{\mathbf{v}}_2\right\},$$

where

$$\frac{d}{dt}(\mathbf{v}_2\cdot\mathbf{F}) = \frac{\partial}{\partial t}(\mathbf{v}_2\cdot\mathbf{F})+(\mathbf{v}_2\cdot\nabla)(\mathbf{v}_2\cdot\mathbf{F})$$

is the total time derivative (differentiation with respect to both ends of the vector $\mathbf{R}$!) and can be dropped from the Lagrangian. The accelerations are eliminated from the resulting expression by using the equation of motion of the first approximation: $m\dot{\mathbf{v}}_1 = -e^2\mathbf{n}/R^2$, $m\dot{\mathbf{v}}_2 = e^2\mathbf{n}/R^2$. After a rather long computation, we finally get:

$$L^{(4)} = \frac{e^2}{8c^4 R}\Big\{[-v_1^2 v_2^2+2(\mathbf{v}_1\cdot\mathbf{v}_2)^2-3(\mathbf{n}\cdot\mathbf{v}_1)^2(\mathbf{n}\cdot\mathbf{v}_2)^2+(\mathbf{n}\cdot\mathbf{v}_1)^2\mathbf{v}_2^2+(\mathbf{n}\cdot\mathbf{v}_2)^2\mathbf{v}_1^2]+$$

$$+\frac{e^2}{mR}[-v_1^2-v_2^2+3(\mathbf{n}\cdot\mathbf{v}_1)^2+3(\mathbf{n}\cdot\mathbf{v}_2)^2]+\frac{2e^4}{m^2R^2}\Big\}+\frac{m}{16c^4}(v_1^6+v_2^6).$$

---

† Here we omit the infinite terms associated with the action on the particles of their "self" fields. This operation corresponds to a "renormalization" of the masses appearing in the Lagrangian (see the footnote on p. 194).

From the symmetry in the two identical particles, it was clear beforehand that $\mathbf{v}_1 = -\mathbf{v}_2$ in the system of reference in which their center of inertia is at rest. Then the fourth order terms in the Lagrangian are:

$$L^{(4)} = \frac{e^2}{8c^4R}\left\{\frac{1}{16}[v^4-3(\mathbf{n}\cdot\mathbf{v})^4+2(\mathbf{n}\cdot\mathbf{v})^2v^2]+\frac{e^2}{2mR}[3(\mathbf{n}\cdot\mathbf{v})^2-v^2]+\frac{2e^4}{m^2R^2}\right\}+\frac{mv^6}{2^9c^4},$$

where $\mathbf{v} = \mathbf{v}_2-\mathbf{v}_1$.

§ 76. Radiation damping in the relativistic case

We derive the relativistic expression for the radiation damping (for a single charge), which is applicable also to motion with velocity comparable to that of light. This force is now a four-vector g_i, which must be included in the equation of motion of the charge, written in four-dimensional form:

$$mc\frac{du_i}{ds} = \frac{e}{c}F_{ik}u_k+g_i. \tag{76.1}$$

To determine g_i we note that for $v \ll c$, its three space components must go over into the components of the vector $\mathbf{f}/c$ (75.8). It is easy to see that the vector $\frac{2e^2}{3c}\frac{d^2u_i}{ds^2}$ has this property. However, it does not satisfy the identity $g_iu_i = 0$, which is valid for any force four-vector. In order to satisfy this condition, we must add to the expression given, a certain auxiliary four-vector, made up from the four-velocity u_i and its derivatives. The three space components of this vector must become zero in the limiting case $\mathbf{v} = 0$, in order not to change the correct values of $\mathbf{f}$ which are already given by $\frac{2e^2}{3c}\frac{d^2u_i}{ds^2}$. The four-vector u_i has this property, and therefore the required auxiliary term has the form αu_i. The scalar α must be chosen so that we satisfy the auxiliary relation $g_iu_i = 0$. As a result we find

$$g_i = \frac{2e^2}{3c}\left(\frac{d^2u_i}{ds^2}+u_iu_k\frac{d^2u_k}{ds^2}\right). \tag{76.2}$$

In accordance with the equations of motion, this expression can be written in another form, by expressing d^2u_i/ds^2 directly in terms of the field tensor of the external field acting on the particle:

$$\frac{du_i}{ds} = \frac{e}{mc^2}F_{ik}u_k,$$

$$\frac{d^2u_i}{ds^2} = \frac{e}{mc^2}\frac{\partial F_{ik}}{\partial x_l}u_ku_l+\frac{e^2}{m^2c^4}F_{ik}F_{kl}u_l.$$

In making substitutions, we must keep in mind that the product of the tensor $\partial F_{ik}/\partial x_l$, which is antisymmetric in the indices i, k, and the symmetric tensor u_iu_k gives identically zero. So,

$$g_i = \frac{2e^3}{3mc^3}\frac{\partial F_{ik}}{\partial x_l}u_ku_l-\frac{2e^4}{3m^2c^5}F_{il}F_{kl}u_k-\frac{2e^4}{3m^2c^5}(F_{kl}u_l)^2u_i. \tag{76.3}$$

The integral of the four-force g_i over the world line of the motion of a charge, passing through a given field, must coincide (except for opposite sign) with the total four-momentum ΔP_l of the radiation from the charge [just as the average value of the work of the force **f** in the nonrelativistic case coincides with the intensity of dipole radiation; see (75.6)]. It is easy to check that this is actually so. The first term in (76.2) goes to zero on performing the integration, since at infinity the particle has no acceleration, i.e., $\frac{du_i}{ds}=0$. We integrate the second term by parts and get:

$$-\int g_i dx_i = -\frac{2e^2}{3c}\int u_k \frac{d^2 u_k}{ds^2}\,ds = \frac{2e^2}{3c}\int \left(\frac{du_k}{ds}\right)^2 ds,$$

which coincides exactly with (73.4).

When the velocity of the particle approaches the velocity of light, those terms in the space components of the four-vector (76.3) increase most rapidly which come from the third derivatives of the components of the four-velocity. Therefore, keeping only these terms in (76.3) and using the relation (9.17) between the space components of the four-vector g_i and the three-dimensional force **f**, we find for the latter:

$$\mathbf{f} = -\frac{2e^4}{3m^2c^5}(F_{kl}u_l)^2\mathbf{v}.$$

Consequently, in this case the force **f** is opposite to the velocity of the particle; choosing the latter as the X axis, and writing out the four-dimensional expressions, we obtain:

$$f_x = -\frac{2e^4}{3m^2c^4}\,\frac{(E_y-H_z)^2+(E_z+H_y)^2}{1-\frac{v^2}{c^2}} \tag{76.4}$$

(where we have set $v=c$ everywhere except in the denominator).

We see that for an ultrarelativistic particle, the radiation damping is proportional to the square of its energy.

Let us call attention to the following interesting situation. Earlier we pointed out that the expression obtained for the radiation damping is applicable only to fields which (in the reference system K_0, in which the particle is at rest) are small compared with m^2c^4/e^3. Let F be the order of magnitude of the external field, transverse to the direction of motion, in the reference system K, in which the particle moves with velocity v. Then in the K_0 frame, the field has the order of magnitude $F/\sqrt{1-v^2/c^2}$ (see the transformation formulas in § 24). Therefore F must satisfy the condition

$$\frac{e^3F}{m^2c^4\sqrt{1-\frac{v^2}{c^2}}} \ll 1. \tag{76.5}$$

At the same time, the ratio of the damping force (76.4) to the external force ($\sim eF$) is of the order of

$$\frac{e^3F}{m^2c^4\left(1-\dfrac{v^2}{c^2}\right)},$$

and we see that, even though the condition (76.5) is satisfied, it may happen (for sufficiently high energy of the particle) that the damping force is large compared with the ordinary Lorentz force acting on the particle in the electromagnetic field.† Thus for an ultrarelativistic particle we can have the case where the radiation damping is the main force acting on the particle.

In this case the loss of (kinetic) energy of the particle per unit length of path can be equated to the damping force f_x alone; keeping in mind that the latter is proportional to the square of the energy of the particle, we write

$$\frac{d\mathcal{E}_{\text{kin}}}{dx} = -k(x)\,\mathcal{E}_{\text{kin}}^2,$$

where we denote by $k(x)$ the coefficient, depending on the x coordinate and expressed in terms of the transverse components of the field in accordance with (76.4). Integrating this differential equation, we find

$$\frac{1}{\mathcal{E}_{\text{kin}}} = \frac{1}{\mathcal{E}_0} + \int_{-\infty}^{x} k(x)\,dx,$$

where $\mathcal{E}_0$ represents the initial energy of the particle (its energy for $x \to -\infty$). In particular, the final energy $\mathcal{E}_1$ of the particle (after passage of the particle through the field) is given by the formula

$$\frac{1}{\mathcal{E}_1} = \frac{1}{\mathcal{E}_0} + \int_{-\infty}^{+\infty} k(x)\,dx.$$

We see that for $\mathcal{E}_0 \to \infty$, the final energy $\mathcal{E}_1$ approaches a constant limit independent of $\mathcal{E}_0$ (I. Pomeranchuk, 1939). In other words, after passing through the field, the energy of the particle cannot exceed the energy $\mathcal{E}_{\text{crit}}$, defined by the equation

$$\frac{1}{\mathcal{E}_{\text{crit}}} = \int_{-\infty}^{+\infty} k(x)\,dx,$$

† We should emphasize that this result does not in any way contradict the derivation given earlier of the relativistic expression for the four-force g_i, in which it was assumed to be "small" compared with the four-force $\frac{e}{c}F_{ik}u_k$. It is sufficient to satisfy the requirement that the components of one vector be small compared to those of another in just one frame of reference; by virtue of relativistic invariance, the four-dimensional formulas obtained on the basis of such an assumption will be valid in any other reference frame.

or, substituting the expression for $k(x)$,

$$\mathcal{E}_{\text{crit}}^{-1} = \frac{2}{3m^2c^4}\left(\frac{e^2}{mc^2}\right)^2 \int_{-\infty}^{+\infty} [(E_y - H_z)^2 + (E_z + H_y)^2]\, dx. \qquad (76.6)$$

Problems

1. Calculate the limiting energy which a particle can have after passing through the field of a magnetic dipole $\mathfrak{m}$; the vector $\mathfrak{m}$ and the direction of motion lie in a plane.

Solution: We choose the plane passing through the vector $\mathfrak{m}$ and the direction of motion as the XZ plane, where the particle moves parallel to the X axis at a distance ϱ from it For the transverse components of the field of the magnetic dipole we have (see 44.4):

$$H_y = 0,$$

$$H_z = \frac{3(\mathfrak{m}\cdot\mathbf{r})z - \mathfrak{m}_z r^2}{r^5} = \frac{\mathfrak{m}}{(\varrho^2 + x^2)^{\frac{5}{2}}}\{3(\varrho\cos\phi + x\sin\phi)\varrho - (\varrho^2 + x^2)\cos\phi\}$$

(ϕ is the angle between $\mathfrak{m}$ and the Z axis). Substituting in (76.6) and performing the integration, we obtain

$$\frac{1}{\mathcal{E}_{\text{crit}}} = \frac{\mathfrak{m}^2\pi}{64\mathrm{m}^2c^4\rho^5}\left(\frac{e^2}{mc^2}\right)^2(15 + 26\cos^2\phi).$$

2. Write the three-dimensional expression for the damping force in the relativistic case.

Solution: Calculating the space components of the four-vector (76.3), we find

$$\mathbf{f} = \frac{2e^3}{3mc^3}\left(1-\frac{v^2}{c^2}\right)^{-\frac{1}{2}}\left\{\left(\frac{\partial}{\partial t} + \mathbf{v}\cdot\nabla\right)\mathbf{E} + \frac{1}{c}\mathbf{v}\times\left(\frac{\partial}{\partial t} + \mathbf{v}\cdot\nabla\right)\mathbf{H}\right\} +$$

$$+ \frac{2e^4}{3m^2c^4}\left\{\mathbf{E}\times\mathbf{H} + \frac{1}{c}\mathbf{H}\times(\mathbf{H}\times\mathbf{v}) + \frac{1}{c}\mathbf{E}(\mathbf{v}\cdot\mathbf{E})\right\} +$$

$$+ \frac{2e^4}{3m^2c^5\left(1-\frac{v^2}{c^2}\right)}\mathbf{v}\left\{\left(\mathbf{E} + \frac{1}{c}\mathbf{v}\times\mathbf{H}\right)^2 - \frac{1}{c^2}(\mathbf{E}\cdot\mathbf{v})^2\right\}.$$

§ 77. Spectral resolution of the radiation in the ultrarelativistic case

Earlier (in § 73) it was shown that the radiation from an ultrarelativistic particle is directed mainly in the forward direction, along the velocity of the particle: it is contained almost entirely within the small range of angles

$$\Delta\theta \sim \sqrt{1-\frac{v^2}{c^2}}$$

around the direction of $\mathbf{v}$.

In evaluating the spectral resolution of the radiation, the relation between the magnitude of the angular range $\Delta\theta$ and the angle of deflection α of the particle in passing through the external electromagnetic field is essential.

The angle α can be calculated as follows. The change in the transverse (to the direction of motion) momentum of the particle is of the order of the product of the transverse force eF† and the time of passage through the field, $t \sim a/v \cong a/c$ (where a is the distance within which the field is significantly different from 0).

The ratio of this quantity to the momentum

$$p = \frac{mv}{\sqrt{1-v^2/c^2}} \cong \frac{mc}{\sqrt{1-v^2/c^2}}$$

determines the order of magnitude of the small angle α:

$$\alpha \sim \frac{eFa}{mc^2}\sqrt{1-\frac{v^2}{c^2}}.$$

Dividing by $\Delta\theta$, we find:

$$\frac{\alpha}{\Delta\theta} \sim \frac{eFa}{mc^2}. \tag{77.1}$$

We call attention to the fact that it does not depend on the velocity of the particle, and is completely determined by the properties of the external field itself.

We assume first that

$$eFa \gg mc^2, \tag{77.2}$$

that is, the total deflection of the particle is large compared with $\Delta\theta$. Then we can say that radiation in a given direction occurs mainly from that portion of the trajectory in which the velocity of the particle is almost parallel to that direction (subtending with it an angle in the interval $\Delta\theta$) and the length of this segment is small compared with a. The field F can be considered constant within this segment, and since a small segment of a curve can be considered as an arc of a circle, we can apply the results obtained in § 74 for radiation during uniform motion in a circle (replacing H by F). In particular, we may state that the main part of the radiation is concentrated in the frequency range

$$\omega \sim \frac{eF}{mc\left(1-\frac{v^2}{c^2}\right)} \tag{77.3}$$

[see (74.14)].

In the opposite limiting case,

$$eFa \ll mc^2, \tag{77.4}$$

the total angle of deflection of the particle is small compared with $\Delta\theta$. In this case the radiation is directed mainly into the narrow angular range $\Delta\theta$ around the direction of motion, while radiation arrives at a given point from the whole trajectory.

† If we choose the X axis along the direction of motion of the particle, then $(eF)^2$ is the sum of the squares of the y and z components of the Lorentz force, $e\mathbf{E}+e\mathbf{v}/c\times\mathbf{H}$, in which we can here set $v \cong c$:

$$F^2 = (E_y - H_z)^2 + (E_z + H_y)^2.$$

To compute the spectral distribution of the intensity, it is convenient to start in this case from the Lienard-Wiechert expressions (73.8) for the field in the wave zone. Let us compute the Fourier component

$$\mathbf{E}_\omega = \frac{1}{2\pi} \int_{-\infty}^{\infty} \mathbf{E} e^{i\omega t}\, dt.$$

The expression on the right of formula (73.8) is a function of the retarded time t', which is determined by the condition $t' - t - R(t')/c$. At large distances from a particle which is moving with an almost constant velocity $\mathbf{v}$, we have:

$$t' \cong t - \frac{R_0}{c} + \frac{1}{c}\mathbf{n}\cdot\mathbf{r}(t') \cong t - \frac{R_0}{c} + \frac{1}{c}\mathbf{n}\cdot\mathbf{v}t'$$

($\mathbf{r} = \mathbf{r}(t) \cong \mathbf{v}t$ is the radius vector of the particle), or

$$t = t'\left(1 - \frac{\mathbf{n}\cdot\mathbf{v}}{c}\right) + \frac{R_0}{c}.$$

We replace the t integration by an integration over t', by setting

$$dt = dt'\left(1 - \frac{\mathbf{n}\cdot\mathbf{v}}{c}\right),$$

and obtain:

$$\mathbf{F}_\omega = \frac{e}{2\pi c^2} \frac{e^{ikR_0}}{R_0\left(1 - \frac{\mathbf{n}\cdot\mathbf{v}}{c}\right)^2} \int_{-\infty}^{\infty} \mathbf{n}\times\left\{\left(\mathbf{n} - \frac{\mathbf{v}}{c}\right)\times\mathbf{w}(t')\right\} e^{i\omega t'\left(1-\frac{\mathbf{n}\cdot\mathbf{v}}{c}\right)} dt'.$$

We treat the velocity $\mathbf{v}$ as constant; only the acceleration $\mathbf{w}(t')$ is variable. Introducing the notation

$$\omega' = \omega\left(1 - \frac{\mathbf{n}\cdot\mathbf{v}}{c}\right), \qquad (77.5)$$

and the corresponding frequency component of the acceleration, we write $\mathbf{E}_\omega$ in the form

$$\mathbf{E}_\omega = \frac{e}{c^2} \frac{e^{ikR_0}}{R_0} \left(\frac{\omega}{\omega'}\right)^2 \mathbf{n}\times\left\{\left(\mathbf{n} - \frac{\mathbf{v}}{c}\right)\times\mathbf{w}_{\omega'}\right\}.$$

Finally from (66.9) we get for the energy radiated into solid angle do, with frequency in $d\omega$:

$$d\mathcal{E}_{\mathbf{n}\omega} = \frac{e^2}{c^3}\left(\frac{\omega}{\omega'}\right)^4 \left|\mathbf{n}\times\left\{\left(\mathbf{n} - \frac{\mathbf{v}}{c}\right)\times\mathbf{w}_{\omega'}\right\}\right|^2 do\, d\omega. \qquad (77.6)$$

An estimate of the order of magnitude of the frequencies in which the radiation is mainly concentrated in the case of (77.4) is easily made by noting that the Fourier component $\mathbf{w}_{\omega'}$ is significantly different from zero only if the time $1/\omega'$, or

$$\frac{1}{\omega\left(1-\frac{v^2}{c^2}\right)}$$

is of the same order as the time $a/v \sim a/c$ during which the acceleration of the particle changes significantly. Therefore we find:

$$\omega \sim \frac{c}{a\left(1-\frac{v^2}{c^2}\right)}. \tag{77.7}$$

In the treatment of both cases (77.2) and (77.4) it was assumed that the total loss of energy by the particle during its passage through the field was relatively small. We shall now show that the first of these cases also covers the problem of the radiation by an ultrarelativistic particle, whose total loss of energy is comparable with its initial energy.

The total loss of energy by the particle in the field can be determined from the work of the Lorentz frictional force. The work done by the force (76.4) over the path $\sim a$ is of order

$$af \sim \frac{e^4F^2a}{m^2c^4\left(1-\frac{v^2}{c^2}\right)}.$$

In order for this to be comparable with the total energy of the particle, $mc^2\Big/\sqrt{1-\frac{v^2}{c^2}}$, the field must exist at distances

$$a \sim \frac{m^3c^6}{e^4F^2}\sqrt{1-\frac{v^2}{c^2}}.$$

But then condition (77.2) is satisfied automatically:

$$aeF \sim \frac{m^3c^6}{e^3F}\sqrt{1-\frac{v^2}{c^2}} \gg mc^2,$$

since the field F must necessarily satisfy condition (76.5)

$$\frac{F}{\sqrt{1-\frac{v^2}{c^2}}} \ll \frac{m^2c^4}{e^3},$$

since otherwise we could not even apply ordinary electrodynamics.

Problems

1. Determine the spectral distribution of the total (over all directions) radiation intensity for the condition (77.2).

Solution: For each element of length of the trajectory, the radiation is determined by (74.11), where we must replace H by the value of the transverse force F at the given point and, in addition, we must go over from a discrete to a continuous frequency spectrum. This transformation is accomplished by formally multiplying by dn and the replacement

$$I_n\,dn = I_n \frac{dn}{d\omega}\,d\omega = I_n \frac{d\omega}{\omega_0}.$$

Next, integrating over all time, we obtain the spectral distribution of the total radiation in the following form:

$$d\mathcal{E}_\omega = -\,d\omega \frac{2e^2\omega}{\sqrt{\pi}\,c}\left(1-\frac{v^2}{c^2}\right)\int_{-\infty}^{+\infty}\left[\frac{1}{u}\Phi'(u)+\frac{1}{2}\int_u^\infty \Phi(u)\,du\right]dt,$$

where $\Phi(u)$ is the Airy function of the argument

$$u = \left[\frac{mc\omega}{eF}\left(1-\frac{v^2}{c^2}\right)\right]^{\frac{2}{3}}.$$

The integrand depends on the integration variable t implicitly through the quantity u (F and with it u, varies along the trajectory of the particle; for a given motion this variation can be considered as a time dependence).

2. Determine the spectral distribution of the total (over all directions) radiated energy for the condition (77.4).

Solution: Keeping in mind that the main role is played by the radiation at small angles to the direction of motion, we write:

$$\omega' = \omega\left(1-\frac{v}{c}\cos\theta\right) \cong \omega\left(1-\frac{v}{c}+\frac{\theta^2}{2}\right) \cong \frac{\omega}{2}\left(1-\frac{v^2}{c^2}+\theta^2\right).$$

We replace the integration over angles $do = \sin\theta\,d\theta\,d\phi \simeq \theta\,d\theta\,d\phi$ in (77.6) by an integration over $d\phi\,d\omega'/\omega$. In writing out the square of the vector triple product in (77.6) it must be remembered that in the ultrarelativistic case the longitudinal component of the acceleration is small compared with the transverse component $\left(\text{in the ratio } 1-\dfrac{v^2}{c^2}\right)$, and that in the present case we can, to sufficient accuracy, consider $\mathbf{w}$ and $\mathbf{v}$ to be mutually perpendicular. As a result, we find for the spectral distribution of the total radiation the following formula:

$$d\mathcal{E}_\omega = \frac{2\pi e^2\omega\,d\omega}{c^3}\int_{\frac{\omega}{2}\left(1-\frac{v^2}{c^2}\right)}^{\infty}\frac{|\mathbf{w}_{\omega'}|^2}{\omega'^2}\left[1-\frac{\omega}{\omega'}\left(1-\frac{v^2}{c^2}\right)+\frac{\omega^2}{2\omega'^2}\left(1-\frac{v^2}{c^2}\right)^2\right]d\omega'.$$

§ 78. Scattering by free charges

If an electromagnetic wave falls on a system of charges, then under its action the charges are set in motion. This motion in turn produces radiation in all directions; there occurs, we say, a *scattering* of the original wave.

The scattering is most conveniently characterized by the ratio of the amount of energy emitted by the scattering system in a given direction per unit time, to the energy flux density of the incident radiation. This ratio clearly has dimensions of area, and is called the *effective scattering cross section*.

Let dI be the energy radiated by the system into solid angle do per second for an incident wave with Poynting vector **S**. Then the effective cross section for scattering (into the solid angle do) is

$$d\sigma = \frac{\overline{dI}}{\overline{S}} \tag{78.1}$$

(the dash over a symbol means a time average). The integral σ of $d\sigma$ over all directions is the *total* effective scattering cross section.

Let us consider the scattering produced by a free charge at rest. Suppose there is incident on this charge a plane monochromatic linearly polarized wave. Its electric field can be written in the form

$$\mathbf{E} = \mathbf{E}_0 \cos(\mathbf{k}\cdot\mathbf{r} - \omega t + \alpha).$$

We shall assume that the velocity acquired by the charge under the influence of the incident wave is small compared with the velocity of light (which is usually the case). Then we can consider the force acting on the charge to be $e\mathbf{E}$, while the force $\frac{e}{c}\mathbf{v}\times\mathbf{H}$ due to the magnetic field can be neglected. In this case we can also neglect the effect of the displacement of the charge during its vibrations under the influence of the field. If the charge carries out vibrations around the coordinate origin, then we can assume that the field which acts on the charge at all times is the same as that at the origin, that is,

$$\mathbf{E} = \mathbf{E}_0 \cos(\omega t - \alpha).$$

Since the equation of motion of the charge is

$$m\ddot{\mathbf{r}} = e\mathbf{E}$$

and its dipole moment $\mathbf{d} = e\mathbf{r}$, then

$$\ddot{\mathbf{d}} = \frac{e^2}{m}\mathbf{E}. \tag{78.2}$$

The calculate the scattered radiation, we use formula (67.7) for dipole radiation (this is justified, since the velocity acquired by the charge under the influence of the incident wave is small compared with the velocity of light). We also note that the frequency of the wave radiated by the charge (i.e., scattered by it) is clearly the same as the frequency of the incident wave.

Substituting (78.2) in (67.7), we find

$$dI = \frac{e^4}{4\pi m^2 c^3}(\mathbf{E}\times\mathbf{n})^2\, do.$$

On the other hand, the Poynting vector of the incident wave is

$$S = \frac{c}{4\pi}E^2.$$

From this we find, for the effective cross section for scattering into the solid angle do,

$$d\sigma = \left(\frac{e^2}{mc^2}\right)^2 \sin^2\theta\, do, \tag{78.3}$$

where θ is the angle between the direction of scattering (the vector **n**), and the direction of the electric field **E** of the incident wave. We see that the effective scattering cross section of a free charge is independent of frequency.

We determine the total effective cross section σ. To do this, we choose the polar axis along **E**. Then $do = \sin\theta\, d\theta\, d\phi$; substituting this and integrating with respect to θ from 0 to π, and over ϕ from 0 to 2π, we find

$$\sigma = \frac{8\pi}{3}\left(\frac{e^2}{mc^2}\right)^2. \tag{78.4}$$

(This is the *Thomson formula*).

Finally, we calculate the effective cross section $d\sigma$ in the case where the incident wave is unpolarized (ordinary light). To do this we must average (78.3) over all directions of the vector **E** in a plane perpendicular to the direction of propagation of the incident wave (direction of the wave vector **k**). We introduce a coordinate system with Z axis along **k** and X axis along **E**. Then the cosine of the angle θ between the directions of **n** and **E**, that is, the projection of the unit vector **n** on the X axis, is $\cos\theta = \sin\Theta \cos\phi$ where Θ and ϕ are the polar axis and azimuth of the direction **n**. Averaging over all directions of **E** in the plane perpendicular to **k** is equivalent to averaging over the azimuth ϕ. We have

$$\overline{\sin^2\theta} = 1 - \frac{\sin^2\Theta}{2} = \frac{1+\cos^2\Theta}{2}$$

and, substituting in (78.3), we find for the effective cross section for the scattering of an unpolarized wave by a free charge

$$d\sigma = \frac{1}{2}\left(\frac{e^2}{mc^2}\right)^2 (1+\cos^2\Theta)\, do, \tag{78.5}$$

where Θ is the angle between the directions of the incident and scattered waves (the *scattering angle*).

The occurrence of scattering leads, in particular, to the appearance of a certain force acting on the scattering particle. One can verify this by the following considerations. On the average, in unit time, the wave incident on the particle loses energy $c\overline{W}\sigma$, where $\overline{W}$ is the average energy density, and σ is the total effective scattering cross section. Since the momentum of the field is equal to its energy divided by the velocity of light, the incident wave loses momentum equal in magnitude to $\overline{W}\sigma$. On the other hand, in a system of reference in which the charge carries out only small vibrations under the action of the force $e\mathbf{E}$, and its velocity v is small, the total flux of momentum in the scattered wave is zero, to terms of higher order in v/c (in § 73 it was shown that in a reference system in which $v = 0$, radiation of momentum by the particle does not occur). Therefore all the momentum lost by the incident wave is "absorbed" by the scattering particle. The average force $\overline{\mathbf{f}}$ acting on the particle is equal to the average momentum absorbed per unit time, i.e.,

$$\overline{\mathbf{f}} = \sigma \overline{W} \mathbf{n}_0 \tag{78.6}$$

($\mathbf{n}_0$ is a unit vector in the direction of propagation of the incident wave). We note that the average force appears as a second order quantity in the field of the incident wave, while the "instantaneous" force (the main part of which is $e\mathbf{E}$) is of first order in the field.

Formula (78.6) can also be obtained directly by averaging the damping force (75.10). The first term, proportional to $\mathbf{E}$, goes to zero on averaging, as does the average of the main part of the force, $e\mathbf{E}$. The second term gives

$$\overline{\mathbf{f}} = \frac{2e^4}{3m^2c^4} \overline{E^2} \mathbf{n}_0 = \frac{8\pi}{3} \left(\frac{e^2}{mc^2}\right)^2 \frac{\overline{E^2}}{4\pi} \mathbf{n}_0,$$

which, using (78.4), coincides with (78.6).

Problems

1. Determine the effective cross section for scattering of an elliptically polarized wave by a free charge.

Solution: The field of the wave has the form $\mathbf{E} = \mathbf{A}\cos(\omega t + a) + \mathbf{B}\sin(\omega t + a)$, where $\mathbf{A}$ and $\mathbf{B}$ are mutually perpendicular vectors (see § 48). By a derivation similar to the one in the text, we find

$$d\sigma = \left(\frac{e^2}{mc^2}\right)^2 \frac{(\mathbf{A}\times\mathbf{n})^2 + (\mathbf{B}\times\mathbf{n})^2}{A^2+B^2} do.$$

2. Determine the effective cross section for scattering of a linearly polarized wave by a charge carrying out small vibrations under the influence of an elastic force (oscillator).

Solution: The equation of motion of the charge in the incident field $\mathbf{E} = \mathbf{E}_0 \cos(\omega t + a)$ is

$$\ddot{\mathbf{r}} + \omega_0^2 \mathbf{r} = \frac{e}{m} \mathbf{E}_0 \cos(\omega t + a),$$

where ω_0 is the frequency of its free vibrations. For the forced vibrations, we then have

$$\mathbf{r} = \frac{e\mathbf{E}_0 \cos(\omega t + a)}{m(\omega_0^2 - \omega^2)}.$$

Calculating $\ddot{\mathbf{d}}$ from this, we find

$$d\sigma = \left(\frac{e^2}{mc^2}\right)^2 \frac{\omega^4}{(\omega_0^2-\omega^2)^2} \sin^2\theta \, do$$

(θ is the angle between $\mathbf{E}$ and $\mathbf{n}$).

3. Determine the total effective cross section for scattering of light by an electric dipole which, mechanically, is a rotator. The frequency ω of the wave is assumed to be large compared with the frequency $\mathbf{\Omega}_0$ of free rotation of the rotator.

Solution: Because of the condition $\omega \gg \Omega_0$, we can neglect the free rotation of the rotator, and consider only the forced rotation under the action of the moment of the forces $\mathbf{d}\times\mathbf{E}$ exerted on it by the scattered wave. The equation for this motion is: $J\dot{\mathbf{\Omega}} = \mathbf{d}\times\mathbf{E}$, where J is the moment of inertia of the rotator and $\mathbf{\Omega}$ is the angular velocity of rotation. The change in the dipole moment vector, as it rotates without changing its absolute value, is given by the formula $\dot{\mathbf{d}} = \mathbf{\Omega}\times\mathbf{d}$. From these two equations, we find (omitting the quadratic term in the small quantity $\mathbf{\Omega}$):

$$\ddot{\mathbf{d}} = \frac{1}{J}(\mathbf{d}\times\mathbf{E})\times\mathbf{d} = \frac{1}{J}[\mathbf{E}d^2-(\mathbf{E}\cdot\mathbf{d})\,\mathbf{d}].$$

Assuming that all orientations of the dipole in space are equally probable, and averaging $\overline{\ddot{\mathbf{d}}^2}$ over them, we find for the total effective cross section,

$$\sigma = \frac{16\pi d^4}{9c^4J^2}.$$

4. Determine the degree of depolarization in the scattering of ordinary light by a free charge.

Solution: From symmetry considerations, it is clear that the two incoherent polarized components of the scattered light (see § 50) will be linearly polarized: one in the plane of scattering (the plane passing through the incident and scattered waves) and the other perpendicular to this plane. The intensities of these components are determined by the components of the field of the incident wave in the plane of scattering ($\mathbf{E}_{\parallel}$) and perpendicular to it ($\mathbf{E}_{\perp}$), and, according to (78.3), are proportional respectively to

$$(\mathbf{E}_{\parallel}\times\mathbf{n})^2 = E_{\parallel}^2\cos^2\Theta \quad\text{and}\quad (\mathbf{E}_{\perp}\times\mathbf{n})^2 = E_{\perp}^2$$

(where Θ is the angle of scattering). Since for the ordinary incident light, $\overline{E_{\parallel}^2} = \overline{E_{\perp}^2}$, the degree of depolarization [see the definition in (50.9)] is:

$$\varrho = \cos^2\Theta.$$

5. Determine the frequency ω' of the light scattered by a moving charge.

Solution: In a system of coordinates in which the charge is at rest, the frequency of the light does not change on scattering ($\omega = \omega'$). This relation can be written in invariant form as

$$k_i' u_i = k_i u_i,$$

where u_i is the four-velocity of the charge. From this we find without difficulty

$$\omega'\left(1-\frac{v}{c}\cos\theta'\right) = \omega\left(1-\frac{v}{c}\cos\theta\right),$$

where θ and θ' are the angles made by the incident and scattered waves with the direction of motion (v is the velocity of the charge).

6. Determine the angular distribution of the scattering of a linearly polarized wave by a charge moving with velocity v in the direction of propagation of the wave.

Solution: The scattered intensity is given by (73.14), where the acceleration $\mathbf{w}$ of the particle must be expressed in terms of the fields $\mathbf{E}$ and $\mathbf{H}$ of the incident wave by the formulas obtained in the problem in § 17; in doing this we must keep in mind that $\mathbf{v}$ is perpendicular to $\mathbf{E}$ and $\mathbf{H}$. Dividing the intensity dI by the Poynting vector of the incident wave, we get the following expression for the effective scattering cross section:

$$d\sigma = \left(\frac{e^2}{mc^2}\right)^2 \frac{\left(1-\frac{v^2}{c^2}\right)\left(1-\frac{v}{c}\right)^2}{\left(1-\frac{v}{c}\sin\theta\cos\phi\right)^6}\left[\left(1-\frac{v}{c}\sin\theta\cos\phi\right)^2-\left(1-\frac{v^2}{c^2}\right)\cos^2\theta\right]do,$$

where θ and ϕ are the polar angle and azimuth of the direction **n** relative to a system of coordinates with Z axis along **E**, and X axis along **v** ($\cos(\mathbf{n}, \mathbf{E}) = \cos\theta$; $\cos(\mathbf{n}, \mathbf{v}) = \sin\theta \cos\phi$).

7. Calculate the motion of a charge under the action of the average force exerted upon it by the wave scattered by it.

Solution: The force (78.6), and therefore the velocity of the motion under consideration, is along the direction of propagation of the incident wave (X axis). In the auxiliary reference system K_0, in which the particle is at rest (we recall that we are dealing with the motion averaged over the period of the small vibrations), the force acting on it is $\sigma \overline{W}_0$, and the acceleration acquired by it under the action of this force is

$$w_0 = \frac{\sigma}{m} \overline{W}_0$$

(the index zero refers to the reference system K_0). The transformation to the original reference system K (in which the charge moves with velocity v) is given by the formulas obtained in the problem of §7 and by formula (47.7), and gives:

$$\frac{d}{dt} \frac{v}{\sqrt{1 - \frac{v^2}{c^2}}} = \frac{1}{\left(1 - \frac{v^2}{c^2}\right)^{\frac{3}{2}}} \frac{dv}{dt} = \frac{\overline{W}\sigma}{m} \frac{1 - \frac{v}{c}}{1 + \frac{v}{c}}.$$

Integrating this expression, we find

$$\frac{\overline{W}\sigma}{mc} t = \frac{1}{3} \sqrt{\frac{1 + \frac{v}{c}}{1 - \frac{v}{c}}} \cdot \frac{2 - \frac{v}{c}}{1 - \frac{v}{c}} - \frac{2}{3},$$

which determines the velocity $v = dx/dt$ as an implicit function of the time (the integration constant has been chosen so that $v = 0$ at $t = 0$).

8. Determine the average force exerted on a charge moving in an electromagnetic field consisting of a superposition of waves in all directions with an isotropic distribution of directions of propagation.

Solution: We write the equation of motion of the charge in four-dimensional form,

$$mc \frac{du_i}{ds} = g_i.$$

To determine the four-vector g_i, we note that in a system of reference in which the charge is at rest at a given moment, in the presence of a single wave propagating along a definite direction (say, along the X axis), the equation of motion is ($v_x \equiv v$)

$$m \frac{dv}{dt} = \sigma W$$

(we omit the average sign throughout). This means that the X-component of the vector g_i must become $\frac{W}{c}\sigma$. The four-vector $-\frac{\sigma}{c} T_{ik} u_k$ has this property, where T_{ik} is the energy-momentum tensor of the wave, and u_i is the four-velocity of the charge. In addition, g_i must satisfy the condition $g_i u_i = 0$. This can be achieved by adding to the previous expression a four-vector of the form $a u_i$, where a is a scalar. Determining a suitably, we obtain

$$mc \frac{du_i}{ds} = -\frac{\sigma}{c} (T_{ik} u_k + u_i u_k u_l T_{kl}). \tag{1}$$

In an electromagnetic field of isotropic radiation, the Poynting vector vanishes because of symmetry, and the stress tensor $T_{\alpha\beta}$ must have the form const $\delta_{\alpha\beta}$. Noting also that we must have $T_{ii} = 0$, we find for the components of T_{ik},

$$T_{\alpha\beta} = \frac{W}{3}\delta_{\alpha\beta}, \quad T_{\alpha 4} = 0, \quad T_{44} = -W.$$

Substituting these expressions in (1), we find for the force acting on the charge:

$$\frac{d}{dt}\left(\frac{mv}{\sqrt{1-\frac{v^2}{c^2}}}\right) = -\frac{4W\sigma v}{3c\left(1-\frac{v^2}{c^2}\right)}.$$

This force acts in the direction opposite to the motion of the charge, i.e., the charge experiences a retardation. We note that for $v \ll c$, the retarding force is proportional to the velocity of the charge:

$$m\frac{dv}{dt} = -\frac{4W\sigma v}{3c}.$$

9. Determine the effective cross section for scattering of a linearly polarized wave by an oscillator, taking into account the radiation damping.

Solution: We write the equation of motion of the charge in the incident field in the form

$$\ddot{\mathbf{r}} + \omega_0^2 \mathbf{r} = \frac{e}{m}\mathbf{E}_0 e^{-i\omega t} + \frac{2e^2}{3mc^3}\dddot{\mathbf{r}}.$$

In the damping force, we can substitute approximately $\dddot{\mathbf{r}} = -\omega_0^2 \dot{\mathbf{r}}^2$; then we find

$$\ddot{\mathbf{r}} + \gamma\dot{\mathbf{r}} + \omega_0^2 \mathbf{r} = \frac{e}{m}\mathbf{E}_0 e^{-i\omega t},$$

where $\gamma = \frac{2e^2}{3mc^3}\omega_0^2$. From this we obtain

$$\mathbf{r} = \frac{e}{m}\mathbf{E}_0 \frac{e^{-i\omega t}}{\omega_0^2 - \omega^2 - i\omega\gamma}.$$

The effective cross section is

$$\sigma = \frac{8\pi}{3}\left(\frac{e^2}{mc^2}\right)^2 \frac{\omega^4}{(\omega_0^2-\omega^2)^2 + \omega^2\gamma^2}$$

§ 79. Scattering of low-frequency waves

The scattering of a wave by a system of charges differs from the scattering by a single charge (at rest), first of all in the fact that because of the presence of internal motion of the charges of the system, the frequency of the scattered radiation can be different from the frequency of the incident wave. Namely, in the spectral resolution of the scattered wave there appear, in addition to the frequency ω of the incident wave, frequencies ω' differing from ω by one of the internal frequencies of motion of the scattering system. The scattering with changed frequency is called incoherent (or combinational), in contrast to the coherent scattering without change in frequency.

Assuming that the field of the incident wave is weak, we can represent the current density in the form $\mathbf{j} = \mathbf{j}_0 + \mathbf{j}'$, where $\mathbf{j}_0$ is the current density in the absence of the external field, and $\mathbf{j}'$ is the change in the current under the action of the incident wave. Correspondingly, the vector potential (and other quantities) of the field of the system also has the form $\mathbf{A} = \mathbf{A}_0 + \mathbf{A}'$, where $\mathbf{A}_0$ and $\mathbf{A}'$ are determined by the currents $\mathbf{j}_0$ and $\mathbf{j}'$. Clearly, $\mathbf{A}'$ describes the wave scattered by the system.

Let us consider the scattering of a wave whose frequency ω is small compared with all the internal frequencies of the system. The scattering will consist of an incoherent as well as a coherent part, but we shall here consider only the coherent scattering.

In calculating the field of the scattered wave, for sufficiently low frequency ω, we can use the expansion of the retarded potentials which was presented in §§ 67 and 71, even if the velocities of the particles of the system are not small compared with the velocity of light. Namely, for the validity of the expansion of the integral

$$\mathbf{A}' = \frac{1}{cR_0}\int \mathbf{j}'_{t-\frac{R_0}{c}+\frac{\mathbf{r}\cdot\mathbf{n}}{c}}\,dV,$$

it is necessary only that the time $\mathbf{r}\cdot\mathbf{n}/c \sim a/c$ be small compared with the time $1/\omega$; for sufficiently low frequencies ($\omega \ll c/a$), this condition is fulfilled independently of the velocities of the particles of the system.

The first terms in the expansion give

$$\mathbf{H}' = \frac{1}{c^2R_0}\{\ddot{\mathbf{d}}'\times\mathbf{n} + (\ddot{\mathfrak{m}}'\times\mathbf{n})\times\mathbf{n}\},$$

where $\mathbf{d}'$, $\mathfrak{m}'$ are the parts of the dipole and magnetic moments of the system which are produced by the radiation falling on the system. The succeeding terms contain higher time derivatives than the second, and we drop them.

The component $\mathbf{H}'_\omega$ of the spectral resolution of the field of the scattered wave, with frequency equal to that of the incident wave, is given by this same formula, when we substitute for all quantities their Fourier components: $\ddot{\mathbf{d}}'_\omega = -\omega^2\mathbf{d}'_\omega$, $\ddot{\mathfrak{m}}'_\omega = -\omega^2\mathfrak{m}'_\omega$. Then we obtain

$$\mathbf{H}'_\omega = \frac{\omega^2}{c^2R_0}\{\mathbf{n}\times\mathbf{d}'_\omega + \mathbf{n}\times(\mathfrak{m}'_\omega\times\mathbf{n})\}. \tag{79.1}$$

The later terms in the expansion of the field would give quantities proportional to higher powers of the small frequency. If the velocities of all the particles of the system are small ($v \ll c$), then in (79.1) we can neglect the second term in comparison to the first, since the magnetic moment contains the ratio v/c. Then

$$\mathbf{H}'_\omega = \frac{1}{c^2R_0}\,\omega^2\mathbf{n}\times\mathbf{d}'_\omega. \tag{79.2}$$

If the total charge of the system is zero, then for $\omega \to 0$, $\mathbf{d}'_\omega$ and $\mathfrak{m}'_\omega$ approach constant limits (if the sum of the charges were different from zero, then for $\omega = 0$, i.e., for a constant field, the system would begin to move as a whole). Therefore for low frequencies ($\omega \ll v/a$) we can consider $\mathbf{d}'_\omega$ and $\mathfrak{m}'_\omega$ as independent of frequency, so that the field of the scattered wave is proportional to the square of the frequency. Its intensity is consequently proportional to ω^4. Thus for the scattering of a low-frequency wave, the effective cross section for (coherent) scattering is proportional to the fourth power of the frequency of the incident radiation.†

§ 80. Scattering of high-frequency waves

We consider the scattering of a wave by a system of charges in the opposite limit, when the frequency ω of the wave is large compared with the fundamental internal frequencies of the system. The latter have the order of magnitude $\omega_0 \sim v/a$, so that ω must satisfy the condition

$$\omega \gg \omega_0 \sim \frac{v}{a}. \tag{80.1}$$

In addition, we assume that the velocities of the charges of the system are small ($v \ll c$).

According to condition (80.1), the periods of the motion of the charges of the system are large compared with the period of the wave. Therefore during a time interval of the order of the period of the wave, the motion of the charges of the system can be considered uniform. This means that in considering the scattering of short waves, we need not take into account the interaction of the charges of the system with each other, that is, we can consider them as free.

Thus in calculating the velocity $\mathbf{v}'$, acquired by a charge in the field of the incident wave, we can consider each of the charges in the system separately, and write for it an equation of motion of the form

$$m\frac{d\mathbf{v}'}{dt} = e\mathbf{E} = e\mathbf{E}_0 e^{-i(\omega t - \mathbf{k}\cdot\mathbf{r})},$$

where $\mathbf{k} = \frac{\omega}{c}\mathbf{n}$ is the wave vector of the incident wave. The radius vector of the charge is, of course, a function of the time. In the exponent on the right side of this equation the time rate of change of the first term is large compared with that of the second (the first is ω, while the second is of order $kv \sim v\frac{\omega}{c} \ll \omega$). Therefore in integrating the equation of motion, we can consider the term $\mathbf{r}$ on the right side as constant. Then

$$\mathbf{v}' = -\frac{e}{i\omega m}\mathbf{E}_0 e^{-i(\omega t - \mathbf{k}\cdot\mathbf{r})}. \tag{80.2}$$

† This also applies to the scattering of light by ions as well as by neutral atoms. Because of the large mass of the nucleus, the scattering resulting from the motion of the ion as a whole can be neglected.

For the vector potential of the scattered wave (at large distances from the system), we have from the general formula (66.2):

$$\mathbf{A}' = \frac{1}{cR_0}\int \mathbf{j}'_{t-\frac{R_0}{c}+\frac{\mathbf{r}\cdot\mathbf{n}'}{c}}\,dV = \frac{1}{cR_0}\sum (e\mathbf{v}')_{t-\frac{R_0}{c}+\frac{\mathbf{r}\cdot\mathbf{n}'}{c}},$$

where the sum goes over all the charges of the system; $\mathbf{n}'$ is a unit vector in the direction of scattering. Substituting (80.2), we find

$$\mathbf{A}' = -\frac{1}{icR_0\omega}e^{-i\omega\left(t-\frac{R_0}{c}\right)}\mathbf{E}_0\sum\frac{e^2}{m}e^{-i\mathbf{q}\cdot\mathbf{r}}, \tag{80.3}$$

where $\mathbf{q} = \mathbf{k}'-\mathbf{k}$ is the difference between the wave vector $\mathbf{k} = \frac{\omega}{c}\mathbf{n}$ of the incident wave, and the wave vector $\mathbf{k}' = \frac{\omega}{c}\mathbf{n}'$ of the scattered wave.† The value of the sum in (80.3) must be taken at the time $t' = t-\frac{R_0}{c}$ (for brevity as usual, we omit the index t' on $\mathbf{r}$); the change of $\mathbf{r}$ in the time $\mathbf{r}\cdot\mathbf{n}'/c$ can be neglected in view of our assumption that the velocities of the particles are small. The absolute value of the vector $\mathbf{q}$ is

$$q = 2\frac{\omega}{c}\sin\frac{\theta}{2}, \tag{80.4}$$

where θ is the scattering angle.

For scattering by an atom (or molecule), we can neglect the terms in the sum in (80.3) which come from the nuclei, because their masses are large compared with the electron mass. Later we shall be looking at just this case, so that we remove the factor e^2/m from the summation sign, and understand by e and m the charge and mass of the electron.

For the field $\mathbf{H}'$ of the scattered wave we find from (66.3):

$$\mathbf{H}' = \frac{\mathbf{n}'\times\mathbf{E}_0}{c^2R_0}e^{-i\omega\left(t-\frac{R_0}{c}\right)}\frac{e^2}{m}\sum e^{-i\mathbf{q}\cdot\mathbf{r}} \tag{80.5}$$

The energy flux into an element of solid angle in the direction $\mathbf{n}'$ is

$$\frac{c|\mathbf{H}'|^2}{8\pi}R_0^2\,do = \frac{e^4}{8\pi c^3m^2}(\mathbf{n}'\times\mathbf{E}_0)^2\left|\sum e^{-i\mathbf{q}\cdot\mathbf{r}}\right|^2 do.$$

Dividing this by the energy flux $\frac{c}{8\pi}|\mathbf{E}_0|^2$ of the incident wave, and introducing the angle θ between the direction of the field $\mathbf{E}$ of the incident wave and the

† Strictly speaking, the wave vector $\mathbf{k}' = \omega'\mathbf{n}'/c$, where the frequency ω' of the scattered wave may differ from ω. However, in the present case of high frequencies the difference $\omega'-\omega\sim\omega_0$ can be neglected.

direction of scattering, we finally obtain the effective scattering cross section in the form

$$do = \left(\frac{e^2}{mc^2}\right)^2 \overline{\left|\sum e^{-i\mathbf{q}\cdot\mathbf{r}}\right|^2} \sin^2\theta \, do. \tag{80.6}$$

The dash means a time average, i.e., an average over the motion of the charges of the system; it appears because the scattering is observed over a time interval large compared with the periods of motion of the charges of the system.

For the wavelength of the incident radiation, there follows from the condition (80.1) the inequality $\lambda \ll \frac{c}{v} \cdot a$. As for the relative values of λ and a, both the limiting cases $\lambda \gg a$ and $\lambda \ll a$ are possible. In both these cases the general formula (80.6) simplifies considerably.

In the case of $\lambda \gg a$, in the expression (80.6) $\mathbf{q}\cdot\mathbf{r} \ll 1$, since $q \sim 1/\lambda$, and r is of order of a. Replacing $e^{-i\mathbf{q}\cdot\mathbf{r}}$ by unity in accordance with this, we have:

$$d\sigma = \left(\frac{Zc^2}{mc^2}\right)^2 \sin^2\theta \, do \tag{80.7}$$

that is, the scattering is proportional to the square of the atomic number Z.

We now go over to the case of $\lambda \ll a$. In the square of the sum which appears in (80.6), in addition to the square modulus of each term, there appear products of the form $e^{-i\mathbf{q}\cdot(\mathbf{r}_1-\mathbf{r}_2)}$.

In averaging over the motion of the charges, i.e., over their mutual separations, $\mathbf{r}_1$ $\mathbf{r}_2$ takes on values in an interval of order a. Since $q \sim 1/\lambda$, $\lambda \ll a$, the exponential factor $e^{-i\mathbf{q}\cdot(\mathbf{r}_1-\mathbf{r}_2)}$ is a rapidly oscillating function in this interval, and its average value vanishes. Thus for $\lambda \ll a$, the effective scattering cross section is

$$d\sigma = Z\left(\frac{e^2}{mc^2}\right)^2 \sin^2\theta \, do, \tag{80.8}$$

that is, the scattering is proportional to the first power of the atomic number. We note that this formula is not applicable for small angles of scattering $\left(\theta \sim \frac{\lambda}{a}\right)$, since in this case $q \sim \frac{\theta}{\lambda} \sim \frac{1}{a}$ and the exponent $\mathbf{q}\cdot\mathbf{r}$ is not large compared to unity.

To determine the effective coherent scattering cross section, we must separate out that part of the field of the scattered wave which has the frequency ω. The expression (80.5) depends on the time through the factor $e^{-i\omega t}$, and also involves the time in the sum $\sum e^{-i\mathbf{q}\cdot\mathbf{r}}$. This latter dependence leads to the result that in the field of the scattered wave there are contained, along with the frequency ω, other (though close to ω) frequencies. That part of the field which has the frequency ω (i.e., depends on the time only through the factor $e^{-i\omega t}$), is obtained if we average the sum $\sum e^{-i\mathbf{q}\cdot\mathbf{r}}$ over time. In accordance with this, the expression for the effective coherent scattering cross section $d\sigma_{\text{coh}}$, differs from the total cross section $d\sigma$ in that it contains, in place of the average value of the square modulus of the sum, the square modulus of the average value of the sum,

$$d\sigma_{\text{coh}} = \left(\frac{e^2}{mc^2}\right)^2 \left|\overline{\sum e^{-i\mathbf{q}\cdot\mathbf{r}}}\right|^2 \tag{80.9}$$

It is useful to note that this average value of the sum is (except for a factor) just the space Fourier component of the distribution $\varrho(\mathbf{r})$ of the electric charge density in the atom:

$$e\overline{\sum e^{-i\mathbf{q}\cdot\mathbf{r}}} = \int \varrho(\mathbf{r})\, e^{-i\mathbf{q}\cdot\mathbf{r}}\, dV = (2\pi)^3 \varrho_{\mathbf{q}}. \tag{80.10}$$

In case $\lambda \gg a$, we can again replace $e^{i\mathbf{q}\cdot\mathbf{r}}$ by unity, so that

$$d\sigma_{\text{coh}} = \left(Z\frac{e^2}{mc^2}\right)^2 \sin^2\theta\, do. \tag{80.11}$$

Comparing this with the total effective cross section (80.7), we see that $d\sigma_{\text{coh}} = d\sigma$, that is, all the scattering is coherent.

If $\lambda \ll a$, then when we average in (80.9) all the terms of the sum (being rapidly oscillating functions of the time) vanish, so that $d\sigma_{\text{coh}} = 0$. Thus in this case the scattering is completely incoherent.

CHAPTER 10

PARTICLE IN A GRAVITATIONAL FIELD

§ 81. Gravitational fields in nonrelativistic mechanics

In addition to electromagnetic fields, there exist in nature fields of another type — so-called *gravitational fields*, or fields of gravity. These fields have the basic property that all bodies move in them in the same manner, independently of mass or charge, provided the initial conditions are the same.

For example, the laws of free fall in the gravity field of the earth are the same for all bodies; whatever their mass, all acquire one and the same acceleration.

This property of gravitational fields provides the possibility of establishing an analogy between the motion of a body in a gravitational field and the motion of a body not located in any external field, but which is considered from the point of view of a noninertial system of reference. Namely, in an inertial reference system, the free motion of all bodies is uniform and rectilinear, and if, say, at the initial time their velocities are the same, they will be the same for all times. Clearly, therefore, if we consider this motion in a given noninertial system, then relative to this system all the bodies will move in the same way.

Thus the properties of the motion in a noninertial system are the same as those in an inertial system in the presence of a gravitational field. In other words, a noninertial reference system is equivalent to a certain gravitational field. This is called the *principle of equivalence*.

Let us consider, for example, motion in a uniformly accelerated reference system. A body of arbitrary mass, freely moving in such a system of reference, clearly has relative to this system a constant acceleration, equal and opposite to the acceleration of the system itself. The same applies to motion in a uniform constant gravitational field, e.g., the field of gravity of the earth (over small regions, where the field can be considered uniform). Thus a uniformly accelerated system of reference is equivalent to a constant, uniform external field. A somewhat more general case is a nonuniformly accelerated linear motion of the reference system — it is clearly equivalent to a uniform but variable gravitational field.

However, the fields to which noninertial reference systems are equivalent are not completely identical with "actual" gravitational fields which occur also in inertial frames. For there is a very essential difference with respect to their behavior at infinity. At infinite distances from the bodies producing the field, "actual" gravitational fields always go to zero. Contrary to this, the fields to which noninertial frames are equivalent increase without limit at infinity, or, in any event, remain finite in value. Thus, for example, the centrifugal force which appears in a rotating reference system increases without limit as we move away from the axis of rotation; the field to which a reference system in accelerated linear motion is equivalent is the same over all space and also at infinity.

The fields to which noninertial systems are equivalent vanish as soon as we transform to an inertial system. In contrast to this, "actual" gravitational fields (existing also in an inertial reference frame) cannot be eliminated by any choice of reference system. This is already clear from what has been said above concerning the difference in conditions at infinity between "actual" gravitational fields and fields to which noninertial systems are equivalent; since the latter do not approach zero at infinity, it is clear that it is impossible, by any choice of reference frame, to eliminate an "actual" field, since it vanishes at infinity.

All that can be done by a suitable choice of reference system is to eliminate the gravitational field in a given region of space, sufficiently small so that the field can be considered uniform over it. This can be done by choosing a system in accelerated motion, the acceleration of which is equal to that which would be acquired by a particle placed in the region of the field which we are considering.

The motion of a particle in a gravitational field is determined, in nonrelativistic mechanics, by a Lagrangian having (in an inertial reference frame) the form

$$L=\frac{mv^2}{2}-m\phi, \tag{81.1}$$

where ϕ is a certain function of the coordinates and time which characterizes the field and is called the *gravitational potential.*† Correspondingly, the equation of motion of the particle is

$$\dot{\mathbf{v}} = -\text{grad}\,\phi. \tag{81.2}$$

It does not contain the mass or any other constant characterizing the properties of the particle; this is the mathematical expression of the basic property of gravitational fields.

§ 82. The gravitational field in relativistic mechanics

The fundamental property of gravitational fields which was pointed out in the previous section, that all bodies move in them in the same way, remains valid also in relativistic mechanics. Consequently there remains also

† In what follows we shall seldom have to use the electromagnetic potential ϕ, so that the designation of the gravitational potential by the same symbol cannot lead to misunderstanding.

the analogy between gravitational fields and noninertial reference systems. Therefore in studying the properties of gravitational fields in relativistic mechanics, we naturally also start from this analogy.

In an inertial reference system, in cartesian coordinates, the interval ds is given by the relation:

$$ds^2 = c^2\,dt^2 - dx^2 - dy^2 - dz^2.$$

Upon transforming to any other inertial reference system (i.e., under Lorentz transformation), the interval, as we know, retains the same form. However, if we transform to a noninertial system of reference, ds^2 will no longer be a sum of squares of the four coordinate differentials.

So, for example, when we transform to a uniformly rotating system of coordinates,

$$x = x' \cos\Omega t - y' \sin\Omega t, \qquad y = x' \sin\Omega t + y' \cos\Omega t, \qquad z = z'$$

(Ω is the angular velocity of the rotation, directed along the Z axis), the interval takes on the form

$$ds^2 = [c^2 - \Omega^2(x'^2+y'^2)]\,dt^2 - dx'^2 - dy'^2 - dz'^2 + 2\Omega y'\,dx'\,dt - 2\Omega x'\,dy'\,dt.$$

No matter what the law of transformation of the time coordinate, this expression cannot be represented as a sum of squares of the coordinate differentials.

Thus in a noninertial system of reference the square of an interval appears as a quadratic form of general type in the coordinate differentials, that is, it has the form

$$-ds^2 = g_{ik}\,dx_i\,dx_k, \tag{82.1}$$

where the g_{ik} are certain functions of the space coordinates x_1, x_2, x_3 and the time coordinate x_0. Thus, when we use a noninertial system, the four-dimensional coordinate system x_0, x_1, x_2, x_3 is curvilinear. The quantities g_{ik}, determining all the geometric properties in each curvilinear system of coordinates, represent, we say, the *space-time metric.*

Since ds^2 is no longer always a sum of squares, there is no point in using an imaginary time coordinate $x_4 = ict$. We shall denote the real time coordinate by x_0 (or ct).†

The quantities g_{ik} can clearly always be considered symmetric in the indices i and k ($g_{ki} = g_{ik}$), since they are determined from the symmetric form (82.1), where g_{ik} and g_{ki} enter as factors of one and the same product $dx_i\,dx_k$. In the general case, there are ten different quantities g_{ik} — four with equal, and $4 \cdot 3/2 = 6$ with different indices. In an inertial reference system, when

† Correspondingly, in what follows it is understood that we sum from 0 to 3 over a repeated Latin index, and from 1 to 3 over a Greek index.

we use cartesian space coordinates $x_{1,2,3} = x, y, z$, and the time, $x_0 = ct$, the quantities g_{ik} are

$$g_{11} = g_{22} = g_{33} = 1, \ g_{00} = -1, \ g_{ik} = 0 \text{ for } i \neq k. \tag{82.2}$$

We call a four-dimensional system of coordinates with these values of g_{ik} *Galilean.*

In the previous section it was shown that a noninertial system of reference is equivalent to a certain field of force. We now see that in relativistic mechanics, these fields are determined by the quantities g_{ik}.

The same applies also to "actual" gravitational fields. Any gravitational field is just a change in the metric of space-time, as determined by the quantities g_{ik}. This important fact means that the geometrical properties of space-time (its metric) are determined by physical phenomena, and are not fixed properties of space and time.

The theory of gravitational fields, constructed on the basis of the theory of relativity, is called the *general theory of relativity.* It was established by Einstein (and finally formulated by him in 1916), and represents probably the most beautiful of all existing physical theories. It is remarkable that it was developed by Einstein in a purely deductive manner and only later was substantiated by astronomical observations.

As in nonrelativistic mechanics, there is a fundamental difference between "actual" gravitational fields and fields to which noninertial reference systems are equivalent. Upon transforming to a noninertial reference system, the quadratic form (82.1), i.e., the quantities g_{ik}, are obtained from their Galilean values (82.2) by a simple transformation of coordinates, and can be reduced over all space to their Galilean values by the inverse coordinate transformation. That such forms for g_{ik} are very special is clear from the fact that it is impossible by a mere transformation of the *four* coordinates to bring the *ten* quantities g_{ik} to a pre-assigned form.

An "actual" gravitational field cannot be eliminated by any transformation of coordinates. In other words, in the presence of a gravitational field space-time is such that the quantities g_{ik} determining its metric cannot, by any coordinate transformation, be brought to their Galilean values over all space. Such a space-time is said to be *curved*, in contrast to *flat* space-time, where such a reduction is possible.†

By an appropriate choice of coordinates, we can, however, bring the quantities g_{ik} to Galilean form at any individual point of the non-Galilean space-time: this amounts to the reduction to diagonal form of a quadratic form

† The metric of a flat four-space, defined by the quadratic form $-ds^2 = dx_1^2 + dx_2^2 + dx_3^2 - dx_0^2$, is sometimes said to be pseudo-Euclidean, in constrast to the Euclidean case, where the squares of the differentials of all four (real) coordinates enter with the same sign in $-ds^2$.

with constant coefficients (the values of g_{ik} at the given point). Such a coordinate system is said to be *Galilean for the given point.*†

We note that, after reduction to diagonal form at a given point, the matrix of the quantities g_{ik} has one negative and three positive principal values.‡ From this it follows, in particular, that the determinant g, formed from the quantities g_{ik}, is always negative for a real space-time:

$$g < 0. \tag{82.3}$$

A change in the metric of space-time also means a change in the purely spatial metric. To a Galilean g_{ik} in flat space-time, there corresponds a Euclidean geometry of space. In a gravitational field, the geometry of space becomes non-Euclidean. This applies both to "true" gravitational fields, in which space-time is "curved", as well as to fields resulting from the fact that the reference system is non-inertial, which leave the space-time flat.

The problem of spatial geometry in a gravitational field will be considered in more detail in § 84. It is useful to give here a simple argument which shows pictorially that space will become non-Euclidean when we change to a non-inertial system of reference. Let us consider two reference frames, of which one (K) is inertial, while the other (K') rotates uniformly with respect to K around their common z axis. A circle in the x, y plane of the K system (with its center at the origin) can also be regarded as a circle in the x', y' plane of the K' system. Measuring the length of the circle and its diameter with a yardstick in the K system, we obtain values whose ratio is equal to π, in accordance with the Euclidean character of the geometry in the inertial reference system. Now let the measurement be carried out with a yardstick at rest relative to K'. Observing this process from the K system, we find that the yardstick laid along the circumference suffers a Lorentz contraction, whereas the yardstick placed radially is not changed. It is therefore clear that the ratio of the circumference to the diameter, obtained from such a measurement, will be greater than π.

In the general case of an arbitrary, varying gravitational field, the metric of space is not only non-Euclidean, but also varies with the time.§ This means that the relations between different geometrical distances change with time. As a result, the relative position of "test bodies" introduced into the field cannot remain unchanged in any coordinate system.†† Thus if the particles

† To avoid misunderstanding, we state immediately that the choice of such a coordinate system does not mean that the gravitational field has been eliminated over the corresponding infinitesimal volume of four-space. Such an elimination is also always possible, by virtue of the principle of equivalence, and has a greater significance (see § 87).

‡ This set of signs is called the *signature* of the tensor.

§ For the special case of constant gravitational fields, see § 89.

†† Strictly speaking, the number of particles should be greater than four. Since we can construct a tetrahedron from the six line segments, we can always, by a suitable definition of the reference system, make a system of four particles form an invariant tetrahedron. A fortiori, we can fix the particles relative to one another in systems of three or two particles.

are placed around the circumference of a circle and along a diameter, since the ratio of the circumference to the diameter is not equal to π and changes with time, it is clear that if the separations of the particles along the diameter remain unchanged the separations around the circumference must change, and conversely. Thus in the general theory of relativity it is impossible in general to have a system of bodies which are fixed relative to one another.

This result essentially changes the very concept of a system of reference in the general theory of relativity, as compared to its meaning in the special theory. In the latter we meant by a reference system a set of bodies at rest relative to one another in unchanging relative positions. Such systems of bodies do not exist in the presence of a variable gravitational field, and for the exact determination of the position of a particle in space we must, strictly speaking, have an infinite number of bodies which fill all the space like some sort of "medium". Such a system of bodies with arbitrarily running clocks fixed on them constitutes a reference system in the general theory of relativity.

In connection with the arbitrariness of the choice of a reference system, the laws of nature must be written in the general theory of relativity in a form which is appropriate to any four-dimensional system of coordinates (or, as one says, in "covariant" form). This, of course, does not imply the physical equivalence of all these reference systems (like the physical equivalence of all inertial reference systems in the special theory). On the contrary, the specific appearances of physical phenomena, including the properties of the motion of bodies, become different in all systems of reference.

§ 83. **Curvilinear coordinates**

As we have seen, in studying gravitational fields we are confronted with the necessity of considering phenomena in curvilinear coordinates. In this connection it is necessary to develop four-dimensional geometry in arbitrary curvilinear coordinates. Sections 83, 85 and 86 are devoted to this.

Let us consider the transformation from one coordinate system, x^0, x^1, x^2, x^3, to another, x'^0, x'^1, x'^2, x'^3:

$$x^i = f^i(x'^0, x'^1, x'^2, x'^3),$$

where the f^i are certain functions. When we transform the coordinates, their differentials transform according to the relation

$$dx^i = \frac{\partial x^i}{\partial x'^k} dx'^k. \qquad (83.1)$$

Every aggregate of four quantities A^i ($i = 0, 1, 2, 3$), which under a transformation of coordinates transform like the coordinate differentials, is called a *contravariant* four-vector. Thus, under a coordinate transformation,

$$A^i = \frac{\partial x^i}{\partial x'^k} A'^k. \tag{83.2}$$

We shall designate the components of contravariant vectors by a superscript.†

Let ϕ be some scalar. Under a coordinate transformation, the four quantities $\partial\phi/\partial x^i$ transform according to the formula

$$\frac{\partial \phi}{\partial x^i} = \frac{\partial \phi}{\partial x'^k}\frac{\partial x'^k}{\partial x^i}, \tag{83.3}$$

which is different from formula (83.2). Every aggregate of four quantities A_i which, under a coordinate transformation, transform like the derivatives of a scalar, is called a *covariant* four-vector. Thus, under a coordinate transformation,

$$A_i = \frac{\partial x'^k}{\partial x^i} A'_k. \tag{83.4}$$

We designate the components of covariant vectors by a subscript.

In a cartesian coordinate system, there is no difference between covariant and contravariant vectors — the transformation rules (83.2) and (83.4) are equivalent in this case.‡

Because two types of vectors appear in curvilinear coordinates, there are three types of tensors of the second rank. We call a *contravariant tensor* of the second rank, A^{ik}, an aggregate of 16 quantities which transform like the products of the components of two contravariant vectors, i.e., according to the law

$$A^{ik} = \frac{\partial x^i}{\partial x'^l}\frac{\partial x^k}{\partial x'^m} A'^{lm}. \tag{83.5}$$

† Since the coordinate differentials x^i themselves constitute a contravariant vector, we write the index above the coordinate here and in the sequel. We shall write the index of a particular coordinate as a subscript only occasionally, when it would be inconvenient to write it above (for example, x_2^2 instead of $(x^2)^2$).

‡ It is sufficient to recall that in cartesian coordinates the gradient has the same vector properties as all other vectors. The equivalence of the transformations (83.2) and (83.4) can be verified formally as follows. Transformations from one cartesian system to another are linear transformations of the form

$$x^i = a_{ik} x'^k$$

where the a_{ik} are constants, satisfying the so-called orthogonality conditions $a_{il}a_{kl} = \delta_{ik}$, (which express the invariance of the sum of the squares of the coordinates, $x_i^2 = x_i'^2$). As a consequence, the components of the matrix reciprocal to a_{ik} are $a_{ik}^{-1} = a_{ki}$, so that

$$x'_i = a_{ik}^{-1} x_k = a_{ki} x_k,$$

and the transformations (83.2) and (83.4) become identical.

Similarly, we define a *covariant tensor*, transforming according to the formula

$$A_{ik} = \frac{\partial x'^l}{\partial x^i}\frac{\partial x'^m}{\partial x^k} A'_{lm}, \tag{83.6}$$

and a *mixed tensor*, transforming as follows:

$$A^i_k = \frac{\partial x^i}{\partial x'^l}\frac{\partial x'^m}{\partial x^k} A'^l_m. \tag{83.7}$$

Tensors of higher rank are defined in completely analogous fashion. For example, the tensor A^m_{ikl}, covariant in three indices and contravariant in one, transforms according to the formula

$$A^m_{ikl} = \frac{\partial x'^p}{\partial x^i}\frac{\partial x'^r}{\partial x^k}\frac{\partial x'^s}{\partial x^l}\frac{\partial x^m}{\partial x'^t} A'^t_{prs}.$$

If a tensor is symmetric or antisymmetric in any pair of indices (both of which are covariant, or both contravariant), then it remains so for any coordinate system. For a mixed tensor, say A^i_k, the concept of symmetry or antisymmetry has no meaning, since to the different indices there correspond different laws of transformation, so that when we transform from one coordinate system to another, the symmetry changes.

If a tensor (i.e. every component) is zero in one coordinate system, then it is zero in every other system. The sum of two tensors of the same co- or contravariant character is a tensor of the same character.

Clearly the product of components of the vectors A_i and B_k is a tensor of the form A_{ik}, and of the vectors A_i and B^k is a tensor of the form A^k_i. The product of the vector A_l and the tensor A^{ik} is a tensor of the form A^{ik}_l, etc.

In cartesian coordinates, we can construct from any two vectors a scalar, the scalar product of these vectors. In curvilinear coordinates, we cannot construct a scalar from any two vectors. It is impossible to construct a scalar from two covariant or two contravariant vectors. On the other hand, we can construct a scalar from a contravariant vector A^i and a covariant vector B_k; this scalar is the quantity A^iB_i, called the *scalar product* of the vectors A^i and B_i. It is easy to verify, with the aid of the formulas (83.2) and (83.4), that A^iB_i is actually invariant under coordinate transformations.

The formation of the scalar product from two vectors is a special case of the following law of *contraction* of tensors. If we have a tensor $A::^i_k:::$, then the expression $A:^i_i:$ (summation over i) is a tensor lower in rank by two than the tensor $A::^i_k::$. Thus, for example, from the tensor A^k_i we can form the scalar A^i_i. For, according to (83.7),

$$A^i_i = \frac{\partial x^i}{\partial x'^l}\frac{\partial x'^m}{\partial x^i} A'^l_m = \frac{\partial x'^m}{\partial x'^l} A'^l_m = A'^l_l,$$

that is, A^i_i is actually an invariant. Similarly, the expressions A^{ik}_{ik}, $A^k_i B^i_k$ are scalars, etc. The expression A^i_{kli} is a covariant tensor of the second rank,

$A^i_k B^k$ is a contravariant vector, etc. Note that expressions obtained by summation over two superscripts or two subscripts (for example, A^i_{kll}), are not tensors. In what follows we shall not use such quantities.

The role of unit tensor in curvilinear coordinates is played by the mixed tensor δ^k_i, whose components are $\delta^k_i = 0$ for $i \neq k$, while for $i = k$, they are unity. If A^k is a vector, then on multiplying by δ^i_k we get

$$A^k \delta^i_k = A^i ,$$

that is, the same vector; this also shows that δ^i_k is a tensor.

The square of the line element ds^2 is a quadratic form in the differentials dx^i, that is,

$$-ds^2 = g_{ik}\, dx^i\, dx^k , \tag{83.8}$$

where the g_{ik} are functions of the coordinates; g_{ik} is symmetric in the indices i and k, that is,

$$g_{ik} = g_{ki} . \tag{83.9}$$

Since the (contracted) product of g_{ik} with the contravariant tensor $dx^i\, dx^k$ is a scalar, g_{ik} is a covariant tensor; it is called the *metric tensor.*

Two tensors A_{ik} and B^{ik} are said to be reciprocal to each other if

$$A_{ik} B^{kl} = \delta^l_i .$$

In particular the *contravariant metric tensor* is the tensor g^{ik} reciprocal to the tensor g_{ik}, that is,

$$g_{ik} g^{kl} = \delta^l_i . \tag{83.10}$$

In a cartesian (four-dimensional) system of coordinates, as already pointed out, there is no difference between co- and contravariant vectors; however, this difference arises when we go over to curvilinear coordinates. Therefore, if any physical quantity appears as a vector in a cartesian coordinate system, then on going over to curvilinear coordinates, it can be represented in two forms: in the form of a covariant or a contravariant vector. We shall designate the two forms for one and the same vector by the same symbol, but with super- and subscripts respectively (A^i and A_i).

It is easy to find the formulas by which one transforms from the covariant to the contravariant form of the vector, and conversely. It is clear that the only quantities which can determine the relation between co- and contravariant components are the components of the metric tensor. Furthermore, in a cartesian system (i.e., for $g_{ik} = \delta_{ik}$), the required relations must reduce to $A_i = A^i$.† In order to develop a contravariant from a covariant vector,

† In this and similar places, where in a proof we use a cartesian system of coordinates, one must keep in mind that a cartesian system can be introduced only if the space is Euclidean. In the case of a non-Euclidean space, in our proof we must consider a coordinate system which is cartesian in a given infinitesimal volume element, which can always be done. All derivations then remain unchanged also for non-Euclidean space. Later we shall, in cases like this, always speak of a cartesian system of coordinates; we must keep in mind that all the results are equally applicable to non-Euclidean space.

we must therefore construct, from the components A_i and the components of the metric tensor, a contravariant vector which fulfills the condition we have set. Thus

$$A^i = g^{ik} A_k \tag{83.11}$$

and, inversely,

$$A_i = g_{ik} A^k. \tag{83.12}$$

In a cartesian system of coordinates, $g_{ik} = \delta_{ik}$, and these formulas give, as they should, $A_i = A^i$.

All that has been said applies also to tensors. Every tensor in a cartesian system can, on transformation to curvilinear coordinates, be presented in several forms with different co- and contravariant character. We shall again designate the different forms of one and the same tensor by a single symbol with different positions of the indices. The transformation between the different forms of the tensor is accomplished in a manner similar to that for vectors. Thus,

$$A^i_{kl} = g_{lm} A^{im}_{k}, \quad A^{ik} = g^{il} g^{km} A_{lm}, \text{ etc.}$$

We note that if a tensor of the second rank is not symmetric, then we must distinguish between $A_k{}^i$ and $A^k{}_i$, i.e., the position from which the index was raised.

In a cartesian system of coordinates, the square of the absolute value of a vector is equal to the sum of the squares of its components. It is obvious that in curvilinear coordinates, the square of the absolute value of a vector is the scalar

$$A_i A^i = g_{ik} A^i A^k = g^{ik} A_i A_k. \tag{83.13}$$

It is important to note that indices over which summation occurs in a product of tensors ("dummy" indices) have a certain freedom of movement. Thus, for example,

$$A_{ik} B^{ik} = A^{ik} B_{ik}, \quad A_{i\cdot} B^{lk} = A_i{}^k B^l{}_k, \text{ etc.}$$

An index can be raised in one of the factors, provided the same index is lowered in the other (this is easy to verify, using the relation between covariant and contravariant components of tensors in terms of the tensor g_{ik}).

In § 6 we defined (for cartesian coordinates) the completely antisymmetric unit pseudotensor e_{iklm}. We now transform it to an arbitrary curvilinear system of coordinates. First we note that from the definition of e_{iklm}, we can write for an arbitrary tensor k_{ik}:

$$e_{nrst} k_{ni} k_{rk} k_{sl} k_{tm} = k e_{iklm}, \tag{83.14}$$

where k is the determinant constructed from the quantities k_{ik}, for the different terms of the determinant are obtained by taking four elements, one from each row (so that $n \neq r \neq s \neq t$) and each column (so that $i \neq k \neq l \neq m$), and placing before their product a plus or minus sign according as the ordering of the columns can be brought into coincidence with the ordering of the rows by an even or an odd number of transpositions.

According to the general law of transformation of tensors and using (83.14), we have for the transformation to curvilinear coordinates

$$e_{iklm} = e'_{nrst} \frac{\partial x'^n}{\partial x^i} \frac{\partial x'^r}{\partial x^k} \frac{\partial x'^s}{\partial x^l} \frac{\partial x'^t}{\partial x^m} = e'_{iklm} J, \tag{83.15}$$

where

$$J = \frac{\partial(x'^0, x'^1, x'^2, x'^3)}{\partial(x^0, x^1, x^2, x^3)}$$

is the Jacobian of the transformation from the coordinates x^i to x'^i. This Jacobian can be expressed in terms of the determinant g' made up from the components of the tensor g'_{ik}. For this we note that in a cartesian system, $g_{ik} = \delta_{ik}$, so that according to the transformation formula,

$$\delta_{ik} = g'_{lm} \frac{\partial x'^l}{\partial x^i} \frac{\partial x'^m}{\partial x^k}.$$

Comparing the determinants constructed from the quantities standing on the two sides of this equation, we have $1 = g'J^2$, that is, $\sqrt{g'} = 1/J$; in the future we shall, however, always write $-g$ under the square root, since in reality for all coordinates connected with a real space-time, the determinant g is negative (see § 82). From (83.15), we now have

$$e'_{iklm} = \sqrt{-g'}\, e_{iklm}.$$

Thus in curvilinear coordinates, the antisymmetric unit tensor of the fourth rank must be defined as

$$E_{iklm} = \sqrt{-g}\, e_{iklm}. \tag{83.16}$$

By raising the indices of the tensor $\sqrt{-g}\, e_{iklm}$ it is easy to show that the contravariant antisymmetric unit tensor of the fourth rank is

$$E^{iklm} = \frac{1}{\sqrt{-g}} e^{iklm}. \tag{83.17}$$

In a cartesian coordinate system, the integral of a scalar over $d\Omega = dx^0\, dx^1\, dx^2\, dx^3$ is again a scalar, that is, $d\Omega$ behaves like an invariant in integrations (see § 6). On transforming to curvilinear coordinates, the element of integration $d\Omega$ transforms to

$$d\Omega'/J = \sqrt{-g'}\, d\Omega'.$$

Thus in curvilinear coordinates, when integrating over any region of four-space, $\sqrt{-g}\,d\Omega$ behaves like an invariant.†

All that was said at the end of § 6 concerning elements of integration over hypersurfaces, surfaces, and lines remains valid also for curvilinear coordinates, with the one exception that the definition of the dual tensor is slightly changed. The element of "area" of a hypersurface constructed on three infinitesimal segments is a contravariant antisymmetric tensor dS^{ikl}; the vector dual to this is obtained by multiplying by the tensor $\sqrt{-g}\, e_{iklm}$, that is, is equal to

$$\sqrt{-g}\, dS_i = \tfrac{1}{6} e_{iklm}\, dS^{klm} \sqrt{-g}. \tag{83.18}$$

Similarly, if df^{ik} is an element of surface (two-dimensional) constructed on two infinitesimal segments, then the tensor dual to it is given by

$$\sqrt{-g}\, df^*_{ik} = \tfrac{1}{2} \sqrt{-g}\, e_{iklm}\, df^{lm}. \tag{83.19}$$

We here designate by dS_i and df^*_{ik} the quantities, $\frac{1}{6} e_{klmi}\, dS^{klm}$ and $\frac{1}{2} e_{iklm} df^{lm}$ respectively (and not their products with $\sqrt{-g}$); the rules (6.11)—(6.15) for the transformations of the various integrals into one another remain the same, since their derivation has a purely formal character, not depending on the tensor properties of the corresponding quantities. Of these we need especially the rule for transforming an integral over a hypersurface into an integral over a volume (Gauss' theorem), which is accomplished by the substitution

$$dS_i \to d\Omega \frac{\partial}{\partial x^i}. \tag{83.20}$$

As already pointed out in § 82, in real space-time we can, by a suitable choice of coordinate system, transform the metric tensor not to cartesian, but to Galilean form

$$g^{(0)}_{ik} = \begin{pmatrix} 1 & 0 & 0 & 0 \\ 0 & 1 & 0 & 0 \\ 0 & 0 & 1 & 0 \\ 0 & 0 & 0 & -1 \end{pmatrix} \tag{83.21}$$

(where the contravariant tensor $g^{(0)ik}$ has these same components). Obviously this fact has nothing to do with the proofs given above, in which we used a "cartesian" system of coordinates.‡

---

† If ϕ is a scalar, then the quantity $\sqrt{-g}\,\phi$, which upon integration over $d\Omega$ gives an invariant, is sometimes called a *scalar density*. Similarly, one speaks of *vector* and *tensor densities* $\sqrt{-g}\, A^i$, $\sqrt{-g}\, A^{ik}$, etc. These quantities give vectors or tensors when multiplied by the four-volume element $d\Omega$ (the integral $\int A^i \sqrt{-g}\, d\Omega$ over a finite region, generally speaking, cannot be a vector, since the laws of transformation of the vector A^i are different for different points).

‡ For the formal transition from a Galilean to a cartesian system, it is sufficient to introduce an imaginary fourth coordinate.

However, in a Galilean system unlike a cartesian system, there is not complete identity between the co- and contravariant forms of vectors: the space components A_α and A^α coincide, but the time components A_0 and A^0 differ in sign. The relation of the latter to the quantity A_4, which we used in the special theory of relativity when we chose the imaginary time coordinate $x^4 = ict$, is given by the obvious equations

$$A^0 = -A_0 = \frac{A_4}{i}. \tag{83.22}$$

Analogously, the time components and the mixed (space-time) components of a second rank tensor are related to the quantities A_{44} and $A_{4\alpha}$ used earlier by the equations:

$$\begin{aligned} A^{00} &= A_{00} = -A_0^0 = -A_{44}, \\ A^{0\alpha} &= -A_{0\alpha} = -A_0{}^\alpha = A^0{}_\alpha = \frac{1}{i} A_{4\alpha}. \end{aligned} \tag{83.23}$$

The specific relation of such components with various physical quantities also changes correspondingly.†

PROBLEM

Consider the possible cases of reduction to canonical form of a symmetric tensor of second rank in a pseudo-Euclidean space.

Solution. The reduction of a symmetric tensor A_{ik} to principal axes means that we find "eigenvectors" n^i for which

$$A_{ik} n^k = \lambda n_i. \tag{1}$$

The corresponding principal (or "proper") values λ are obtained from the condition for consistency of Eq. (1), i.e., as the roots of the fourth degree equation

$$|A_{ik} - \lambda g_{ik}| = 0, \tag{2}$$

and are invariants of the tensor. Both the quantities λ and the eigenvectors corresponding to them may be complex. (The components of the tensor A_{ik} itself are of course assumed to be real.)

---

† For convenience of reference, we list here the principal four-vectors and four-tensors introduced in the preceding chapters, with an indication of the meaning of their components in the Galilean coordinates x^1, x^2, x^3, x^0.

The time component of the four-momentum is related to the energy by $p^0 = -p_0 = \mathcal{E}/c$; the spatial components $p^\alpha = p_\alpha$ form the three-dimensional momentum vector $\mathbf{p}$.

The time component of the four-potential of the electromagnetic field is related to the scalar potential φ by $A^0 = -A_0 = \varphi$, while the space components form the vector $\mathbf{A}$. The connection of the components of the four-tensor F_{ik} with the fields $\mathbf{E}$ and $\mathbf{H}$ is given by the formulas:

$$F_{12} = H_z \quad F_{13} = -H_y, \quad F_{23} = H_x,$$
$$F_{10} = E_x, \quad F_{20} = E_y, \quad F_{30} = E_z.$$

The component $T_{00} = T^{00} = -T_0^0$ of the energy-momentum tensor is the energy density; the components $T_\alpha^0/c = -T_{0\alpha}/c = T^{0\alpha}/c$ form the momentum density vector; the quantities $T_\alpha^\beta = T_{\alpha\beta} = T^{\alpha\beta}$ form the tensor of the density of flux of momentum.

From Eq. (1) it is easily shown in the usual fashion that two vectors $n_i^{(1)}$ and $n_i^{(2)}$ which correspond to different principal values $\lambda^{(1)}$ and $\lambda^{(2)}$ are "mutually perpendicular":

$$n_i^{(1)} n^{(2)i} = 0. \tag{3}$$

In particular, if Eq (2) has complex-conjugate roots λ and λ^*, to which there correspond the complex-conjugate vectors n_i and n_i^*, then we must have

$$n_i n^{i*} = 0. \tag{4}$$

The tensor A_{ik} is expressed in terms of its principal values and the corresponding eigenvectors by the formula

$$A_{ik} = \sum \lambda \frac{n_i n_k}{n_l n^l} \tag{5}$$

(so long as none of the quantities $n_l n^l$ *is* equal to zero—cf. below).

Depending on the character of the roots of Eq. (2), the following three situations may occur.

(a) All four eigenvalues λ are real. Then the vectors n_i are also real, and since they are mutually perpendicular, three of them must have spacelike directions and one a timelike direction (and are normalized by the conditions $n_l n^l = 1$ and $n_l n^l = -1$, respectively). Choosing the directions of the coordinates along these vectors, we bring the tensor A_{ik} to the form

$$A_{ik} = \begin{pmatrix} \lambda^{(1)} & 0 & 0 & 0 \\ 0 & \lambda^{(2)} & 0 & 0 \\ 0 & 0 & \lambda^{(3)} & 0 \\ 0 & 0 & 0 & -\lambda^{(0)} \end{pmatrix} \tag{6}$$

(b) Equation (2) has two real roots ($\lambda^{(1)}$, $\lambda^{(2)}$) and two complex-conjugate roots ($\lambda' \pm i\lambda''$). We write the complex-conjugate vectors n_i, n_i^*, corresponding to the last two roots in the form $a_i \pm ib_i$; since they are defined only to within an arbitrary complex factor, we can normalize them by the condition $n_i n^i = n_i^* n^{i*} = 1$. Also using Eq. (4), we find

$$a_i a^i = \tfrac{1}{2}, \quad b_i b^i = -\tfrac{1}{2},$$

i.e., one of these vectors must be spacelike and the other timelike.† Choosing the coordinate axes along the vectors $n^{(1)i}$, $n^{(2)i}$, a^i and b^i, we bring the tensor to the form:

$$A_{ik} = \begin{pmatrix} \lambda^{(1)} & 0 & 0 & 0 \\ 0 & \lambda^{(2)} & 0 & 0 \\ 0 & 0 & \lambda' & \lambda' \\ 0 & 0 & \lambda'' & -\lambda' \end{pmatrix} \tag{7}$$

(c) If the square of one of the vectors n^i is equal to zero ($n_l n^l = 0$), then this vector cannot be chosen as the direction of a coordinate axis. We can however choose one of the planes x^0, x^α so that the vector n^i lies in it. Suppose this is the x^0, x^3 plane; then it follows from $n_l n^l = 0$ that $n^0 = n^3$, and from Eq. (1) we have $A_{33}+A_{30} = \lambda$, $A_{00}+A_{03} = -\lambda$, so that $A_{33} = \lambda+\mu$, $A_{00} = -\lambda+\mu$, $A_{03} = -\mu$, where μ is a quantity which is not invariant but changes under rotations in the x^0, x^3 plane; it can always be made real by a suitable ro-

† Since only one of the vectors can have a timelike direction, it then follows that Eq. (2) cannot have two pairs of complex-conjugate roots.

tation. Choosing the axes x^1, x^2 along the other two (spacelike) vectors $n^{(1)i}$, $n^{(2)i}$, we bring the tensor A_{ik} to the form

$$A_{ik} = \begin{pmatrix} \lambda^{(1)} & 0 & 0 & 0 \\ 0 & \lambda^{(2)} & 0 & 0 \\ 0 & 0 & \lambda+\mu & -\mu \\ 0 & 0 & -\mu & -\lambda+\mu \end{pmatrix} \tag{8}$$

This case corresponds to the situation when two of the roots ($\lambda^{(0)}$, $\lambda^{(3)}$) of Eq. (2) are equal.†

§ 84. Distances and time intervals

We have already said that in the general theory of relativity the choice of a coordinate system is not limited in any way; the triplet of space coordinates x^1, x^2, x^3, can be any quantities defining the position of bodies in space, and the time coordinate x^0 can be defined by an arbitrarily running clock. The question arises of how, in terms of the values of the quantities x^1, x^2, x^3, x^0, we can determine actual distances and time intervals.

First we find the relation of the proper time, which from now on we shall denote by τ, to the coordinate x^0. To do this we consider two infinitesimally separated events, occuring at one and the same point in space. Then the interval ds between the two events is, as we know, just $cd\tau$, where $d\tau$ is the (proper) time interval between the two events. Setting $dx^1 = dx^2 = dx^3 = 0$ in the general expression $-ds^2 = g_{ik}\,dx^i dx^k$, we consequently find

$$ds^2 = c^2\,d\tau^2 = -g_{00}dx_0^2,$$

from which

$$d\tau = \frac{1}{c}\sqrt{-g_{00}}\,dx^0, \tag{84.1}$$

or else, for the time between any two events occurring at the same point in space,

$$\tau = \frac{1}{c}\int \sqrt{-g_{00}}\,dx^0. \tag{84.2}$$

This relation determines the actual time interval (or as it is also called, the *proper time* for the given point in space) for a change of the coordinate

---

† We note that for the physical energy-momentum tensor T_{ik} of matter moving with velocities less than the velocity of light only case (a) can occur; this is related to the fact that there must always exist a reference system in which the flux of the energy of the matter, i.e., the components $T_{\alpha 0}$ are equal to zero. For the energy-momentum tensor of electromagnetic waves we have case (c) with $\lambda^{(1)} = \lambda^{(2)} = \lambda = 0$ (cf. p. 93); it can be shown that if this were not the case there would exist a reference frame in which the energy flux would exceed the value c times the energy density.

x^0. We note in passing that the quantity g_{00}, as we see from these formulas, is negative:

$$g_{00} < 0. \tag{84.3}$$

It is necessary to emphasize the difference between the meaning of (84.3) and the meaning of the condition that three principal values of the tensor g_{ik} must be positive and one negative (§ 82). A tensor g_{ik} which does not satisfy the second of these conditions cannot correspond to any real gravitational field, i.e., cannot be the metric of a real space-time. Nonfulfilment of the condition (84.3) would mean only that the corresponding system of reference cannot be realized with real bodies; if the condition on the principal values is fulfilled, then a suitable transformation of the coordinates can make g_{00} negative (an example of such a system is given by the rotating system of coordinates, see § 90).

We now determine the element dl of *spatial distance*. In the special theory of relativity we can define dl as the interval between two infinitesimally separated events occurring at one and the same time. In the general theory of relativity, it is usually impossible to do this, i.e., it is impossible to determine dl by simply setting $dx^0 = 0$ in ds. This is related to the fact that in a gravitational field the proper time at different points in space has a different dependence on the coordinate x^0.

To find dl, we now proceed as follows.

Suppose a light signal is directed from some point B in space (with coordinates $x^\alpha + dx^\alpha$) to a point A infinitely near to it (and having coordinates x^α), and then back over the same path. Obviously, the time (as observed from the one point B) required for this, when multiplied by c, is twice the distance between the two points.

Let us write the interval, separating the space and time coordinates:

$$-ds^2 = g_{\alpha\beta}\, dx^\alpha\, dx^\beta + 2g_{0\alpha}\, dx^0\, dx^\alpha + g_{00}\, dx_0^2, \tag{84.4}$$

where it is understood that we sum over repeated Greek indices from 1 to 3. The interval between the events corresponding to the departure and arrival of the signal from one point to the other is equal to zero. Solving the equation $ds^2 = 0$ with respect to dx^0, we find two roots:

$$\begin{aligned} dx_0^{(1)} &= \frac{1}{-g_{00}}\left\{g_{0\alpha}\, dx^\alpha - \sqrt{(g_{0\alpha}g_{0\beta} - g_{\alpha\beta}g_{00})\, dx^\alpha\, dx^\beta}\right\}, \\ dx_0^{(2)} &= \frac{1}{-g_{00}}\left\{g_{0\alpha}\, dx^\alpha + \sqrt{(g_{0\alpha}g_{0\beta} - g_{\alpha\beta}g_{00})\, dx^\alpha\, dx^\beta}\right\}, \end{aligned} \tag{84.5}$$

corresponding to the propagation of the signal in the two directions between A and B. If x^0 is the moment of arrival of the signal at A, the times when it left B and when it will return to B are, respectively, $x^0+dx_0^{(1)}$ and $x^0+dx_0^{(2)}$. In the schematic diagram of Fig. 17, the solid lines are the world lines corresponding to the given coordinates x^α and $x^\alpha+dx^\alpha$, while the dashed lines are the world lines of the signals.† It is clear that the total interval of "time" between the departure of the signal and its return to the original point is equal to

$$dx_0^{(2)}-dx_0^{(1)} = \frac{2}{-g_{00}}\sqrt{(g_{0\alpha}g_{0\beta}-g_{\alpha\beta}g_{00})\,dx^\alpha\,dx^\beta}.$$

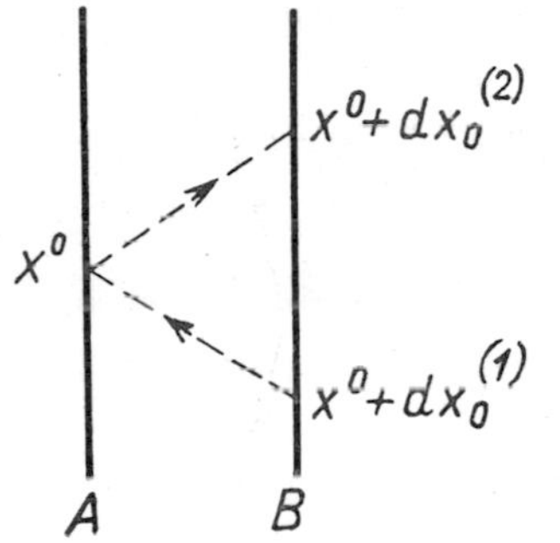

FIG. 17.

The corresponding interval of proper time is obtained, according to (84.1), by multiplying by $\sqrt{-g_{00}}/c$, and the distance dl between the two points by multiplying once more by $c/2$. As a result, we obtain

$$dl^2 = \left(g_{\alpha\beta}-\frac{g_{0\alpha}g_{0\beta}}{g_{00}}\right)dx^\alpha\,dx^\beta.$$

This is the required expression, defining the distance in terms of the space coordinate elements. We rewrite it in the form

$$dl^2 = \gamma_{\alpha\beta}\,dx^\alpha\,dx^\beta, \tag{84.6}$$

where

$$\gamma_{\alpha\beta} = \left(g_{\alpha\beta}-\frac{g_{0\alpha}g_{0\beta}}{g_{00}}\right) \tag{84.7}$$

is the three-dimensional metric tensor, determining the metric, i.e., the geometric properties of the space. The relations (84.7) give the connection be-

---

† In Fig. 17, it is assumed that $dx_0^{(2)} > 0$, $dx_0^{(1)} < 0$, but this is not necessary: $dx_0^{(1)}$ and $dx_0^{(2)}$ may have the same sign. The fact that in this case the value $x^{(0)}(A)$ at the moment of arrival of the signal at A might be less than the value $x^{(0)}(B)$ at the moment of its departure from B contains no contradiction, since the rates of clocks at different points in space are not assumed to be synchronized in any way.

tween the metric of real space and the metric of the four-dimensional space-time.†

However, we must remember that the g_{ik} generally depend on x^0, so that the space metric (84.6) also changes with time. For this reason, it is meaningless to integrate dl; such an integral would depend on the world line chosen between the two given space points. Thus, generally speaking, in the general theory of relativity the concept of a definite distance between bodies loses its meaning, remaining valid only for infinitesimal distances. The only case where the distance can be defined also over a finite domain is that in which the g_{ik} do not depend on the time, so that the integral $\int dl$ along a space curve has a definite meaning.

It is worth noting that the tensor $\gamma_{\alpha\beta}$ is the reciprocal of the contravariant three-dimensional tensor $g^{\alpha\beta}$. In fact, from $g^{ik} g_{kl} = \delta^i_l$, we have, in particular,

$$g^{\alpha\beta} g_{\beta\gamma} + g^{\alpha 0} g_{0\gamma} = \delta^\alpha_\gamma, \; g^{\alpha\beta} g_{\beta 0} + g^{\alpha 0} g_{00} = 0.$$

Determining $g^{\alpha 0}$ from the second equation and substituting in the first, we obtain:

$$g^{\alpha\beta} \gamma_{\beta\gamma} = \delta^\alpha_\gamma. \tag{84.8}$$

We also state that the determinants g and γ, formed respectively from the quantities g_{ik} and $\gamma_{\alpha\beta}$, are related to one another by

$$g = g_{00} \gamma. \tag{84.9}$$

We now turn to the definition of the concept of simultaneity in the general theory of relativity. In other words, we discuss the question of the possibility of synchronizing clocks located at different points in space, i.e. the setting up of a correspondence between the readings of these clocks.

Such a synchronization must obviously be achieved by means of an exchange of light signals between the two points. We again consider the pro-

---

† The quadratic form (84.6) must clearly be positive definite. For this, its coefficients must, as we know from the theory of forms, satisfy the conditions

$$\gamma_{11} > 0, \quad \begin{vmatrix} \gamma_{11} & \gamma_{12} \\ \gamma_{21} & \gamma_{22} \end{vmatrix} > 0, \quad \begin{vmatrix} \gamma_{11} & \gamma_{12} & \gamma_{13} \\ \gamma_{21} & \gamma_{22} & \gamma_{33} \\ \gamma_{31} & \gamma_{32} & \gamma_{33} \end{vmatrix} > 0.$$

Expressing γ_{ik} in terms of g_{ik}, it is easy to show that these conditions take the form

$$\begin{vmatrix} g_{00} & g_{01} \\ g_{10} & g_{11} \end{vmatrix} < 0, \quad \begin{vmatrix} g_{00} & g_{01} & g_{02} \\ g_{10} & g_{11} & g_{12} \\ g_{20} & g_{21} & g_{22} \end{vmatrix} < 0, \quad g < 0.$$

These conditions, together with the condition (84.3), must be satisfied by the components of the metric tensor in every system of reference which can be realized with the aid of real bodies.

cess of propagation of signals between two infinitely near points A and B, as shown in Fig. 17. We should regard as simultaneous with the moment x^0 at the point A that reading of the clock at point B which is halfway between the moments of departure and return of the signal to that point, i.e. the moment

$$x^0+\Delta x^0 = x^0+\tfrac{1}{2}\,(dx_0^{(2)}+dx_0^{(1)}).$$

Substituting (84.5), we thus find that the difference in the values of the "time" x^0 for two simultaneous events occurring at infinitely near points is given by

$$\Delta x^0 = \frac{g_{0\alpha}\,dx^\alpha}{-g_{00}}. \tag{84.10}$$

This relation enables us to synchronize clocks in any infinitesimal region of space. Carrying out a similar synchronization from the point A, we can synchronize clocks, i.e., we can define simultaneity of events, along any open curve.†

However, synchronization of clocks along a closed contour turns out to be impossible in general. In fact, starting out along the contour and returning to the initial point, we would obtain for Δx^0 a value different from zero. Thus it is, a fortiori, impossible to synchronize clocks over all space. The exceptional cases are those reference systems in which all the components $g_{0\alpha}$ are equal to zero.‡

It should be emphasized that the impossibility of synchronization of all clocks is a property of the arbitrary reference system, and not of the space-time itself. In any gravitational field, it is always possible (in infinitely many ways) to choose the reference system so that the three quantities $g_{0\alpha}$ become identically equal to zero, and thus make possible a complete synchronization of clocks.

Even in the special theory of relativity, proper time elapses differently for clocks moving relative to one another. In the general theory of relativity, proper time elapses differently even at different points of space in the same reference system. This means that the interval of proper time between two events occurring at some point in space, and the interval of time between two events simultaneous with these at another point in space, are in general different from one another.

---

† Multiplying (84.10) by g_{00} and bringing both terms to one side, we can state the condition for synchronization in the form $dx_0 = g_{0i}\,dx^i = 0$: the "covariant differential" dx_0 between two infinitely near simultaneous events must be equal to zero.

‡ We should also assign to this class those cases where the $g_{0\alpha}$ can be made equal to zero by a simple transformation of the time coordinate, which does not involve any choice of the system of objects serving for the definition of the space coordinates.

§ 85. Covariant differentiation

In cartesian coordinates† the differentials dA_i of a vector A_i form a vector, and the derivatives $\partial A_i/\partial x^k$ of the components of a vector with respect to the coordinates form a tensor. In curvilinear coordinates this is not so; dA_i is not a vector, and $\partial A_i/\partial x^k$ is not a tensor. This is due to the fact that dA_i is the difference of vectors located at different (infinitesimally separated) points of space; at different points in space vectors transform differently, since the coefficients in the transformation formulas (83.2), (83.4) are functions of the coordinates.

It is also easy to verify these statements directly. To do this we determine the transformation formulas for the differentials dA_i in curvilinear coordinates. A covariant vector is transformed according to the formula

$$A_i = \frac{\partial x'^k}{\partial x^i} A'_k;$$

therefore

$$dA_i = \frac{\partial x'^k}{\partial x^i} dA'_k + A'_k\, d\frac{\partial x'^k}{\partial x^i} = \frac{\partial x'^k}{\partial x^i} dA'_k + A'_k \frac{\partial^2 x'^k}{\partial x^i\, \partial x^l} dx^l.$$

Thus dA_i does not transform at all like a vector (the same also applies, of course, to the differential of a contravariant vector). Only if the second derivatives $\partial^2 x'^k/\partial x^i\, \partial x^l = 0$, i.e., if the x'^k are linear functions of the x^k, do the transformation formulas have the form

$$dA_i = \frac{\partial x'^k}{\partial x^i} dA'_k,$$

that is, dA_i transforms like a vector.

We now undertake the definition of a tensor which in curvilinear coordinates plays the same role as $\partial A_i/\partial x^k$ in cartesian coordinates. In other words, we must transform $\partial A_i/\partial x^k$ from cartesian to curvilinear coordinates.

In curvilinear coordinates, in order to obtain a differential of a vector which behaves like a vector, it is necessary that the two vectors to be subtracted from each other be located at the same point in space. In other words, we must somehow "translate" one of the vectors (which are separated infinitesimally from each other) to the point where the second is located, after which we determine the difference of two vectors which now refer to one and the same point in space. The operation of translation itself must be defined so that in cartesian coordinates the difference shall coincide with the ordinary differential dA_i. Since dA_i is just the difference of the components of two infinitesimally separated vectors, this means that when we use cartesian coordinates the components of the vector should not change as a result

† And also in oblique coordinates; in general, whenever the quantities g_{ik} are constant.

of the translation operation. But such a translation is precisely the translation of a vector parallel to itself. Under a *parallel translation* of a vector, its components in cartesian coordinates do not change. If, on the other hand, we use curvilinear coordinates, then in general the components of the vector will change under such a translation. Therefore in curvilinear coordinates, the difference in the components of the two vectors after translating one of them to the point where the other is located will not coincide with their difference before the translation (i.e., with the differential dA_i).

Thus to compare two infinitesimally separated vectors we must subject one of them to a parallel translation to the point where the second is located. Let us consider an arbitrary contravariant vector; if its value at the point x^i is A^i, then at the neighboring point x^i+dx^i it is equal to A^i+dA^i. We subject the vector A^i to an infinitesimal parallel displacement to the point x^i+dx^i; the change in the vector which results from this we denote by δA^i. Then the difference DA^i between the two vectors which are now located at the same point is

$$DA^i = dA^i - \delta A^i. \tag{85.1}$$

The change δA^i in the components of a vector under an infinitesimal parallel displacement depends on the values of the components themselves, where this dependence must clearly be linear. This follows directly from the fact that the sum of two vectors must transform according to the same law as each of the constituents. Thus δA^i has the form

$$\delta A^i = -\Gamma^i_{kl} A^k \, dx^l, \tag{85.2}$$

where the Γ^i_{kl} are certain functions of the coordinates. Their form depends, of course, on the coordinate system; for a cartesian coordinate system $\Gamma^i_{kl} = 0$.

From this it is already clear that the quantities Γ^i_{kl} do not form a tensor, since a tensor which is equal to zero in one coordinate system is equal to zero in every other one. In a non-Euclidean space it is, of course, impossible to make all the Γ^i_{kl} vanish over all of space. But we can choose a coordinate system for which the Γ^i_{kl} become zero over a given infinitesimal region (see the end of this section†). The quantities Γ^i_{kl} are called *Christoffel symbols.* In addition to the quantities Γ^i_{kl} we shall later also use quantities $\Gamma_{i,kl}$‡ defined as follows:

$$\Gamma_{i,kl} = g_{im}\Gamma^m_{kl}. \tag{85.3}$$

Conversely,

$$\Gamma^i_{kl} = g^{im}\,\Gamma_{m,kl} \tag{85.4}$$

---

† This is precisely the coordinate system which we have in mind in arguments where we, for brevity's sake, speak of a "cartesian" system; still all the proofs remain applicable not only to Euclidean, but also to non-Euclidean space.

‡ In place of Γ^i_{kl} and $\Gamma_{i,kl}$, the symbols $\left\{ {kl \atop i} \right\}$ and $\left[{kl \atop i} \right]$ are sometimes used.

It is also easy to relate the change in the components of a covariant vector under a parallel displacement to the Christoffel symbols. To do this we note that under a parallel displacement, a scalar is unchanged. In particular, the scalar product of two vectors does not change under a parallel displacement.

Let A_i and B^i be any covariant and contravariant vectors. Then from $\delta(A_i B^i) = 0$, we have

$$B^i\, \delta A_i = -A_i\, \delta B^i = \Gamma^i_{kl} B^k A_i\, dx^l$$

or, changing the indices,

$$B^i\, \delta A_i = \Gamma^k_{il} A_k B^i\, dx^l.$$

From this, in view of the arbitrariness of the B^i,

$$\delta A_i = \Gamma^k_{il} A_k\, dx^l, \tag{85.5}$$

which determines the change in a covariant vector under a parallel displacement.

Substituting (85.2) and $dA^i = \dfrac{\partial A^i}{\partial x^l} dx^l$ in (85.1), we have

$$DA^i = \left(\frac{\partial A^i}{\partial x^l} + \Gamma^i_{kl} A^k\right) dx^l. \tag{85.6}$$

Similarly, we find for a covariant vector,

$$DA_i = \left(\frac{\partial A_i}{\partial x^l} - \Gamma^k_{il} A_k\right) dx^l. \tag{85.7}$$

The expressions in parentheses in (85.6) and (85.7) are tensors, since when multiplied by the vector dx^l they give a vector. Clearly, these are the tensors which, in curvilinear coordinates, play the same role as the tensor $\partial A^i/\partial x^k$ in cartesian coordinates. These tensors are called the *covariant derivatives* of the vectors A^i and A_i respectively. We shall denote them by $A^i{}_{;k}$ and $A_{i;k}$. Thus,

$$DA^i = A^i{}_{;l}\, dx^l; \qquad DA_i = A_{i;l}\, dx^l, \tag{85.8}$$

while the covariant derivatives themselves are:

$$A^i{}_{;l} = \frac{\partial A^i}{\partial x^l} + \Gamma^i_{kl} A^k, \tag{85.9}$$

$$A_{i;l} = \frac{\partial A_i}{\partial x^l} - \Gamma^k_{il} A_k. \tag{85.10}$$

In cartesian coordinates, $\Gamma^i_{kl} = 0$, and covariant differentiation reduces to ordinary differentiation.

It is also easy to calculate the covariant derivative of a tensor. To do this we must determine the change in the tensor under an infinitesimal parallel displacement. For example, let us consider any contravariant tensor, expressible as a product of two contravariant vectors A^iB^k. Under parallel displacement,

$$\delta(A^iB^k) = A^i\delta B^k + B^k\delta A^i = -A^i\Gamma^k_{lm}B^l dx^m - B^k\Gamma^i_{lm}A^l dx^m.$$

By virtue of the linearity of this transformation we must also have, for an arbitrary tensor A^{ik},

$$\delta A^{ik} = -(A^{im}\Gamma^k_{ml} + A^{mk}\Gamma^i_{ml})\, dx^l. \tag{85.11}$$

Substituting this in

$$DA^{ik} = dA^{ik} - \delta A^{ik} \equiv A^{ik}{}_{;l}\, dx^l,$$

we get the covariant derivative of the tensor A^{ik} in the form

$$A^{ik}{}_{;l} = \frac{\partial A^{ik}}{\partial x^l} + \Gamma^i_{ml}A^{mk} + \Gamma^k_{ml}A^{im}. \tag{85.12}$$

In completely similar fashion we obtain the covariant derivative of the mixed tensor A^i_k and the covariant tensor A_{ik} in the form

$$A^i_{k;l} = \frac{\partial A^i_k}{\partial x^l} - \Gamma^m_{kl}A^i_m + \Gamma^i_{ml}A^m_k, \tag{85.13}$$

$$A_{ik;l} = \frac{\partial A_{ik}}{\partial x^l} - \Gamma^m_{il}A_{mk} - \Gamma^m_{kl}A_{im}. \tag{85.14}$$

One can similarly determine the covariant derivative of a tensor of arbitrary rank. In doing this one finds the following rule of covariant differentiation. To obtain the covariant derivative of the tensor $A^{\dots}_{\dots}$ with respect to x^l, we add to the ordinary derivative $\partial A^{\dots}_{\dots}/\partial x^l$ for each covariant index $i(A^{\cdot\cdot}_{\cdot i \cdot})$ a term $-\Gamma^k_{il}A^{\cdot\cdot}_{\cdot k\cdot}$, and for each contravariant index $i(A^{\cdot i \cdot}_{\cdot\cdot})$ a term $+\Gamma^i_{kl}A^{\cdot k \cdot}_{\cdot\cdot}$.

One can easily verify that the covariant derivative of a product is found by the same rule as for ordinary differentiation of products. In doing this we must consider the covariant derivative of a scalar ϕ as an ordinary derivative, that is, as the covariant vector $\phi_k = \partial\phi/\partial x^k$, in accordance with the fact that for a scalar $\delta\phi = 0$, and therefore $D\phi = d\phi$. For example, the covariant derivative of the product A_iB_k is

$$(A_iB_k)_{;l} = A_{i;l}B_k + A_iB_{k;l}.$$

If in a covariant derivative we raise the index signifying the differentiation, we obtain the so-called *contravariant derivative*. Thus,

$$A_i^{;k} = g^{kl}A_{i;l}, \qquad A^{i;k} = g^{kl}A^i{}_{;l}.$$

We prove that the Christoffel symbols Γ^l_{kl} are symmetric in the subscripts. Since the covariant derivative of a vector $A_{i;k}$ is a tensor, the difference $A_{i;k} - A_{k;i}$ is also a tensor. Let the vector A_i be the gradient of a scalar, that is, $A_i = \partial\phi/\partial x^i$. Since $\partial A_i/\partial x^k = \partial^2\phi/\partial x^k\partial x^i = \partial A_k/\partial x^i$, with the help of (85.10) we have

$$A_{k;i} - A_{i;k} = (\Gamma^l_{ik} - \Gamma^l_{ki})\frac{\partial\phi}{\partial x^l}.$$

In a cartesian coordinate system the covariant derivative reduces to the ordinary derivative, and therefore the left side of our equation becomes zero. But since $A_{k;i}-A_{i;k}$ is a tensor, then being zero in one system it must also be zero in any coordinate system. Thus we find that

$$\Gamma^i_{kl} = \Gamma^i_{lk}. \tag{85.15}$$

Clearly, also,

$$\Gamma_{i,kl} = \Gamma_{i,lk}. \tag{85.16}$$

In general, there are altogether 40 different quantities Γ^i_{kl}; for each of the four values of the index i there are 10 different pairs of values of the indices k and l (counting pairs obtained by interchanging k and l as the same).

In concluding this section we present the formulas for transforming the Christoffel symbols from one coordinate system to another. These formulas can be obtained by comparing the laws of transformation of the two sides of the equations defining the covariant derivatives, and requiring that these laws be the same for both sides. A simple calculation gives

$$\Gamma^i_{kl} = \Gamma'^m_{np}\frac{\partial x^i}{\partial x'^m}\frac{\partial x'^n}{\partial x^k}\frac{\partial x'^p}{\partial x^l}+\frac{\partial^2 x'^m}{\partial x^k\,\partial x^l}\frac{\partial x^i}{\partial x'^m}. \tag{85.17}$$

From this formula it is clear that the quantity Γ^i_{kl} behaves like a tensor only under linear transformations [for which the second term in (85.17) drops out].

Formula (85.17) enables us to prove easily the assertion made above that t is always possible to choose a coordinate system in which all the Γ^i_{kl} become zero at a previously assigned point (such a system is said to be *locally-inertial* or *locally-geodesic* (see § 87).†

In fact, let the given point be chosen as the origin of coordinates, and let the values of the Γ^i_{kl} at it be initially (in the coordinates x^i) equal to $(\Gamma^i_{kl})_0$. In the neighborhood of this point, we now make the transformation

$$x'^i = x^i+\tfrac{1}{2}\,(\Gamma^i_{kl})_0 x^k x^l. \tag{85.18}$$

Then

$$\left(\frac{\partial^2 x'^m}{\partial x^k \partial x^l}\frac{\partial x^i}{\partial x'^m}\right)_0 = (\Gamma^i_{kl})_0$$

and according to (85.17), all the Γ'^m_{np} become equal to zero.

We note that for the transformation (85.18).

$$\left(\frac{\partial x'^i}{\partial x^k}\right)_0 = \delta^i_k,$$

so that it does not change the value of any tensor (including the tensor g_{ik}) at the given point, so that we can make the Christoffel symbols vanish at the same time as we bring the g_{ik} to Galilean form.

† It can also be shown that, by a suitable choice of the coordinate system, one can make all the Γ^i_{kl} go to zero not just at a point but all along a given curve.

§ 86. The relation of the Christoffel symbols to the metric tensor

Let us show that the covariant derivative of the metric tensor g_{ik} is zero. To do this we note that the relation

$$DA_i = g_{ik}DA^k$$

is valid for the vector DA_i, as for any vector. On the other hand, $A_i = g_{ik}A^k$, so that

$$DA_i = D(g_{ik}A^k) = g_{ik}DA^k + A^k Dg_{ik}.$$

Comparing with $DA_i = g_{ik}DA^k$, and remembering that the vector A^k is arbitrary,

$$Dg_{ik} = 0.$$

Therefore the covariant derivative

$$g_{ik;l} = 0. \tag{86.1}$$

Thus g_{ik} may be considered as a constant during covariant differentiation.

The equation $g_{ik;l} = 0$ can be used to express the Christoffel symbols Γ^i_{kl} in terms of the metric tensor g_{ik}. To do this we write in accordance with the general definition (85.14) of the covariant derivative of a tensor,

$$g_{ik;l} = \frac{\partial g_{ik}}{\partial x^l} - g_{mk}\Gamma^m_{il} - g_{im}\Gamma^m_{kl} = \frac{\partial g_{ik}}{\partial x^l} - \Gamma_{k,il} - \Gamma_{i,kl} = 0.$$

Thus the derivatives of g_{ik} are expressed in terms of the Christoffel symbols.† We write the values of the derivatives of g_{ik}, permuting the indices i, k, l:

$$\frac{\partial g_{ik}}{\partial x^l} = \Gamma_{k,il} + \Gamma_{i,kl},$$

$$\frac{\partial g_{li}}{\partial x^k} = \Gamma_{i,kl} + \Gamma_{l,ik},$$

$$-\frac{\partial g_{kl}}{\partial x^i} = -\Gamma_{l,ki} - \Gamma_{k,li}.$$

Taking half the sum of these equations, we find (remembering that $\Gamma_{i,kl} = \Gamma_{i,lk}$)

$$\Gamma_{i,kl} = \frac{1}{2}\left(\frac{\partial g_{ik}}{\partial x^l} + \frac{\partial g_{il}}{\partial x^k} - \frac{\partial g_{kl}}{\partial x^i}\right). \tag{86.2}$$

From this we have for the symbols $\Gamma^i_{kl} = g^{im}\Gamma_{m,kl}$,

$$\Gamma^i_{kl} = \frac{1}{2}g^{im}\left(\frac{\partial g_{mk}}{\partial x^l} + \frac{\partial g_{ml}}{\partial x^k} - \frac{\partial g_{kl}}{\partial x^m}\right). \tag{86.3}$$

These formulas give the required expressions for the Christoffel symbols in terms of the metric tensor.

---

† Choosing a locally-geodesic system of coordinates therefore means that at the given point all the first derivatives of the components of the metric tensor vanish.

We now derive an expression for the contracted Christoffel symbol Γ^i_{ki} which will be important later on. To do this we calculate the differential dg of the determinant g made up from the components of the tensor g_{ik}; dg can be obtained by taking the differential of each component of the tensor g_{ik} and multiplying it by its coefficient in the determinant, i.e., by the corresponding minor. On the other hand, the components of the tensor g^{ik} reciprocal to g_{ik} are equal to the minors of the determinant of the g_{ik}, divided by the determinant. Therefore the minors of the determinant g are equal to gg^{ik}. Thus,

$$dg = gg^{ik}\,dg_{ik} = -gg_{ik}\,dg^{ik} \tag{86.4}$$

(since $g_{ik}g^{ik} = \delta^i_i = 4$, $g^{ik}\,dg_{ik} = -g_{ik}\,dg^{ik}$).

From (86.3), we have

$$\Gamma^i_{ki} = \frac{1}{2}g^{im}\left(\frac{\partial g_{mk}}{\partial x^i} + \frac{\partial g_{mi}}{\partial x^k} - \frac{\partial g_{ki}}{\partial x^m}\right).$$

Changing the positions of the indices m and i in the third and first terms in parentheses, we see that these two terms cancel each other, so that

$$\Gamma^i_{ki} = \frac{1}{2}g^{im}\frac{\partial g_{im}}{\partial x^k},$$

or, according to (86.4),

$$\Gamma^i_{ki} = \frac{1}{2g}\frac{\partial g}{\partial x^k} = \frac{\partial \ln\sqrt{-g}}{\partial x^k}. \tag{86.5}$$

It is important to note also the expression for the quantity $g^{kl}\Gamma^i_{kl}$; we have

$$g^{kl}\Gamma^i_{kl} = \frac{1}{2}g^{kl}g^{im}\left(\frac{\partial g_{mk}}{\partial x^l} + \frac{\partial g_{lm}}{\partial x^k} - \frac{\partial g_{kl}}{\partial x^m}\right) = g^{kl}g^{im}\left(\frac{\partial g_{mk}}{\partial x^l} - \frac{1}{2}\frac{\partial g_{kl}}{\partial x^m}\right).$$

With the help of (86.4) this can be transformed to

$$g^{kl}\Gamma^i_{kl} = -\frac{1}{\sqrt{-g}}\frac{\partial(\sqrt{-g}\,g^{ik})}{\partial x^k}. \tag{86.6}$$

For various calculations it is important to remember that the derivatives of the contravariant tensor g^{ik} are related to the derivatives of g_{ik} by the relations

$$g_{il}\frac{\partial g^{lk}}{\partial x^m} = -g^{lk}\frac{\partial g_{il}}{\partial x^m} \tag{86.7}$$

(which are obtained by differentiating the equality $g_{il}g^{lk} = \delta^k_i$). Finally we point out that the derivatives of g^{ik} can also be expressed in terms of the quantities Γ^i_{kl}. Namely, from the identity $g^{ik}{}_{;l} = 0$ it follows directly that

$$\frac{\partial g^{ik}}{\partial x^l} = -\Gamma^i_{ml}g^{mk} - \Gamma^k_{ml}g^{im}. \tag{86.8}$$

With the aid of the formulas which we have obtained we can put the expression for $A^i{}_{;i}$, the generalized divergence of a vector in curvilinear coordinates, in convenient form. Using (86.5), we have

$$A^i{}_{;i} = \frac{\partial A^i}{\partial x^i} + \Gamma^i_{li}A^l = \frac{\partial A^i}{\partial x^i} + A^l \frac{\partial \ln \sqrt{-g}}{\partial x^l}$$

or, finally,

$$A^i{}_{;i} = \frac{1}{\sqrt{-g}} \frac{\partial(\sqrt{-g}\, A^i)}{\partial x^i}. \tag{86.9}$$

We derive an analogous expression for the divergence of an antisymmetric tensor A^{ik}. From (85.12), we have

$$A^{ik}{}_{;k} = \frac{\partial A^{ik}}{\partial x^k} + \Gamma^i_{mk}A^{mk} + \Gamma^k_{mk}A^{im}.$$

But, since $A^{mk} = -A^{km}$,

$$\Gamma^i_{mk}A^{mk} = -\Gamma^i_{km}A^{km} = 0.$$

Substituting the expression (86.5) for Γ^k_{mk}, we obtain

$$A^{ik}{}_{;k} = \frac{1}{\sqrt{-g}} \frac{\partial(\sqrt{-g}\, A^{ik})}{\partial x^k}. \tag{86.10}$$

Now suppose A_{ik} is a symmetric tensor; we calculate the expression $A^k_{i;k}$ for its mixed components. We have

$$A^k_{i;k} = \frac{\partial A^k_i}{\partial x^k} + \Gamma^k_{lk} A^l_i - \Gamma^l_{ik} A^k_l = \frac{1}{\sqrt{-g}} \frac{\partial(A^k_i \sqrt{-g})}{\partial x^k} - \Gamma^l_{ki} A^k_l.$$

The last term here is equal to

$$\frac{1}{2}\left(\frac{\partial g_{il}}{\partial x^k} + \frac{\partial g_{kl}}{\partial x^i} - \frac{\partial g_{ik}}{\partial x^l}\right) A^{kl}.$$

Because of the symmetry of the tensor A^{kl}, two of the terms in parentheses cancel each other, leaving

$$A^k_{i;k} = \frac{1}{\sqrt{-g}} \frac{\partial(\sqrt{-g}\, A^k_i)}{\partial x^k} - \frac{1}{2} \frac{\partial g_{kl}}{\partial x^i} A^{kl}. \tag{86.11}$$

In cartesian coordinates, $\partial A_i/\partial x^k - \partial A_k/\partial x^i$ is an antisymmetric tensor. In curvilinear coordinates this tensor is $A_{i;k} - A_{k;i}$. However, with the help of the expression for $A_{i;k}$ and since $\Gamma^i_{kl} = \Gamma^i_{lk}$, we have

$$A_{i;k} - A_{k;i} = \frac{\partial A_i}{\partial x^k} - \frac{\partial A_k}{\partial x^i}. \tag{86.12}$$

Finally, we transform to curvilinear coordinates the sum $\partial^2\phi/\partial x_i^2$ of the second derivatives of a scalar ϕ. It is clear that in curvilinear coordinates this sum goes over into $\phi_{:i}^{:i}$. But $\phi_{:i} = \partial\phi/\partial x^i$, since covariant differentiation of a scalar reduces to ordinary differentiation. Raising the index i, we have

$$\phi^{:i} = g^{ik}\frac{\partial\phi}{\partial x^k},$$

and using formula (86.9), we find

$$\phi_{:i}^{:i} = \frac{1}{\sqrt{-g}}\frac{\partial}{\partial x^i}\left(\sqrt{-g}\, g^{ik}\frac{\partial\phi}{\partial x^k}\right). \tag{86.13}$$

It is important to note that Gauss' theorem (83.20) for the transformation of the integral of a vector over a hypersurface into an integral over a four-volume can, in view of (86.9), be written as

$$\oint A^i\sqrt{-g}\, dS_i = \int A^i{}_{:i}\sqrt{-g}\, d\Omega. \tag{86.14}$$

§ 87. Motion of a particle in a gravitational field

The motion of a free material particle is determined in the special theory of relativity from the principle of least action,

$$\delta S = -mc\,\delta\int ds = 0, \tag{87.1}$$

according to which the particle moves so that its world line is an extremal between a given pair of world points, in our case a straight line (in ordinary three-dimensional space this corresponds to uniform rectilinear motion).

The motion of a particle in a gravitational field is determined by the principle of least action in this same form (87.1), since the gravitational field is nothing but a change in the metric of space-time, manifesting itself only in a change in the expression for ds in terms of the dx^i. Thus, in a gravitational field the particle moves so that its world point moves along an extremal or, as it is called, a *geodesic line* in the four-space x^0, x^1, x^2, x^3; however, since in the presence of the gravitational field space-time is not Galilean, this line is not a "straight line", and the real spatial motion of the particle is neither uniform nor rectilinear.

Instead of starting once again directly from the principle of least action (see the problem at the end of this section), it is simpler to obtain the equation of motion of a particle in a gravitational field by an appropriate generalization of the differential equation for the free motion of a particle in the special theory of relativity, i.e. in a Galilean four-dimensional coordinate system. These equations are $du^i/ds = 0$ or $du^i = 0$, where $u^i = dx^i/ds$ is the four-velocity. Clearly, in curvilinear coordinates this equation is generalized to the equation

$$Du^i = 0. \tag{87.2}$$

From the expression (85.6) for the covariant differential of a vector, we have

$$du^i + \Gamma^i_{kl} u^k \, dx^l = 0.$$

Dividing this equation by ds, we have

$$\frac{d^2x^i}{ds^2} + \Gamma^i_{kl} \frac{dx^k}{ds} \frac{dx^l}{ds} = 0. \tag{87.3}$$

This is the required equation of motion. We see that the motion of a particle in a gravitational field is determined by the quantities Γ^i_{kl}. The derivative $d^2x^i/ds^2 = du^i/ds$ is the four-acceleration of the particle. Therefore we may call the quantity $-m\Gamma^i_{kl}u^k u^l$ the "four-force," acting on the particle in the gravitational field. Here, the tensor g_{ik} plays the role of the "potential" of the gravitational field—its derivatives determine the field "intensity" Γ^i_{kl}.

In § 85 it was shown that by a suitable choice of the coordinate system one can always make all the Γ^i_{kl} zero at an arbitrary point of space-time. We now see that the choice of such a locally-inertial system of reference means the elimination of the gravitational field in the given infinitesimal element of space-time, and the possibility of making such a choice is an expression of the principle of equivalence in the relativistic theory of gravitation.

As before, we define the four-momentum of a particle in a gravitational field as

$$p^i = mcu^i. \tag{87.4}$$

Its square is

$$p_i p^i = -m^2c^2. \tag{87.5}$$

Substituting $\partial S/\partial x^i$ for p_i, we find the Hamilton-Jacobi equation for a particle in a gravitational field:

$$g^{ik} \frac{\partial S}{\partial x^i} \frac{\partial S}{\partial x^k} + m^2c^2 = 0. \tag{87.6}$$

The equation of a geodesic in the form (87.3) is not applicable to the propagation of a light signal, since along the world line of the propagation of a light ray the interval ds, as we know, is zero, so that all the terms in equation (87.3) become infinite. To get the equations of motion in the form needed for this case, we use the fact that the direction of propagation of a light ray in geometrical optics is determined by the wave vector tangent to the ray. We can therefore write the four-dimensional wave vector in the form $k^i = dx^i/d\lambda$, where λ is some parameter varying along the ray. In the special theory of relativity, i.e., in Euclidean space, in the propagation of light in vacuum the wave vector does not vary along the path, that is, $dk^i = 0$ (see § 53). In a gravitational field this equation clearly goes over into $Dk^i = 0$ or

$$\frac{dk^i}{d\lambda} + \Gamma^i_{kl} k^k k^l = 0 \tag{87.7}$$

(these equations also determine the parameter λ).

The absolute square of the wave four-vector, as we know (see § 48) is zero, that is,

$$k_i k^i = 0. \tag{87.8}$$

Substituting $\partial\psi/\partial x^i$ in place of k_i (ψ is the eikonal), we find the eikonal equation in a gravitational field in the form

$$g^{ik}\frac{\partial\psi}{\partial x^i}\frac{\partial\psi}{\partial x^k} = 0. \tag{87.9}$$

In the limiting case of small velocities, the relativistic equations of motion of a particle in a gravitational field must go over into the corresponding nonrelativistic equations. In this we must keep in mind that the assumption of small velocity implies the requirement that the gravitational field itself be weak; if this were not so a particle located in it would acquire a high velocity.

Let us examine how, in this limiting case, the metric tensor g_{ik} determining the field is related to the nonrelativistic potential ϕ of the gravitational field.

In nonrelativistic mechanics the motion of a particle in a gravitational field is determined by the Lagrangian (81.1). We now write it in the form

$$L = -mc^2 + \frac{mv^2}{2} - m\phi,$$

adding the constant $-mc^2$. This must be done so that the nonrelativistic Lagrangian in the absence of the field, $L = -mc^2 + mv^2/2$, shall be the same exactly as that to which the corresponding relativistic function $L = -mc^2\sqrt{1-v^2/c^2}$ reduces in the limit as $v/c \to 0$.

Consequently, the nonrelativistic action function S for a particle in a gravitational field has the form

$$S = \int L\,dt = -mc\int\left(c - \frac{v^2}{2c} + \frac{\phi}{c}\right)dt.$$

Comparing this with the expression $S = -mc\int ds$. we see that in the limiting case under consideration ds is

$$ds = \left(c - \frac{v^2}{2c} + \frac{\phi}{c}\right)dt.$$

Squaring and dropping terms which vanish for $c \to \infty$, we find

$$ds^2 = (c^2 + 2\phi)\,dt^2 - d\mathbf{r}^2. \tag{87.10}$$

when we have used the fact that $\mathbf{v}\,dt = d\mathbf{r}$.

Thus in the limiting case the component g_{00} of the metric tensor is

$$g_{00} = -1 - \frac{2\phi}{c^2}\,. \tag{87.11}$$

As for the other components, from (87.10) it would follow that $g_{\alpha\beta} = \delta_{\alpha\beta}$, $g_{0\alpha} = 0$. Actually, however, the corrections to them are, generally speaking, of the same order of magnitude as the corrections to g_{00} (for more detail, see § 105). The impossibility of determining these corrections by the method given above is related to the fact that the corrections to the $g_{\alpha\beta}$, though of the same order of magnitude as the correction to g_{00}, would give rise to terms in the Lagrangian of a much higher order of smallness (because in the expression for ds^2 the components $g_{\alpha\beta}$ are not multiplied by c^2, while this is the case for g_{00}).

PROBLEM

Derive the equation of motion (87.3) from the principle of least action (87.1).

Solution: We have:

$$-\delta ds^2 = -2ds\,\delta ds = \delta(g_{ik}\,dx^i\,dx^k) = dx^i\,dx^k\frac{\partial g_{ik}}{\partial x^l}\delta x^l + 2g_{ik}\,dx^i\,d\delta x^k.$$

Therefore

$$\delta S = mc\int\left\{\frac{1}{2}\frac{dx^i}{ds}\frac{dx^k}{ds}\frac{\partial g_{ik}}{\partial x^l}\delta x^l + g_{ik}\frac{dx^i}{ds}\frac{d\delta x^k}{ds}\right\}ds =$$

$$= mc\int\left\{\frac{1}{2}\frac{dx^i}{ds}\frac{dx^k}{ds}\frac{\partial g_{ik}}{\partial x^l}\delta x^l - \frac{d}{ds}\left(g_{ik}\frac{dx^i}{ds}\right)\delta x^k\right\}ds$$

(in integrating by parts, we use the fact that $\delta x^k = 0$ at the limits). In the second term in the integral, we replace the index k by the index l. We then find, by equating to zero the coefficient of the arbitrary variation δx^l:

$$\frac{1}{2}u^i u^k\frac{\partial g_{ik}}{\partial x^l} - \frac{d}{ds}(g_{il}u^i) = \frac{1}{2}u^i u^k\frac{\partial g_{ik}}{\partial x^l} - g_{il}\frac{du^i}{ds} - u^i u^k\frac{\partial g_{il}}{\partial x^k} = 0.$$

Noting that the third term can be written as

$$-\frac{1}{2}u^i u^k\left(\frac{\partial g_{il}}{\partial x^k} + \frac{\partial g_{kl}}{\partial x^i}\right),$$

and introducing the Christoffel symbols $\Gamma_{l,ik}$ in accordance with (86.2), we have:

$$g_{il}\frac{du^i}{ds} + \Gamma_{l,ik}u^i u^k = 0.$$

Equation (87.3) is obtained from this by raising the index l.

§ 88. The equations of electrodynamics in the presence of a gravitational field

The electromagnetic field equations of the special theory of relativity can be easily generalized so that they are applicable in an arbitrary four-dimensional curvilinear system of coordinates, i.e., in the presence of a gravitational field.

The electromagnetic field tensor in the special theory of relativity is defined as $F_{ik} = (\partial A_k/\partial x^i)-(\partial A_i/\partial x^k)$. Clearly it must now be defined correspondingly as $F_{ik} = A_{k;\,i}-A_{i;\,k}$. But because of (86.12),

$$F_{ik} = A_{k;i}-A_{i;k} = \frac{\partial A_k}{\partial x^i}-\frac{\partial A_i}{\partial x^k}, \tag{88.1}$$

and therefore the relation of F_{ik} to the potential A_k does not change. Consequently the first pair of Maxwell equations (26.5) also does not change its form,

$$\frac{\partial F_{ik}}{\partial x^l}+\frac{\partial F_{li}}{\partial x^k}+\frac{\partial F_{kl}}{\partial x^i} = 0. \tag{88.2}$$

In order to write the second pair of Maxwell equations, we must first determine the current four-vector in curvilinear coordinates. We do this in a fashion completely analogous to that which we followed in § 28. The charge located in the element of volume $dV = dx^1\,dx^2\,dx^3$ can be written in the form $de = \varrho\, dV$, where the density $\varrho = \sum_a e_a\,\delta(\mathbf{r}-\mathbf{r}_a)$ [see (28.1)]. Multiplying $de = \varrho\, dV$ on both sides by dx^i, we have

$$de\,dx^i = \varrho\,dV\,dx^i = \frac{\varrho}{\sqrt{-g}}\frac{dx^i}{dx^0}\sqrt{-g}\,dV\,dx^0.$$

The invariant element of four-volume is $\sqrt{-g}\,dV\,dx^0 = \sqrt{-g}\,d\Omega$, so that the current four-vector is equal to

$$j^i = \frac{\varrho c}{\sqrt{-g}}\frac{dx^i}{dx^0}, \tag{88.3}$$

where dx^i/dx^0 is the velocity measured in units of the "time" x^0 (dx^i/dx^0 is not a vector). The component j^0 of the current four-vector multiplied by $\frac{1}{c}\sqrt{-g}$ is the spatial density of charge.

In the special theory of relativity, the second pair of Maxwell equations (30.2) has the form

$$\frac{\partial F^{ik}}{\partial x^k} = \frac{4\pi}{c}j^i.$$

In a gravitational field they have, correspondingly, the form

$$F^{ik}{}_{;k} = \frac{4\pi}{c}j^i,$$

or, according to (86.10),

$$\frac{1}{\sqrt{-g}}\frac{\partial}{\partial x^k}(\sqrt{-g}\,F^{ik}) = \frac{4\pi}{c}j^i. \tag{88.4}$$

The equation of continuity $\partial j^i/\partial x^i = 0$ (29.4) now takes the form

$$j^i{}_{;i} = \frac{1}{\sqrt{-g}} \frac{\partial}{\partial x^i} (\sqrt{-g}\, j^i) = 0 \qquad (88.5)$$

[from (86.9)].

Finally, it is easy to write the equations of motion of a charged particle in the presence of both gravitational and electromagnetic fields by a simple generalization of equations (23.5) to curvilinear coordinates. Writing Du^i in them in place of du^i, we find

$$mc\frac{Du^i}{ds} = \frac{e}{c} F^i{}_k u^k = mc\left(\frac{du^i}{ds} + \Gamma^i_{kl} u^k u^l\right). \qquad (88.6)$$

§ 89. The constant gravitational field

A gravitational field is said to be *constant* if one can choose a system of reference in which all the components of the metric tensor are independent of the time coordinate x^0; the latter is then called the *world time.*

The choice of a world time is not completely unique. Thus, if we add to x^0 an arbitrary function of the space coordinates, the g_{ik} will still not contain x^0; this transformation corresponds to the arbitrariness in the choice of the time origin at each point in space.† In addition, of course, the world time can be multiplied by an arbitrary constant, i.e. the units for measuring it are arbitrary.

Strictly speaking, only the field produced by a single body can be constant. In a system of several bodies, their mutual gravitational attraction will give rise to motion, as a result of which the field produced by them cannot be constant.

If the body producing the field is fixed (in the reference system in which the g_{ik} do not depend on x^0), then both directions of time are equivalent. For a suitable choice of the time origin at all the points in space, the interval ds should in this case not be changed when we change the sign of x^0, and therefore all the components $g_{0\alpha}$ of the metric tensor must be identically equal to zero. Such constant gravitational fields are said to be *static.*

However, for the field produced by a body to be constant, it is not necessary for the body to be at rest. Thus the field of an axially symmetric body rotating uniformly about its axis will also be constant. However in this case the two time directions are no longer equivalent by any means — if the sign of the time is changed, the sign of the angular velocity is changed. Therefore in such constant gravitational fields (we shall call them *stationary* fields) the components $g_{0\alpha}$ of the metric tensor are in general different from zero.

† It is easy to see that under such a transformation the spatial metric, as expected, does not change.

The meaning of the world time in a constant gravitational field is that an interval of world time between events at a certain point in space coincides with the interval of world time between any other two events at any other point in space, if these events are respectively simultaneous (in the sense explained in § 84) with the first pair of events. But to the same interval of world time x^0 there correspond, at different points of space, different intervals of proper time τ.

The relation between world time and proper time, formula (84.1), can now be written in the form

$$\tau = \frac{1}{c}\sqrt{-g_{00}}\, x^0, \tag{89.1}$$

applicable to any finite time interval.

If the gravitational field is weak, then we may use the approximate expression (87.11), and (89.1) gives

$$\tau = \frac{x^0}{c}\sqrt{1+\frac{2\phi}{c^2}},$$

and to the same accuracy,

$$\tau = \frac{x^0}{c}\left(1+\frac{\phi}{c^2}\right). \tag{89.2}$$

Thus proper time elapses the more slowly the smaller the gravitational potential at a given point in space, i.e., the larger its absolute value (later, in § 96, it will be shown that the potential ϕ is negative). If one of two identical clocks is placed in a gravitational field for some time, the clock which has been in the field will thereafter appear to be slow.

As was already indicated above, in a static gravitational field the components $g_{0\alpha}$ of the metric tensor are zero. According to the results of § 84, this means that in such a field synchronization of clocks is possible over all space. We note also that the element of spatial distance dl is equal in a static field simply to

$$dl^2 = g_{\alpha\beta}\, dx^\alpha\, dx^\beta. \tag{89.3}$$

In a stationary field the $g_{0\alpha}$ are different from zero and the synchronization of clocks over all space is impossible. Since the g_{ik} do not depend on x^0, formula (84.10) for the difference between the values of world time for two simultaneous events occurring at different points in space can be written in the form

$$\Delta x^0 = -\int \frac{g_{0\alpha}\, dx^\alpha}{g_{00}} \tag{89.4}$$

for any two points on the line along which the synchronization of clocks is carried out. In the synhronization of clocks along a closed ocntour, the difference in the value of the world time which would be recorded upon returning to the starting point is equal to the integral

$$\Delta x^0 = -\oint \frac{g_{0\alpha}\, dx^\alpha}{g_{00}} \tag{89.5}$$

taken along the closed contour.†

Let us consider the propagation of a light ray in a constant gravitational field. We have seen in § 53 that the frequency of the light is the time derivative of the eikonal ψ (with opposite sign). The frequency expressed in terms of the world time x^0/c is therefore $\omega_0 = -c\dfrac{\partial\psi}{\partial x^0}$. Since the eikonal equation (87.9) in a constant field does not contain x^0 explicitly, the frequency ω_0 remains constant during the propagation of the light ray. The frequency measured in terms of the proper time is $\omega = -\dfrac{\partial\psi}{\partial\tau}$; this frequency is different at different points of space.

From the relation

$$\frac{\partial\psi}{\partial\tau} = \frac{\partial\psi}{\partial x^0}\frac{\partial x^0}{\partial\tau} = \frac{\partial\psi}{\partial x^0}\frac{c}{\sqrt{-g_{00}}},$$

we have

$$\omega = \frac{\omega_0}{\sqrt{-g_{00}}}. \tag{89.6}$$

In a weak gravitational field we obtain from this, approximately,

$$\omega = \omega_0\left(1 - \frac{\phi}{c^2}\right). \tag{89.7}$$

We see that the light frequency increases with increasing absolute value of the potential of the gravitational field, i.e., as we approach the bodies producing the field; conversely, as the light recedes from these bodies the frequency decreases. If a ray of light, emitted at a point where the gravitational potential is ϕ_1, has (at that point) the frequency ω, then upon arriving at a point where the potential is ϕ_2, it will have a frequency (measured in units of the proper time at that point) equal to

$$\frac{\omega}{1-\dfrac{\phi_1}{c^2}}\left(1-\frac{\phi_2}{c^2}\right) = \omega\left(1+\frac{\phi_1-\phi_2}{c^2}\right).$$

A line spectrum emitted by some atoms located, for example, on the sun, looks the same there as the spectrum emitted by the same atoms located on

† The integral (89.5) is identically zero if the sum $g_{0\alpha}dx^\alpha/g_{00}$ is an exact differential of some function of the space coordinates. However such a case would simply mean that we are actually dealing with a static field, and that all the $g_{0\alpha}$ could be made equal to zero by a transformation of the form $x^0 \to x^0 + \varphi(x^\alpha)$.

the earth would appear on it. If, however, we observe on the earth the spectrum emitted by the atoms located on the sun, then, as follows from what has been said above, its lines appear to be shifted with respect to the lines of the same spectrum emitted on the earth. Namely, each line with frequency ω will be shifted through the interval $\Delta\omega$ given by the formula

$$\Delta\omega = \frac{\phi_1 - \phi_2}{c^2}\,\omega, \tag{89.8}$$

where ϕ_1 and ϕ_2 are the potentials of the gravitational field at the points of emission and observation of the spectrum respectively. If we observe on the earth a spectrum emitted on the sun or the stars, then $|\phi_1| > |\phi_2|$, and from (89.8) it follows that $\Delta\omega < 0$, i.e., the shift occurs in the direction of lower frequency. The phenomenon we have described is called the "*red shift*".

The occurrence of this phenomenon can be explained directly on the basis of what has been said above about world time. Because the field is constant, the interval of world time during which a certain vibration in the light wave propagates from one given point of space to another is independent of x^0. Therefore it is clear that the number of vibrations occurring in a unit interval of world time will be the same at all points along the ray. But to one and the same interval of world time there corresponds a larger and larger interval of proper time, the further away we are from the bodies producing the field. Consequently, the frequency, i.e., the number of vibrations per unit proper time, will decrease as the light recedes from these masses.

During the motion of a particle in a constant field, its energy is defined as $\left(-c\dfrac{\partial S}{\partial x^0}\right)$, the derivative of the action with respect to the world time; this follows, for example, from the fact that x^0 does not appear explicitly in the Hamilton-Jacobi equation. The energy defined in this way is the time component of the covariant four-vector of momentum $p_k = mcu_k = mcg_{ki}u^i$. In a static field, $ds^2 = -g_{00}\,dx_0^2 - dl^2$, and we have for the energy, which we here denote by $\mathcal{E}_0$,

$$\mathcal{E}_0 = -mc^2 g_{00}\frac{dx^0}{ds} = -mc^2 g_{00}\frac{dx^0}{\sqrt{-g_{00}\,dx_0^2 - dl^2}}\,.$$

We introduce the velocity

$$v = \frac{dl}{d\tau} = \frac{c\,dl}{\sqrt{-g_{00}}\,dx^0}$$

of the particle, measure in terms of the proper time; that is, by an observer located at the given point. Then we obtain for the energy

$$\mathcal{E}_0 = \frac{mc^2\sqrt{-g_{00}}}{\sqrt{1-\dfrac{v^2}{c^2}}}. \tag{89.9}$$

This is the quantity which is conserved during the motion of the particle.

It is easy to show that the expression (89.9) remains valid also for a stationary field, if only the velocity v is measured in terms of the proper time, as determined by clocks synchronized along the trajectory of the particle. If the particle departs from point A at the moment of world time x^0 and arrives at the infinitesimally distant point B at the moment x^0+dx^0, then to determine the velocity we must now take, not the time interval $(x^0+dx^0)-x^0 = dx^0$, but rather the difference between x^0+dx^0 and the moment $x^0-\frac{g_{0\alpha}}{g_{00}}dx^\alpha$ which is simultaneous at the point B with the moment x_0 at the point A.

$$(x^0+dx^0)-\left(x^0-\frac{g_{0\alpha}}{g_{00}}dx^\alpha\right) = dx^0+\frac{g_{0\alpha}}{g_{00}}dx^\alpha.$$

Multiplying by $\sqrt{-g_{00}}/c$, we obtain the corresponding interval of proper time, so that the velocity is

$$v^\alpha = \frac{c\,dx^\alpha}{\sqrt{h}\,(dx^0-g_\alpha dx^\alpha)}, \tag{89.10}$$

where we have introduced the notation

$$h=-g_{00}, \qquad g_\alpha = -\frac{g_{0\alpha}}{g_{00}}. \tag{89.11}$$

We note that with such a definition, the interval ds is expressed in terms of the velocity in the usual fashion:

$$ds^2 = -g_{00}\,dx_0^2-2g_{0\alpha}\,dx^0\,dx^\alpha-g_{\alpha\beta}\,dx^\alpha\,dx^\beta = \\ = h\,(dx^0-g_\alpha\,dx^\alpha)^2-dl^2 = h\,(dx^0-g_\alpha\,dx^\alpha)^2\left(1-\frac{v^2}{c^2}\right), \tag{89.12}$$

where v^2 is to be understood as the square of a three-dimensional vector in the space with the metric tensor $\gamma_{\alpha\beta}$:

$$v^2 = v_\alpha v^\alpha, \qquad v_\alpha = \gamma_{\alpha\beta}v^\beta. \tag{89.13}$$

The components of the four-velocity $u^i = \frac{dx^i}{ds}$ are

$$u^\alpha = \frac{v^\alpha}{c\sqrt{1-\frac{v^2}{c^2}}}, \qquad u^0 = \frac{1}{\sqrt{h}\sqrt{1-\frac{v^2}{c^2}}}+\frac{g_\alpha v^\alpha}{c\sqrt{1-\frac{v^2}{c^2}}}. \tag{89.14}$$

The energy is

$$\mathcal{E}_0 = -mc^2 g_{0i}u^i = mc^2 h\,(u^0-g_\alpha u^\alpha),$$

and after substituting (89.14), takes the form (89.9).

In the limiting case of a weak gravitational field and low velocities, by substituting $-g_{00} = 1+\frac{2\varphi}{c^2}$ in (89.9), we get approximately:

$$\mathscr{E}_0 = mc^2 + \frac{mv^2}{2} + m\varphi, \tag{89.15}$$

where $m\varphi$ is the potential energy of the particle in the gravitational field, which is in agreement with the Lagrangian (81.1).

Problems

1. Determine the force acting on a particle in a constant gravitational field.

Solution: For the components of Γ^i_{kl} which we need, we find the following expressions:

$$\begin{aligned}
\Gamma^{\alpha}_{00} &= \frac{1}{2}h^{;\alpha},\\
\Gamma^{\alpha}_{0\beta} &= \frac{h}{2}(g^{\alpha}_{;\beta} - g_{\beta}^{;\alpha}) - \frac{1}{2}g_{\beta}h^{;\alpha},\\
\Gamma^{\alpha}_{\beta\gamma} &= \lambda^{\alpha}_{\beta\gamma} + \frac{h}{2}\,[g_{\beta}\,(g_{\gamma}^{;\alpha} - g^{\alpha}_{;\gamma}) + g_{\gamma}(g_{\beta}^{;\alpha} - g^{\alpha}_{;\beta})] + \frac{1}{2}g_{\beta}g_{\gamma}h^{;\alpha}.
\end{aligned} \tag{1}$$

In these expressions all the tensor operations (covariant differentiation, raising and lowering of indices) are carried out in the three-dimensional space with metric $\gamma_{\alpha\beta}$, on the three-dimensional vector g^{α} and the three-dimensional scalar h (89.11); $\lambda^{\alpha}_{\beta\gamma}$ is the three-dimensional Christoffel symbol, constructed from the components of the tensor $\gamma_{\alpha\beta}$ in just the same way as Γ_{kl} is constructed from the components of g_{ik}; in the computations, the fact is used that the components of the contravariant tensor g^{ik} are equal to

$$g^{\alpha\beta} = \gamma^{\alpha\beta}, \quad g^{0\alpha} = g^{\alpha} \equiv \gamma^{\alpha\beta}g_{\beta}\,.$$

Substituting (1) in the equation of motion

$$\frac{du^{\alpha}}{ds} = -\Gamma^{\alpha}_{00}\,(u^0)^2 - 2\Gamma^{\alpha}_{0\beta}u^0u^{\beta} - \Gamma^{\alpha}_{\beta\gamma}u^{\beta}u^{\gamma}$$

and using the expression (89.14) for the components of the four-velocity, we find after some simple transformations:

$$\frac{d}{ds}\frac{v^{\alpha}}{c\sqrt{1-\frac{v^2}{c^2}}} = -\frac{h^{;\alpha}}{2h\left(1-\frac{v^2}{c^2}\right)} - \frac{\sqrt{h}\,(g^{\alpha}{}_{;\beta} - g_{\beta}{}^{;\alpha})v^{\beta}}{c\left(1-\frac{v^2}{c^2}\right)} - \frac{\lambda^{\alpha}_{\beta\gamma}v^{\beta}v^{\gamma}}{c^2\left(1-\frac{v^2}{c^2}\right)}\,. \tag{2}$$

The force $\mathbf{f}$ acting on the particle is the derivative of its momentum $\mathbf{p}$ with respect to the (synchronized) proper time, as defined by the three-dimensional covariant differential:

$$f^{\alpha} = c\sqrt{1-\frac{v^2}{c^2}}\frac{Dp^{\alpha}}{ds} = c\sqrt{1-\frac{v^2}{c^2}}\frac{d}{ds}\frac{mv^{\alpha}}{\sqrt{1-\frac{v^2}{c^2}}} + \lambda^{\alpha}_{\beta\gamma}\frac{mv^{\beta}v^{\gamma}}{\sqrt{1-\frac{v^2}{c^2}}}\,.$$

From (2) we therefore have (for convenience we lower the index α):

$$f_{\alpha} = \frac{mc^2}{\sqrt{1-\frac{v^2}{c^2}}}\left\{-\frac{\partial}{\partial x^{\alpha}}\ln\sqrt{h} + \sqrt{h}\left(\frac{\partial g_{\beta}}{\partial x^{\alpha}} - \frac{\partial g_{\alpha}}{\partial x^{\beta}}\right)\frac{v^{\beta}}{c}\right\},$$

or, in the usual three-dimensional notation,

$$\mathbf{f} = \frac{mc^2}{\sqrt{1-\frac{v^2}{c^2}}}\left\{-\nabla \ln \sqrt{h} + \sqrt{h}\frac{\mathbf{v}}{c} \times (\nabla \times \mathbf{g}).\right\}. \tag{3}$$

We note that if the body is at rest, then the force acting on it [the first term in (3)] has a potential. For low velocities of motion the second term in (3) has the form $mc\sqrt{h}\,\mathbf{v}\times(\nabla\times\mathbf{g})$ analogous to the Coriolis force which would appear (in the absence of the field) in a coordinate system rotating with angular velocity

$$\mathbf{\Omega} = \frac{c}{2}\sqrt{h}\,\nabla\times\mathbf{g}.$$

2. Derive Fermat's principle for the propagation of a ray in a constant gravitational field.

Solution: Fermat's principle (§ 53) states:

$$\delta\int k_\alpha\, dx^\alpha = 0,$$

where the integral is taken along the ray, and the integrand must be expressed in terms of the frequency ω_0 (which is constant along the ray) and the coordinate differentials. Noting that $k_0 = \frac{\partial\psi}{\partial x^0} = -\frac{\omega_0}{c}$, we write:

$$\frac{\omega_0}{c} = -k_0 = -g_{0i}k^i = -g_{00}k^0 - g_{0\alpha}k^\alpha = h(k^0 - g_\alpha k^\alpha).$$

Substituting this in the relation $k_ik^i = g_{ik}k^ik^k = 0$, written in the form

$$-h(k^0 - g_\alpha k^\alpha)^2 + \gamma_{\alpha\beta}k^\alpha k^\beta = 0,$$

we obtain:

$$-\frac{1}{h}\left(\frac{\omega_0}{c}\right)^2 + \gamma_{\alpha\beta}k^\alpha k^\beta = 0.$$

Noting that the vector k^α must have the direction of the vector dx^α, we then find:

$$k^\alpha = \frac{\omega_0}{c\sqrt{h}}\frac{dx^\alpha}{dl},$$

where dl (84.6) is the element of spatial distance along the ray. In order to obtain the expression for k_α, we write

$$k^\alpha = g^{\alpha i}k_i = g^{\alpha 0}k_0 + g^{\alpha\beta}k_\beta = -g^\alpha\frac{\omega_0}{c} + \gamma^{\alpha\beta}k_\beta,$$

so that

$$k_\alpha = \gamma_{\alpha\beta}\left(k^\beta + \frac{\omega_0}{c}g^\beta\right) = \frac{\omega_0}{c}\left(\frac{\gamma_{\alpha\beta}}{\sqrt{h}}\frac{dx^\beta}{dl} + g_\alpha\right).$$

Finally, multiplying by dx^α, we obtain Fermat's principle in the form (dropping the constant factor $\frac{\omega_0}{c}$):

$$\delta\int\left(\frac{dl}{\sqrt{h}} + g_\alpha\, dx^\alpha\right) = 0.$$

In a static field, we have simply:

$$\delta \int \frac{dl}{\sqrt{h}} = 0.$$

We call attention to the fact that in a gravitational field the ray does not propagate along the shortest line in space, since the latter would be defined by the equation $\delta \int dl = 0$.

3. Write the Maxwell equations, in a given constant gravitational field, in three-dimensional form.

Solution: We introduce two three dimensional vectors **E** and **B**, which are related to the components of the covariant tensor F_{ik} in the same way as are the vectors **B** and **H** for the case of Galilean coordinates (see p. 269); similarly, we relate the components $\sqrt{-g_{00}}\, F^{ik}$ with the components of two vectors which we denote by **D** and **H**. By simple algebraic transformations, we can then represent the relation $F^{ik} = g^{il}g^{km}F_{lm}$ in the form of a pair of vector equations:

$$\mathbf{D} = \frac{\mathbf{E}}{\sqrt{h}} + \mathbf{H}\times\mathbf{g}, \quad \mathbf{B} = \frac{\mathbf{H}}{\sqrt{h}} + \mathbf{g}\times\mathbf{E}.$$

With this same notation, the four-dimensional equations (88.2) and (88.4) can be written as three-dimensional equations:

$$\nabla\times\mathbf{E} = -\frac{1}{c}\frac{\partial\mathbf{B}}{\partial t}, \quad \nabla\cdot\mathbf{D} = 0,$$

$$\nabla\times\mathbf{H} = \frac{1}{c}\frac{\partial\mathbf{D}}{\partial t}, \quad \nabla\cdot\mathbf{B} = 0,$$

in which the vector operations are carried out in a three-dimensional space with metric $\gamma_{\alpha\beta}$.

We call attention to the formal analogy of these equations with the Maxwell equations for the electromagnetic field in material media.† In particular, in a static gravitational field the quantity $1/\sqrt{h}$ plays the role of the electric and magnetic "permeability".

90. **Rotation**

As a special case of a stationary gravitational field, let us consider a uniformly rotating reference system. To calculate the interval ds we carry out the transformation from a system at rest (inertial system) to the uniformly rotating one. In the coordinates r', ϕ', z', t of the system at rest (we use cylindrical coordinates r', ϕ', z'), the interval has the form

$$ds^2 = c^2\, dt^2 - dr'^2 - r'^2\, d\phi'^2 - dz'^2. \tag{90.1}$$

Let the cylindrical coordinates in the rotating system be r, ϕ, z. If the axis of rotation coincides with the axes Z and Z', then we have $r' = r$, $z' = z$, $\phi' = \phi + \Omega t$, where Ω is the angular velocity of rotation. Substituting in (90.1), we find the required expression for ds^2 in the rotating system of reference:

$$ds^2 = (c^2 - \Omega^2 r^2)\, dt^2 - 2\Omega r^2\, d\phi\, dt - dz^2 - r^2\, d\phi^2 - dr^2. \tag{90.2}$$

It is necessary to note that the rotating system of reference can be used only out to distances equal to c/Ω. In fact, from (90.2) we see that for $r > c/\Omega$, g_{00} becomes positive, which is not admissible. The inapplicability of the rotating reference system at large distances is related to the fact that

† See *Electrodynamics of Continuous Media.*

there the velocity would become greater than the velocity of light, and therefore such a system cannot be made up from real bodies.

As in every stationary field, clocks on the rotating body cannot be uniquely synchronized at all points. Proceeding with the synchronization along any closed curve, we find, upon returning to the starting point, a time differing from the initial value by an amount [see (89.5)]

$$\Delta t = -\frac{1}{c}\oint \frac{g_{0\alpha}}{g_{00}}\,dx^\alpha - \frac{1}{c^2}\oint \frac{\Omega r^2 d\phi}{1-\dfrac{\Omega^2 r^2}{c^2}}$$

or, assuming that $\Omega r/c \ll 1$ (i.e., that the velocity of the rotation is small compared with the velocity of light),

$$\Delta t = \frac{\Omega}{c^2}\int r^2 d\phi = \pm\frac{2\Omega}{c^2}S, \tag{90.3}$$

where S is the projected area of the contour on a plane perpendicular to the axis of rotation (the sign $+$ or $-$ holding according as we traverse the contour in, or opposite to, the direction of rotation).

Let us assume that a ray of light propagates along a certain closed contour. Let us calculate to terms of order v/c the time t that elapses between the starting out of the light ray and its return to the initial point. The velocity of light, by definition, is always equal to c, if the times are synchronized along the given closed curve and if at each point we use the proper time. Since the difference between proper and world time is of order v^2/c^2, then in calculating the required time interval t to terms of order v/c this difference can be neglected. Therefore we have

$$t = \frac{L}{c} \pm \frac{2\Omega}{c^2}S,$$

where L is the length of the contour. Corresponding to this, the velocity of light, measured as the ratio L/t, appears equal to

$$c \pm 2\Omega\frac{S}{L}. \tag{90.4}$$

This formula, like the first approximation for the Doppler effect, can also be easily derived in a purely classical manner.

Problem

Calculate the element of spatial distance in a rotating coordinate system.

Solution: With the help of (84.6) and (84.7), we find

$$dl^2 = dr^2 + dz^2 + \frac{r^2 d\phi^2}{1-\Omega^2\dfrac{r^2}{c^2}},$$

which determines the spatial geometry in the rotating reference system. We note that the ratio of the circumference of a circle in the plane z=constant (with center on the axis of rotation) to its radius r is

$$2\pi/\sqrt{1-\Omega^2 r^2/c^2},$$

i.e., larger than 2π.

CHAPTER 11

THE GRAVITATIONAL FIELD EQUATIONS

§ 91. The curvature tensor

Let us go back once more to the concept of parallel displacement of a vector. As we said in § 85, in the general case of a non-Euclidean space, the infinitesimal parallel displacement of a vector is defined as a displacement in which the components of the vector are not changed in a system of coordinates which is cartesian in the given infinitesimal volume element.

If $x^i = x^i(s)$ is the parametric equation of a certain curve (s is the arc length measured from some point), then the vector $u^i = dx^i/ds$ is a unit vector tangent to the curve. If the curve we are considering is a geodesic, then along it $Du^i = 0$ [see (87.2)]. This means that if the vector u^i is subjected to a parallel displacement from a point x^i on a geodesic curve to the point $x^i + dx^i$ on the same curve, then it coincides with the vector $u^i + du^i$ tangent to the curve at the point $x^i + dx^i$. Thus when the tangent to a geodesic moves along the curve, it is displaced parallel to itself.

On the other hand, during the parallel displacement of two vectors, the "angle" between them clearly remains unchanged. Therefore we may say that during the parallel displacement of any vector along a geodesic curve, the angle between the vector and the tangent to the geodesic remains unchanged. In other words, during the parallel displacement of a vector, its component along the geodesic must be the same at all points of the path.

Now the very important result appears that in a non-Euclidean space the parallel displacement of a vector from one given point to another gives different results if the displacement is carried out over different paths. In particular, it follows from this that if we displace a vector parallel to itself along some closed contour, then upon returning to the starting point, it will not coincide with its original value.

In order to make this clear, let us consider a non-Euclidean two-dimensional space, i.e., any curved surface. Figure 18 shows a portion of such a surface, bounded by three geodesic curves. Let us subject the vector 1 to a parallel displacement along the contour made up of these three curves. In moving along the line AB, the vector 1, always retaining its angle with the curve unchanged, goes over into the vector 2. In the same way, on moving along BC it goes over into 3. Finally, on moving from C to A along the curve CA, maintaining a constant angle with this curve, the vector under consideration goes over into 1′, not coinciding with the vector 1.

We derive the general formula for the change in a vector after parallel displacement around any infinitesimal closed contour. This change ΔA_k can clearly be written in the form $\oint dA_k$, where the integral is taken over the given contour. Substituting in place of dA_k the expression (85.5), we have

$$\Delta A_k = \oint \Gamma^i_{kl} A_i dx^l \tag{91.1}$$

(the vector A_k which appears in the integrand changes as we move along the contour).

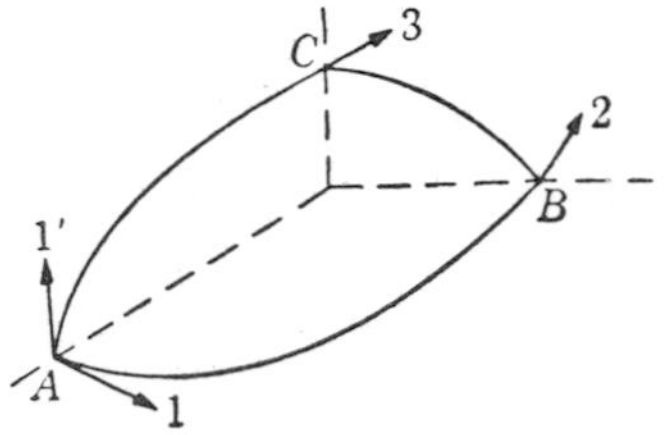

FIG. 18.

For the further transformation of this integral, we must note the following. The values of the vector A_i at points inside the contour are not unique; they depend on the path along which we approach the particular point. However, as we shall see from the result obtained below, this non-uniqueness is related to terms of second order. We may therefore, with the first order accuracy which is sufficient for the transformation, regard the components of the vector A_i at points inside the infinitesimal contour as being uniquely determined by their values on the contour itself by the formulas $\delta A_i = \Gamma^n_{il} A_n dx^l$, i.e., by the derivatives

$$\frac{\partial A_i}{\partial x^l} = \Gamma^n_{il} A_n. \tag{91.2}$$

Now applying Stokes' theorem (6.15) to the integral (91.1) and considering that the area enclosed by the contour has the infinitesimal value Δf^{lm}, we get:

$$\Delta A_k = \frac{1}{2}\left[\frac{\partial(\Gamma^i_{km} A_i)}{\partial x^l} - \frac{\partial(\Gamma^i_{kl} A_i)}{\partial x^m}\right]\Delta f^{lm}$$

$$= \frac{1}{2}\left[\frac{\partial \Gamma^i_{km}}{\partial x^l} A_i - \frac{\partial \Gamma^i_{kl}}{\partial x^m} A_i + \Gamma^i_{km}\frac{\partial A_i}{\partial x^l} - \Gamma^i_{kl}\frac{\partial A_i}{\partial x^m}\right]\Delta f^{lm}.$$

Substituting the values of the derivatives (91.2), we get finally:

$$\Delta A_k = \tfrac{1}{2} R^i_{klm} A_i \Delta f^{lm}, \tag{91.3}$$

where R^i_{klm} is a tensor of the fourth rank:

$$R^i_{klm} = \frac{\partial \Gamma^i_{km}}{\partial x^l} - \frac{\partial \Gamma^i_{kl}}{\partial x^m} + \Gamma^i_{nl}\Gamma^n_{km} - \Gamma^i_{nm}\Gamma^n_{kl}. \tag{91.4}$$

That R^i_{klm} is a tensor is clear from the fact that in (91.3) the left side is a vector — the difference ΔA_k between the values of vectors at one and the same point. The tensor R^i_{klm} is called the *curvature tensor* or the *Riemann tensor.*

It is easy to obtain a similar formula for a contravariant vector A^k. To do this we note, since under parallel displacement a scalar does not change, that $\Delta(A^k B_k) = 0$, where B_k is any covariant vector. With the help of (91.3), we then have

$$\Delta(A^k B_k) = A^k \Delta B_k + B_k \Delta A^k = \tfrac{1}{2} A^k B_i R^i_{klm} \Delta f^{lm} + B_k \Delta A^k =$$
$$= B_k(\Delta A^k + \tfrac{1}{2} A^i R^k_{ilm} \Delta f^{lm}) = 0,$$

or, in view of the arbitrariness of the vector B_k,

$$\Delta A^k = -\tfrac{1}{2} R^k_{ilm} A^i \Delta f^{lm}. \tag{91.5}$$

If we twice differentiate a vector A_i covariantly with respect to x^k and x^l, then the result generally depends on the order of differentiation, contrary to the situation for ordinary differentiation. It turns out that the difference $A_{i;k;l} - A_{i;l;k}$ is given by the same curvature tensor which we introduced above. Namely, one finds the formula

$$A_{i;k;l} - A_{i;l;k} = A_m R^m_{ikl}, \tag{91.6}$$

which is easily verified by direct calculation in the locally-geodesic coordinate system. Similarly, for a contravariant vector,†

$$A^i{}_{;k;l} - A^i{}_{;l;k} = -A^m R^i_{mkl}. \tag{91.7}$$

Finally, it is easy to obtain similar formulas for the second derivatives of tensors [this is done most easily by considering, for example, a tensor of the form $A_i B_k$, and using formulas (91.6) and (91.7); because of the linearity, the formulas thus obtained must be valid for an arbitrary tensor A_{ik}] Thus

$$A_{ik;l;m} - A_{ik;m;l} = A_{in} R^n_{klm} + A_{nk} R^n_{ilm} \tag{91.8}$$

Clearly, in a Euclidean space the curvature tensor is zero, for, in a Euclidean space, we can choose coordinates such that over all the space all the $\Gamma^i_{kl} = 0$, and therefore also $R^i_{klm} = 0$. Because of the tensor character of R^i_{klm} it is then equal to zero also in any other coordinate system. This is related to the fact that in a Euclidean space parallel displacement is a single-valued operation, so that in making a circuit of a closed contour a vector does not change.

The converse theorem is also valid: if $R^i_{klm} = 0$, then the space is Euclidean. Namely, in any space we can choose a coordinate system which is cartesian over a given infinitesimal region. If $R^i_{klm} = 0$, then parallel displacement

† Formula (91.7) can also be obtained directly from (91.6) by raising the index i and using the symmetry properties of the tensor R_{iklm} (§ 92).

is a unique operation, and then by a parallel displacement of the cartesian system from the given infinitesimal region to all the rest of the space, we can construct a cartesian system over the whole space, which proves that the space is Euclidean.

Thus the vanishing or nonvanishing of the curvature tensor is a criterion which enables us to determine whether a space is Euclidean or not.

We note that although in a non-Euclidean space we can also choose a coordinate system which will be cartesian at a given point, that is, such that at a given point all the Γ^i_{kl} vanish, at the same time the curvature tensor at this same point does not go to zero (since the derivatives of the Γ^i_{kl} do not become zero along with the Γ^i_{kl}).

§ 92. Properties of the curvature tensor

From the expression (91.4) for the tensor R^i_{klm} it follows immediately that the curvature tensor is antisymmetric in the indices l and m:

$$R^i_{klm} = -R^i_{kml}. \tag{92.1}$$

Furthermore, one can easily verify that the following identity is valid:

$$R^i_{klm}+R^i_{mkl}+R^i_{lmk} = 0. \tag{92.2}$$

In addition to the mixed curvature tensor R^i_{klm}, one also uses the covariant curvature tensor †

$$R_{iklm} = g_{in} R^n_{klm}. \tag{92.3}$$

By means of simple transformations it is easy to obtain the following expressions for R_{iklm}:

$$R_{iklm} = \frac{1}{2}\left(\frac{\partial^2 g_{im}}{\partial x^k \partial x^l} + \frac{\partial^2 g_{kl}}{\partial x^i \partial x^m} - \frac{\partial^2 g_{il}}{\partial x^k \partial x^m} - \frac{\partial^2 g_{km}}{\partial x^i \partial x^l}\right) + g_{np}(\Gamma^n_{kl}\Gamma^p_{im} - \Gamma^n_{km}\Gamma^p_{il}). \tag{92.4}$$

From this expression one sees immediately the following symmetry properties:

$$R_{iklm} = -R_{kilm}, \tag{92.5}$$

$$R_{iklm} = -R_{ikml}, \tag{92.6}$$

$$R_{iklm} = R_{lmik}. \tag{92.7}$$

From these formulas it follows, in particular, that all components R_{iklm}, in which $i = k$ or $l = m$ are zero.

Finally, for R_{iklm} as for R^i_{klm}, the identity (92.2) is valid:

$$R_{iklm}+R_{imkl}+R_{ilmk} = 0. \tag{92.8}$$

---

† In this connection it would be more correct to use the notation $R^i{}_{klm}$ which clearly shows the position of the index which has been raised.

Furthermore, from the relations (92.5)–(92.7) it follows that if we cyclically permute any three indices in R_{iklm} and add the three components obtained, then the result will be zero.

Finally, we also prove the *Bianchi identity*:

$$R^n_{ikl;m}+R^n_{imk;l}+R^n_{ilm;k}=0. \tag{92.9}$$

It is most conveniently veriefied by using a locally-geodesic coordinate system. Because of its tensor character, the relation (92.9) will then be valid in any other system. Differentiating (91.4) and then substituting in it $\Gamma^i_{kl}=0$, we find for the point under consideration

$$R^n_{ikl;m}=\frac{\partial R^n_{ikl}}{\partial x^m}=\frac{\partial^2\Gamma^n_{il}}{\partial x^m\,\partial x^k}-\frac{\partial^2\Gamma^n_{ik}}{\partial x^m\,\partial x^l}.$$

With the aid of this expression it is easy to verify that (92.9) actually holds.

From the curvature tensor we can, by contraction, construct a tensor of the second rank. This contraction can be carried out in only one way: contraction of the tensor R_{iklm} on the indices i and k or l and m gives zero because of the antisymmetry in these indices, while contraction on any other pair always gives the same result, except for sign. We define the tensor R_{ik} as

$$R_{ik}=g^{lm}R_{limk}=R^l_{ilk}. \tag{92.10}$$

According to (91.4), we have:

$$R_{ik}=\frac{\partial\Gamma^l_{ik}}{\partial x^l}-\frac{\partial\Gamma^l_{il}}{\partial x^k}+\Gamma^l_{ik}\Gamma^m_{lm}-\Gamma^m_{il}\Gamma^l_{km}, \tag{92.11}$$

or, by using (86.5),

$$R_{ik}=\frac{1}{\sqrt{-g}}\frac{\partial}{\partial x^l}\left(\Gamma^l_{ik}\sqrt{-g}\right)-\frac{\partial^2}{\partial x^i\,\partial x^k}\ln\sqrt{-g}-\Gamma^m_{il}\Gamma^l_{km}. \tag{92.11a}$$

This tensor is clearly symmetric:

$$R_{ik}=R_{ki}. \tag{92.12}$$

Finally, contracting R_{ik}, we obtain the invariant

$$R=g^{ik}R_{ik}=g^{il}g^{km}R_{iklm}, \tag{92.13}$$

which is called the *scalar curvature* of the space.

Because of the relations (92.5)–(92.8), not all the components of the curvature tensor are independent. Let us determine the number of independent components of the tensor R_{iklm}.

We consider first the case of a space with two dimensions ,i.e., an ordinary surface; then the indices i, k, l, m, can have the values 1, 2. Components in which i and k, or l and m, are simultaneously 1 or 2 are zero. All the nonzero components are either equal to one another or differ in sign; thus the curvature tensor in this case has only one independent component, for example R_{1212}. It is easy to show that the scalar curvature $R=g^{il}g^{km}R_{iklm}$ in this case is equal to

$$R=2R_{1212}/g$$

(g is the determinant formed from the g_{ik}). $R/2$ turns out to be equal to the familiar *Gaussian curvature* of the surface, that is, the reciprocal of the product of the principal radii of curvature.

Now we determine the number of independent components of the curvature tensor in three-dimensional space. Let us consider those components in which there are only two different indices, that is, components of the form R_{abab}. A pair of values for a and b can be chosen from the values 1, 2, 3, in three ways. Because of the relations (92.5)–(92.7), each pair a and b gives only one independent component; thus there are altogether three components of this type. There are also altogether three components with three different indices, that is, components of the form R_{abac}: R_{1213}, R_{2123}, R_{3231}; all others are either equal to these or differ from them only in sign. Thus in three-dimensional space, the curvature tensor has six independent components. The symmetric tensor R_{ik} has this same number of components. Therefore, from the linear relations $R_{ik} = g^{ml}R_{limk}$, all the components of the tensor R_{iklm} can be expressed in terms of the R_{ik} and the metric tensor g_{ik}. (See problem 2.) If we choose a coordinate system which is cartesian at a given point, then by a suitable rotation we can bring the tensor R_{ik} to principal axes.† Thus in a three-dimensional space, the curvature at each point is determined by a triplet of values.

Finally we go to four-dimensional space. There are altogether six components of the curvature tensor with two different indices (i.e., of the form R_{abab}); the indices a and b can be chosen from the values 0, 1, 2, 3, in six ways, and each pair gives one independent component. There are 12 components with three indices different: three different indices can be chosen from 0, 1, 2, 3, in four ways, and each triplet of values gives three independent components (e.g., R_{1213}, R_{2123}, R_{3132}). Finally, there are three components in which all four indices are different: R_{1230}, R_{1023}, R_{1302}; the others are equal to these or differ only in sign. But of these three components, only two are independent, since the three are related to each other by the identity (92.8) $R_{1230}+R_{1023}+R_{1302} = 0$. Thus, in four-dimensional space the curvature tensor has altogether 20 independent components. Choosing a coordinate system which is cartesian at a given point, and considering transformations which rotate this cartesian system (so that the values of the g_{ik} do not change at the point under consideration) we can arrange that six components of the curvature tensor become zero. (Six is the number of possible independent rotations of a four-dimensional coordinate system.) Thus the curvature of a four-dimensional space at each point is given by 14 quantities.

---

† We note that for t actual determination of the principal values of the tensor R_{ik} there is no need to transform to a coordinate system which is cartesian at the given point. These values can be found by determining the roots λ of the equation $|R_{ik}-\lambda g_{ik}| = 0$.

Problems

1. Calculate the components of the tensors R_{iklm} and R_{ik} for a metric in which $g_{ik}=0$ for $i\neq k$ (B. K. Harrison, 1960).

Solution. We represent the nonzero components of the metric tensor in the form

$$g_{ii}=e_i e^{2F_i}, \quad e_0=-1, \quad e_\alpha=1.$$

The calculation according to formula (92.4) gives the following expressions for the nonzero components of the curvature tensor:

$$R_{lilk}=e_l e^{2F_l}[F_{l,k}F_{k,i}+F_{i,k}F_{l,i}-F_{l,i}F_{l,k}-F_{l,i,k}], \quad i\neq k\neq l;$$

$$R_{lili}=e_l e^{2F_l}(F_{i,i}F_{l,i}-F_{l,i}^2-F_{l,i,i})+e_i e^{2F_i}(F_{l,l}F_{i,l}-F_{i,l}^2-F_{i,l,l})-$$
$$-e_l e^{2F_l}\sum_{m\neq i,l} e_i e_m e^{2(F_i-F_m)}F_{i,m}F_{l,m}, \quad i\neq l$$

(no summation over repeated indices!). The subscripts preceded by a comma denote ordinary differentiation with respect to the corresponding coordinate.

Contracting the curvature tensor on two indices, we obtain:

$$R_{ik}=\sum_{l\neq i,k}(F_{l,k}F_{k,i}+F_{i,k}F_{l,i}-F_{l,i}F_{l,k}-F_{l,i,k}), \quad i\neq k;$$

$$R_{ii}=\sum_{l\neq i}[F_{i,i}F_{l,i}-F_{l,i}^2-F_{l,i,i}+$$
$$+e_i e_l e^{2(F_i-F_l)}(F_{l,l}F_{i,l}-F_{i,l}^2-F_{i,l,l}-F_{i,l}\sum_{m\neq i,l}F_{m,l})].$$

2. Express the fourth-rank curvature tensor $P_{\alpha\beta\gamma\delta}$ of three-dimensional space in terms of the second-rank tensor $P_{\alpha\beta}$.

Solution: We look for $P_{\alpha\beta\gamma\delta}$ in the form

$$P_{\alpha\beta\gamma\delta}=A_{\alpha\gamma}\gamma_{\beta\delta}-A_{\alpha\delta}\gamma_{\beta\gamma}+A_{\beta\delta}\gamma_{\alpha\gamma}-A_{\beta\gamma}\gamma_{\alpha\delta},$$

which satisfies the symmetry conditions; here $A_{\alpha\beta}$ is some symmetric tensor whose relation tp $P_{\alpha\beta}$ is determined by contracting the expression we have written on the indices α and γ We thus find:

$$P_{\alpha\beta}=A\gamma_{\alpha\beta}+A_{\alpha\beta}, \quad A_{\alpha\beta}=P_{\alpha\beta}-\tfrac{1}{4}P\gamma_{\alpha\beta},$$

and finally,

$$P_{\alpha\beta\gamma\delta}=P_{\alpha\gamma}\gamma_{\beta\delta}-P_{\alpha\delta}\gamma_{\beta\gamma}+P_{\beta\delta}\gamma_{\alpha\gamma}-P_{\beta\gamma}\gamma_{\alpha\delta}+\frac{P}{2}(\gamma_{\alpha\delta}\gamma_{\beta\gamma}-\gamma_{\alpha\gamma}\gamma_{\beta\delta}).$$

3. Consider the possible types of canonical forms for the curvature tensor (A. Z. Petrov, 1954).†

Solution. We shall assume in the following that the metric is reduced to galilean form in the given point of the 4-space, so that we have to deal with the pseudo-euclidean metric. We represent the set of 20 independent components of the tensor R_{iklm} as a set of components of three three-dimensional tensors defined as follows: a symmetric tensor $A_{\alpha\beta}$ with components

$$A_{11}=R_{0101}, \quad A_{12}=R_{0102}, \quad A_{22}=R_{0202},\ldots, \qquad (1)$$

† It is to be emphazised that this classification has a local charakter: tha curvature tensor in different points of the 4-space in the same gravitational field can refer to different types.

a symmetric tensor $C_{\alpha\beta}$, in which the indices 1, 2, 3 correspond to the pairs of indices 23, 31, 12 of the antisymmetric tensor R_{iklm}:

$$C_{11} = R_{2323}, \quad C_{22} = R_{3131}, \quad C_{33} = R_{1212}, \quad C_{12} = R_{2331}, \ldots, \tag{2}$$

and an asymmetric tensor $B_{\alpha\beta}$ with components

$$B_{11} = R_{0123}, \quad B_{22} = R_{0231}, \quad B_{12} = R_{0131}, \quad B_{21} = R_{0223}, \ldots, \tag{3}$$

in which

$$B_{11}+B_{22}+B_{33} = 0 \tag{4}$$

[by virtue of the symmetry property (92.8)].

We shall assume that the tensor R_{iklm} satisfies the conditions $R_{km} = g^{il} R_{iklm} = 0$ [the conditions which are satisfied by the curvature tensor of the gravitational field in vacuum, cf. (95.9)].†

It is easy to see that these conditions are equivalent to the following relations between the components of the three-dimensional tensors which we have introduced:‡

$$A_{\alpha\alpha} = 0, \quad B_{\alpha\beta} = B_{\beta\alpha}, \quad A_{\alpha\beta} = -C_{\alpha\beta} \tag{5}$$

(since the three-dimensional metric is Euclidean, there is no need to distinguish between subscripts and superscripts in the summations).

Furthermore we introduce the symmetric complex tensor

$$D_{\alpha\beta} = \tfrac{1}{2}(A_{\alpha\beta}+2i B_{\alpha\beta}-C_{\alpha\beta}) = A_{\alpha\beta}+iB_{\alpha\beta}. \tag{6}$$

This joining of the two real three-dimensional tensors $A_{\alpha\beta}$ and $B_{\alpha\beta}$ into a single complex tensor corresponds precisely to the procedure in § 25 where we combined the two vectors **E** and **H** into the complex vector **F**, and the resulting relation between $D_{\alpha\beta}$ and the four-tensor R_{iklm} corresponds to the relation between **F** and the four-tensor F_{ik}. From this it follows that four-dimensional transformations (Lorentz transformations) of the tensor R_{iklm} are equivalent to three-dimensional complex rotations applied to the tensor $D_{\alpha\beta}$.

With respect to these rotations we can define eigenvalues $\lambda = \lambda' + i\lambda''$ and eigenvectors n_α (complex, in general) as solutions of the system of equations

$$D_{\alpha\beta} n_\beta = \lambda n_\alpha. \tag{7}$$

The quantities λ are invariants of the curvature tensor. Since the trace $D_{\alpha\alpha} = 0$, the sum of the three roots of Eq. (7) is also equal to zero: $\lambda_1+\lambda_2+\lambda_3 = 0$.

Depending on the number of independent eigenvectors n_α, we arrive at the following classification of the possible cases of reduction of the tensor R_{iklm} to canonical form.

(a) There are three independent eigenvectors. Their squares $n_\beta n^\beta$ are different from zero; by a suitable rotation we can bring the tensor $D_{\alpha\beta}$, and with it $A_{\alpha\beta}$ and $B_{\alpha\beta}$, to diagonal form:

$$A_{\alpha\beta} = \begin{pmatrix} \lambda_1' & 0 & 0 \\ 0 & \lambda_2' & 0 \\ 0 & 0 & -\lambda_1'-\lambda_2' \end{pmatrix}, \quad B_{\alpha\beta} = \begin{pmatrix} \lambda_1'' & 0 & 0 \\ 0 & \lambda_2'' & 0 \\ 0 & 0 & -\lambda_1''-\lambda_2'' \end{pmatrix} \tag{8}$$

In this case the curvature tensor has four independent invariants $\lambda_1', \lambda_2', \lambda_1'', \lambda_2''$.

(b) There are two independent eigenvectors. The square of one of them is then equal to zero, so that it cannot be chosen as the direction of one of the coordinate axes. However one can take it to lie in the x_1, x_2 plane; then $n_2 = i n_1$, $n_3 = 0$. The corresponding Eq. (7) give $D_{11}+i D_{12}=\lambda$, $D_{22} - i D_{12} = \lambda$, so that $D_{11} = \lambda - i\mu$, $D_{22} = \lambda+i\mu$, $D_{12} = \mu$.

† If this is not the case, then all the following results will apply to the tensor

$$R_{iklm}-\tfrac{1}{2}R_{il}g_{km}+\tfrac{1}{2}R_{im}g_{kl}+\tfrac{1}{2}R_{kl}g_{im}-\tfrac{1}{2}R_{km}g_{il}+\tfrac{1}{6}R(g_{il}g_{km}-g_{im}g_{kl}),$$

for which the analogous conditions are fulfilled.

‡ We are assuming that the metric tensor has been brought to Galilean form at the particular point in four-space.

The complex quantity $\lambda = \lambda' + i\lambda''$ is a scalar and cannot be changed. But the quantity μ can be given any nonzero value by a suitable complex rotation, so we can, without loss of generality, assume that it is real. As a result we get the following canonical type:

$$A_{\alpha\beta} = \begin{pmatrix} \lambda' & \mu & 0 \\ \mu & \lambda' & 0 \\ 0 & 0 & -2\lambda' \end{pmatrix}, \quad B_{\alpha\beta} = \begin{pmatrix} \lambda''-\mu & 0 & 0 \\ 0 & \lambda''+\mu & 0 \\ 0 & 0 & -2\lambda'' \end{pmatrix} \tag{9}$$

In this case there are two invariants λ' and λ''.

(c) There is just one eigenvector, and its square is equal to zero. All the eigenvalues λ are then identical and consequently equal to zero. The solutions of Eqs. (7) can be brought to the form $D_{11} = D_{22} = D_{12} = 0$, $D_{13} = \mu$, $D_{23} = i\mu$, so that

$$A_{\alpha\beta} = \begin{pmatrix} 0 & 0 & \mu \\ 0 & 0 & 0 \\ \mu & 0 & 0 \end{pmatrix}, \quad B_{\alpha\beta} = \begin{pmatrix} 0 & 0 & 0 \\ 0 & 0 & \mu \\ 0 & \mu & 0 \end{pmatrix} \tag{10}$$

In this case the curvature tensor has no invariants at all, and we have a peculiar situation: the four-space is curved, but there are no invariants which could be used as a measure of its curvature. [The same situation occurs in the case of (9) with $\lambda' = \lambda'' = 0$.]

§ 93. The action function for the gravitational field

To arrive at the equations determining the gravitational field, it is necessary first to determine the action S_g for this field. The required equations can then be obtained by varying the sum of the actions of field plus material particles.

Just as for the electromagnetic field, the action S_g must be expressed in terms of a scalar integral $\int G\sqrt{-g}\,d\Omega$, taken over all space and over the time coördinate x^0 between two given values. To determine this scalar we shall start from the fact that the equations of the gravitational field must contain derivatives of the "potential" no higher than the second (just as is the case for the electromagnetic field). Since the field equations are obtained by varying the action, then it is necessary that the integrand G contain derivatives of g_{ik} no higher than first order; thus G must contain only the tensor g_{ik} and the quantities Γ^i_{kl}.

However, it is impossible to construct an invariant from the quantities g_{ik} and Γ^i_{kl} alone. This is immediately clear from the fact that by a suitable choice of coordinate system we can always make all the quantities Γ^i_{kl} zero at a given point. There is, however, the scalar R (the curvature of the four-space), which though it contains in addition to the g_{ik} and its first derivatives also the second derivatives of g_{ik}, is linear in the second derivatives. Because of this linearity, the invariant integral $\int R\sqrt{-g}\,d\Omega$ can be transformed by means of Gauss' theorem to the integral of an expression not containing the second derivatives. Namely, $\int R\sqrt{-g}\,d\Omega$ can be presented in the form

$$\int R\sqrt{-g}\,d\Omega = \int G\sqrt{-g}\,d\Omega + \int \frac{\partial(\sqrt{-g}\,w^i)}{\partial x^i}\,d\Omega,$$

where G contains only the tensor g_{ik} and its first derivatives, and the integrand of the second integral has the form of a divergence of a certain quantity w^i (the detailed calculation is given at the end of this section). According to Gauss' theorem, this second integral can be transformed into an integral over a hypersurface surrounding the four-volume over which the integration is carried out in the other two integrals. When we vary the action, the variation of the second term on the right vanishes, since in the principle of least action, the variations of the field at the limits of the region of integration are zero. Consequently, we may write

$$\delta \int R\sqrt{-g}\, d\Omega = \delta \int G\sqrt{-g}\, d\Omega.$$

The left side is a scalar; therefore the expression on the right is also a scalar (the quantity G itself is, of course, not a scalar).

The quantity G satisfies the condition imposed above, since it contains only the g_{ik} and its first derivatives. Thus we may write

$$\delta S_g = \frac{c^3}{16\pi k}\delta \int G\sqrt{-g}\, d\Omega = \frac{c^3}{16\pi k}\delta \int R\sqrt{-g}\, d\Omega, \qquad (93.1)$$

where k is a new universal constant. Just as was done for the action of the electromagnetic field in § 27, we can see that the constant k must be positive (see the end of this section).

The constant k is called the *gravitational constant*. The dimensions of k follow from (93.1). The action has dimensions gm-cm^2-sec^{-1}; all the coordinates have the dimensions cm, the g_{ik} are dimensionless, and so R has dimensions cm^{-2}. As a result, we find that k has the dimensions cm^3-gm^{-1}-sec^{-2}. Its numerical value is

$$k = 6.67\times 10^{-8}\ \text{cm}^3\text{-gm}^{-1}\text{-sec}^{-2}. \qquad (93.2)$$

We note that we could have set k equal to unity (or any other dimensionless constant). However, this would fix the unit of mass.†

Finally, let us calculate the quantity G of (93.1). From the expression (92.11) for R_{ik}, we have

$$\sqrt{-g}\, R = \sqrt{-g}\, g^{ik} R_{ik} = \sqrt{-g}\left\{g^{ik}\frac{\partial \Gamma^l_{ik}}{\partial x^l} - g^{ik}\frac{\partial \Gamma^l_{il}}{\partial x^k} + g^{ik}\Gamma^l_{ik}\Gamma^m_{lm} - g^{ik}\Gamma^m_{il}\Gamma^l_{km}\right\}.$$

In the first two terms on the right, we have

$$\sqrt{-g}\, g^{ik}\frac{\partial \Gamma^l_{ik}}{\partial x^l} = \frac{\partial}{\partial x^l}(\sqrt{-g}\, g^{ik}\Gamma^l_{ik}) - \Gamma^l_{ik}\frac{\partial}{\partial x^l}(\sqrt{-g}\, g^{ik}),$$

$$\sqrt{-g}\, g^{ik}\frac{\partial \Gamma^l_{il}}{\partial x^k} = \frac{\partial}{\partial x^k}(\sqrt{-g}\, g^{ik}\Gamma^l_{il}) - \Gamma^l_{il}\frac{\partial}{\partial x^k}(\sqrt{-g}\, g^{ik}).$$

† If one sets $k = c^2$, the mass is measured in cm, where 1 cm $= 1.35\times 10^{28}$ gm. Sometimes one uses in place of k the quantity

$$\varkappa = \frac{8\pi k}{c^2} = 1.86\times 10^{-27}\ \text{cm gm}^{-1},$$

which is called the Einstein gravitational constant.

Dropping the total derivatives, we find

$$\sqrt{-g}\,G = \Gamma^m_{im}\frac{\partial}{\partial x^k}(\sqrt{-g}\,g^{ik}) - \Gamma^l_{ik}\frac{\partial}{\partial x^l}(\sqrt{-g}\,g^{ik}) - (\Gamma^m_{il}\Gamma^l_{km} - \Gamma^l_{ik}\Gamma^m_{lm})g^{ik}\sqrt{-g}.$$

With the aid of formulas (86.5)–(86.8), we find that the first two terms on the right are equal to $\sqrt{-g}$ multiplied by

$$2\Gamma^l_{ik}\Gamma^i_{lm}g^{mk} - \Gamma^m_{im}\Gamma^i_{kl}g^{kl} - \Gamma^l_{ik}\Gamma^m_{lm}g^{ik} = g^{ik}(2\Gamma^l_{mk}\Gamma^m_{li} - \Gamma^m_{lm}\Gamma^l_{ik} - \Gamma^l_{ik}\Gamma^m_{lm})$$
$$= 2g^{ik}(\Gamma^m_{il}\Gamma^l_{km} - \Gamma^l_{ik}\Gamma^m_{lm}).$$

Finally, we have

$$G = g^{ik}(\Gamma^m_{il}\Gamma^l_{km} - \Gamma^l_{ik}\Gamma^m_{lm}). \tag{93.3}$$

The components of the metric tensor are the quantities which determine the gravitational field. Therefore in the principle of least action for the gravitational field it is the quantities g_{ik} which are subjected to variation. However, it is necessary here to make the following fundamental reservation. Namely, we cannot claim now that in an actually realizable field the action integral has a minimum (and not just an extremum) with respect to *all* possible variations of the g_{ik}. This is related to the fact that not every change in the g_{ik} is associated with a change in the space-time metric, i.e., with a real change in the gravitational field. The components g_{ik} also change under a simple transformation of coordinates connected merely with the shift from one system to another in one and the same space-time. Each such coordinate transformation is generally an aggregate of four independent transformations. In order to exclude such changes in g_{ik} which are not associated with a change in the metric, we can impose four auxiliary conditions and require the fulfillment of these conditions under the variation. Thus, when the principle of least action is applied to a gravitational field, we can assert only that we can impose auxiliary conditions on the g_{ik}, such that when they are fulfilled the action has a minimum with respect to variations of the g_{ik}.†

Keeping these remarks in mind, we now show that the gravitational constant must be positive. As the four auxiliary conditions mentioned, we use the vanishing of the three components $g_{0\alpha}$, and the constancy of the determinant $|g_{\alpha\beta}|$ made up from the components of $g_{\alpha\beta}$:

$$g_{0\alpha} = 0, \quad |g_{\alpha\beta}| = \text{const};$$

from the last of these conditions we have

$$g^{\alpha\beta}\frac{\partial g_{\alpha\beta}}{\partial x^\gamma} = \frac{\partial}{\partial x^\gamma}|g_{\alpha\beta}| = 0.$$

† We must emphasize, however, that everything we have said has no effect on the derivation of the field equations from the principle of least action (§ 95). These equations are already obtained as a result of the requirement that the action be an extremum (i.e., vanishing of the first derivative), and not definitely a minimum. Therefore in deriving them we can vary all of the g_{ik} independently.

We are here interested in those terms in the integrand of the expression for the action which contain derivatives of g_{ik} with respect to x^0 (cf. p. 77). A simple calculation using (93.3) shows that these terms in G are

$$\frac{1}{4}g^{\alpha\beta}g^{\gamma\delta}\frac{\partial g_{\alpha\gamma}}{\partial x^0}\frac{\partial g_{\beta\delta}}{\partial x^0}.$$

It is easy to see that this quantity is essentially positive. Namely, choosing a spatial system of coordinates which is cartesian at a given point at a given moment of time (so that $g_{\alpha\beta} = g^{\alpha\beta} = \delta_{\alpha\beta}$), we obtain $\frac{1}{4}(\partial g_{\alpha\beta}/\partial x^0)^2$, i.e., a sum of squares.

By a sufficiently rapid change of the components $g_{\alpha\beta}$ with the time x^0 (within the time interval between the limits of integration of x^0) the quantity G can consequently be made as large as one likes. If the constant k were negative, the action would then decrease without limit (taking on negative values of arbitrarily large absolute magnitude), that is, there could be no minimum.

§ 94. The energy-momentum tensor

In § 32 the general rule was given for calculating the energy-momentum tensor of any physical system whose action is given in the form of an integral (32.1) over four-space. In curvilinear coordinates this integral must be written in the form

$$S = \frac{1}{c}\int \Lambda\sqrt{-g}\,d\Omega \tag{94.1}$$

(in Galilean coordinates $g = -1$, and S goes over into $\int \Lambda\,dV\,dt$). The integration extends over all the three-dimensional space and over the time between two given moments, i.e., over the infinite region of four-space contained between two hypersurfaces.

As already discussed in § 32, the energy-momentum tensor, calculated from the formula (32.5), is generally not symmetric, as it should be. In order to symmetrize it, we had to add to (32.5) suitable terms of the form $\frac{\partial}{\partial x^l}\psi_{ikl}$, where ψ_{ikl} was antisymmetric in the indices k and l. We shall now give another method of calculating the energy-momentum tensor which has the advantage of leading at once to the correct expression.

In (94.1) we carry out a transformation from the coordinates x^i to the coordinates $x'^i = x^i+\xi^i$, where the ξ^i are small quantities. Under this transformation the g^{ik} are transformed according to the formulas:

$$g'^{ik}(x'^l) = g^{lm}(x^l)\frac{\partial x'^i}{\partial x^l}\frac{\partial x'^k}{\partial x^m} = g^{lm}\left(\delta^i_l+\frac{\partial\xi^i}{\partial x^l}\right)\left(\delta^k_m+\frac{\partial\xi^k}{\partial x^m}\right)$$

$$\approx g^{ik}(x^l)+g^{im}\frac{\partial\xi^k}{\partial x^m}+g^{kl}\frac{\partial\xi^i}{\partial x^l}.$$

Here the tensor g'^{ik} is a function of the x'^l, while the tensor g^{ik} is a function of the original coordinates x^l. In order to present all terms as functions of one and the same variables, we expand $g'^{ik}(x^l+\xi^l)$ in powers of ξ^l. Furthermore, if we neglect terms of higher order in ξ^l, we can in all terms containing ξ^l, replace g'^{ik} by g^{ik}. Thus we find

$$g'^{ik}(x^l) = g^{ik}(x^l) - \xi^l \frac{\partial g^{ik}}{\partial x^l} + g^{il}\frac{\partial \xi^k}{\partial x^l} + g^{kl}\frac{\partial \xi^i}{\partial x^l}.$$

It is easy to verify by direct trial that the last three terms on the right can be written as a sum $\xi^{i;k}+\xi^{k;i}$ of contravariant derivatives of the ξ^i. Thus we finally obtain the transformation of the g^{ik} in the form

$$g'^{ik} = g^{ik}+\delta g^{ik}, \qquad \delta g^{ik} = \xi^{i;k}+\xi^{k;i}. \tag{94.2}$$

For the covariant components, we have:

$$g'_{ik} = g_{ik}+\delta g_{ik}, \qquad \delta g_{ik} = -\xi_{i;k}-\xi_{k;i} \tag{94.3}$$

(so that, to terms of first order we satisfy the condition $g'_{il}g'^{kl} = \delta_i^k$).

Since the action S is a scalar, it does not change under a transformation of coordinates. On the other hand, the change δS in the action under a transformation of coordinates can be written in the following form. As in § 32, let q denote the quantities defining the physical system to which the action S applies. Under coordinate transformation the quantities q change by δq. In calculating δS we need not write terms containing the changes in q. All such terms must cancel each other by virtue of the "equations of motion" of the physical system, since these equations are obtained by equating to zero the variation of S with respect to the quantities q. Therefore it is sufficient to write the terms associated with changes in the g_{ik}. Using Gauss' theorem, and setting $\delta g^{ik}=0$ at the integration limits, we find δS in the form†

$$\delta S = \frac{1}{c}\int\left\{\frac{\partial\sqrt{-g}\Lambda}{\partial g^{ik}}\delta g^{ik} + \frac{\partial\sqrt{-g}\Lambda}{\partial\frac{\partial g^{ik}}{\partial x^l}}\delta\frac{\partial g^{ik}}{\partial x^l}\right\}d\Omega$$

$$= \frac{1}{c}\int\left\{\frac{\partial\sqrt{-g}\Lambda}{\partial g^{ik}} - \frac{\partial}{\partial x^l}\frac{\partial\sqrt{-g}\Lambda}{\partial\frac{\partial g^{ik}}{\partial x^l}}\right\}\delta g^{ik}\,d\Omega.$$

† It is necessary to note that the notation of differentiation with respect to the components of the symmetric tensor g_{ik}, which we introduce here, has in a certain sense a symbolic character. Namely, the derivative $\partial F/\partial g^{ik}$ (F is some function of the g_{ik}) actually has a meaning only as the expression of the fact that $dF = \frac{\partial F}{\partial g^{ik}}dg_{ik}$. But in the sum $\frac{\partial F}{\partial g^{ik}}dg_{ik}$, the terms with differentials dg_{ik}, of components of the symmetric tensor with $i\neq k$, appear twice. Therefore in differentiating the actual expression for F with respect to any definite component g_{ik} with $i\neq k$, we would obtain a value which is twice as large as that which we denote by $\partial F/\partial g^{ik}$. This remark must be kept in mind if we assign definite values to the indices i,k, in formulas in which the derivatives with respect to g_{ik} appear.

Here we introduce the notation

$$\frac{1}{2}\sqrt{-g}\,T_{ik} = \frac{\partial}{\partial x^l}\frac{\partial\sqrt{-g}\,\Lambda}{\partial\dfrac{\partial g^{ik}}{\partial x^l}} - \frac{\partial\sqrt{-g}\,\Lambda}{\partial g^{ik}}. \tag{94.4}$$

Then δS takes the form†

$$\delta S = -\frac{1}{2c}\int T_{ik}\,\delta g^{ik}\sqrt{-g}\,d\Omega = \frac{1}{2c}\int T^{ik}\delta g_{ik}\sqrt{-g}\,d\Omega \tag{94.5}$$

(note that $g^{ik}\,\delta g_{lk} = -g_{lk}\,\delta g^{ik}$, and therefore $T^{ik}\,\delta g_{ik} = -T_{ik}\,\delta g^{ik}$). Substituting for δg^{ik} the expression (94.2), we have, making use of the symmetry of the tensor T_{ik},

$$\delta S = -\frac{1}{2c}\int T_{ik}(\xi^{i;k}+\xi^{k;i})\sqrt{-g}\,d\Omega = -\frac{1}{c}\int T_{ik}\xi^{i;k}\sqrt{-g}\,d\Omega.$$

Furthermore, we transform this expression in the following way:

$$\delta S = -\frac{1}{c}\int (T_i^k\xi^i)_{;k}\sqrt{-g}\,d\Omega + \frac{1}{c}\int T^k_{i;k}\xi^i\sqrt{-g}\,d\Omega. \tag{94.6}$$

Using (86.9), the first integral can be written in the form

$$-\frac{1}{c}\int\frac{\partial}{\partial x^k}(\sqrt{-g}\,T_i^k\xi^i)\,d\Omega,$$

and transformed into an integral over a hypersurface. Since the ξ^i vanish at the limits of integration, this integral drops out.

Thus, equating δS to zero, we find

$$\delta S = \frac{1}{c}\int T^k_{i;k}\xi^i\sqrt{-g}\,d\Omega = 0.$$

Because of the arbitrariness of the ξ^i it then follows that

$$T^k_{i;k} = 0. \tag{94.7}$$

Comparing this with equation (32.4) $\partial T_{ik}/\partial x^k = 0$, valid in Galilean coordinates, we see that the tensor T_{ik}, defined by formula (94.4), must be identical with the energy-momentum tensor — at least to within a constant factor. It is easy to verify, carrying out, for example, the calculation from formula (94.4) for the electromagnetic field $\left(\Lambda = -\frac{1}{16\pi}F_{ik}F^{ik} = -\frac{1}{16\pi}F_{ik}F_{lm}g^{il}g^{km}\right)$, that this factor is equal to unity, that is, that T_{ik} from (94.4) is exactly the energy-momentum tensor.

† We call attention to the fact that in the case we are considering, the ten quantities δg_{ik} are not independent, since they are the result of a transformation of the coordinates. of which there are only four. Therefore from the vanishing of δS it does not follow that $T_{ik} = 0$.

Thus, formula (94.4) enables us to calculate the energy-momentum tensor by differentiating the function Λ with respect to the components of the metric tensor (and their derivatives). The tensor T_{ik} obtained in this way is symmetric. Formula (94.4) is convenient for calculating the energy-momentum tensor not only in the case of the presence of a gravitational field, but also in its absence, in which case the metric tensor has no independent significance and the transition to curvilinear coordinates occurs formally as an intermediary step in the calculation of T_{ik}.

The expression (33.1) for the energy-momentum tensor of the electromagnetic field must be written in curvilinear coordinates in the form

$$T_{ik} = \frac{1}{4\pi}\left(F_{il}F_k{}^l - \frac{1}{4}F_{lm}F^{lm}g_{ik}\right), \tag{94.8}$$

or, for the components of the mixed tensor,

$$T_i^k = \frac{1}{4\pi}\left(F_{il}F^{kl} - \frac{1}{4}F_{lm}F^{lm}\delta_i^k\right).$$

Similarly, the covariant components of the energy-momentum tensor of a macroscopic body (35.2) are

$$T_{ik} = (p+\epsilon)u_i u_k + p g_{ik}, \tag{94.9}$$

and the mixed components

$$T_i^k = (p+\epsilon)u_i u^k + p\delta_i^k.$$

We note that the quantity T_{00} is always positive:†

$$T_{00} \geqslant 0. \tag{94.10}$$

No general statement can be made about the mixed component T_0^0.

§ 95. The gravitational field equations

We can now proceed to the derivation of the equations of the gravitational field. These equations are obtained from the principle of least action $\delta(S_m+S_g) = 0$, where S_g and S_m are the actions of the gravitational field and matter respectively. We now subject the gravitational field, that is, the quantities g_{ik}, to variation.

---

† We have $T_{00}=\epsilon u_0^2+p(u_0^2+g_{00})$. The first term is always positive. In the second term we write $u_0 = g_{00}u^0+g_{0\alpha}u^\alpha = \frac{g_{00}dx^0+g_{0\alpha}dx^\alpha}{ds}$ and obtain after a simple transformation $-g_{00}p\left(\frac{dl}{ds}\right)^2$, where dl is the element of spatial distance (94.8); from this it is clear that the second term of T_{00} is also positive. The same result can also be shown for the tensor (94.8).

Calculating the variation δS_g, we have

$$\delta\int R\sqrt{-g}\,d\Omega = \delta\int g^{ik}R_{ik}\sqrt{-g}\,d\Omega$$
$$= \int\{R_{ik}\sqrt{-g}\,\delta g^{ik}+R_{ik}g^{ik}\delta\sqrt{-g}+g^{ik}\sqrt{-g}\,\delta R_{ik}\}\,d\Omega.$$

From formula (86.4), we have

$$\delta\sqrt{-g} = -\frac{1}{2\sqrt{-g}}\,\delta g = -\frac{1}{2}\sqrt{-g}\,g_{ik}\delta g^{ik};$$

substituting this, we find

$$\delta\int R\sqrt{-g}\,d\Omega = \int(R_{ik}-\tfrac{1}{2}g_{ik}R)\delta g^{ik}\sqrt{-g}\,d\Omega+\int g^{ik}\,\delta R_{ik}\sqrt{-g}\,d\Omega. \quad (95.1)$$

For the calculation of δR_{ik} we note that although the quantities Γ^i_{kl} do not constitute a tensor, their variations $\delta\Gamma^i_{kl}$ do form a tensor, for $\Gamma^k_{il}A_k\,dx^l$ is the change in a vector under parallel displacement [see (85.5)] from some point P to an infinitesimally separated point P'. Therefore $\delta\Gamma^k_{il}A_k\,dx^l$ is the difference between the two vectors, obtained as the result of two parallel displacements (one with the unvaried, the other with the varied Γ^i_{kl}) from the point P to one and the same point P'. The difference between two vectors at the same point is a vector, and therefore $\delta\Gamma^i_{kl}$ is a tensor.

Let us use a system of coordinates which is inertial at a given point. Then at that point all the $\Gamma^i_{kl}=0$. With the help of expression (92.11) for the R_{ik}, we have (remembering that the first derivatives of the g^{ik} are now equal to zero)

$$g^{ik}\delta R_{ik} = g^{ik}\left\{\frac{\partial}{\partial x^l}\,\delta\Gamma^l_{ik}-\frac{\partial}{\partial x^k}\,\delta\Gamma^l_{il}\right\} = g^{ik}\frac{\partial}{\partial x^l}\,\delta\Gamma^l_{ik}-g^{il}\frac{\partial}{\partial x^l}\,\delta\Gamma^k_{ik} = \frac{\partial w^l}{\partial x^l},$$

where

$$w^l = g^{ik}\delta\Gamma^l_{ik}-g^{il}\delta\Gamma^k_{ik}.$$

Since w^l is a vector, we may write the relation we have obtained, in an arbitrary coordinate system, in the form

$$g^{ik}\delta R_{ik} = \frac{1}{\sqrt{-g}}\frac{\partial}{\partial x^l}(\sqrt{-g}\,w^l)$$

[replacing $\partial w^l/\partial x^l$ by $w^l_{\ ;l}$ and using (86.9)]. Consequently the second integral on the right side of (95.1) is equal to

$$\int g^{ik}\delta R_{ik}\sqrt{-g}\,d\Omega = \int\frac{\partial(\sqrt{-g}\,w^l)}{\partial x^l}\,d\Omega,$$

and by Gauss' theorem can be transformed into an integral of w^l over the hypersurface surrounding the whole four-volume. Since the variations of the field are zero at the integration limits, this term drops out. Thus, the variation δS_g is equal to †

$$\delta S_g = \frac{c^3}{16\pi k} \int \left(R_{ik} - \frac{1}{2} g_{ik} R \right) \delta g^{ik} \sqrt{-g}\, \delta\Omega. \tag{95.2}$$

We note that if we had started from the expression

$$S_g = \frac{c^3}{16\pi k} \int G \sqrt{-g}\, d\Omega$$

for the action of the field, then we would have obtained

$$\delta S_g = \frac{c^3}{16\pi k} \int \left\{ \frac{\partial (G\sqrt{-g})}{\partial g^{ik}} - \frac{\partial}{\partial x^l} \frac{\partial (G\sqrt{-g})}{\partial \frac{\partial g^{ik}}{\partial x^l}} \right\} \delta g^{ik}\, d\Omega.$$

Comparing this with (95.2), we find the following relation:

$$R_{ik} - \frac{1}{2} g_{ik} R = \frac{1}{\sqrt{-g}} \left\{ \frac{\partial (G\sqrt{-g})}{\partial g^{ik}} - \frac{\partial}{\partial x^l} \frac{\partial (G\sqrt{-g})}{\partial \frac{\partial g^{ik}}{\partial x^l}} \right\}. \tag{95.3}$$

For the variation of the action of the matter we can write immediately from (94.5):

$$\delta S_m = -\frac{1}{2c} \int T_{ik}\, \delta g^{ik} \sqrt{-g}\, d\Omega, \tag{95.4}$$

where T_{ik} is the energy-momentum tensor of the matter (including the electromagnetic field). Gravitational interaction plays a role only for bodies with sufficiently large mass (because of the smallness of the gravitational constant), and therefore in studying the gravitational field we usually have to deal with macroscopic bodies. Corresponding to this we must usually write for T_{ik} the expression (94.9).

Thus, from the principle of least action $\delta S_m + \delta S_g = 0$ we find, using the relations (95.2) and (95.4):

$$\frac{c^3}{16\pi k} \int \left(R_{ik} - \frac{1}{2} g_{ik} R - \frac{8\pi k}{c^4} T_{ik} \right) \delta g^{ik} \sqrt{-g}\, d\Omega = 0,$$

from which, in view of the arbitrariness of the δg^{ik}:

$$R_{ik} - \frac{1}{2} g_{ik} R = \frac{8\pi k}{c^4} T_{ik}, \tag{95.5}$$

---

† We note here the following curious fact. If we calculate the variation $\delta \int R \sqrt{-g}\, d\Omega$ [with R_{ik} from (92.11)], considering the Γ^i_{kl} as independent variables and the g_{ik} as constants, and then use expression (86.3) for the Γ^i_{kl}, we would obtain, as one easily verifies, indentically zero. Conversely, one could determine the relation between the Γ^i_{kl} and the metric tensor by requiring that the variation we have mentioned should vanish.

or, in mixed components,

$$R_i^k - \frac{1}{2}\delta_i^k R = \frac{8\pi k}{c^4} T_i^k. \tag{95.6}$$

This is the required *equation of the gravitational field* — the basic equation of the general theory of relativity.

Contracting (95.6) on the indices i and k, we find

$$R = -\frac{8\pi k}{c^4} T; \tag{95.7}$$

($T = T_i^i$). Therefore the equation of the field can also be written in the form

$$R_{ik} = \frac{8\pi k}{c^4}\left(T_{ik} - \frac{1}{2}g_{ik}T\right). \tag{95.8}$$

Note that the equations of the gravitational field are nonlinear equations. Therefore for gravitational fields the principle of superposition is not valid, contrary to the case for the electromagnetic field in the special theory of relativity.

It is necessary, however, to remember that actually one has usually to deal with weak gravitational fields, for which the equations of the field in first approximation are linear (see the following section). For such fields, in this approximation, the principle of superposition is valid.

In empty space $T_{ik} = 0$, and the equations of the gravitational field reduce to the equation

$$R_{ik} = 0. \tag{95.9}$$

We mention that this does not at all mean that in vacuum, spacetime is flat; for this we would have the stronger conditions $R^i_{klm} = 0$.

The energy-momentum tensor of the electromagnetic field has the property that $T_i^i = 0$ [see (33.2)]. From (95.7), it follows that in the presence of an electromagnetic field without any masses the scalar curvature of spacetime is zero.

As we know, the divergence $T^k_{i;k}$ of the tensor T_i^k is zero (§ 94), therefore the divergence of the left side of equation (95.6) must be zero. It is easy from this to verify the validity of the identity

$$R^k_{i;k} - \frac{1}{2}(\delta_i^k R)_{;k} = R^k_{i;k} - \frac{1}{2}\frac{\partial R}{\partial x^i} = 0. \tag{95.10}$$

It also follows directly from the identity (92.9) on multiplying the latter by $g^{ik}\delta^l_n$.

Thus the equation $T^k_{i;k} = 0$ is essentially contained in the field equations (95.6). On the other hand, the equation $T^k_{i;k} = 0$, expressing the law of conservation of energy and momentum, contains the equation of motion of the physical system to which the energy-momentum tensor under consideration refers (i.e., the equations of motion of the material particles or the second pair of Maxwell equations). Thus the equations of the gravitational field also contain the equations for the matter which produces this field. In contrast to this, the electromagnetic field equations (Maxwell equations) contain only the equation of conservation of the total charge (continuity equation), but not the equations of motion of the charges producing the field.

Therefore in the case of the electromagnetic field, the distribution and motion of the charges can be assigned arbitrarily, provided only that the total charge is constant; the assignment of this charge distribution then determines, through Maxwell's equations, the field produced by the charges. In a gravitational field, the distribution and motion of the matter producing it cannot at all be assigned arbitrarily — on the contrary it must be determined (by solving the field equations for given initial conditions) simultaneously with the field produced by this same matter.

It is however, necessary to note that the equations of the gravitational field do not determine the distribution and motion of the matter completely. Namely, these equations do not contain the equation of state of the material, i.e., the equation which relates its pressure and density. This equation must be given along with the field equations.†

The four coordinates x^i can be subjected to an arbitrary transformation. By means of these transformations we can arbitrarily assign four of the ten components of the tensor g_{ik}. Therefore there are only six independent quantities g_{ik}. Furthermore, the four components of the four-velocity u^i, which appear in the energy-momentum tensor of the matter, are related to one another by $u^i u_i = -1$, so that only three of them are independent. Thus, the ten field equations (95.5) actually determine the ten unknowns, namely, the six components g_{ik}, the three components of u^i, and the density ϵ/c^2 of the matter (or its pressure p).

The equations of gravitation are a system of second order partial differential equations. If we are interested in solving these equations for given initial conditions, then we are faced with the question of how many quantities can be assigned initial spatial distributions.

To answer this question, we must note that the equations (95.5) do not contain the second time derivatives of all ten components g_{ik}. In fact, from expression (92.4) it is immediately clear that second derivatives with respect to the time are contained only in the components $R_{\alpha 0 \beta 0}$ of the curvature tensor,

---

†Actually the equation of state relates to one another not two but three thermodynamic quantities, for example the pressure, density and temperature of the matter. In applications in the theory of gravitation, this point is however not important, since the approximate equations of state used here actually do not depend on the temperature (as, for example, the equation $p = 0$ for rarefied matter, the limiting extreme-relativistic equation $p = \epsilon/3$ for highly compressed matter, etc).

in the form of the term $-\frac{1}{2}\frac{\partial^2 g_{\alpha\beta}}{\partial x_0^2}$; the second derivatives of the components $g_{0\alpha}$ and g_{00} of the metric tensor do not appear at all. It is therefore clear that the tensor R_{ik}, which is obtained by contracting the curvature tensor, and with it equation (95.5), also contains the second time derivatives of only the six spatial components $g_{\alpha\beta}$. Therefore as initial conditions we can assign only the first time derivatives of these six quantities. Adding to these the initial distributions of the 14 quantities which appear in the equations of gravitation (10 components g_{ik}, 3 components u^i and, for example, the density), we get altogether 20 arbitrary functions.

However, among these there are also some functions whose arbitrariness is related simply to the arbitrariness in the choice of the four-dimensional coordinate system. The number of "physically different" functions, which cannot be reduced by any choice of reference system, is much smaller. From physical considerations it is easy to see that there are 8: for the initial conditions, we must assign the distribution of the density of matter and of its three components of velocity, as well as four quantities (see § 101) characterizing the free gravitational field (not coupled to the matter).

Problem

Write the equations for a constant gravitational field.

Solution: We introduce the notation $g_{00} = -h$, $g_{0\alpha} = hg_\alpha$ (89.11) and the three-dimensional velocity v^α (89.10). In the following all operations of raising and lowering indices and of covariant differentiation are carried out in three-dimensional space with the metric $\gamma_{\alpha\beta}$, on the three-dimensional vectors g_α, v^α and the three-dimensional scalar h.

The desired equations must be invariant with respect to the transformation $x^0 \to x^0+\varphi(x^\alpha)$, which does not change the stationary character of the field. But under such a transformation, as is easily shown, $g_\alpha \to g_\alpha - \frac{\partial\varphi}{\partial x^\alpha}$, while the scalar h and the tensor $\gamma_{\alpha\beta} = g_{\alpha\beta}+hg_\alpha g_\beta$ are invariant. It is therefore clear that the required equations, when expressed in terms of $\gamma_{\alpha\beta}$, h and g_α, can contain g_α only in the combination

$$f_{\alpha\beta} = g_{\beta;\alpha}-g_{\alpha;\beta} = \frac{\partial g_\beta}{\partial x^\alpha}-\frac{\partial g_\alpha}{\partial x^\beta},$$

which is invariant under such a transformation. Taking this fact into account, we can drastically simplify the computations, setting (after computing all the derivatives appearing in R_{ik}) $g_\alpha = 0$ and $g_{\alpha;\beta}+g_{\beta;\alpha} = 0$.†

---

† To avoid any misunderstandings, we emphasize, however, that such a procedure would not be applicable to the computation of the components of the tensor R_{ik} themselves; correct values would be obtained only for the component R_{00} and the scalar R, which are invariant under such a transformation:

$$R_{00} = \sqrt{h}\,(\sqrt{h})_{;\alpha}^{;\alpha}+\frac{h^2}{4}f_{\alpha\beta}f^{\alpha\beta},$$

$$R = P+\frac{h}{4}f_{\alpha\beta}f^{\alpha\beta}-\frac{2}{\sqrt{h}}(\sqrt{h})_{;\alpha}^{;\alpha}.$$

As a result of the computation, we get the following equations [the components$_{00}$, $^{\alpha}_{0}$, $^{\alpha}_{\beta}$ of equation (95.8)]:

$$\frac{1}{\sqrt{h}}(\sqrt{h})_{;\alpha}^{;\alpha}+\frac{h}{4}f_{\alpha\beta}f^{\alpha\beta}=\frac{8\pi k}{c^4}\left(\frac{\epsilon+p}{1-\frac{v^2}{c^2}}-\frac{\epsilon-p}{2}\right), \tag{1}$$

$$\frac{\sqrt{h}}{2}f^{\alpha\beta}_{;\beta}+\frac{3}{2}f^{\alpha\beta}(\sqrt{h})_{;\beta}=-\frac{8\pi k}{c^4}\frac{p+\epsilon}{1-\frac{v^2}{c^2}}\frac{v^\alpha}{c}, \tag{2}$$

$$P^{\alpha}_{\beta}+\frac{h}{2}f^{\alpha\gamma}f_{\beta\gamma}-\frac{1}{\sqrt{h}}(\sqrt{h})_{;\beta}^{;\alpha}=\frac{8\pi k}{c^4}\left[\frac{(p+\epsilon)v^\alpha v_\beta}{c^2\left(1-\frac{v^2}{c^2}\right)}+\frac{\epsilon-p}{2}\delta^{\alpha}_{\beta}\right]. \tag{3}$$

Here P^{α}_{β} is a three-dimensional tensor, expressed in terms of $\gamma_{\alpha\beta}$ in the same way as R_i^k is expressed in terms of g_{ik}.

§ 96. Newton's Law

In the gravitational field equations which we have obtained, we now carry out the transition to the limit of nonrelativistic mechanics. As was stated in § 87, the assumption of small velocities of all particles requires also that the gravitational field be weak.

The expression for the component g_{00} of the metric tensor (the only one which we need) was found, for the limiting case which we are considering, in § 87:

$$g_{00}=-1-\frac{2\phi}{c^2}.$$

Further, we can use for the components of the energy-momentum tensor the expression (35.4) $T_i^k=\mu c^2 u_i u^k$, where μ is the mass density of the body (the sum of the rest masses of the particles in a unit volume; we drop the subscript 0 on μ). As for the four-velocity u^i, since the macroscopic motion is also considered to be slow, we must neglect all its space components and retain only the time component, that is, we must set $u^\alpha=0$, $u^0=-u_0=1$. Of all the components T_i^k, there thus remains only

$$T_0^0=-\mu c^2. \tag{96.1}$$

The scalar $T=T_i^i$ will be equal to this same value $-\mu c^2$.

We write the field equations in the form (95.8):

$$R_i^k=\frac{8\pi k}{c^4}\left(T_i^k-\frac{1}{2}\delta_i^k T\right);$$

for $i=k=0$

$$R_0^0=-\frac{4\pi k}{c^2}\mu.$$

One easily verifies that in the approximation we are considering all the other equations vanish identically.

For the calculation of R_0^0 from the general formula (92.11), we note that terms containing derivatives of the quantities Γ^i_{kl} are in every case quantities of the second order. Terms containing derivatives with respect to $x^0 = ct$ are small (compared with terms with derivatives with respect to the coordinates x^α) since they contain extra powers of $1/c$. As a result, there remains $R_{00} = -R_0^0 = \partial\Gamma^\alpha_{00}/\partial x^\alpha$. Substituting

$$\Gamma^\alpha_{00} \simeq -\frac{1}{2} g^{\alpha\beta} \frac{\partial g_{00}}{\partial x^\beta} = \frac{1}{c^2} \frac{\partial \phi}{\partial x^\alpha},$$

we find

$$R_0^0 = -\frac{1}{c^2} \frac{\partial^2 \phi}{\partial x^{\alpha 2}} = -\frac{1}{c^2} \Delta\phi.$$

Thus the field equations give

$$\Delta\phi = 4\pi k \mu. \tag{96.2}$$

This is the equation of the gravitational field in nonrelativistic mechanics. It is completely analogous to the Poisson equation (36.4) for the electric potential, where here in place of the charge density we have the mass density multiplied by $-k$. Therefore we can immediately write the general solution of equation (96.2) by analogy with (36.8) in the form

$$\phi = -k \int \frac{\mu \, dV}{R}. \tag{96.3}$$

This formula determines the potential of the gravitational field of an arbitrary mass distribution in the nonrelativistic approximation.

In particular, we have for the potential of the field of a single particle of mass m

$$\phi = -\frac{km}{R} \tag{96.4}$$

and, consequently, the force $F = -m' \frac{\partial \phi}{\partial R}$, acting in this field on another particle (mass m'), is equal to

$$F = -\frac{kmm'}{R^2}. \tag{96.5}$$

This is the well-known *law of attraction of Newton.*

The potential energy of a particle in a gravitational field is equal to its mass multiplied by the potential of the field, in analogy to the fact that the potential energy in an electric field is equal to the product of the charge and the potential of the field. Therefore, we may write, by analogy with (37.1), for the potential energy of an arbitrary mass distribution, the expression

$$U = \frac{1}{2}\int \mu\phi \, dV. \tag{96.6}$$

For the Newtonian potential of a constant gravitational field at large distances from the masses producing it, we can give an expansion analogous to that obtained in §§ 40–41 for the electrostatic field. We choose the coordinate origin at the inertial center of the masses. Then the intergal $\int \mu \mathbf{r} \, dV$, which is analogous to the dipole moment of a system of charges, vanishes identically. Thus, unlike the case of the electrostatic field, in the case of the gravitational field we can always eliminate the "dipole terms". Consequently, the expansion of the potential ϕ has the form:

$$\phi = -k\left\{\frac{M}{R_0} + \frac{1}{6}D_{\alpha\beta}\frac{\partial^2}{\partial X_\alpha \, \partial X_\beta}\frac{1}{R_0} + \cdots\right\}, \tag{96.7}$$

where $M = \int \mu \, dV$ is the total mass of the system, and the qunatity

$$D_{\alpha\beta} = \int \mu(3x_\alpha x_\beta - r^2\delta_{\alpha\beta}) \, dV \tag{96.8}$$

may be called the *mass quadrupole moment tensor.*† It is related to the usual *moment of inertia tensor*

$$J_{\alpha\beta} = \int \mu \, (r^2 \, \delta_{\alpha\beta} - x_\alpha x_\beta) \, dV$$

by the obvious relation

$$D_{\alpha\beta} = J_{\gamma\gamma}\delta_{\alpha\beta} - 3J_{\alpha\beta}. \tag{96.9}$$

The determination of the Newtonian potential from a given distribution of masses is the subject of one of the branches of mathematical physics; the exposition of the various methods for this is not the subject of the present book. Here we shall for reference purposes give only the formulas for the potential of the gravitational field produced by a homogeneous ellipsoidal body.‡

Let the surface of the ellipsoid be given by the equation

$$\frac{x^2}{a^2} + \frac{y^2}{b^2} + \frac{z^2}{c^2} = 1, \qquad a > b > c. \tag{96.10}$$

---

†We here write all indices α, β as subscripts, not distinguishing between co- and contravariant components, in accordance with the fact that all operations are carried out in ordinary Newtonian (Euclidean) space.

‡ The derivation of these formulas can be found in the book of L. N. Sretenskii, *Theory of the Newtonian Potential*, Gostekhizdat, 1946.

Then the potential of the field at an arbitrary point outside the body is given by the following formula:

$$\varphi = -\pi\mu abck \int\limits_{\xi}^{\infty} \left(1 - \frac{x^2}{a^2+s} - \frac{y^2}{b^2+s} - \frac{z^2}{c^2+s}\right) \frac{ds}{R_s} \tag{96.11}$$

$$R_s = \sqrt{(a^2+s)(b^2+s)(c^2+s)},$$

where ξ is the positive root of the equation

$$\frac{x^2}{a^2+\xi} + \frac{y^2}{b^2+\xi} + \frac{z^2}{c^2+\xi} = 1. \tag{96.12}$$

The potential of the field in the interior of the ellipsoid is given by the formula

$$\varphi = -\pi\mu abck \int\limits_{0}^{\infty} \left(1 - \frac{x^2}{a^2+s} - \frac{y^2}{b^2+s} - \frac{z^2}{c^2+s}\right) \frac{ds}{R_s}, \tag{96.13}$$

which differs from (96.11) in having the lower limit replaced by zero; we note that this expression is a quadratic function of the coordinates x, y, z.

The gravitational energy of the body is obtained, according to (96.6), by integrating the expression (96.13) over the volume of the ellipsoid. This integral can be done by elementary methods,† and gives:

$$U = \frac{3km^2}{8} \int\limits_{0}^{\infty} \left[\frac{1}{5}\left(\frac{a^2}{a^2+s} + \frac{b^2}{b^2+s} + \frac{c^2}{c^2+s}\right) - 1\right] \frac{ds}{R_s}$$

$$= \frac{3km^2}{8} \int\limits_{0}^{\infty} \left[\frac{2}{5} sd\left(\frac{1}{R_s}\right) - \frac{2}{5}\frac{ds}{R_s}\right] \tag{96.14}$$

$\left(m = \frac{4\pi}{3} abc\,\mu \text{ is the total mass of the body}\right)$; integrating the first term by parts, we obtain finally:

$$U = -\frac{3km^2}{10} \int\limits_{0}^{\infty} \frac{ds}{R_s}. \tag{96.15}$$

All the integrals appearing in formulas (96.11)—(96.14) can be expressed in terms of elliptic integrals of the first and second kind. For ellipsoids of rotation, these integrals are expressed in terms of elementary functions. In particular, the gravitational energy of an oblate ellipsoid of rotation ($a = b > c$) is

$$U = -\frac{3km^2}{5\sqrt{a^2-c^2}} \cos^{-1}\frac{c}{a}, \tag{96.16}$$

† The integration of the squares x^2, y^2, z^2 is most simply done by making the substitution $x = ax'$, $y = by'$, $z = cz'$, which reduces the integral over the volume of the ellipsoid to an integral over the volume of the unit sphere.

and for a prolate ellipsoid of rotation ($a > b = c$):

$$U = -\frac{3km^2}{5\sqrt{a^2-c^2}}\cosh^{-1}\frac{a}{c}. \qquad (96.17)$$

For a sphere ($a = c$) both formulas give the value $U = -3km^2/5a$, which, of course, can also be obtained by elementary methods.†

PROBLEM

Determine the equilibrium shape of a homogeneous gravitating mass of liquid which is rotating as a whole.

Solution: The condition of equilibrium is the constancy on the surface of the body of the sum of the gravitational potential and the potential of the centrifugal forces:

$$\varphi - \frac{\Omega^2}{2}(x^2+y^2) = \text{const.}$$

(Ω) is the angular velocity; the axis of rotation is the z axis). The required shape is that of an oblate ellipsoid of rotation. To determine its parameters we substitute (96.13) in the condition of equilibrium, and eliminate z^2 by using equation (96.10); this gives:

$$(x^2+y^2)\left[\int_0^\infty \frac{ds}{(a^2+s)^2\sqrt{c^2+s}} - \frac{\Omega^2}{2\pi\mu k a^2 c} - \frac{c^2}{a^2}\int_0^\infty \frac{ds}{(a^2+s)(c^2+s)^{3/2}}\right] = \text{const.},$$

from which it follows that the expression in the square brackets must vanish. Performing the integration, we get the equation

$$\frac{(a^2+2c^2)c}{(a^2-c^2)^{3/2}}\cos^{-1}\frac{c}{a} - \frac{3c^2}{a^2-c^2} - \frac{\Omega^2}{2\pi k\mu} = \frac{25}{6}\left(\frac{4\pi}{3}\right)^{1/3}\frac{M^2\mu^{1/3}}{m^{10/3}k}\left(\frac{c}{a}\right)^{4/3}$$

($M = \frac{2}{5}ma^2\Omega$ is the angular momentum of the body around the z axis), which determines the ratio of the semiaxes c/a for given Ω or M. The dependence of the ratio c/a on M is single-valued; c/a increases monotonically with increasing M.

However, it turns out that the symmetrical form which we have found is stable (with respect to small perturbations) only for not too large values of M.‡ The stability is lost for $M = 2.89\, k^{1/2}\, m^{5/3}\, \mu^{-1/6}$ (when $c/a = 0.58$). With further increase of M, the equilibrium shape becomes a general ellipsoid with gradually decreasing values of b/a and c/a (from 1 and from 0.58 respectively). This shape in turn becomes unstable for $M = 3.84\, k^{1/2}\, m^{5/3}\, \mu^{-1/6}$ (when $a{:}b{:}c = 1{:}0.43{:}0.34$).

§ 97. The centrally symmetric gravitational field

Let us consider a gravitational field possessing central symmetry. Such a field can be produced by any centrally symmetric distribution of matter; for this, of course, not only the distribution but also the motion of the matter must be centrally symmetric, i.e., the velocity at each point must be directed along the radius.

† The potential of the field inside a homogeneous sphere of radius a is

$$\varphi = -2\pi k\mu\left(a^2 - \frac{r^2}{3}\right).$$

‡ References to the literature concerning this question can be found in the book by H. Lamb, *Hydrodynamics*, Chap. XII.

The central symmetry of the field means that the space-time metric, that is, the expression for the interval ds, must be the same for all points located at the same distance from the center. In Euclidean space this distance is equal to the radius vector; in a non-Euclidean space, such as we have in the presence of a gravitational field, there is no quantity which has all the properties of the Euclidean radius vector (for example, to be equal both to the distance from the center and to the length of the circumference divided by 2π). Therefore the choice of a "radius vector" is now arbitrary.

If we use "spherical" space coordinates r, θ, ϕ, then the most general centrally symmetric expression for ds^2 is

$$ds^2 = h(r, t)\, dr^2 + k(r, t)\, (\sin^2\theta\, d\phi^2 + d\theta^2) + l(r, t)\, dt^2 + a(r, t)\, dr\, dt, \qquad (97.1)$$

where a, h, k, l are certain functions of the "radius vector" r and the "time" t. But because of the arbitrariness in the choice of a reference system in the general theory of relativity, we can still subject the coordinates to any transformation which does not destroy the central symmetry of ds^2; this means that we can transform the coordinates r and t according to the formulas

$$r = f_1(r', t'), \quad t = f_2(r', t'),$$

where f_1, f_2 are any functions of the new coordinates r', t'.

Making use of this possibility, we choose the coordinate r and the time t in such a way that, first of all, the coefficient $a(r, t)$ of $dr\, dt$ in the expression for ds^2 vanishes and, secondly, the coefficient $k(r, t)$ becomes equal simply to $-r^2$.† The latter condition implies that the radius vector r is defined in such a way that the circumference of a circle with center at the origin of coordinates is equal to $2\pi r$ (the element of arc of a circle in the plane $\theta = \pi/2$ is equal to $dl = r\, d\phi$). It will be convenient to write the quantities h and l in exponential form, as $-e^{\lambda}$ and $c^2 e^{\nu}$ respectively, where λ and ν are some functions of r and t. Thus we obtain the following expression for ds^2:

$$ds^2 = e^{\nu} c^2\, dt^2 - r^2(d\theta^2 + \sin^2\theta\, d\phi^2) - e^{\lambda}\, dr^2. \qquad (97.2)$$

Denoting by x^1, x^2, x^3, x^0, respectively, the coordinates r, θ, ϕ, ct, we have for the nonzero components of the metric tensor the expressions

$$g_{11} = e^{+\lambda}, \quad g_{22} = r^2, \quad g_{33} = r^2 \sin^2\theta, \qquad g_{00} = -e^{\nu}.$$

Clearly,

$$g^{11} = e^{-\lambda}, \quad g^{22} = r^{-2}, \quad g^{33} = r^{-2} \sin^{-2}\theta, \quad g^{00} = -e^{-\nu}.$$

With these values it is easy to calculate the Γ^i_{kl} from formula (86.3). The calculation leads to the following expressions (the prime means differen-

† These conditions do not determine the choice of the time coordinate uniquely. It can till be subjected to an arbitrary transformation $t = f(t')$, not containing r.

tiation with respect to r, while a dot on a symbol means differentiation with respect to ct):

$$\Gamma^1_{11} = \frac{\lambda'}{2}, \qquad \Gamma^0_{10} = \frac{\nu'}{2}, \qquad \Gamma^2_{33} = -\sin\theta\cos\theta,$$

$$\Gamma^0_{11} = \frac{\dot\lambda}{2} e^{\lambda-\nu}, \qquad \Gamma^1_{22} = -re^{-\lambda}, \qquad \Gamma^1_{00} = \frac{\nu'}{2} e^{\nu-\lambda},$$

$$\Gamma^2_{12} = \Gamma^3_{13} = \frac{1}{r}, \qquad \Gamma^3_{23} = \cot\theta, \qquad \Gamma^0_{00} = \frac{\dot\nu}{2}. \tag{97.3}$$

$$\Gamma^1_{10} = \frac{\dot\lambda}{2}, \qquad \Gamma^1_{33} = -r\sin^2\theta e^{-\lambda}.$$

All other components (except for those which differ from the ones we have written by a transposition of the indices k and l) are zero.

To get the equations of gravitation we must calculate the components of the tensor R^i_k according to formula (92.11). A simple calculation leads to the following equations:

$$\frac{8\pi k}{c^4} T^1_1 = \frac{8\pi k}{c^4} \frac{\left(p + \epsilon\frac{v^2}{c^2}\right)}{\left(1 - \frac{v^2}{c^2}\right)} = e^{-\lambda}\left(\frac{\nu'}{r} + \frac{1}{r^2}\right) - \frac{1}{r^2}, \tag{97.4}$$

$$\frac{8\pi k}{c^4} T^2_2 = \frac{8\pi k}{c^4} T^3_3 = \frac{8\pi k}{c^4} p = \frac{1}{2} e^{-\lambda}\left(\nu'' + \frac{\nu'^2}{2} + \frac{\nu' - \lambda'}{r} - \frac{\nu'\lambda'}{2}\right) - \frac{1}{2} e^{-\nu}\left(\ddot\lambda + \frac{\dot\lambda^2}{2} - \frac{\dot\lambda\dot\nu}{2}\right), \tag{97.5}$$

$$\frac{8\pi k}{c^4} T^0_0 = -\frac{8\pi k}{c^4} \frac{\left(\epsilon + p\frac{v^2}{c^2}\right)}{\left(1 - \frac{v^2}{c^2}\right)} = e^{-\lambda}\left(\frac{1}{r^2} - \frac{\lambda'}{r}\right) - \frac{1}{r^2}, \tag{97.6}$$

$$\frac{8\pi k}{c^4} T^1_0 = -\frac{8\pi k}{c^4} \frac{(p+\epsilon)ve^{(\nu-\lambda)/2}}{c\left(1 - \frac{v^2}{c^2}\right)} = e^{-\lambda}\frac{\dot\lambda}{r}. \tag{97.7}$$

Here $v^2 = v_\alpha v^\alpha = v_1 v^1 = e^\lambda (v^1)^2$. The other components vanish identically.

The equations of gravitation can be integrated exactly in the very important case of a centrally symmetric field in vacuum, that is, outside of the masses producing the field (K. Schwarzschild, 1916). Setting the energy-momentum tensor equal to zero, we get the following equations:

$$e^{-\lambda}\left(\frac{\nu'}{r}+\frac{1}{r^2}\right)-\frac{1}{r^2}=0, \tag{97.8}$$

$$e^{-\lambda}\left(\frac{\lambda'}{r}-\frac{1}{r^2}\right)+\frac{1}{r^2}=0, \tag{97.9}$$

$$\dot{\lambda}=0 \tag{97.10}$$

[we do not write the fourth equation, that is, Eq. (97.5), since it follows from the other three equations].

From (97.10) we see directly that λ does not depend on the time. Further, adding Eqs. (97.8) and (97.9), we find $\lambda'+\nu'=0$, that is,

$$\lambda+\nu=f(t), \tag{97.11}$$

where $f(t)$ is a function only of the time. But when we chose the interval, ds^2 in the form (97.2), there still remained the possibility of an arbitrary transformation of the time of the form $t=f(t')$. Such a transformation is equivalent to adding to ν an arbitrary function of the time, and with its aid we can always make $f(t)$ in (97.11) vanish. And so, without any loss in generality, we can set $\lambda+\nu=0$, that is, $\lambda=-\nu$. Note that the centrally symmetric gravitational field in vacuum is automatically static.

The equation (97.9) is easily integrated and gives:

$$e^{-\lambda}=e^{\nu}=1+\frac{\text{const}}{r}. \tag{97.12}$$

Thus, at infinity ($r\to\infty$), $e^{-\lambda}=e^{\nu}=1$, that is, far from the gravitating bodies the metric automatically becomes Galilean. The constant is easily expressed in terms of the mass of the body by requiring that at large distances, where the field is weak, Newton's law should hold. In other words, we should have $g_{00}=-1-\frac{2\phi}{c^2}$, where the potential ϕ has its Newtonian value (96.4) $\phi=-\frac{km}{r}$ (m is the total mass of the bodies producing the field). From this it is clear that const $=-\frac{2km}{c^2}$.†

Thus we finally obtain for the interval ds,

$$ds^2=\left(c^2-\frac{2km}{r}\right)dt^2-r^2(\sin^2\theta\, d\phi^2+d\theta^2)-\frac{dr^2}{1-\frac{2km}{c^2 r}}. \tag{97.13}$$

† For the field in the interior of a spherical cavity in a centrally symmetric distribution, we must have const $=0$, since otherwise the metric would have a singularity at $r=0$. Thus the metric inside such a cavity is automatically Galilean.

This expression completely determines the gravitational field in vacuum produced by any centrally symmetric distribution of masses. We emphasize that this solution holds not only for masses at rest, but also for moving masses, provided only that this motion also has central symmetry (for example, centrally symmetric vibration).

The spatial metric is determined by the expression for the element of spatial distance:

$$dl^2 = r^2(\sin^2\theta \cdot d\phi^2 + d\theta^2) + \frac{dr^2}{1 - \frac{2km}{c^2 r}}. \tag{97.14}$$

The distance from the center to any point in space is $\int_0^r \sqrt{g_{11}}dr$, and since $g_{11} \geqslant 1$,

$$\int_0^r \sqrt{g_{11}}\, dr \geqslant r \tag{97.15}$$

(the equality sign holds only for points at infinity). The circumference of the circle drawn through the given point (with center at the origin) is $2\pi r$. Consequently we see that the ratio of the circumference of a circle to its radius is less than 2π.

Furthermore, we see that $-g_{00} \leqslant 1$. Combining with the formula (84.1) $d\tau = \sqrt{-g_{00}}\, dt$, defining the proper time, it follows that

$$d\tau \leqslant dt. \tag{97.16}$$

The equality sign holds only at infinity, where t coincides with the proper time. Thus at finite distances from the masses there is a "slowing down" of the time compared with the time at infinity.

Finally, we present an approximate expression for ds^2 at large distances from the origin of coordinates:

$$ds^2 = ds_0^2 - \frac{2km}{c^2 r}(dr^2 + c^2\, dt^2). \tag{97.17}$$

The second term represents a small correction to the Galilean metric ds_0^2. At large distances from the masses producing it, every field appears centrally symmetric. Therefore (97.17) determines the metric at large distances from any system of bodies.

Certain general considerations can also be made concerning the behavior of a centrally symmetric gravitational field in the interior of the gravitating masses. From Eq. (97.6) we see that for $r \to 0$, λ must also vanish at least like r^2; if this were not so the right side of the equation would become infinite for $r \to 0$, that is, T_0^0 would have a singular point at $r = 0$, which is physically impossible. Formally integrating (97.6) with the limiting condition $\lambda|_{r=0} = 0$, we obtain

$$\lambda = -\ln\left\{1 + \frac{8\pi k}{c^4 r}\int_0^r T_0^0 r^2\,dr\right\}. \tag{97.18}$$

Since $T_0^0 = -e^{-\nu}T_{00} \leqslant 0$, it is clear that $\lambda \geqslant 0$, that is,

$$e^\lambda \geqslant 1. \tag{97.19}$$

Subtracting equation (97.6) term by term from (97.4), we get:

$$\frac{e^{-\lambda}}{r}(\nu' + \lambda') = \frac{8\pi k}{c^4}(T_1^1 - T_0^0) \geqslant 0,$$

i.e. $\nu' + \lambda' \geqslant 0$. But for $r \to \infty$ (far from the masses) the metric becomes Galilean, i.e. $\nu \to 0$, $\lambda \to 0$. Therefore, from $\nu' + \lambda' \geqslant 0$ it follows that over all space

$$\nu + \lambda \leqslant 0. \tag{97.20}$$

Since $\lambda \geqslant 0$, it then follows that $\nu \leqslant 0$, i.e.

$$e^\nu \leqslant 1. \tag{97.21}$$

The inequalities obtained show that the above properties (97.15) and (97.16) of the spatial metric and the behavior of clocks in a centrally symmetric field in vacuum apply equally well to the field in the interior of the gravitating masses.

If the gravitational field is produced by a spherical body of "radius" a, then for $r > a$, we have $T_0^0 = 0$. For points with $r > a$, formula (97.18) therefore gives

$$\lambda = -\ln\left\{1 + \frac{8\pi k}{c^4 r}\int_0^a T_0^0 r^2\,dr\right\}.$$

On the other hand, we can here apply the expression (97.13) referring to vacuum, according to which

$$\lambda = -\ln\left(1 - \frac{2km}{c^2 r}\right).$$

Equating the two expressions, we get the formula

$$m = -\frac{4\pi}{c^2}\int_0^a T_0^0 r^2\,dr, \tag{97.22}$$

expressing the total mass of a body in terms of its energy-momentum tensor.

In the element of interval in the gravitational field in vacuum (97.13), at the point $r = r_0$, where

$$r_0 = \frac{2mk}{c^2} \tag{97.23}$$

(this quantity is called the *gravitational radius* of the body) g_{00} goes to zero and g_{11} to infinity. This fact might seem to give the basis for concluding that there is a singularity in the space-time, and that therefore it is impossible for bodies to exist with a "radius" (for a given mass m) which is less than the value given above; however such conclusions would actually not be correct.† This is already indicated by the fact that the determinant $g = -r^4 \sin^2\theta$ has no singularity at $r = r_0$, so that the condition $g < 0$ (82.3) is not violated. We shall see that actually we have only the result that for $r < r_0$ it is impossible to realize the corresponding system of reference.

To investigate the essential character of the space-time metric in this region, we make a transformation of coordinates, introducing in place of t a new variable τ:

$$ct = c\tau \pm r_0 \ln\left(\frac{r}{r_0} - 1\right); \tag{97.24}$$

then

$$ds^2 = c^2\left(1 - \frac{r_0}{r}\right)d\tau^2 \pm \frac{2r_0}{r}\,c\,d\tau\,dr - \left(1 + \frac{r_0}{r}\right)dr^2 - r^2(d\theta^2 + \sin^2\theta\,d\phi^2) \tag{97.25}$$

(D. Finkelstein, 1958). In this expression there is no longer a singularity of the metric at $r = r_0$; the change in sign of g_{00} for $r = r_0$ in these coordinates means only that the coordinate ceases to have a timelike character; it does not violate the necessary conditions, since g_{00} no longer is one of the principal values of the metric tensor.‡

Let us consider the propagation of radial light signals. The equation $ds^2 = 0$ (for $\theta = \text{const}$, $\phi = \text{const}$) gives two possible values for the derivative $\frac{d\tau}{dr}$ along the ray:

$$c\frac{d\tau}{dr} = \pm 1, \quad c\frac{d\tau}{dr} = \mp\frac{r + r_0}{r - r_0}, \tag{97.26}$$

where the two signs correspond to the two signs in (97.25). In Fig. 19 are shown the "light cones" corresponding to the propagation of signals from different points on the r axis [for definiteness, we choose the lower sign in (97.26)]. For $r > r_0$, along the world lines of the two signals (the two conical surfaces) the signs of $\frac{d\tau}{dr}$ are usually different. In the region $r < r_0$, $\frac{d\tau}{dr} < 0$

† The considerations presented below have a fundamental interest, even though the gravitational radius of real bodies is negligibly small (compared to their radius), so that the problem considered here does not arise. We remark that it is meaningless to apply the problem formulated here to elementary particles, since the whole theory propounded in this book ceases to be applicable, because of quantum phenomena, already for dimensions far exceeding (by a factor $\sim 10^{40}$) the value of km/c^2.

‡ The fact that t is complex for $r < r_0$ and real values of τ again shows that, for $r < r_0$, a system of reference with time coordinate t is not realizable.

for both signals. Since no causally related events can lie on the world line outside the light cone, it then follows first of all that in this region no particle can be at rest: the world line of a particle at rest would run parallel to the τ axis outside the light cone. Thus a system of reference for $r < r_0$ can be realized only by means of moving bodies, whose motion is directed toward the center; it is only in this direction that all interactions or signals propagate.†

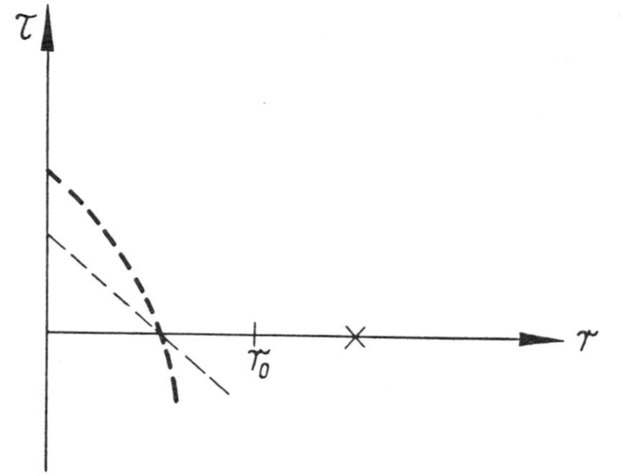

FIG. 19.

The case of the lower sign in (97.25) is then obtained simply by changing the sign of τ, i.e. all the same conclusions are valid with the one difference that the motion of bodies and propagation of signals occurs only along the direction out from the center.

PROBLEMS

1. Determine the spatial curvature in a centrally symmetric gravitational field in vacuum.

Solution: The spatial curvature tensor $P^{\alpha}_{\beta\gamma\delta}$ is expressed in terms of the spatial metric tensor $\gamma_{\alpha\beta}$ in the same way as R^{i}_{klm} is expressed in terms of the g_{ik}. The components of the tensor $P^{\alpha}_{\beta\gamma\delta}$ can be expressed in terms of the components of the tensor $P_{\alpha\beta} = P^{\gamma}_{\alpha\gamma\beta}$ (and the $\gamma_{\alpha\beta}$), so that it is sufficient to calculate the $P_{\alpha\beta}$ (see problem 2, § 92). With the values of the $\gamma_{\alpha\beta}$ from (97.14) we obtain, after computation, the following values for the components of the tensor:

$$P^{\theta}_{\theta} = P^{\phi}_{\phi} = \frac{r_0}{2r^3}, \quad P^{r}_{r} = -\frac{r_0}{r^3},$$

† The total time for "falling in" of bodies from a given point to the center is always finite, since the two boundary surfaces of the light "cone" intersect the τ axis at finite distances (as shown in Fig 19 by the dotted lines).

Doubts may arise as to whether the sign of τ determines which half of the light cone is the region of the future and which the past (with respect to the moment $\tau = 0$), since the coordinate τ does not have timelike character for $r < r_0$. However, such doubts are eliminated by considerations of continuity in the transition from the region $r > r_0$, in which the condition that τ be timelike is fulfilled.

and $P^\alpha_\beta = 0$ for $\alpha \neq \beta$, so that the tensor P^β_α is diagonal. Note that P^θ_θ, P^ϕ_ϕ are positive, while P^r_r is negative. This means that the spatial geometry is such that in "planes" passing through the origin, the sum of the angles of a triangle is greater than π, while in "planes" "perpendicular" to the radius vector it is less than π.

2. Determine the form of the surface of rotation on which the geometry would be the same as on a "plane" passing through the origin in a centrally symmetric gravitational field in vacuo.

Solution: The geometry on the surface of rotation $z = z(r)$ is determined (in cylindrical coordinates) by the element of length:

$$dl^2 = dr^2 + dz^2 + r^2 d\phi^2 = dr^2(1+z'^2) + r^2 d\phi^2.$$

Comparing with the element of length (97.4) in the "plane" $\theta = \pi/2$

$$dl^2 = r^2 d\phi^2 + \frac{dr^2}{1-\dfrac{2mk}{c^2 r}},$$

we find

$$1+z'^2 = \left(1-\frac{r_0}{r}\right)^{-1},$$

from which

$$z = 2\sqrt{r_0(r-r_0)}.$$

For $r = r_0$ this function has a singularity—a branch point. The reason for this is that the spatial metric (97.14) in contrast to the space-time metric (97.13), actually has a singularity at $r = r_0$.

3. Transform the interval (97.13) to such coordinates that its element of spatial distance dl is proportional to its Euclidean expression.

Solution: Setting

$$r = \left(1+\frac{r_0}{4r_1}\right)^2 r_1,$$

we get from (97.13)

$$ds^2 = \left(\frac{1-\dfrac{r_0}{4r_1}}{1+\dfrac{r_0}{4r_1}}\right)^2 c^2 dt^2 - \left(1+\frac{r_0}{4r_1}\right)^4 (dr_1^2 + r_1^2 d\theta^2 + r_1^2 \sin^2\theta\, d\phi^2).$$

The coordinates r_1, θ, ϕ are called *isotropic spherical coordinates*.

4. Derive the equations of the centrally symmetric gravitational field in a system of coordinates moving at each point with the material located at that point (such a system of reference is said to be *comoving*).

Solution: We make use of the two possible transformations of the coordinates r, t in the element of interval (97.1), first, to make the coefficient $a(r, t)$ zero, and second, to make the radial velocity $\dot{r}$ of the matter zero at all points (the remaining components of the velocity are zero because of the central symmetry). After that, the coordinates r and t can still be subjected to an arbitrary transformation of the form $r = r(r')$, $t = t(t')$.

We denote the radial coordinate and time thus selected by R and τ, and let the coefficients h, k, l respectively be $-e^\omega$, $-e^\mu$, $c^2 e^\sigma$, (where ω, μ, σ are functions of R and τ). Then for the interval we have:

$$ds^2 = c^2 e^\sigma d\tau^2 - e^\mu (d\theta^2 + \sin^2\theta d\phi^2) - e^\omega dR^2. \tag{1}$$

The components of the energy-momentum tensor are equal to

$$T_1^1 = T_2^2 = T_3^3 = p,\ T_0^0 = -\epsilon. \tag{2}$$

A rather lengthy calculation leads to the following equations of gravitation:

$$\frac{8\pi k}{c^4} T_1^1 = \frac{8\pi k}{c^4} p = \tfrac{1}{2} e^{-\omega}\left(\frac{\mu'^2}{2}+\mu'\sigma'\right) - e^{-\sigma}(\ddot{\mu}-\tfrac{1}{2}\dot{\mu}\dot{\sigma}+\tfrac{3}{4}\dot{\mu}^2) - e^{-\mu}, \tag{3}$$

$$\frac{8\pi k}{c^4} T_2^2 = \frac{8\pi k}{c^4} p = \tfrac{1}{4} e^{-\omega}(2\sigma''+\sigma'^2+2\mu''+\mu'^2-\mu'\omega'-\sigma'\omega'+\mu'\sigma')+$$
$$+\tfrac{1}{4} e^{-\sigma}(\dot{\omega}\dot{\sigma}+\dot{\mu}\dot{\sigma}-\dot{\omega}\dot{\mu}-2\ddot{\omega}-\dot{\omega}^2-2\ddot{\mu}-\dot{\mu}^2), \tag{4}$$

$$\frac{8\pi k}{c^4} T_0^0 = -\frac{8\pi k}{c^4}\epsilon = e^{-\omega}\left(\mu''+\tfrac{3}{4}\mu'^2-\frac{\mu'\omega'}{2}\right) - \tfrac{1}{2} e^{-\sigma}\left(\dot{\omega}\dot{\mu}+\frac{\dot{\mu}^2}{2}\right) - e^{-\mu}, \tag{5}$$

$$\frac{8\pi k}{c^4} T_0^1 = 0 = \tfrac{1}{2} e^{-\omega}(-2\dot{\mu}'-\dot{\mu}\mu'+\dot{\omega}\mu'+\sigma'\dot{\mu}) \tag{6}$$

(where the prime denotes differentiation with respect to R and the dot with respect to $c\tau$).

Certain general relations for ω, μ, σ can be easily obtained by starting from the equations $T^k_{i;k} = 0$ which are contained in the equations of gravitation. Using formula (86.11), and substituting for T_i^k and g_{ik} from (1) and (2), we obtain the following two equations:

$$\dot{\omega}+2\dot{\mu} = -\frac{2\dot{\epsilon}}{p+\epsilon},\quad \sigma' = -\frac{2p'}{p+\epsilon}. \tag{7}$$

If p is known as a function of ϵ, the equations (7) are integrable in the form

$$\omega+2\mu = -2\int \frac{d\epsilon}{p+\epsilon} + f_1(R),\quad \sigma = -2\int \frac{dp}{p+\epsilon} + f_2(\tau), \tag{8}$$

where the functions $f_1(R)$ and $f_2(\tau)$ can be chosen arbitrarily, because of the possibility mentioned above of making an arbitrary transformation of the form $R = R(R')$, $\tau = \tau(\tau')$.

5. Find the general solution of the equations of the centrally symmetric gravitational field in the "comoving" coordinate system, when the pressure of the matter is equal to zero.

Solution: From equation (7) we see that if $p = 0$ we can set $\sigma = 0$ (which establishes a unique choice of the time τ). In place of $\mu(R, \tau)$ we introduce the function

$$r(R, \tau) = e^{\frac{\mu}{2}},$$

which represents a "radius", defined so that $2\pi r$ is the length of the circle (with center at the origin); then the interval is given by

$$ds^2 = c^2 d\tau^2 - r^2(R.\tau)(d\theta^2+\sin^2\theta d\phi^2) - e^{\omega} dR^2.$$

Equation (6) takes the form $\dot{\omega} r' = 2\dot{r}'$, and is immediately integrated over the time, giving

$$e^{\omega} = \frac{r'^2}{1+f}, \tag{9}$$

where $f(R)$ is an arbitrary function, satysfying only the requirement that $1+f > 0$. Substituting this expression in equation (3) [substitution in (4) gives nothing new] we get:

$$2r\ddot{r}+\dot{r}-f = 0.$$

The first integral of this equation is

$$\dot{r}^2 = f(R)+\frac{F(R)}{r}. \tag{10}$$

where $F(R)$ is again an arbitrary function. Integrating once more, we have:

$$c[\tau-\tau_0(R)] = \frac{1}{f}\sqrt{fr^2+Fr}-\frac{F}{f^{3/2}}\sinh^{-1}\sqrt{\frac{fr}{F}} \quad \text{for } f>0, \tag{11}$$

$$c[\tau-\tau_0(R)] = \frac{1}{f}\sqrt{fr^2+Fr}+\frac{F}{(-f)^{3/2}}\sin^{-1}\sqrt{\frac{-fr}{F}} \quad \text{for } f<0;$$

$$r = \left(\frac{3c}{2}\right)^{2/3} F^{1/3}(\tau-\tau_0)^{2/3} \quad \text{for } f=0.$$

For ϵ, we find by substituting (9) in equation (5) and eliminating f by means of (10):

$$\frac{8\pi k}{c^4}\epsilon = \frac{F'}{r'r^2}. \tag{12}$$

Formulas (9), (11) and (12) define the required general solution (R. Tolman, 1934). We note that it depends, in general, not on three but only on two arbitrary functions, which determine the relation between f, F and ϵ, since the coordinate R itself can still be subjected to an arbitrary transformation $R = R(R')$.

This number corresponds precisely to the maximum number of "physically different" arbitrary functions for the present case (see p. 318): the initial centrally symmetric distribution is specified by two quantities (the distribution of density and radial velocity) while there exists no free gravitational field with central symmetry.

For $\tau \to \tau_0(R)$, the function $r(R, \tau)$ tends to zero according to the law

$$r^2 \cong \left(\frac{3c}{2}\right)^{4/3} F^{2/3}(\tau_0-\tau)^{4/3},$$

while the function e^{ω} goes to infinity as

$$e^{\omega} \cong c^2\left(\frac{2}{3c}\right)^{2/3}\frac{\tau_0'^2 F^{2/3}}{1+f}(\tau_0-\tau)^{-2/3}.$$

This means that all radial separations (in the "comoving" coordinate system which we are using) tend to infinity, and all circumferential distances tend toward zero, in such a way that all volumes tend to zero.† Correspondingly. the density of matter increases without limit:

$$\frac{8\pi k}{c^4}\epsilon \cong \frac{2F'}{3c^2F\tau_0'(\tau_0-\tau)}.$$

Thus there is a contraction of all the matter into one point.

† The geometry on a "plane" passing through the center is thus the same as it would be on a conical surface of rotation, which stretches in the course of time along its generator and simultaneously contracts along all circles about its axis.

In the special case when the function $\tau_0(R) = \text{const}$, the falling in has a different character. In this case

$$r^2 \cong \left(\frac{3c}{2}\right)^{4/3} F^{2/3}(\tau_0-\tau)^{4/3}, \qquad e^{\omega} \cong \left(\frac{2}{3c}\right)^{2/3} \frac{c^2F'^2}{4F^{4/3}(f+1)}(\tau_0-\tau)^{4/3},$$

$$\frac{8\pi k}{c^4}\epsilon \cong \frac{4}{3c^2(\tau_0-\tau)^2},$$

i.e., for $\tau \to \tau_0$ all separations, both azimuthal as well as radial, tend toward zero according to the same law $[\sim(\tau_0-\tau)^{4/3}]$; the density of matter tends to infinity like $(\xi_0-\xi)^{-2}$, where in the limit its distribution becomes uniform.

The nature of the relation between the pictures of the contraction as seen from the convected system and as seen by an external observer (i.e. one who is in a reference system which is not attached to the body and which is Galilean at infinity) is clear from our remarks at the end of § 97. For the external observer, the "radius" of the contracting body cannot become less than its gravitational radius r_0; it tends asymptotically toward this value as $t \to \infty$. To this time t in the system of the external observer, there corresponds in the convected system a certain moment $\tau < \tau_0(R_0)$. (The radius R_0 of the body is, by definition, constant in this system). There is no logical contradiction in all this since, after the moment $\tau_0(R_0)$, the observer moving with the matter could not send a light signal out into the external space.

§ 98. Motion in a centrally symmetric gravitational field

Let us consider the motion of a body in a centrally symmetric gravitational field. As in every centrally symmetric field, the motion occurs in a single "plane" passing through the origin; we choose this plane as the plane $\theta = \pi/2$.

To determine the trajectory of the body (with mass m), we use the Hamilton-Jacobi equation:

$$g^{ik}\frac{\partial S}{\partial x^i}\frac{\partial S}{\partial x^k} + m^2c^2 = 0.$$

Using the g^{ik} given in the expression (97.13) for the interval, we find the following equation:

$$e^{-\nu}\left(\frac{\partial S}{c\partial t}\right)^2 - e^{\nu}\left(\frac{\partial S}{\partial r}\right)^2 - \frac{1}{r^2}\left(\frac{\partial S}{\partial \phi}\right)^2 - m^2c^2 = 0, \tag{98.1}$$

where

$$e^{\nu} = 1 - \frac{r_0}{r} \tag{98.2}$$

(m' is the mass of the body producing the field; r_0 is its gravitational radius). By the general procedure for solving the Hamilton-Jacobi equation, we look for an S in the form

$$S = -\mathcal{E}_0 t + M\phi + S_r(r), \tag{98.3}$$

with constant energy $\mathcal{E}_0$ and angular momentum M. Substituting this in (98.1), we find the equation

$$e^{-\nu}\frac{\mathcal{E}_0^2}{c^2}-\frac{M^2}{r^2}-e^{\nu}\left(\frac{\partial S_r}{\partial r}\right)^2=m^2c^2,$$

from which

$$S_r=\int\sqrt{\frac{\mathcal{E}_0^2}{c^2}e^{-2\nu}-\left(m^2c^2+\frac{M^2}{r^2}\right)e^{-\nu}}\cdot dr=$$

$$=\int\left[\frac{r^2(\mathcal{E}_0^2-m^2c^4)+m^2c^4rr_0}{c^2(r-r_0)^2}-\frac{M^2}{r(r-r_0)}\right]^{1/2}dr. \qquad (98.4)$$

The trajectory is determined† by the equation $\dfrac{\partial S}{\partial M}=\text{const}$, from which

$$\phi=\int\frac{M\,dr}{r^2\sqrt{\dfrac{\mathcal{E}_0^2}{c^2}-\left(m^2c^2+\dfrac{M^2}{r^2}\right)\left(1-\dfrac{r_0}{r}\right)}}. \qquad (98.5)$$

This integral reduces to an elliptic integral.

For the motion of a planet in the field of attraction of the Sun, the relativistic theory leads to only an insignificant correction compared to Newton's theory, since the velocities of the planets are very small compared to the velocity of light. In the integrand in the equation (98.5) for the trajectory, this corresponds to a small value for the ratio r_0/r, where r_0 is the gravitational radius of the Sun.

To investigate the relativistic corrections to the trajectory, it is convenient to start from the expression (98.4) for the radial part of the action, before differentiation with respect to M.

We make a transformation of the integration variable, writing

$$r(r-r_0)=r'^2,\quad \text{i.e.,}\quad r-\frac{r_0}{2}\cong r',$$

as a result of which the second term under the square root takes the form M^2/r'^2. In the first term we make an expansion in powers of r_0/r', and obtain to the required accuracy:

$$S_r=\int\left[\left(2\mathcal{E}'m+\frac{\mathcal{E}'^2}{c^2}\right)+\frac{1}{r}(2m^2m'k+4\mathcal{E}'mr_0)-\frac{1}{r^2}\left(M^2-\frac{3m^2c^2r_0^2}{2}\right)\right]^{1/2}dr, \qquad (98.6)$$

where for brevity we have dropped the prime on r' and introduced the non-relativistic energy $\mathcal{E}'$ (without the rest energy).

The correction terms in the coefficients of the first two terms under the square root have only the not particularly interesting effect of changing

† See *Mechanics*, § 47.

the relation between the energy and momentum of the particle and changing the parameters of its Newtonian orbit (ellipse). But the change in the coefficient of $1/r^2$ leads to a more fundamental effect — to a systematic (secular) shift in the perihelion of the orbit.

Since the trajectory is defined by the equation $\phi+\frac{\partial S_r}{\partial M}=$ const, the change of the angle ϕ after one revolution of the planet in its orbit is

$$\Delta\phi = -\frac{\partial}{\partial M}\Delta S_r,$$

where ΔS_r is the corresponding change in S_r. Expanding S_r in powers of the small correction to the coefficient of $1/r^2$, we get:

$$\Delta S_r = \Delta S_r^{(0)} - \frac{3}{2}m^2c^2r_0^2\frac{\partial}{\partial(M^2)}\Delta S_r^{(0)} = \Delta S_r^{(0)} - \frac{3m^2c^2r_0^2}{4M}\frac{\partial \Delta S_r^{(0)}}{\partial M},$$

where $\Delta S_r^{(0)}$ corresponds to the motion in the closed ellipse which is unshifted. Differentiating this relation with respect to M, and using the fact that

$$-\frac{\partial}{\partial M}\Delta S_r^{(0)} = \Delta\phi^{(0)} = 2\pi,$$

we find:

$$\Delta\phi = 2\pi + \frac{3\pi m^2c^2r_0^2}{2M^2} = 2\pi + \frac{6\pi k^2m^2m'^2}{c^2M^2}.$$

The second term is the required angular displacement $\delta\phi$ of the Newtonian ellipse during one revolution, i.e. the shift in the perihelion of the orbit. Expressing it in terms of the length a of the semimajor axis and the eccentricity e of the ellipse by means of the formula $\frac{M^2}{km'm^2} = a(1-e^2)$, we obtain:†

$$\delta\phi = \frac{6\pi km'}{c^2a(1-e^2)}. \tag{98.7}$$

Next we consider the path of a light ray in a centrally symmetric gravitational field. This path is determined by the eikonal equation (87.9)

$$g^{ik}\frac{\partial\psi}{\partial x^i}\frac{\partial\psi}{\partial x^k} = 0,$$

which differs from the Hamilton-Jacobi equation only in having m set equal to zero. Therefore the trajectory of the ray can be obtained immediately from (98.5) by setting $m = 0$; at the same time, in place of the energy $\mathcal{E}_0 = -\frac{\partial S}{\partial t}$

† Numerical values of the shifts determined from formula (98.7) for Mercury and Earth are equal, respectively, to 43.0″ and 3.8″ per century. Astronomical measurements give 42.6″±0.9″ and 4.6″ ±2.7″, in excellent agreement with theory.

of the particle we must write the frequency of the light, $\omega_0 = -\frac{\partial\psi}{\partial t}$. Also introducing in place of the constant M a constant ϱ defined by $\varrho = cM/\omega_0$, we get:

$$\phi = \int \frac{dr}{r^2\sqrt{\frac{1}{\varrho^2}-\frac{1}{r^2}\left(1-\frac{r_0}{r}\right)}}. \tag{98.8}$$

If we neglect the relativistic corrections ($r_0 \to 0$), this equation gives $r = \varrho/\cos\phi$, i.e. a straight line passing at a distance ϱ from the origin. To study the relativistic corrections, we proceed in the same way as in the previous case.

For the radial part of the eikonal we have [see (98.4)]:

$$\psi_r(r) = \frac{\omega_0}{c}\int\sqrt{\frac{r^2}{(r-r_0)^2}-\frac{\varrho^2}{r(r-r_0)}}\,dr.$$

Making the same transformations as were used to go from (98.4) to (98.6), we find:

$$\psi_r(r) = \frac{\omega_0}{c}\int\sqrt{1+\frac{2r_0}{r}-\frac{\varrho^2}{r^2}}\,dr.$$

Expanding the integrand in powers of r_0/r, we have:

$$\psi_r = \psi_r^{(0)} + \frac{r_0\omega_0}{c}\int\frac{dr}{\sqrt{r^2-\varrho^2}} = \psi_r^{(0)} + \frac{r_0\omega_0}{c}\cosh^{-1}\frac{r}{\varrho},$$

where $\psi_r^{(0)}$ corresponds to the classical straight ray.

The total change in ψ_r during the propagation of the light from some very large distance R to the point $r = \varrho$ nearest to the center and then back to the distance R is equal to

$$\Delta\psi_r = \Delta\psi_r^{(0)} + 2\frac{r_0\omega_0}{c}\cosh^{-1}\frac{R}{\varrho}.$$

The corresponding change in the polar angle ϕ along the ray is obtained by differentiation with respect to $M = \varrho\omega_0/c$:

$$\Delta\phi = -\frac{\partial\Delta\psi_r}{\partial M} = -\frac{\partial\Delta\psi_r^{(0)}}{\partial M} + \frac{2r_0R}{\varrho\sqrt{R^2-\varrho^2}}.$$

Finally, going to the limit $R \to \infty$, and noting that the straight ray corresponds to $\Delta\phi = \pi$, we get:

$$\Delta\phi = \pi + \frac{2r_0}{\varrho}.$$

This means that under the influence of the field of attraction the light ray is bent: its trajectory is a curve which is concave toward the center (the ray is "attracted" toward the center), so that the angle between its two asymptotes differs from π by

$$\delta\phi = \frac{2r_0}{\varrho} = \frac{4km'}{c^2\varrho}; \tag{98.9}$$

in other words, the ray of light, passing at a distance ϱ from the center of the field, is deflected through an angle $\delta\phi$.†

§ 99. The synchronous reference system

As we know from § 84, the condition for it to be possible to synchronize clocks at different points in space is that the components $g_{0\alpha}$ of the metric tensor be equal to zero. If, in addition, $-g_{00} = 1$, the time coordinate $x^0 = ct$ is the proper time at each point in space. A reference system satisfying the conditions

$$g_{0\alpha} = 0, \quad -g_{00} = 1 \tag{99.1}$$

is said to be synchronous. The interval element in such a system is given by the expression

$$-ds^2 = -c^2\,dt^2 + g_{\alpha\beta}\,dx^\alpha\,dx^\beta. \tag{99.2}$$

The three-dimensional tensor $g_{\alpha\beta}$ determines the spatial metric.

In the synchronous reference system the time lines are geodesics in the four-space. The four-vector $u^i = dx^i/ds$, which is tangent to the world line x^1 x^2, $x^3 =$ const, has components $u^\alpha = 0$, $u^0 = 1$, and automatically satisfies the geodesic equations:

$$\frac{du^i}{ds} + \Gamma^i_{kl}u^k u^l = \Gamma^i_{00} = 0,$$

since, from the conditions (99.1), the Christoffel symbols Γ^α_{00} and Γ^0_{00} vanish identically.

It is also easy to see that these lines are normal to the hypersurfaces $t =$ const. In fact, the four-vector normal to such a hypersurface, $n_i = -c\,\partial t/\partial x^i$, has covariant components $n_\alpha = 0$, $n_0 = -1$. With the conditions (99.1), the corresponding contravariant components are $n^\alpha = 0$, $n^0 = 1$, i.e., they coincide with the components of the four-vector u^i which is tangent to the time lines.

Conversely, these properties can be used for the geometrical construction of a synchronous reference system in any space-time. For this purpose we choose as our starting surface any spacelike hypersurface, i.e., a hypersurface whose normals at each point have a time-like direction (they lie inside the light cone with its vertex at this point); all elements of interval on such a hypersurface are spacelike. Next we construct the family of geodesic lines normal

† For a ray just skirting the edge of the Sun, $\delta\phi = 1.75''$.

to this hypersurface. If we now choose these lines as the time coordinate lines and determine the time coordinate ct as the length s of the geodesic line measured from the initial hypersurface, we obtain a synchronous reference system.

It is clear that such a construction, and the selection of a synchronous reference system, is always possible in principle.

Furthermore this choice is still not unique. A metric of the form (99.2) allows any transformation of the space coordinates which does not affect the time, and also transformations corresponding to the arbitrariness in the choice of the initial hypersurface for the geometrical construction.

The transformation to the synchronous reference system can, in principle, be done analytically by using the Hamilton-Jacobi equation; the basis of this method is the fact that the trajectories of a particle in a gravitational field are just the geodesic lines.

The Hamilton-Jacobi equation for a particle (whose mass we set equal to unity) in a gravitational field is

$$c^2 g^{ik} \frac{\partial \tau}{\partial x^i} \frac{\partial \tau}{\partial x^k} = -1, \tag{99.3}$$

(where we denote the action by τc^2). Its complete integral has the form:

$$\tau = f(\xi^\alpha, x^i) + A(\xi^\alpha), \tag{99.4}$$

where f is a function of the four coordinates x^i and the three parameters ξ^α; the fourth constant A we treat as an arbitrary function of the three ξ^α. With such a representation for τ, the equations for the trajectory of the particle can be obtained by equating the derivatives $\partial\tau/\partial\xi^\alpha$ to zero, i.e.,

$$\frac{\partial f}{\partial \xi^\alpha} = -\frac{\partial A}{\partial \xi^\alpha}. \tag{99.5}$$

For each set of assigned values of the parameters ξ^α, the right sides of Eqs. (99.5) have definite constant values, and the world line determined by these equations is one of the possible trajectories of the particle. Choosing the quantities ξ^α, which are constant along the trajectory, as new space coordinates, and the quantity τ as the new time coordinate, we get the synchronous reference system; the transformation which takes us from the old coordinates to the new is given by Eqs. (99.4-5). In fact it is guaranteed that for such a transformation the time lines will be geodesics and will be normal to the hypersurfaces $\tau =$ const. The latter point is obvious from the mechanical analogy: the four-vector $c\, \partial\tau/\partial x^i$ which is normal to the hypersurface coincides in mechanics with the four-momentum of the particle, and therefore coincides in direction with its four-velocity u_i, i.e., with the four-vector tangent to the trajectory. Finally the condition $-\, g_{00} = 1$ is obviously satisfied, since the derivative

$-c\, d\tau/ds$ of the action along the trajectory is the mass of the particle, which we set equal to 1; therefore $|c\, d\tau/ds| = 1$.

We write the equations of the gravitational field in the synchronous reference system, separating the operations of space and time differentiation in the equations.

We introduce the notation

$$\varkappa_{\alpha\beta} = \frac{\partial g_{\alpha\beta}}{c\partial t} \tag{99.6}$$

for the time derivatives of the three-dimensional metric tensor; these quantities also form a three-dimensional tensor. We note that the sum $\varkappa_\alpha^\alpha$ is the logarithmic derivative of the determinant $-g$: from (86.4) we have

$$\varkappa_\alpha^\alpha = g^{\alpha\beta}\frac{\partial g_{\alpha\beta}}{c\partial t} = \frac{\partial}{c\partial t}\ln(-g). \tag{99.7}$$

For the Christoffel symbols we find the expressions:

$$\begin{gathered} \Gamma^0_{00} = \Gamma^\alpha_{00} = \Gamma^0_{0\alpha} = 0, \\ \Gamma^0_{\alpha\beta} = \tfrac{1}{2}\varkappa_{\alpha\beta}, \qquad \Gamma^\alpha_{0\beta} = \tfrac{1}{2}\varkappa^\alpha_\beta, \qquad \Gamma^\alpha_{\beta\gamma} = \lambda^\alpha_{\beta\gamma}, \end{gathered} \tag{99.8}$$

where $\lambda^\alpha_{\beta\gamma}$ are the three-dimensional Christoffel symbols formed from the tensor $g_{\alpha\beta}$. A calculation using formula (92.11) gives the following expressions for the components of the tensor R_{ik}:

$$\begin{aligned} R_{00} &= -\frac{1}{2c}\frac{\partial}{\partial t}\varkappa_\alpha^\alpha - \frac{1}{4}\varkappa_\alpha^\beta\varkappa_\beta^\alpha, \\ R_{0\alpha} &= \frac{1}{2}(\varkappa^\beta_{\alpha;\beta} - \varkappa^\beta_{\beta;\alpha}), \\ R_{\alpha\beta} &= \frac{1}{2c}\frac{\partial}{\partial t}\varkappa_{\alpha\beta} + \frac{1}{4}(\varkappa_{\alpha\beta}\varkappa^\gamma_\gamma - 2\varkappa^\gamma_\alpha\varkappa_{\beta\gamma}) + P_{\alpha\beta}. \end{aligned} \tag{99.9}$$

Here $P_{\alpha\beta}$ is a three-dimensional tensor which is expressed in terms of $g_{\alpha\beta}$ in the same way as R_{ik} is expressed in terms of g_{ik}. All operations of raising indices and of covariant differentiation are carried out in the three-dimensional space with the metric $g_{\alpha\beta}$.

We write the equations of the gravitational field in mixed components. They are:

$$R_0^0 = \frac{1}{2c}\frac{\partial}{\partial t}\varkappa_\alpha^\alpha + \frac{1}{4}\varkappa_\alpha^\beta\varkappa_\beta^\alpha = \frac{8\pi k}{c^4}(T_0^0 - \tfrac{1}{2}T), \tag{99.10}$$

$$R_\alpha^0 = \frac{1}{2}(\varkappa^\beta_{\beta;\alpha} - \varkappa^\beta_{\alpha;\beta}) = \frac{8\pi k}{c^4}T_\alpha^0, \tag{99.11}$$

$$R_\alpha^\beta = P_\alpha^\beta + \frac{1}{2c\sqrt{-g}}\frac{\partial}{\partial t}(\sqrt{-g}\,\varkappa_\alpha^\beta) = \frac{8\pi k}{c^4}(T_\alpha^\beta - \tfrac{1}{2}\delta_\alpha^\beta T). \tag{99.12}$$

PROBLEMS

1. Find the general form of the infinitesimal transformation from one synchronous reference system to another.

Solution: The transformation has the form

$$t \to t+\phi(x^1, x^2, x^3),\ x^\alpha \to x^\alpha+\xi^\alpha(x^1, x^2, x^3, t),$$

where ϕ and ξ^α are small quantities. We are guaranteed that the condition $-g_{00} = 1$ is satisfied by keeping ϕ independent of t; to maintain the condition $g_{0\alpha} = 0$, we must satisfy the equations

$$g_{\alpha\beta}\frac{\partial \xi^\beta}{\partial t} - c\frac{\partial \phi}{\partial x^\alpha},$$

from which

$$\xi^\alpha = c\frac{\partial \phi}{\partial x^\beta}\int g^{\alpha\beta}\,dt+f^\alpha(x^1, x^2, x^3),$$

where the f^α are again small quantities.

Thus the transformation contains four arbitrary functions (ϕ, f^α) of the space coordinates.

2. Calculate the components of the curvature tensor R_{iklm} in the synchronous reference system.

Solution: The computation according to formula (92.4), using the Christoffel symbols (99.8) gives:

$$R_{\alpha\beta\gamma\delta} = P_{\alpha\beta\gamma\delta}+\frac{1}{4}(\varkappa_{\alpha\gamma}\varkappa_{\beta\delta}-\varkappa_{\alpha\delta}\varkappa_{\beta\gamma}),$$

$$R_{0\alpha\beta\gamma} = \frac{1}{2}(\varkappa_{\alpha\beta;\gamma}-\varkappa_{\alpha\gamma;\beta}),$$

$$R_{0\alpha0\beta} = -\frac{1}{2c}\frac{\partial}{\partial t}\varkappa_{\alpha\beta}+\frac{1}{4}\varkappa_{\alpha\gamma}\varkappa^\gamma_\beta,$$

where $P_{\alpha\beta\gamma\delta}$ is the three-dimensional curvature tensor.

§ 100. The energy-momentum pseudotensor

In the absence of a gravitational field, the law of conservation of energy and momentum of the material (and electromagnetic field) is expressed by the equation $\partial T_{ik}/\partial x^k = 0$. The generalization of this equation to the case where a gravitational field is present is Eq. (94.7):

$$T^k_{i;k} = \frac{1}{\sqrt{-g}}\frac{\partial(T^k_i\sqrt{-g})}{\partial x^k} - \frac{1}{2}\frac{\partial g_{kl}}{\partial x^i}T^{kl} = 0. \qquad (100.1)$$

In this form, however, this equation does not generally express any conservation law whatever.† This is related to the fact that in a gravitational field the four-momentum of the matter alone must not be conserved, but

† Because the integral $\int T^k_i\sqrt{-g}\,dS_k$ is conserved only if the condition $\dfrac{\partial(\sqrt{-g}T^k_i)}{\partial x^k} = 0$ is fulfilled, and not (100.1). This is easily verified by carrying out in curvilinear coordinates all those calculations which in § 29 were done in cartesian coordinates. Besides it is sufficient simply to note that these calculations have a purely formal character not connected with the tensor properties of the corresponding quantities, like the proof of Gauss' theorem, which has the same form (83.20) in curvilinear as in cartesian coordinates.

rather the four-momentum of matter plus gravitational field; the latter is not included in the expression for T_i^k.

To determine the conservation of the total four-momentum for a gravitational field plus the matter located in it, we proceed as follows.† We choose a system of coordinates of such form that at some particular point in spacetime all the first derivatives of the g_{ik} vanish (the g_{ik} need not, for this, necessarily have their Galilean values). Then at this point the second term in equation (100.1) vanishes, and in the first term we can take $\sqrt{-g}$ out from under the derivative sign, so that there remains

$$\frac{\partial}{\partial x^k} T_i^k = 0,$$

or, in contravariant components,

$$\frac{\partial}{\partial x^k} T^{ik} = 0.$$

Quantities T^{ik}, identically satisfying this equation, can be written in the form

$$T^{ik} = \frac{\partial}{\partial x^l} \eta^{ikl},$$

where the η^{ikl} are quantities antisymmetric in the indices k, l;

$$\eta^{ikl} = -\eta^{ilk}.$$

Actually it is not difficult to bring T^{ik} to this form. To do this we start from the field equation

$$T^{ik} = \frac{c^4}{8\pi k}\left(R^{ik} - \frac{1}{2} g^{ik} R\right),$$

and for R^{ik} we have, according to (92.4)

$$R^{ik} = \frac{1}{2} g^{im} g^{kp} g^{ln} \left\{ \frac{\partial^2 g_{lp}}{\partial x^m \partial x^n} + \frac{\partial^2 g_{mn}}{\partial x^l \partial x^p} - \frac{\partial^2 g_{ln}}{\partial x^m \partial x^p} - \frac{\partial^2 g_{mp}}{\partial x^l \partial x^n} \right\}$$

(we recall that at the point under consideration, all the $\Gamma^i_{kl} = 0$). After simple transformations the tensor T^{ik} can be put in the form

$$T^{ik} = \frac{\partial}{\partial x^l} \left\{ \frac{c^4}{16\pi k} \frac{1}{(-g)} \frac{\partial}{\partial x^m} [(-g)(g^{ik} g^{lm} - g^{il} g^{km})] \right\}.$$

The expression in the curly brackets is antisymmetric in k and l, and is the quantity which we designated above as η^{ikl}. Since the first derivatives

---

† One might get the notion to apply to the gravitational field the formula (94.4), substituting $\Lambda = \frac{c^4}{16\pi k} G$. We emphasize, however, that this formula applies only to physical systems described by quantities q different from the g_{ik}; therefore it cannot be applied to the gravitational field which is determined by the quantities g_{ik} themselves. Note, by the way, that upon substituting G in place of Λ in (94.4) we would obtain simply zero, as is immediately clear from the relation (95.3) and the equation of the field in vacuum.

of g_{ik} are zero at the point under consideration, the factor $1/(-g)$ can be taken out from under the sign of differentiation $\partial/\partial x^l$. We introduce the notation

$$h^{ikl} = \frac{c^4}{16\pi k}\frac{\partial}{\partial x^m}[(-g)(g^{ik}g^{lm}-g^{il}g^{km})]. \tag{100.2}$$

These quantities are antisymmetric in k and l:

$$h^{ikl} = -h^{ilk}. \tag{100.3}$$

Then we can write

$$\frac{\partial h^{ikl}}{\partial x^l} = (-g)T^{ik}.$$

This relation, derived under the assumption $\partial g_{ik}/\partial x^l = 0$, is no longer valid when we go to an arbitrary system of coordinates. In the general case, the difference $\partial h^{ikl}/\partial x^l - (-g)T^{ik}$ is different from zero; we denote it by $(-g)t^{ik}$. Then we have, by definition,

$$(-g)\,(T^{ik}+t^{ik}) = \frac{\partial h^{ikl}}{\partial x^l}. \tag{100.4}$$

The quantities t^{ik} are symmetric in i and k:

$$t^{ik} = t^{ki}. \tag{100.5}$$

This is clear immediately from their definition, since like the tensor T^{ik}, the derivatives $\partial h^{ikl}/\partial x^l$ are symmetric quantities.† Expressing T^{ik} in terms of R^{ik}, according to the gravitational equations, and using expression (100.2) for the h^{ikl}, one can obtain, after a rather lengthy calculation, the following expression for t^{ik}:

$$\begin{aligned} t^{ik} = \frac{c^4}{16\pi k}\{ &(2\Gamma^n_{lm}\Gamma^p_{np}-\Gamma^n_{lp}\Gamma^p_{mn}-\Gamma^n_{ln}\Gamma^p_{mp})(g^{il}g^{km}-g^{ik}g^{lm})+ \\ &+g^{il}g^{mn}(\Gamma^k_{lp}\Gamma^p_{mn}+\Gamma^k_{mn}\Gamma^p_{lp}-\Gamma^k_{np}\Gamma^p_{lm}-\Gamma^k_{lm}\Gamma^p_{np})+ \\ &+g^{kl}g^{mn}(\Gamma^i_{lp}\Gamma^p_{mn}+\Gamma^i_{mn}\Gamma^p_{lp}-\Gamma^i_{np}\Gamma^p_{lm}-\Gamma^i_{lm}\Gamma^p_{np})+ \\ &+g^{lm}g^{np}(\Gamma^i_{ln}\Gamma^k_{mp}-\Gamma^i_{lm}\Gamma^k_{np}), \end{aligned} \tag{100.6}$$

or, in terms of derivatives of the components of the metric tensor,

$$\begin{aligned} (-g)t^{ik} = \frac{c^4}{16\pi k}\{ &\mathfrak{g}^{ik}{}_{,l}\,\mathfrak{g}^{lm}{}_{,m}-\mathfrak{g}^{il}{}_{,l}\,\mathfrak{g}^{km}{}_{,m}+\tfrac{1}{2}g^{ik}g_{lm}\,\mathfrak{g}^{ln}{}_{,p}\,\mathfrak{g}^{pm}{}_{,n}- \\ &-(g^{il}g_{mn}\,\mathfrak{g}^{kn}{}_{,p}\,\mathfrak{g}^{mp}{}_{,l}+g^{kl}g_{mn}\,\mathfrak{g}^{in}{}_{,p}\,\mathfrak{g}^{mp}{}_{,l})+g_{lm}g^{np}\,\mathfrak{g}^{il}{}_{,n}\,\mathfrak{g}^{km}{}_{,p}+ \\ &+\tfrac{1}{8}(2g^{il}g^{km}-g^{ik}g^{lm})(2g_{np}g_{qr}-g_{pq}g_{nr})\,\mathfrak{g}^{nr}{}_{,l}\,\mathfrak{g}^{pq}{}_{,m}\}, \end{aligned} \tag{100.7}$$

where $\mathfrak{g}^{ik} = \sqrt{-g}\,g^{ik}$, while the index $,i$ denotes a simple differentiation with respect to x^i.

† For just this reason we took $(-g)$ out from under the derivative sign in the expression for T^{ik}. If this had not been done, $\partial h^{ikl}/\partial x^l$ and therefore also t^{ik} would turn out not to be symmetric in i and k.

An essential property of the t^{ik} is that they do not constitute a tensor; this is clear from the fact that in $\partial h^{ikl}/\partial x^l$ there appears the ordinary, and not the covariant derivative. However, t^{ik} is expressed in terms of the quantities Γ^i_{kl}, and the latter behave like a tensor with respect to linear transformations of the coordinates (see § 85), so the same applies to the t^{ik}.

From the definition (100.4) it follows that for the sum $T^{ik}+t^{ik}$ the equation

$$\frac{\partial}{\partial x^k}(-g)(T^{ik}+t^{ik}) = 0 \tag{100.8}$$

is identically satisfied. This means that there is a conservation law for the quantities

$$P^i = \frac{1}{c}\int (-g)\,(T^{ik}+t^{ik})\,dS_k. \tag{100.9}$$

In the absence of a gravitational field, in Galilean coordinates, $t^{ik} = 0$, and the integral we have written goes over into $\frac{1}{c}\int T^{ik}\,dS_k$, that is, into the four-momentum of the material. Therefore the quantity (100.9) must be identified with the total four-momentum of matter plus gravitational field. The aggregate of quantities t^{ik} is called the *energy-momentum pseudotensor* of the gravitational field.

The integration in (100.9) can be taken over any infinite hypersurface, including all of the three-dimensional space. If we choose for this the hypersurface $x^0 = \text{const}$, then P^i can be written in the form of a three-dimensional space integral:

$$P^i = \frac{1}{c}\int (-g)\,(T^{i0}+t^{i0})\,dV. \tag{100.10}$$

This fact, that the total four-momentum of matter plus field is expressible as an integral of the quantity $(-g)\,(T^{ik}+t^{ik})$ which is symmetric in the indices i, k, is very important. It means that there is a conservation law for the angular momentum, defined as (see § 32)†

$$M^{ik} = \int (x^i\,dP^k - x^k\,dP^i) = \frac{1}{c}\int \{x^i\,(T^{kl}+t^{kl}) - x^k(T^{il}+t^{il})\}\,(-g)\,dS_l. \tag{100.11}$$

† It is necessary to note that the expression obtained by us for the four-momentum of matter plus field is by no means the only possible one. On the contrary, one can, in an infinity of ways (see for example, the problem in this section), form expressions which in the absence of a field reduce to T^{ik}, and which upon integration over dS_k, give conservation of some quantity. However, the choice made by us is the only one for which the energy-momentum pseudotensor of the field contains only first (and not higher) derivatives of g_{ik} (a condition which is completely natural from the physical point of view), and is also symmetric, so that it is possible to formulate a conservation law for the angular momentum.

Thus, also in the general theory of relativity, for a closed system of gravitating bodies the total angular momentum is conserved, and moreover one can again define a center of inertia which carries out a uniform motion. This latter point is related to the conservation of the components $M^{0\alpha}$ (see § 14), which is expressed by the equation

$$x^0 \int (T^{\alpha 0}+t^{\alpha 0})(-g)\,dV - \int x^\alpha (T^{00}+t^{00})(-g)\,dV = \text{const},$$

so that the coordinates of the center of inertia are given by the formula

$$X^\alpha = \frac{\int x^\alpha (T^{00}+t^{00})(-g)\,dV}{\int (T^{00}+t^{00})(-g)dV}. \tag{100.12}$$

By choosing a coordinate system which is inertial in a given volume element, we can make all the t^{ik} vanish at any point in space-time (since then all the Γ^i_{kl} vanish). On the other hand, we can get values of the t^{ik} different from zero in flat space, i.e., in the absence of a gravitational field, if we simply use curvilinear coordinates instead of cartesian. Thus, in any case, it has no meaning to speak of a definite localization of the energy of the gravitational field in space. If the tensor T_{ik} is zero at some world point, then this is the case for any reference system, since we may say that at this point there is no matter or electromagnetic field. On the other hand, from the vanishing of a pseudotensor at some point in one reference system it does not at all follow that this is so for another reference system, so that it is meaningless to talk of whether or not there is gravitational energy at a given place. This corresponds completely to the fact that by a suitable choice of coordinates, we can "annihilate" the gravitational field in a given volume element, in which case, from what has been said, the pseudotensor t^{ik} also vanishes in this volume element.

The quantities P^i (the four-momentum of field plus matter) have a completely definite meaning and are independent of the choice of reference system to just the extent that it is necessary on the basis of physical considerations.

Let us draw around the masses under consideration a region of space sufficiently large so that outside of it we may say that there is no gravitational field. In the course of time, this region cuts out a "channel" in four-dimensional space-time. Outside of this channel there is no field, so that four-space is flat. Because of this we must, when calculating the energy and momentum of the field, choose a four-dimensional reference system such that outside the channel it goes over into a Galilean system and all the t^{ik} vanish.

By this requirement the reference system is, of course, not at all uniquely determined — it can still be chosen arbitrarily in the interior of the channel. However the P^i, in full accord with their physical meaning, turn out to be completely independent of the choice of coordinate system in the interior of the channel. Consider two coordinate systems, different in the interior of the channel, but reducing outside of it to one and the same Galilean system, and compare the values of the four-momentum P^i and P'^i in these two systems at definite moments of "time" x^0 and x'^0. Let us introduce a third coordinate system, coinciding in the interior of the channel at the moment x^0 with the first system, and at the moment x'^0 with the second, while outside of the channel it is Galilean. But by vritue of the law of conservation of energy and momentum the quantities P^i are constant ($\partial P^i/\partial x^0 = 0$). This is the case for the third coordinate system as well as for the first two, and from this it follows that $P^i = P'^i$.

Earlier it was mentioned that the quantities t^{ik} behave like a tensor with respect to linear transformations of the coordinates. Therefore the quantities P^i form a vector with respect to such transformations, in particular with respect to Lorentz transformations which, at infinity, take one Galilean reference frame into another.† Substituting (100.4) in (100.9), we find

$$P^i = \frac{1}{c}\int \frac{\partial h^{ikl}}{\partial x^l}\, dS_k.$$

This integral can be transformed into an integral over an ordinary surface by means of (6.13):

$$P_i = \frac{1}{2c}\oint h^{ikl}\, df^*_{kl}. \tag{100.13}$$

If for the surface of integration in (100.9) we choose the hypersurface $x^0 = \text{const}$, then in (100.13) the surface of integration turns out to be a surface in ordinary space.‡ Thus we find an expression for the four-momentum of the matter and gravitational field in a certain region of three-dimensional space in the form of an integral over the surface bounding this volume:

$$P^i = \frac{1}{c}\oint h^{i0\alpha}\, df_\alpha. \tag{100.14}$$

To derive the analogous formula for the angular momentum, we write formula (100.2) in the form

$$h^{ikl} = \frac{\partial}{\partial x^m}\lambda^{iklm}; \tag{100.15}$$

†Strictly speaking, in the definition (100.9) P^i is a four-vector only with respect to linear transformations with determinant equal to unity; among these are the Lorentz transformations, which alone are of physical interest. If we also admit transformations with determinant not equal to unity, then we must introduce into the definition of P^i the value of g at infinity by writing $\sqrt{-g_\infty}\, P^i$ in place of P^i on the left side of (100.9).

‡ The quantity df^*_{kl} is the "normal" to the surface element, related to the "tangential" element df^{ik} by (16.9): $df^*_{ik} = \frac{1}{2}e_{iklm}\, df^{lm}$. On the surface bounding the hypersurface which is perpendicular to the x^0 axis, the only nonzero components of df^{lm} are those with $l, m = 1, 2, 3$, and so df^*_{ik} has only those components in which one of i and k is 0. The components $df^*_{0\alpha}$ are just the components of the three-dimensional element of ordinary surface, which we denote by df_α.

the expression for the quantities λ^{iklm} in terms of the components of the metric tensor is obvious from (100.2). Substituting (100.4) in (100.11) and integrating by parts, we obtain:

$$M^{ik}=\frac{1}{c}\int\left(x^i\frac{\partial^2\lambda^{klmn}}{\partial x^m\,\partial x^n}-x^k\frac{\partial^2\lambda^{ilmn}}{\partial x^m\,\partial x^n}\right)dS_l$$

$$=\frac{1}{2c}\int\left(x^i\frac{\partial\lambda^{klmn}}{\partial x^n}-x^k\frac{\partial\lambda^{ilmn}}{\partial x^n}\right)df^*_{lm}-\frac{1}{c}\int\left(\delta^i_m\frac{\partial\lambda^{klmn}}{\partial x^n}-\delta^k_m\frac{\partial\lambda^{ilmn}}{\partial x^n}\right)dS_l$$

$$=\frac{1}{2c}\int(x^ih^{klm}-x^kh^{ilm})\,df^*_{lm}-\frac{1}{c}\int\frac{\partial}{\partial x^n}(\lambda^{klin}-\lambda^{ilkn})\,dS_l.$$

From the definition of the quantities λ^{iklm} it is easy to see that

$$\lambda^{ilkn}-\lambda^{klin}=\lambda^{ilnk},\qquad \lambda^{inlk}=-\lambda^{ilnk}.$$

Thus the remaining integral over dS_l is equal to

$$\frac{1}{c}\int\frac{\partial\lambda^{ilnk}}{\partial x^n}dS_l=\frac{1}{2c}\int\lambda^{ilnk}\,df^*_{ln}.$$

Finally, again choosing a purely spatial surface for the integration, we obtain:

$$M^{ik}=\frac{1}{c}\int(x^ih^{k0\alpha}-x^kh^{i0\alpha}+\lambda^{i0\alpha k})\,df_\alpha. \tag{100.16}$$

We remind the reader that in applying formulas (100.14) and (100.16), in accordance with what was said above, the system of space coordinates should be chosen so that at inifinity the g_{ik} tend toward their constant Galilean values. Thus for the calculation according to formula (100.14) of the four-momentum of an isolated system of bodies which always remain close to the origin of coordinates, we can use for the metric at large distances from the bodies the expression (100.14), transforming it from spherical spatial coordinates to cartesian (for which we must replace dr by $n_\alpha dx^\alpha$, where $\mathbf{n}$ is a unit vector along the direction of $\mathbf{r}$); the corresponding metric tensor is

$$g_{00}=-\left(1-\frac{2km}{c^2r}\right),\quad g_{\alpha\beta}=\delta_{\alpha\beta}+\frac{2km}{c^2}\frac{n_\alpha n_\beta}{r},\quad g_{0\alpha}=0, \tag{100.17}$$

where m is the total mass of the system. Computing the required components of h^{ikl} using formula (100.2), we obtain to the required accuracy (we keep terms $\sim 1/r^2$):

$$h^{\alpha 0\beta}=0,$$

$$h^{00\alpha}=\frac{c^4}{16\pi k}\frac{\partial}{\partial x^\beta}(g^{00}g^{\alpha\beta})=\frac{mc^2}{8\pi}\frac{\partial}{\partial x^\beta}\left(-\frac{\delta^{\alpha\beta}}{r}+\frac{x^\alpha x^\beta}{r^3}\right)=\frac{mc^2}{4\pi}\frac{n^\alpha}{r^2}.$$

Now integrating (100.14) over a sphere of radius r, we obtain finally:

$$P^\alpha=0,\quad P^0=mc, \tag{100.18}$$

a result which was to be expected. It is an expression to the equality of "gravitational" and "interial" mass. (*Gravitational* mass means the mass which determines the gravitational field produced by a body; this is the mass which enters in the expression for the interval in a gravitational field, or, in particular, in Newton's law. The *inertial* mass determines the relation between momentum and energy of a body and, in particular, the rest energy of a body is equal to this mass multiplied by c^2.)

In the case of a constant gravitational field it turns out to be possible to derive a simple expression for the total energy of matter plus field in the form of an integral extended only over the space occupied by the matter. To obtain this expression one can, for example, start from the following identity, valid (as one easily verifies) when all quantities are independent of x^0:†

$$R_0^0 = \frac{1}{\sqrt{-g}} \frac{\partial}{\partial x^\alpha} (\sqrt{-g}\, g^{i0} \Gamma_{0i}^\alpha).$$

Integrating $R_0^0\sqrt{-g}$ over (three-dimensional) space and applying Gauss' theorem, we obtain

$$\int R_0^0 \sqrt{-g}\, dV = \oint \sqrt{-g}\, g^{i0} \Gamma_{0i}^\alpha\, df_\alpha .$$

We choose a sufficiently distant surface of integration and use on it the expressions for the g_{ik} given by formula (100.17), and obtain after a simple calculation

$$\int R_0^0 \sqrt{-g}\, dV = -\frac{4\pi k}{c^2} m = -\frac{4\pi k}{c^3} P^0.$$

Noting also from the equations of the field that

$$R_0^0 = \frac{8\pi k}{c^4}\left(T_0^0 - \frac{1}{2} T\right) = \frac{4\pi k}{c^4} (T_0^0 - T_1^1 - T_2^2 - T_3^3),$$

we get the required expression

$$P^0 = mc = \frac{1}{c} \int (T_1^1 + T_2^2 + T_3^3 - T_0^0) \sqrt{-g}\, dV . \tag{100.19}$$

---

† From (92.11), we have

$$R_0^0 = g^{0i} R_{i0} = g^{0i} \left(\frac{\partial \Gamma_{i0}^l}{\partial x^l} + \Gamma_{i0}^l \Gamma_{lm}^m - \Gamma_{il}^m \Gamma_{0m}^l \right),$$

and with the aid of (86.5) and (86.6), we find that this expression can be written as

$$R_0^0 = \frac{1}{\sqrt{-g}} \frac{\partial}{\partial x^l} (\sqrt{-g}\, g^{0i} \Gamma_{i0}^l) + g^{im} \Gamma_{ml}^0 \Gamma_{i0}^l .$$

With the help of these same relations (86.8), one can easily verify that the second term on the right is identically equal to $-\frac{1}{2}\Gamma_{lm}^0 \frac{\partial g^{lm}}{\partial x^0}$, and vanishes as a consequence of the fact that all quantities are independent of x^0. Finally, for the same reason, replacing the summation over l in the first term by a summation over α, we obtain the formula of the text.

This formula expresses the total energy of matter plus constant gravitational field (i.e., the total mass of the bodies) in terms of the energy-momentum tensor of the matter alone (R. Tolman, 1930). We recall that in the case of central symmetry of the field, we had still another expression for this same quantity, formula (97.22).

PROBLEM

Find the expression for the total four-momentum of matter plus gravitational field, using formulae (32.5).

Solution: In curvilinear coordinates one has

$$S = \int \Lambda \sqrt{-g}\, dV\, dt,$$

and therefore to obtain a quantity which is conserved we must in (32.5) write $\Lambda \sqrt{-g}$ in place of Λ, so that the four-momentum has the form

$$P_i = \frac{1}{c}\int \left\{ \Lambda \sqrt{-g}\, \delta_i^k - \sum \frac{\partial q^{(l)}}{\partial x^i} \frac{\partial (\sqrt{-g}\, \Lambda)}{\partial \dfrac{\partial q^{(l)}}{\partial x^k}} \right\} dS_k .$$

In applying this formula to matter, for which the quantities $q^{(l)}$ are different from the g_{ik}, we can take $\sqrt{-g}$ out from under the sign of differentiation, and the integrand turns out to be equal to $\sqrt{-g}\, T_i^k$, where T_i^k is the energy-momentum tensor of the matter. When applying this same formula to the gravitational field, we must set $\Lambda = \frac{c^4}{16\pi k} G$, while the quantities $q^{(l)}$ are the components g_{ik} of the metric tensor. The total four-momentum of field plus matter is thus equal to

$$P_i = \frac{1}{c}\int T_i^k \sqrt{-g}\, dS_k + \frac{c^3}{16\pi k}\int \left[G\sqrt{-g}\, \delta_i^k - \frac{\partial g^{lm}}{\partial x^i} \frac{\partial (G\sqrt{-g})}{\partial \dfrac{\partial g^{lm}}{\partial x^k}} \right] dS_k .$$

Using the expression (93.3) for G, we can rewrite this expression in the form:

$$P_i = \frac{1}{c}\int \left\{ T_i^k \sqrt{-g} + \frac{c^4}{16\pi k}\left[G\sqrt{-g}\, \delta_i^k + \Gamma_{lm}^k \frac{\partial (g^{lm}\sqrt{-g})}{\partial x^i} - \Gamma_{ml}^l \frac{\partial (g^{mk}\sqrt{-g})}{\partial x^i} \right] \right\} dS_k .$$

The second term in the curly brackets gives the four-momentum of the gravitational field in the absence of matter. The integrand is not symmetric in the indices i, k, so that one cannot formulate a law of conservation of angular momentum.

§ 101. Gravitational waves

Let us consider a weak gravitational field in vacuo. In a weak field the space-time metric is "almost Galilean", i.e., we can choose a system of reference in which the components of the metric tensor are almost equal to their Galilean values, which we denote by

$$g_{\alpha\beta}^{(0)} = \delta_{\alpha\beta}, \quad g_{\alpha 0}^{(0)} = 0, \quad g_{00}^{(0)} = -1. \tag{101.1}$$

We can therefore write the g_{ik} in the form

$$g_{ik} = g_{ik}^{(0)} + h_{ik}, \tag{101.2}$$

where the h_{ik} are small corrections, determined by the gravitational field.

With small h_{ik}, the components Γ^i_{kl}, which are expressed in terms of the derivatives of g_{ik}, are also small. Neglecting powers of h_{ik} higher than the first, we may retain in the tensor R_{iklm} (92.4) only the terms in the first bracket:

$$R_{iklm} = \frac{1}{2}\left(\frac{\partial^2 h_{im}}{\partial x^k \partial x^l} + \frac{\partial^2 h_{kl}}{\partial x^i \partial x^m} - \frac{\partial^2 h_{km}}{\partial x^i \partial x^l} - \frac{\partial^2 h_{il}}{\partial x^k \partial x^m}\right). \tag{101.3}$$

For the contracted tensor R_{ik}, we have to this same accuracy

$$R_{ik} = g^{lm} R_{limk} \approx g^{(0)lm} R_{limk}$$

or

$$R_{ik} = \frac{1}{2}\left(-g^{(0)lm}\frac{\partial^2 h_{ik}}{\partial x^l \partial x^m} + \frac{\partial^2 h^l_i}{\partial x^k \partial x^l} + \frac{\partial^2 h^l_k}{\partial x^i \partial x^l} - \frac{\partial^2 h}{\partial x^i \partial x^k}\right), \tag{101.4}$$

where $h = h^i_i$.†

We have chosen our reference system so that the g_{ik} differ little from the $g^{(0)}_{ik}$. But this condition is also fulfilled for any infinitesimal coordinate transformation, so that we can still apply to the h_{ik} four conditions (equal to the number of coordinates) which do not violate the condition that the h_{ik} be small. We choose for these auxiliary conditions the equations

$$\frac{\partial \psi^k_i}{\partial x^k} = 0,$$

$$\psi^k_i = h^k_i - \frac{1}{2}\delta^k_i h. \tag{101.5}$$

It should be pointed out that even with these conditions the coordinates are not uniquely determined; let us see what transformations are still admissible. Under the transformation $x'^i = x^i + \xi^i$, where the ξ^i are small quantities, the tensor g_{ik} goes over into

$$g'_{ik} = g_{ik} - \frac{\partial \xi_i}{\partial x^k} - \frac{\partial \xi_k}{\partial x^i},$$

i.e.

$$h'_{ik} = h_{ik} - \frac{\partial \xi_i}{\partial x^k} - \frac{\partial \xi_k}{\partial x^i} \tag{101.6}$$

[see formula (94.3)], in which the covariant differentiation reduces for the present case to ordinary differentiation, because of the constancy of $g^{(0)}_{ik}$).

† In accordance with the approximation, all operations of raising and lowering indices of small tensors and vectors are performed here and in the sequel using the "unperturbed" metric tensor $g^{(0)}_{ik}$. Thus $h^k_i = g^{(0)kl} h_{il}$, etc.

Then we have for the contravariant components g^{ik}:

$$g^{ik} = g^{(0)ik} - h^{ik}$$

(so that, to terms of first order, the condition $g_{il}g^{lk} = \delta^k_i$ is satisfied).

It is then easy to show that, if the h_{ik} satisfy the condition (101.5), the h'_{ik} will also satisfy this condition, if the ξ_i are solutions of the equation

$$\Box \xi_i = 0, \tag{101.7}$$

where $\Box$ denotes the d'Alembertian operator

$$\Box = g^{(0)lm} \frac{\partial^2}{\partial x^l \partial x^m} = \frac{\partial^2}{\partial x_\alpha^2} - \frac{1}{c^2} \frac{\partial^2}{\partial t^2}.$$

From condition (101.5), the last three terms in the expression (101.4) for R_{ik} cancel one another, and we find:

$$R_{ik} = -\frac{1}{2} \Box h_{ik}.$$

Thus the equation for the gravitational field in vacuum takes on the form

$$\Box h_i^k = 0. \tag{101.8}$$

This is the ordinary wave equation. Thus gravitational fields, like electromagnetic fields, propagate in vacuum with the velocity of light.

Let us consider a plane gravitational wave. In such a wave the field changes only along one direction in space; for this direction we choose the axis $x^1 = x$. Equation (101.8) then changes to

$$\left(\frac{\partial^2}{\partial x^2} - \frac{1}{c^2} \frac{\partial^2}{\partial t^2} \right) h_i^k = 0, \tag{101.9}$$

the solution of which is any function of $t \pm x/c$ (§ 47).

Consider a wave propagating in the positive direction along the x axis. Then all the quantities h_i^k are functions of $t - x/c$. The auxiliary condition (101.5) in this case gives $\dot{\psi}_i^1 - \dot{\psi}_i^0 = 0$, where the dot denotes differentiation with respect to t. This equality can be integrated by simply dropping the sign of differentiation — the integration constant can be set equal to zero since we are here interested only (as in the case of electromagnetic waves) in the varying part of the field. Thus, among the components ψ_i^k that are left, we have the relations

$$\psi_1^1 = \psi_1^0, \quad \psi_2^1 = \psi_2^0, \quad \psi_3^1 = \psi_3^0, \quad \psi_0^1 = \psi_0^0. \tag{101.10}$$

As was pointed out, the conditions (101.5) still do not determine the system of reference uniquely. We can still subject the coordinates to a transformation of the form $x'^i = x^i + \xi^i(t - x/c)$. These transformations can be employed to make the four quantities $\psi_1^0, \psi_2^0, \psi_3^0, \psi_2^2 + \psi_3^3$ vanish; from the equalities (101.10) it then follows that the components $\psi_1^1, \psi_2^1, \psi_3^1, \psi_0^0$ also vanish. As for the remaining quantities $\psi_2^3, \psi_2^2 - \psi_3^3$, they cannot be made to vanish by any choice of reference system since, as we see from (101.6), these components do not change under a transformation $x'^i = x^i + \xi^i(t - x/c)$. We note that $\psi = \psi_i^i$ also vanishes, and therefore $\psi_i^k = h_i^k$.

Thus a plane gravitational wave is determined by two quantities, h_{23} and $h_{22} = -h_{33}$. In other words, gravitational waves are transverse waves whose polarization is determined by a symmetric tensor of the second rank in the yz plane, the sum of whose diagonal terms, $h_{22}+h_{33}$, is zero.

We calculate the energy flux in a plane gravitational wave. The energy flux in a gravitational field is determined by the quantities $-cgt^{0\alpha}$. In a wave propagating along the x^1 axis, it is clear that only the component t^{10} is different from zero.

The pseudotensor t^{ik} is of second order; we must calculate the t^{01} only to this accuracy. A calculation making use of the formula (100.6), and the fact that in a plane wave the only components of h_{ik} different from zero are h_{23}, $h_{22} = -h_{33}$, leads to the result:

$$t^{01} = -\frac{c^3}{32\pi k}\left(\frac{\partial h_{22}}{\partial x}\frac{\partial h_{22}}{\partial t}+\frac{\partial h_{33}}{\partial x}\frac{\partial h_{33}}{\partial t}+2\frac{\partial h_{23}}{\partial x}\frac{\partial h_{23}}{\partial t}\right).$$

If all quantities are functions only of $t-x/c$, then we get from this, finally,

$$t^{01} = \frac{c^2}{16\pi k}\left[\dot{h}_{23}^2+\tfrac{1}{4}(\dot{h}_{22}-\dot{h}_{33})^2\right]. \tag{101.11}$$

Since it has a definite energy, a gravitational wave produces around itself a certain additional gravitational field. This field is a quantity of higher (second) order compared to the field of the wave itself, since the energy producing it is a quantity of second order.

As initial conditions for the arbitrary field of a gravitational wave we must assign four arbitrary functions of the coordinates: because of the transversality of the field there are just two independent components of $h_{\alpha\beta}$, in addition to which we must also assign their first time derivatives, Although we have made this enumeration here by starting from the properties of a weak gravitational field, it is clear that the result, the number 4, cannot be related to this assumption and applies for any free gravitational field, i.e. for any field which is not associated with gravitating masses.

§ 102. Exact solutions of the gravitational field equations depending on one variable

In this section we shall consider the possible types of exact solutions of the gravitational field equations in vacuum, in which all the components of the metric tensor, for a suitable choice of reference system, are functions of a single variable. This variable may have either timelike or spacelike character; to be specific, we shall assume first that it is timelike, and shall denote it by $x^0 = t$†.

As we shall see, essentially different types of solutions are obtained depending on whether or not it is possible to choose a reference system for which all the

† In this section, to simplify the writing of formulas, we set $c = 1$.

components $g_{0\alpha}=0$ while at the same time all other components still depend on only a single variable.

The last condition obviously permits transformations of the coordinates x^α of the form

$$x^\alpha \to x^\alpha + \phi^\alpha(t)$$

where the ϕ^α are arbitrary functions of t. For such a transformation,

$$g_{0\alpha} \to g_{0\alpha} + g_{\alpha\beta}\dot{\phi}^\beta$$

(where the dot denotes differentiation with respect to t). If the determinant $|g_{\alpha\beta}| \neq 0$, the system of equations

$$g_{0\alpha} + g_{\alpha\beta}\dot{\phi}^\beta = 0 \qquad (102.1)$$

determines functions $\phi^\alpha(t)$ which accomplish the transformation to a reference system with $g_{0\alpha}=0$. By a transformation of the variable t according to $\sqrt{-g_{00}}\,dt \to dt$, we can then make $-g_{00}$ equal to unity, so that we obtain a synchronous reference system, in which

$$g_{00} = -1, \qquad g_{0\alpha} = 0, \qquad g_{\alpha\beta} = g_{\alpha\beta}(t). \qquad (102.2)$$

We can now use the equations of gravitation in the form (99.10)–(99.12). Since the quantities $g_{\alpha\beta}$, and with them the components of the three-dimensional tensor $\varkappa_{\alpha\beta} = \dot{g}_{\alpha\beta}$, do not depend on the coordinates x^α, $R^0_\alpha \equiv 0$. For the same reason, $P_{\alpha\beta} \equiv 0$, and as a result the equations of the gravitational field in vacuum reduce to the following system:

$$R^0_0 = \tfrac{1}{2}\dot{\varkappa}^\alpha_\alpha + \tfrac{1}{4}\varkappa^\beta_\alpha \varkappa^\alpha_\beta = 0, \qquad (102.3)$$

$$R^\beta_\alpha = \frac{1}{2\sqrt{-g}}\left(\sqrt{-g}\,\varkappa^\beta_\alpha\right)^{\cdot} = 0. \qquad (102.4)$$

From Eq. (102.4) it follows that

$$\sqrt{-g}\,\varkappa^\beta_\alpha = 2\lambda^\beta_\alpha, \qquad (102.5)$$

where the λ^β_α are constants. Contracting on the indices α and β, we then obtain

$$\varkappa^\alpha_\alpha = \frac{\dot{g}}{g} = \frac{2}{\sqrt{-g}}\lambda^\alpha_\alpha,$$

from which we see that $-g = \text{const}\cdot t^2$; without loss of generality we may set the constant equal to unity (simply by a scale change of the coordinates x^α); then $\lambda^\alpha_\alpha = 1$. Substitution of (102.5) into Eq. (102.3) now gives the relation

$$\lambda^\beta_\alpha \lambda^\alpha_\beta = 1 \qquad (102.6)$$

which relates the constants λ^β_α.

Next we lower the index β in Eqs. (102.5) and rewrite them as a system of ordinary differential equations:

$$\dot{g}_{\alpha\beta} = \frac{2}{t}\lambda^{\gamma}_{\alpha} g_{\gamma\beta}. \tag{102.7}$$

The set of coefficients $\lambda^{\gamma}_{\alpha}$ may be regarded as the matrix of some linear substitution. By a suitable linear transformation of the coordinates x^1, x^2, x^3 (or, what is equivalent, of $g_{1\beta}$, $g_{2\beta}$, $g_{3\beta}$), we can in general bring this matrix to diagonal form. We shall denote its principal values (roots of the characteristic equation) by $\partial p_1, \partial p_2, \partial p_3$, and assume that they are all real and distinct (concerning other cases, cf. below); the unit vectors along the corresponding principal axes are $\mathbf{n}^{(1)}$, $\mathbf{n}^{(2)}$ and $\mathbf{n}^{(3)}$. Then the solution of Eqs. (102.7) can be written in the form

$$g_{\alpha\beta} = t^{2p_1} n^{(1)}_{\alpha} n^{(1)}_{\beta} + t^{2p_2} n^{(2)}_{\alpha} n^{(2)}_{\beta} + t^{2p_3} n^{(3)}_{\alpha} n^{(3)}_{\beta} \tag{102.8}$$

(where the coefficients of the powers of t have been made equal to unity by a suitable scale change of the coordinates). Finally, choosing the directions of the vectors $\mathbf{n}^{(1)}$, $\mathbf{n}^{(2)}$, $\mathbf{n}^{(3)}$ as the directions of our axes (we call them x, y, z), we bring the metric to the final form

$$-ds^2 = -dt^2 + t^{2p_1}\,dx^2 + t^{2p_2}\,dy^2 + t^{2p_3}\,dz^2. \tag{102.9}$$

Here p_1, p_2 and p_3 are any three numbers satisfying the two relations

$$p_1+p_2+p_3 = 1, \quad p_1^2+p_2^2+p_3^2 = 1 \tag{102.10}$$

[the first of these follows from $-g = t^2$, and the second — from (102.6)]. This solution was first found by E. Kasner (1922).

The three numbers p_1, p_2 and p_3 obviously cannot all have the same value The case where two of them are equal occurs for the triples 0,0,1 and $-1/3$, $2/3$, $2/3$. In all other cases the numbers p_1, p_2 and p_3 are all different, one of them being negative and the other two positive. If we arrange them in the order $p_1 < p_2 < p_3$, their values will lie in the intervals†

$$-\tfrac{1}{3} \leqslant p_1 \leqslant 0, \quad 0 \leqslant p_2 \leqslant \tfrac{2}{3}, \quad \tfrac{2}{3} \leqslant p_3 \leqslant 1.$$

Thus the metric (102.9) corresponds to a homogeneous but anisotropic space whose total volume increases (with increasing t) proportionally to t; the linear distances along two of the axes (y and z) increase, while they decrease along the third axis (x). The moment $t = 0$ is a singular point of the solution; at this point the metric has a singularity which cannot be eliminated by any transformation of the reference system. The only exception

† The solutions of the algebraic equations (102.10) can be represented in parametric form,

$$p_1 = \frac{-s}{1+s+s^2}, \quad p_2 = \frac{s(1+s)}{1+s+s^2}, \quad p_3 = \frac{1+s}{1+s+s^2},$$

where the parameter s runs through the values from 0 to 1.

is the case where $p_1 = p_2 = 0$, $p_3 = 1$. For these values we simply have a flat space-time; by the transformation $t \sinh z \to z$, $t \cosh z \to t$ we can bring the metric (102.9) to Galilean form†.

A solution of the type of (102.9) also exists in the case where the parameter is timelike; we need only make the appropriate changes of sign, for example,

$$-ds^2 = -x^{2p_1}\, dt^2 + dx^2 + x^{2p_2}\, dy^2 + x^{2p_3}\, dz^2.$$

However, in this case there also exist solutions of another type, which occur when the characteristic equation of the matrix λ_α^β in Eqs. (102.7) has complex or coincident roots (cf. Problems 1 and 2). For the case of a timelike parameter t, these solutions are not possible, since the determinant g in them would not satisfy the necessary condition $g < 0$.

A completely different type of solution corresponds to the case where the determinant of the tensor $g_{\alpha\beta}$ which appears in Eqs. (102.1) is equal to zero. In this case there is no reference system satisfying conditions (102.2). Instead we can now choose the reference frame so that:

$$g_{10} = 1, \quad g_{00} = g_{20} = g_{30} = 0, \quad g_{\alpha\beta} = g_{\alpha\beta}(x^0),$$

where the determinant $|g_{\alpha\beta}| = 0$. The variable x^0 then has "lightlike" character: for $dx^\alpha = 0$, $dx^0 \neq 0$, the interval goes to zero; we denote this variable by $x^0 = \eta$. The corresponding interval element can be represented in the form

$$-ds^2 = 2dx^1\, d\eta + g_{ab}(dx^a + g^a\, dx^1)(dx^b + g^b\, dx^1).$$

Here and in the following equations the indices $a, b, c, \ldots$ run through the values 2,3; we may treat g_{ab} as a two-dimensional tensor and g^a as the components of a two-dimensional vector. Computation of the quantities R_{ab}, which we shall omit here, gives the following field equations:

$$R_{ab} = -\tfrac{1}{2} g_{ac}\, \dot{g}^c g_{bd}\, \dot{g}^d = 0$$

(where the dot denotes differentiation with respect to η). From this it follows that $g_{ac}\,\dot{g}^c = 0$, or $\dot{g}^c = 0$, i.e., $g^c = \text{const}$. By the transformation $x^a + g^a x^1 \to x^a$ we can therefore bring the metric to the form

$$-ds^2 = 2dx^1\, d\eta + g_{ab}(\eta)\, dx^a\, dx^b. \tag{102.11}$$

The determinant $-g$ of this metric tensor coincides with the determinant $|g_{ab}|$, while the only Christoffel symbols which are different from zero are the following:

$$\Gamma^a_{b0} = \tfrac{1}{2}\varkappa^a_b, \qquad \Gamma^1_{ab} = -\tfrac{1}{2}\varkappa_{ab},$$

† Whether or not the singularity can be eliminated can be judged from the behavior of the scalars formed from the components of the curvature tensor R_{iklm}. Thus, for the metric (102.9) the scalar $R_{iklm}R^{iklm}$ goes to infinity like t^{-4} for $t \to 0$. For the case where, $p_1 = p_2 = 0$, $p_3 = 1$, all the components of R_{iklm} are equal to zero.

where we have introduced the two-dimensional tensor $\varkappa_{ab} = \dot{g}_{ab}$. The only component of the tensor R_{ik} which is not identically zero is R_{00}, so that we have the equation

$$R_{00} = \tfrac{1}{2}\dot{\varkappa}_a^a + \tfrac{1}{4}\varkappa_a^b\varkappa_b^a = 0. \tag{102.12}$$

Thus the three functions $g_{22}(\eta)$, $g_{33}(\eta)$, $g_{23}(\eta)$ must satisfy just one equation. Therefore two of them may be assigned arbitrarily. It is convenient to write Eq. (102.12) in another form, by representing the quantities g_{ab} as

$$g_{ab} = \chi^2\gamma_{ab}, \qquad |\gamma_{ab}| = 1. \tag{102.13}$$

Then the determinant $-g = |g_{ab}| = \chi^4$, and substitution in (102.12) and a simple transformation gives:

$$\ddot{\chi} + \tfrac{1}{8}(\dot{\gamma}_{ac}\gamma^{bc})(\dot{\gamma}_{bd}\gamma^{ad})\chi = 0 \tag{102.14}$$

(where γ^{ab} is the two-dimensional tensor which is the inverse of γ_{ab}). If we arbitrarily assign the functions $\gamma_{ab}(\eta)$ (which are related to one another by the relation $|\gamma_{ab}| = 1$), the function $\chi(\eta)$ is determined by this equation.

We thus arrive at a solution containing two arbitrary functions. It is easy to see that it represents a generalization of the treatment in § 101 of a weak plane gravitational wave (propagating along one direction).† The latter is obtained if we make the transformation

$$\eta = \frac{x+t}{\sqrt{2}}, \qquad x^1 = \frac{x-t}{\sqrt{2}},$$

and set $\gamma_{ab} = \delta_{ab} + h_{ab}(\eta)$ (where the h_{ab} are small quantities, which are subjected to the condition $h_{22}+h_{33} = 0$) and $\chi = 1$; a constant value of χ satisfies Eq. (102.14) if we neglect terms of second order.

Suppose that a weak gravitational wave of finite extension (a "wave packet") passes through some point x in space. Before the arrival of the packet we have $h_{ab} = 0$ and $\chi = 1$; after its passage we again have $h_{ab} = 0, \partial^2\chi/\partial t^2 = 0$, but the inclusion of second order terms in Eq. (102.14) leads to the appearance of a nonzero negative value of $\partial\chi/\partial t$:

$$\frac{\partial\chi}{\partial t} \cong -\tfrac{1}{8}\int\left(\frac{\partial h_{ab}}{\partial t}\right)^2 dt < 0$$

(where the integral is taken over the time during which the wave passes). Thus after the passage of the wave we will have $\chi = 1 - \text{const}\cdot t$, and after some finite time interval has elapsed χ will change sign. But a null value of χ means that the determinant g of the metric tensor is zero, i.e. there is a singularity of the metric. However this singularity is not physically significant; it is related only to the inadequacy of the reference system furnished by the

† The possibility of such a generalization was first pointed out by I. Robinson and H. Bondi (1957).

passing gravitational wave and can be eliminated by appropriate transformation; after passage of the wave the space-time will again be flat.

One can show this directly. If we measure the values of the parameter η from its value for the singular point, then $\chi = \eta$, so that

$$-ds^2 = 2\,d\eta\,dx_1 + \eta^2(dx_2^2 + dx_3^2).$$

It is easily seen that for this metric $R_{iklm} = 0$, so that the corresponding space-time is flat. And, in fact, after the transformation

$$\eta x^2 = y, \qquad \eta x^3 = z, \qquad x^1 = \xi + \frac{y^2+z^2}{2\eta},$$

we get

$$-ds^2 = 2\,d\eta\,d\xi + dy^2 + dz^2,$$

after which the substitution $\eta = (x+t)/\sqrt{2}$, $\xi = (x-t)/\sqrt{2}$ finally brings the metric to Galilean form.

This property of a gravitational wave — the appearance of a fictitious singularity — is, of course, not related to the fact that the wave is weak, but also occurs in the general solution of Eq. (102.12).† As in the example treated here, near the singularity $\chi \sim \eta$, i.e., $-g \sim \eta^4$.

Finally we point out that, in addition to the general solution given above, Eq. (102.12) also has special solutions of the form

$$-ds^2 = 2\,d\eta\,dx_1 + \eta^{2s_2}\,dx_2^2 + \eta^{2s_3}\,dx_3^2, \tag{102.15}$$

where s_2, s_3 are numbers related to one another by the relation

$$s_2 + s_3 = s_2^2 + s_3^2.$$

In these solutions the metric has a true singular point (at $\eta = 0$) which cannot be eliminated by any transformation of the reference system.

Problems

1. Find the solution of Eqs. (102.7) corresponding to the case where the characteristic equation of the matrix λ_α^β has one real (p_3) and two complex ($p_{1,2} = p' + ip''$) roots.

Solution. In this case the parameter x^0, on which all the quantities depend, must have spacelike character; we denote it by x. Correspondingly, we must now have $g_{00} = +1$ in (102.2). Equations (102.3–4) are not changed (since only the common sign of R_0^0 and R_α^β is changed).

The vectors $\mathbf{n}^{(1)}$, $\mathbf{n}^{(2)}$ in (102.8) become complex: $\mathbf{n}^{(1,2)} = (\mathbf{n}' \pm i\,\mathbf{n}'')/\sqrt{2}$, where $\mathbf{n}'$, $\mathbf{n}''$ are unit vectors. Choosing the axes x^1, x^2, x^3 along the directions $\mathbf{n}'$, $\mathbf{n}''$, $\mathbf{n}^{(3)}$, we obtain the solution in the form

$$g_{11} = -g_{22} = x^{2p'}\cos\left(2p''\ln\frac{x}{a}\right), \quad g_{12} = x^{2p'}\sin\left(2p''\ln\frac{x}{a}\right),$$

$$g_{33} = x^{2p_3}, \qquad g = g_{00}\,|g_{\alpha\beta}| = -x^2,$$

† This can be shown by using Eq. (102.12) in exactly the same way as will be done in § 110 for the analogous three-dimensional equation.

where a is a constant (which can no longer be eliminated by a scale change along the x axis, without changing other coefficients in the expressions given). The numbers, p_1, p_2, p_3 again satisfy the relations (102.10), where the real number p_3 is either $< -1/3$ or > 1.

2. Do the same for the case where two of the roots coincide ($p_2 = p_3$).

Solution. We known from the general theory of linear differential equations that in this case the system (102.7) can be brought to the following canonical form:

$$\dot{g}_{11} = \frac{2p_1}{x} g_{11}, \qquad \dot{g}_{2\alpha} = \frac{2p_2}{x} g_{2\alpha}, \qquad \dot{g}_{3\alpha} = \frac{2p_2}{x} g_{3\alpha} + \frac{\lambda}{x} g_{2\alpha}, \qquad \alpha = 2, 3,$$

where λ is a constant. If $\lambda = 0$, we return to (102, 9). If $\lambda \neq 0$, we can put $\lambda = 1$; then

$$g_{11} = t^{2p_1}, \qquad g_{2\alpha} = a_\alpha t^{2p_2}, \qquad g_{3\alpha} = a_\alpha t^{2p_2} + b_\alpha t^{2p_2} \ln t.$$

From the condition $g_{23} = g_{32}$, we find that $b_2 = 0$, $a_2 = a_3$. By appropriate choice of scale along the x^1 and x^2 axes, we finally bring the metric to the following form:

$$-ds^2 = dx^2 + x^{2p_1} dx_1^2 + 2x^{2p_2} dx_2 dx_3 \pm x^{2p_2} \ln \frac{x}{a} dx_3^2.$$

The numbers p_1, p_2 can have the values 1,0 or $-1/3$, $2/3$.

3. Find the motion for small values of t of matter (with the equation of state $p = \epsilon/3$) which is uniformly distributed in a space with metric (102.9); we neglect the back reaction of the matter on the gravitational field.

Solution. We use the hydrodynamical equations of motion,

$$\frac{1}{\sqrt{-g}} \frac{\partial}{\partial x^i} (\sqrt{-g}\sigma u^i) = 0, \qquad (p+\epsilon) u^k \left[\frac{\partial u_i}{\partial x^k} - \tfrac{1}{2} u^l \frac{\partial g_{kl}}{\partial x^i} \right] = -\frac{\partial p}{\partial x^i} - u_i u^k \frac{\partial p}{\partial x^k},$$

which are contained in the equations $T^k_{i:k} = 0$.† Here σ is the entropy density; for the equation of state $p = \epsilon/3$, we have $\sigma \sim \epsilon^{3/4}$. In this case all quantities depend only on the time, and these equations give

$$\frac{\partial}{\partial t} (t u_0 \epsilon^{3/4}) = 0, \qquad 4\epsilon \frac{\partial u_\alpha}{\partial t} + u_0 \frac{\partial \epsilon}{\partial t} = 0,$$

from which

$$t u_0 \epsilon^{3/4} = \text{const}, \qquad u_\alpha \epsilon^{1/4} = \text{const},$$

while from the identity $u_i u^i = -1$, we find

$$u_0^2 \cong u_3 u^3 = (u_3)^2 t^{-2p_3}$$

(for small t we keep only the term with the highest power of $1/t$). From these relations we find

$$\epsilon \cong \epsilon^{(0)} t^{-2(1-p_3)}, \qquad u_\alpha \cong u_\alpha^{(0)} t^{\frac{1-p_3}{2}},$$

where $\epsilon^{(0)}$ and $u_\alpha^{(0)}$ are constants.

† Cf. *Fluid Mechanics*, § 126.

For $t \to 0$, the energy density ϵ tends to ∞. The direction of the three-dimensional velocity v^α tends toward the z axis ($v^3 = t^{-2p_3} v_3 \gg v^1, v^2$) while its magnitude ($v^2 = v_\alpha v^\alpha$) tends toward the velocity of light according to the law

$$\sqrt{1-v^2} \sim t^{\frac{3p_3-1}{2}}.$$

§ 103. Gravitational fields at large distances from bodies

Let us consider the stationary gravitational field at large distances r from the body witch produces it, and determine the first terms of its expansion in powers of $1/r$.

In the first approximation, to terms of order $1/r$, the small corrections to the Galilean values are given by the corresponding terms in the expansion of the Schwarzschild solution (97.13), i.e. by the formulas already given in (100.17):

$$h_{00}^{(1)} = \frac{2km}{c^2 r}, \quad h_{\alpha\beta}^{(1)} = \frac{2km}{c^2} \frac{n_\alpha n_\beta}{r}, \quad h_{0\alpha}^{(1)} = 0. \tag{103.1}$$

Among the second order terms, proportional to $1/r^2$, there are terms which come from two different sources. Some of the terms arise, as a result of the nonlinearity of the equations of gravitation, from the first order terms. Since the latter depend only on the total mass (and on no other characteristics) of the body, these second order terms also can only depend on the total mass. It is therefore clear that these terms can be obtained by expanding the Schwarzschild solution (97.13), from which we find.†

$$h_{00}^{(2)} = 0, \; h_{\alpha\beta}^{(2)} = \frac{4k^2 m^2}{c^4 r^2} n_\alpha n_\beta. \tag{103.2}$$

The remaining second order terms appear as solutions of the already linearized equations of the field. To calculate them, we use the linearized equations in the form (101.8). In the stationary case, the wave equation reduces to the Laplace equation

$$\Delta h_i^k = 0. \tag{103.3}$$

---

† It should be noted that the specific appearance of the $h_{\alpha\beta}^{(1)}$, $h_{\alpha\beta}^{(2)}$, $h_{00}^{(2)}$ depends on the particular choice of the spatial coordinates (Galilean at infinity); the form given in the text corresponds to just that definition of r for which the Schwarzschild solution is given by (97.13). So the transformation $x'^\alpha = x^\alpha + \xi^\alpha$, $\xi^\alpha = ax^\alpha/2r$ results [see (101.6)] in the addition to $h_{\alpha\beta}^{(1)}$ of the term $\frac{a}{r}(\delta_{\alpha\beta} - n_\alpha n_\beta)$, and by a suitable choice of a we can obtain:

$$h_{\alpha\beta}^{(1)} = \frac{2km}{c^2} \frac{\delta_{\alpha\beta}}{r}, \tag{103.1a}$$

which corresponds to the Schwarzschild solution in the form given in problem 3 of § 97.

The quantities h_i^k are coupled by the auxiliary conditions (101.5), which take the following form, since the h_i^k are independent of the time:

$$\frac{\partial}{\partial x^\beta}(h_\alpha^\beta - \tfrac{1}{2}h\delta_\alpha^\beta) = 0, \tag{103.4}$$

$$\frac{\partial}{\partial x^\beta} h_0^\beta = 0. \tag{103.5}$$

The component h_{00} must be given by a scalar solution of the Laplace equation. We know that such a solution, proportional to $1/r^2$, has the form $\mathbf{a} \cdot \nabla \frac{1}{r}$, where $\mathbf{a}$ is a constant vector. But a term of this type in h_{00} can always be eliminated by a simple displacement of the coordinate origin in the first order term in $1/r$. Thus the presence of such a term in h_{00} would simply indicate that we had made a poor choice of the coordinate origin, and is therefore not of interest.

The components $h_{0\alpha}$ are given by a vector solution of the Laplace equation, i.e. they must have the form

$$h_{0\alpha} = \lambda_{\alpha\beta} \frac{\partial}{\partial x^\beta} \frac{1}{r}.$$

where $\lambda_{\alpha\beta}$ is a constant tensor. The condition (103.5) gives:

$$\lambda_{\alpha\beta} \frac{\partial^2}{\partial x^\alpha \partial x^\beta} \frac{1}{r} = 0,$$

from which it follows that $\lambda_{\alpha\beta}$ must have the form

$$\lambda_{\alpha\beta} = a_{\alpha\beta} + \lambda\delta_{\alpha\beta},$$

where $a_{\alpha\beta}$ is an antisymmetric tensor. But a solution of the form $\lambda \frac{\partial}{\partial x^\alpha} \frac{1}{r}$ can be eliminated by the transformation $x'^0 = x^0 + \xi^0$, with $\xi^0 = \lambda/r$ [see (101.6)]. Therefore the only solution which has a real meaning is of the form

$$h_{0\alpha} = a_{\alpha\beta} \frac{\partial}{\partial x^\beta} \frac{1}{r}, \qquad a_{\alpha\beta} = -a_{\beta\alpha}. \tag{103.6}$$

Finally, by a similar but more complicated argument, one can show that by a suitable transformation of the space coordinates one can always eliminate the quantities $h_{\alpha\beta}$ given by a tensor (symmetric in α, β) solution of the Laplace equation.

There remains the task of examining the meaning of the tensor $a_{\alpha\beta}$ in (103.6). For this purpose we use (100.16) to compute the total angular momentum tensor $M_{\alpha\beta}$ in terms of the expressions we have found for the $h_{0\alpha}$ (assuming that all other components of h_{ik} are absent).

To terms of second order in the $h_{o\alpha}$ we have from formula (100.2) (we note that $g^{\alpha 0} = -h^{\alpha 0} = h_{\alpha 0}$):

$$h^{\alpha 0\beta} = \frac{c^4}{16\pi k}\frac{\partial}{\partial x^\gamma}(g^{\alpha 0}g^{\beta\gamma} - g^{\gamma 0}g^{\alpha\beta}) = \frac{c^4}{16\pi k}\frac{\partial}{\partial x^\gamma}(h_{\alpha 0}\delta_{\beta\gamma} - h_{\gamma 0}\delta_{\alpha\beta}) =$$

$$= \frac{c^4}{16\pi k}\frac{\partial}{\partial x^\beta}h_{\alpha 0} = \frac{c^4}{16\pi k}a_{\alpha\gamma}\frac{\partial^2}{\partial x^\beta\,\partial x^\gamma}\frac{1}{r} = \frac{c^4}{16\pi k}a_{\alpha\gamma}\frac{3n_\beta n_\gamma - \delta_{\beta\gamma}}{r^3}$$

(where **n** is a unit vector along the radius vector). By means of these expressions, we find, after performing the integration over a sphere of radius $r(df_\gamma = n_\gamma r^2 do)$:

$$\frac{1}{c}\int(x^\alpha h^{\beta 0\gamma} - x^\beta h^{\alpha 0\gamma})\,df_\gamma = \frac{c^3}{8\pi k}\int(n_\alpha n_\gamma a_{\beta\gamma} - n_\beta n_\gamma a_{\alpha\gamma})\,do =$$

$$= \frac{c^3}{8\pi k}\frac{4\pi}{3}(\delta_{\alpha\gamma}a_{\beta\gamma} - \delta_{\beta\gamma}a_{\alpha\gamma}) = -\frac{c^3}{3k}a_{\alpha\beta}.$$

A similar calculation gives:

$$\frac{1}{c}\int\lambda^{\alpha 0\gamma\beta}\,df_\gamma = \frac{c^3}{16\pi k}\int(h_{\alpha 0}\,df_\beta - h_{\beta 0}\,df_\alpha) = -\frac{c^3}{6k}a_{\alpha\beta}.$$

Combining these two results, we get:

$$M_{\alpha\beta} = -\frac{c^3}{2k}a_{\alpha\beta}.$$

Thus we finally have:

$$h_{0\alpha}^{(2)} = \frac{2k}{c^3}M_{\alpha\beta}\frac{n_\beta}{r^2}. \tag{103.7}$$

We emphasize that in the general case, when the field near the bodies may not be weak, $M_{\alpha\beta}$ is the angular momentum of the body together with its gravitational field. Only when the field is weak at all distances can its contribution to the angular momentum be neglected. We also note that in the case of a rotating body of spherical shape, producing a weak field everywhere, formula (103.7) is valid over the whole space outside the body.

Formulas (103.1), (103.2) and (103.7) solve our problem to terms of order $1/r^2$. The covariant components of the metric tensor are

$$g_{ik} = g_{ik}^{(0)} + h_{ik}^{(1)} + h_{ik}^{(2)}. \tag{103.8}$$

To this same accuracy, the contravariant components are

$$g^{ik} = g^{(0)ik} - h^{(1)ik} - h^{(2)ik} + h^{(1)i}_{l}h^{(1)lk}. \tag{103.9}$$

Formula (103.7) can be written in vector form as

$$\mathbf{g} = \frac{2k}{c^3 r^2}\mathbf{n}\times\mathbf{M}, \tag{103.10}$$

where we have again introduced (see § 89) the vector **g** with components $g_\alpha = -g_{0\alpha}/g_{00}$. (To the required accuracy, $g_\alpha \cong g_{0\alpha}$.)

In problem 1 of § 89 it was shown that in a stationary gravitational field there acts on the particle a "Coriolis force" equal to that which would act on the particle if it were on a body rotating with angular velocity $\mathbf{\Omega} = \frac{c}{2}\sqrt{-g_{00}}\,\nabla\times\mathbf{g}$. Therefore we may say that in the field produced by a rotating body (with total angular momentum **M**) there acts on a particle distant from the body a force which is equivalent to the Coriolis force which would appear for a rotation with angular velocity

$$\mathbf{\Omega} \cong \frac{c}{2}\nabla\times\mathbf{g} = \frac{k}{c^2 r^3}[\mathbf{M}-3\mathbf{n}(\mathbf{n}\cdot\mathbf{M})].$$

Problem

Determine the systematic ("secular") shift of the orbit of a particle moving in the field of a central body, associated with the rotation of the latter (J. Lense, H. Thirring, 1918).

Solution: Because all the relativistic effects are small, they superpose linearly with one another, so in calculating the effects resulting from the rotation of the central body we can neglect the influence of the non-Newtonian centrally symmetric force field which we considered in § 98; in other words, we can make the computations assuming that of all the h_{ik} only the $h_{0\alpha}$ are different from zero.

The orientation of the classical orbit of the particle is determined by two conserved quantities: the angular momentum of the particle, $\mathbf{M} = \mathbf{r}\times\mathbf{p}$, and the vector

$$\mathbf{A} = \frac{\mathbf{p}}{m}\times\mathbf{M} - \frac{kmm'\mathbf{r}}{r},$$

whose conservation is peculiar to the Newtonian field $\phi = -km'/r$ (where m' is the mass of the central body).† The vector **M** is perpendicular to the plane of the orbit, while the vector **A** is directed along the major axis of the ellipse toward the perihelion (and is equal in magnitude to $kmm'e$, where e is the eccentricity of the orbit). The required secular shift of the orbit can be described in terms of the change in direction of these vectors.

The Lagrangian for a particle moving in the field (103.9) is

$$L = -mc\frac{ds}{dt} = L_0+\delta L,\ \delta L = mc\mathbf{g}\cdot\mathbf{v} = \frac{2km}{c^2 r^3}\mathbf{M}'\cdot\mathbf{v}\times\mathbf{r}$$

(where we denote the angular momentum of the central body by **M′** to distinguish it from the angular momentum **M** of the particle). Then the Hamiltonian is:‡

$$\mathcal{H} = \mathcal{H}_0+\delta\mathcal{H},\ \delta\mathcal{H} = \frac{2k}{c^2 r^3}\mathbf{M}'\cdot\mathbf{r}\times\mathbf{p}$$

Computing the derivative $\dot{\mathbf{M}} = \dot{\mathbf{r}}\times\mathbf{p}+\mathbf{r}\times\dot{\mathbf{p}}$ using the Hamilton equations $\dot{\mathbf{r}} = \frac{\partial\mathcal{H}}{\partial\mathbf{p}}$, $\dot{\mathbf{p}} = -\frac{\partial\mathcal{H}}{\partial\mathbf{r}}$, we get:

$$\dot{\mathbf{M}} = \frac{2k}{c^2 r^3}\mathbf{M}'\times\mathbf{M}.$$

Since we are interested in the secular variation of **M**, we should average this expression over the period of rotation of the particle. The averaging is conveniently done using the

† See *Mechanics*, § 15.

‡ See *Mechanics*, § 40.

parametric representation of the dependence of r on the time for motion in an elliptical orbit, in the form

$$r = a(1-e\cos\xi),\ t = \frac{T}{2\pi}(\xi - e\sin\xi)$$

(a and e are the semimajor axis and eccentricity of the ellipse):†

$$\overline{r^{-3}} = \frac{1}{T}\int_0^T \frac{dt}{r^3} = \frac{1}{2\pi a^3}\int_0^{2\pi} \frac{d\xi}{(1-e\cos\xi)^2} = \frac{1}{a^3(1-e^2)^{3/2}}.$$

Thus the secular change of **M** is given by the formula

$$\frac{d\mathbf{M}}{dt} = \frac{2k\mathbf{M}'\times\mathbf{M}}{c^2a^3(1-e^2)^{3/2}}, \tag{1}$$

i.e. the vector **M** rotates around the axis of rotation of the central body, remaining fixed in magnitude.

An analogous calculation for the vector **A** gives:

$$\dot{\mathbf{A}} = \frac{2k}{c^2r^3}\mathbf{M}'\times\mathbf{A} + \frac{6k}{c^2mr^5}(\mathbf{M}\cdot\mathbf{M}')(\mathbf{r}\times\mathbf{M}).$$

The averaging of this expression is carried out in the same way as before; from symmetry considerations it is clear beforehand that the averaged vector $\overline{\mathbf{r}/r^5}$ will be along the major axis of the ellipse, i.e. along the direction of the vector **A**. The computation leads to the following expression for the secular change of the vector **A**:

$$\frac{d\mathbf{A}}{dt} = \mathbf{\Omega}\times\mathbf{A},\quad \mathbf{\Omega} = \frac{2k\mathbf{M}'}{c^2a^3(1-e^2)^{3/2}}\{\mathbf{n}'-3\mathbf{n}(\mathbf{n}\cdot\mathbf{n}')\} \tag{2}$$

(**n** and **n**′ are unit vectors along the directions of **M** and **M**′), i.e. the vector **A** rotates with angular velocity **Ω**, remaining fixed in magnitude; this last point shows that the eccentricity of the orbit does not undergo any secular change.

Formula (1) can be written in the form

$$\frac{d\mathbf{M}}{dt} = \mathbf{\Omega}\times\mathbf{M},$$

with the same **Ω** as in (2); in other words, **Ω** is the angular velocity of rotation of the ellipse "as a whole". This rotation includes both the additional (compared to that considered in § 98) shift of the perihelion of the orbit, and the secular rotation of its plane about the direction of the axis of the body (where the latter effect is absent if the plane of the orbit coincides with the equatorial plane of the body).

For comparison we note that to the effect considered in § 98 there corresponds

$$\mathbf{\Omega} = \frac{6\pi km'}{c^2a(1-e^2)T}\mathbf{n}.$$

§ 104. Radiation of gravitational waves

Let us consider next a weak gravitational field, produced by arbitrary bodies, moving with velocities small compared with the velocity of light.

Because of the presence of matter, the equations of the gravitational field will differ from the simple wave equation of the form $\Box h_i^k = 0$ (101.8) by

† See *Mechanics*, § 15.

having, on the right side of the equality, terms coming from the energy-momentum tensor of the matter. We write these equations in the form

$$\frac{1}{2}\Box\psi_i^k = -\frac{8\pi k}{c^4}\tau_i^k, \tag{104.1}$$

where we have introduced in place of the h_i^k the quantities $\psi_i^k = h_i^k - \frac{1}{2}\delta_i^k h$, which are more convenient for this case, and where τ_i^k denotes the auxiliary quantities which are obtained upon going over from the exact equations of gravitation to the case of a weak field in the approximation we are considering. It is easy to verify that the components τ_0^0 and τ_α^0 are obtained directly from the corresponding components T_i^k by taking out from them the terms of the order of magnitude in which we are interested; as for the components τ_β^α, they contain along with terms obtained from the T_β^α, also terms of second order from $R_i^k - \frac{1}{2}\delta_i^k R$.

The quantities ψ_i^k satisfy the condition (101.5) $\partial\psi_i^k/\partial x^k = 0$. From (104.1) it follows that this same equation holds for the τ_i^k:

$$\frac{\partial\tau_i^k}{\partial x^k} = 0. \tag{104.2}$$

This equation here replaces the general relation $T_{i;k}^k = 0$.

Using the equations which we have obtained, let us consider the problem of the energy radiated by moving bodies in the form of gravitational waves. The solution of this problem requires the determination of the gravitational field in the "wave zone," i.e., at distances large compared with the wave-length of the radiated waves.

In principle, all the calculations are completely analogous to those which we carried out for electromagnetic waves. Equation (104.1) for a weak gravitational field coincides in form with the equation of the retarded potentials (§ 62). Therefore we can immediately write its general solution in the form

$$\psi_i^k = \frac{4k}{c^4}\int (\tau_i^k)_{t-\frac{R}{c}} \frac{dV}{R}. \tag{104.3}$$

Since the velocities of all the bodies in the system are small, we can write, for the field at large distances from the system (see §§ 66 and 67),

$$\psi_i^k = \frac{4k}{c^4 R_0}\int (\tau_i^k)_{t-\frac{R_0}{c}}\, dV, \tag{104.4}$$

where R_0 is the distance from the origin, chosen anywhere in the interior of the system. From now on we shall, for brevity, omit the index $t - \dfrac{R_0}{c}$ in the integrand.

For the evaluation of these integrals we use Eq. (104.2). Dropping the index on the τ_i^k and separating space and time components, we write (104.2) in the form

$$\frac{\partial \tau_{\alpha\gamma}}{\partial x^\gamma} - \frac{\partial \tau_{\alpha 0}}{\partial x^0} = 0, \qquad \frac{\partial \tau_{0\gamma}}{\partial x^\gamma} - \frac{\partial \tau_{00}}{\partial x^0} = 0. \tag{104.5}$$

Multiplying the first equation by x^β, we integrate over all space,

$$\frac{\partial}{\partial x^0}\int \tau_{\alpha 0} x^\beta\, dV = \int \frac{\partial \tau_{\alpha\gamma}}{\partial x^\gamma} x^\beta\, dV = \int \frac{\partial(\tau_{\alpha\gamma} x^\beta)}{\partial x^\gamma}\, dV - \int \tau_{\alpha\beta}\, dV.$$

Since at infinity $\tau_{ik} = 0$, the first integral on the right, after transformation by Gauss' theorem, vanishes. Taking half the sum of the remaining equation and the same equation with transposed indices, we find

$$\int \tau_{\alpha\beta}\, dV = -\frac{1}{2}\frac{\partial}{\partial x^0}\int (\tau_{\alpha 0} x^\beta + \tau_{\beta 0} x^\alpha)\, dV.$$

Next, we multiply the second equation of (104.5) by $x^\alpha x^\beta$, and again integrate over all space. An analogous transformation leads to

$$\frac{\partial}{\partial x^0}\int \tau_{00} x^\alpha x^\beta\, dV = -\int (\tau_{\alpha 0} x^\beta + \tau_{\beta 0} x^\alpha)\, dV.$$

Comparing the two results, we find

$$\int \tau_{\alpha\beta}\, dV = \frac{1}{2}\frac{\partial^2}{\partial x_0^2}\int \tau_{00} x^\alpha x^\beta\, dV. \tag{104.6}$$

Thus the integrals of all the $\tau_{\alpha\beta}$ appear as expressions in terms of integrals containing only the component τ_{00}. But this component, as was shown earlier, is simply equal to the corresponding component T_{00} of the energy-momentum tensor and can be written to sufficient accuracy [see (96.1)] as:

$$\tau_{00} = \mu c^2. \tag{104.7}$$

Substituting this in (104.6) and introducing the time $t = x^0/c$, we find for (104.4)

$$\psi_{\alpha\beta} = \frac{2k}{c^4 R_0}\frac{\partial^2}{\partial t^2}\int \mu x^\alpha x^\beta\, dV. \tag{104.8}$$

At large distances from the bodies, we can consider the waves as plane (over not too large regions of space). Therefore we can calculate the flux of energy radiated by the system, say along the direction of the x^1 axis, by using formula (101.11). In this formula there enter the components $h_{23} = \psi_{23}$ and $h_{22} - h_{33} = \psi_{22} - \psi_{33}$. From (104.8), we find for them the expressions

$$h_{23} = \frac{2k}{3c^4 R_0}\dddot{D}_{23}, \qquad h_{22} - h_{33} = \frac{2k}{3c^4 R_0}(\ddot{D}_{22} - \ddot{D}_{33})$$

(the dot denotes time differentiation), where we have introduced the tensor

$$D_{\alpha\beta} = \int \mu(3x^{\alpha}x^{\beta} - \delta_{\alpha\beta}x_{\gamma}^2)\, dV, \tag{104.9}$$

the "quadrupole moment" of the mass (see § 96). As a result, we obtain the energy flux along the x^1 axis in the form

$$ct^{10} = \frac{k}{36\pi c^5 R_0^2}\left[\left(\frac{\dddot{D}_{22} - \dddot{D}_{33}}{2}\right)^2 + \dddot{D}_{23}^2\right]. \tag{104.10}$$

Knowing the radiation in the direction of the x^1 axis, it is easy to determine the radiation in an arbitrary direction characterized by the unit vector **n**. To do this we must construct from the components of the tensor $\dddot{D}_{\alpha\beta}$ and the vector n_α a scalar, quadratic in the $\dddot{D}_{\alpha\beta}$, which for $n_1 = 1$, $n_2 = n_3 = 0$ reduces to the expression in square brackets in (104.10).

The result for the intensity of energy radiated into solid angle *do* turns out to be

$$dI = \frac{k}{36\pi c^5}\left[\frac{1}{4}(\dddot{D}_{\alpha\beta}n_\alpha n_\beta)^2 + \frac{1}{2}\dddot{D}_{\alpha\beta}^2 - \dddot{D}_{\alpha\beta}\dddot{D}_{\alpha\gamma}n_\beta n_\gamma\right] do. \tag{104.11}$$

The total radiation in all directions, i.e., the energy loss of the system per unit time $\left(-\frac{d\mathcal{E}}{dt}\right)$, can be found by averaging the flux over all directions and multiplying the result by 4π. The averaging is easily performed using the formulas given in the footnote on p. 217. This averaging leads to the following expression for the energy loss:

$$-\frac{d\mathcal{E}}{dt} = \frac{k}{45c^5}\dddot{D}_{\alpha\beta}^2. \tag{104.12}$$

It is necessary to note that the numerical value of this energy loss, even for astronomical objects, is so small that its effects on the motion, even over cosmic time intervals, is completely negligible (thus, for double stars, the energy loss in a year turns out to be $\sim 10^{-12}$ of the total energy).

Problem

Two bodies attracting each other according to Newton's law move in a circular orbit (around their common center of mass). Calculate the velocity of approach of the two bodies, due to the loss of energy by radiation of gravitational waves.

Solution: If m_1, m_2 are the masses of the bodies, and r their mutual distance (constant for motion in a circular orbit), then a calculation using (104.12) gives

$$-\frac{d\mathcal{E}}{dt} = \frac{32k}{5c^5}\left(\frac{m_1 m_2}{m_1 + m_2}\right)^2 r^4\omega^6,$$

where $\omega = 2\pi/T$, and T is the period of rotation. The frequency ω is related to r by $\omega^2 r^3 = k(m_1+m_2)$. Since $\mathcal{E} = -\frac{km_1m_2}{2r}$, $\dot{r} = \frac{2r^2}{km_1m_2}\frac{d\mathcal{E}}{dt}$,
and we get finally

$$\dot{r} = -\frac{64k^3 m_1 m_2 (m_1+m_2)}{5c^5 r^3}.$$

§ 105. The equations of motion of a system of bodies in the second approximation

The expression (104.12) found in the preceding section for the loss of energy of a system in the form of radiation of gravitational waves contains a factor $1/c^5$, i.e., this loss appears only in the fifth approximation in $1/c$. In the first four approximations, the energy of the system remains constant. From this it follows that a system of gravitating bodies can be described by a Lagrangian correctly to terms of order $1/c^4$ in the absence of an electromagnetic field, for which a Lagrangian exists in general only to terms of second order (§ 65).

Here we shall give the derivation of the Lagrangian of a system of bodies to terms of second order. We thus find the equations of motion of the system in the next approximation after the Newtonian.

We shall neglect the dimensions and internal structure of the bodies, regarding them as "pointlike"; in other words, we shall restrict ourselves to the zero'th approximation in the expansion in powers of the ratios of the dimensions a of the bodies to their mutual separations l.

To solve our problem we must start with the determination, in this same approximation, of the weak gravitational field produced by the bodies at distances large compared to their dimensions, but at the same time small compared to the wavelength λ of the gravitational waves radiated by the system ($a \ll r \ll \lambda \sim lc/v$).

In the first approximation, in equations (104.1) we must neglect terms containing second time derivatives, with the factor $1/c^2$, and of all the components τ_i^k, assume different from zero only the component $\tau_0^0 = -\mu c^2$ which contains c^2 (whereas the other components contain the first or second power of the velocities of the bodies). We then obtain the equations

$$\Delta\psi_\alpha^\beta = 0,\ \Delta\psi_0^\alpha = 0,\ \Delta\psi_0^0 = \frac{16\pi k}{c^2}\mu.$$

We must look for solutions of these equations which go to zero at infinity (Galilean metric). It therefore follows from the first two equations that $\psi_\alpha^\beta = 0$, $\psi_0^\alpha = 0$. Comparing the third equation with equation (96.2) for the Newtonian potential ϕ, we find $\psi_0^0 = 4\phi/c^2$. Then we have for the components of the tensor $h_i^k = \psi_i^k - \frac{1}{2}\psi\,\delta_i^k$ the following values:†

$$h_\alpha^\beta = -\frac{2}{c^2}\phi\,\delta_\alpha^\beta, \tag{105.1}$$

$$h_0^\alpha = 0, \quad h_0^0 = \frac{2}{c^2}\phi, \tag{105.2}$$

and for the interval,

$$ds^2 = \left(1+\frac{2}{c^2}\phi\right)c^2\,dt^2 - \left(1-\frac{2}{c^2}\phi\right)(dx^2+dy^2+dz^2). \tag{105.3}$$

We note that second order terms containing ϕ appear not only in g_{00} but also in $g_{\alpha\beta}$; in § 87 it was already stated that, in the equations of motion of the particle, the correction terms in $g_{\alpha\beta}$ give quantities of higher order than the terms coming from g_{00}; as a consequence, of this, by a comparison with the Newtonian equations of motion we can determine only g_{00}.

As will be seen from the sequel, to obtain the required equations of motion it is sufficient to know the spatial components $h_{\alpha\beta}$ to the accuracy ($\sim 1/c^2$) with which they are given in (105.1); the mixed components (which are absent in the $1/c^2$ approximation) are needed to terms of order $1/c^3$, and the time component h_{00} to terms in $1/c^4$. To calculate them we turn once again to the general equations of gravitation, and consider the terms of corresponding order in these equations.

Disregarding the fact that the bodies are macroscopic, we must write the energy-momentum tensor of the matter in the form (33.4), (33.5). In curvilinear coordinates, this expression is rewritten as

$$T^{ik} = \sum_a \frac{m_a c}{\sqrt{-g}}\frac{dx^i}{ds}\frac{dx^k}{dt}\,\delta(\mathbf{r}-\mathbf{r}_a) \tag{105.4}$$

[for the appearance of the factor $1/\sqrt{-g}$, see the analogous transition in (88.3)]; the summation extends over all the bodies in the system.

The component

$$T_{00} = \sum_a \frac{m_a c^3}{\sqrt{-g}} g_{00}^2 \frac{dt}{ds}\,\delta(\mathbf{r}-\mathbf{r}_a)$$

in first approximation (for Galilean g_{ik}) is equal to $\sum_a m_a c^2 \delta(\mathbf{r}-\mathbf{r}_a)$; in the next approximation, we substitute for g_{ik} from (105.3) and find, after a simple computation:

$$T_{00} = \sum_a m_a c^2\left(1+\frac{5\phi_a}{c^2}+\frac{v_a^2}{2c^2}\right)\delta(\mathbf{r}-\mathbf{r}_a), \tag{105.5}$$

† This result is, of course, in complete agreement with the formulas found in § 103 for $h_{ik}^{(1)}$ [where $h_{\alpha\beta}^{(1)}$ is represented in the form (103.1a)].

where $\mathbf{v}$ is the ordinary three-dimensional velocity $\left(v^\alpha = \frac{dx^\alpha}{dt}\right)$ and ϕ_a is the potential of the field at the point r_a. (As yet we pay no attention to the fact that ϕ_a contains an infinite part — the potential of the self-field of the particle m_a; concerning this, see below).

As regards the components $T_{\alpha\beta}$, $T_{0\alpha}$ of the energy-momentum tensor, in this approximation it is sufficient to keep for them only the first terms in the expansion of the expression (105.4)

$$T_{\alpha\beta} = \sum_a m_a v_{a\alpha} v_{a\beta} \delta(\mathbf{r}-\mathbf{r}_a),$$
$$T_{0\alpha} = -\sum_a m_a c v_{a\alpha} \delta(\mathbf{r}-\mathbf{r}_a). \tag{105.6}$$

Next we proceed to compute the components of the tensor R_{ik}. The calculation is conveniently done using the formula $R_{ik} = g^{lm} R_{limk}$ with R_{limk} given by (92.4). Here we must remember that the quantities $h_{\alpha\beta}$ and h_{00} contain no terms of order lower than $1/c^2$, and $h_{0\alpha}$ no terms lower than $1/c^3$; differentiation with respect to $x^0 = ct$ raises the order of smallness of quantities by unity.

The main terms in R_{00} are of order $1/c^2$; in addition to them we must also keep terms of the next non-vanishing order $1/c^4$. A simple computation gives the result:

$$R_{00} = \frac{1}{c}\frac{\partial}{\partial t}\left(\frac{\partial h_0^\alpha}{\partial x^\alpha} - \frac{1}{2c}\frac{\partial h_\alpha^\alpha}{\partial t}\right) - \frac{1}{2}\frac{\partial^2 h_{00}}{\partial x^{\alpha 2}} + \frac{1}{2} h^{\alpha\beta}\frac{\partial^2 h_{00}}{\partial x^\alpha \partial x^\beta} - \frac{1}{4}\left(\frac{\partial h_{00}}{\partial x^\alpha}\right)^2 + $$
$$+ \frac{1}{4}\frac{\partial h_{00}}{\partial x^\beta}\left(2\frac{\partial h_\beta^\alpha}{\partial x^\alpha} - \frac{\partial h_\alpha^\alpha}{\partial x^\beta}\right).$$

In this computation we have still not used any auxiliary condition for the quantities h_{ik}. Making use of this freedom, we now impose the condition

$$\frac{\partial h_0^\alpha}{\partial x^\alpha} - \frac{1}{2c}\frac{\partial h_\alpha^\alpha}{\partial t} = 0, \tag{105.7}$$

as a result of which all the terms containing the components $h_{0\alpha}$ drop out of R_{00}. In the remaining terms we substitute

$$h_\alpha^\beta = -\frac{2}{c^2}\phi\delta_\alpha^\beta, \quad h_{00} = -\frac{2}{c^2}\phi + O\left(\frac{1}{c^4}\right),$$

and obtain, to the required accuracy,

$$R_{00} = -\frac{1}{2}\Delta h_{00} + \frac{2}{c^4}\phi\Delta\phi - \frac{2}{c^4}(\nabla\phi)^2, \tag{105.8}$$

where we have gone over to three-dimensional notation; here ϕ is the Newtonian potential of the system of point particles, i.e.

$$\phi = -k\sum_a \frac{m_a}{|\mathbf{r}-\mathbf{r}_a|}.$$

In computing the components $R_{0\alpha}$ it is sufficient to keep only the terms of the first nonvanishing order — $1/c^3$. In similar fashion, we find:

$$R_{0\alpha} = \frac{1}{2c}\frac{\partial^2 h_\alpha^\beta}{\partial t\,\partial x^\beta} + \frac{1}{2}\frac{\partial^2 h_0^\beta}{\partial x^\alpha \partial x^\beta} - \frac{1}{2c}\frac{\partial^2 h_\beta^\beta}{\partial t\,\partial x^\alpha} - \frac{1}{2}\frac{\partial^2 h_{0\alpha}}{\partial x^{\beta 2}}$$

and then, using the condition (105.7):

$$R_{0\alpha} = -\frac{1}{2}\Delta h_{0\alpha} + \frac{1}{2c^3}\frac{\partial^2 \phi}{\partial t\,\partial x^\alpha}. \tag{105.9}$$

Using the expressions (105.5) – (105.9), we now write the gravitational equations

$$R_{ik} = \frac{8\pi k}{c^4}\left(T_{ik} - \frac{1}{2}g_{ik}T\right). \tag{105.10}$$

The time component of equation (105.10) gives:

$$\Delta h_{00} - \frac{4}{c^4}\phi\Delta\phi + \frac{4}{c^4}(\nabla\phi)^2 = -\frac{8\pi k}{c^4}\sum_a m_a c^2\left(1 + \frac{5\phi_a}{c^2} + \frac{3v_a^2}{2c^2}\right)\delta(\mathbf{r} - \mathbf{r}_a);$$

making use of the identity

$$4(\nabla\phi)^2 = 2\Delta(\phi^2) - 4\phi\Delta\phi$$

and the equation of the Newtonian potential

$$\Delta\phi = 4\pi k \sum_a m_a \delta(\mathbf{r} - \mathbf{r}_a), \tag{105.11}$$

we rewrite this equation in the form

$$\Delta\left(h_{00} + \frac{2}{c^4}\phi^2\right) = -\frac{8\pi k}{c^2}\sum_a m_a\left(1 + \frac{\phi_a'}{c^2} + \frac{3v_a^2}{2c^2}\right)\delta(\mathbf{r} - \mathbf{r}_a). \tag{105.12}$$

After completing all the computations, we have replaced ϕ_a on the right side of (105.12) by

$$\phi_a' = -k\sum_b{}' \frac{m_b}{|r_a - r_b|},$$

i.e. by the potential at the point $\mathbf{r}_a$ of the field produced by all the particles except for the particle m_a; the exclusion of the infinite self-potential of the particles (in the method used by us, which regards the particles as pointlike) corresponds to a "renormalization" of their masses, as a result of which they take on their true values, which take into account the field produced by the particles themselves (see the footnote on p. 194).†

† Actually, if there is only one particle at rest, the right side of the equation will have simply $-(8\pi k/c^2)m_a\delta(\mathbf{r}-\mathbf{r}_a)$, and this equation will determine correctly (in second approximation) the field produced by the particle.

The solution of (105.12) can be given immediately, using the familiar relation (36.9)

$$\Delta\frac{1}{r} = -4\pi\delta(\mathbf{r}).$$

We thus find:

$$h_{00} = -\frac{2\phi}{c^2} - \frac{2\phi^2}{c^4} + \frac{2k}{c^4}\sum_a \frac{m_a\phi_a'}{|\mathbf{r}-\mathbf{r}_a|} + \frac{3k}{c^4}\sum_a \frac{m_a v_a^2}{|\mathbf{r}-\mathbf{r}_a|}. \tag{105.13}$$

The mixed component of equation (105.10) gives:

$$\Delta h_{0\alpha} = \frac{16\pi k}{c^3}\sum_a m_a v_{a\alpha}\delta(\mathbf{r}-\mathbf{r}_a) + \frac{1}{c^2}\frac{\partial^2\phi}{\partial t\,\partial x^\alpha}. \tag{105.14}$$

The solution of this linear equation is†

$$h_{0\alpha} = -\frac{4k}{c^3}\sum_a \frac{m_a v_{a\alpha}}{|\mathbf{r}-\mathbf{r}_a|} + \frac{1}{c^3}\frac{\partial^2 f}{\partial t\,\partial x^\alpha},$$

where f is the solution of the auxiliary equation

$$\Delta f = \phi = -\sum_a \frac{km_a}{|\mathbf{r}-\mathbf{r}_a|}.$$

Using the relation $\Delta r = 2/r$, we find:

$$f = -\frac{k}{2}\sum_a m_a|\mathbf{r}-\mathbf{r}_a|,$$

and then, after a simple computation, we finally obtain:

$$h_{0\alpha} = -\frac{k}{2c^3}\sum_a \frac{m_a}{|\mathbf{r}-\mathbf{r}_a|}[7v_{a\alpha} + (\mathbf{v}_a\cdot\mathbf{n}_a)n_{a\alpha}], \tag{105.15}$$

where $\mathbf{n}_a$ is a unit vector along the direction of the vector $\mathbf{r}-\mathbf{r}_a$.

The expressions (105.1), (105.13) and (105.15) are sufficient for computing the required Langrangian to terms of second order.

The Lagrangian for a single particle, in a gravitational field produced by other particles and assumed to be given, is

$$L_a = -m_a c\frac{ds}{dt} = -m_a c^2\left(1 - h_{00} - 2h_{0\alpha}\frac{v_a^\alpha}{a} - \frac{v_a^2}{c^2} - h_{\alpha\beta}\frac{v_a^\alpha v_a^\beta}{c^2}\right)^{1/2}.$$

† In the stationary case, the second term on the right of equation (105.14) is absent. At large distances from the system, its solution can be written immediately by analogy with the solution (44.3) of equation (43.4)

$$h_{0\alpha} = -\frac{2k}{c^3 r^2}(\mathbf{M}\times\mathbf{n})_\alpha$$

(where $\mathbf{M} = \int \mathbf{r}\times\mu\mathbf{v}dV = \sum m_a\mathbf{r}_a\times\mathbf{v}_a$ is the angular momentum of the system), in complete agreement with formula (103.10).

Expanding the square root and dropping the irrelevant constant $-m_a c^2$, we rewrite this expression, to the required accuracy, as

$$L_a = \frac{m_a v_a^2}{2} + \frac{m_a v_a^4}{8c^2} + m_a c^2 \left(\frac{h_{00}}{2} + h_{0\alpha} \frac{v_a^\alpha}{c} + \frac{1}{2c^2} h_{\alpha\beta} v_a^\alpha v_a^\beta + \frac{h_{00}^2}{8} + \frac{h_{00}}{4c^2} v_a^2 \right). \tag{105.16}$$

Here the values of all the h_{ik} are taken at the point r_a; again we must drop terms which become infinite, which amounts to a "renormalization" of the mass m_a appearing as a coefficient in L_a.

The further course of the calculations is the following. The total Lagrangian of the system is, of course, not equal to the sum of the Lagrangians L_a for the individual bodies, but must be constructed so that it leads to the correct values of the forces $\mathbf{f}_a$ acting on each of the bodies for a given motion of the others. For this purpose we compute the forces $\mathbf{f}_a$ by differentiating the Lagrangian L_a:

$$\mathbf{f}_a = \left(\frac{\partial L_a}{\partial \mathbf{r}} \right)_{\mathbf{r}=\mathbf{r}_a}$$

(the differentiation is carried out with respect to the running coordinate $\mathbf{r}$ of the "field point" in the expressions for h_{ik}). It is then easy to form the total Lagrangian L, from which all of the forces $\mathbf{f}_a$ are obtained by taking the partial derivatives $\dfrac{\partial L}{\partial \mathbf{r}_a}$.

Omitting the simple intermediate computations, we give immediately the final result for the Lagrangian:†

$$L = \sum_a \frac{m_a v_a^2}{2} \left(1 + 3 \sum_b{}' \frac{k m_b}{c^2 r_{ab}} \right) + \sum_a \frac{m_a v_a^4}{8c^2} + \sum_a \sum_b{}' \frac{k m_a m_b}{2 r_{ab}} -$$
$$- \sum_a \sum_b{}' \frac{k m_a m_b}{4c^2 r_{ab}} [7 \mathbf{v}_a \cdot \mathbf{v}_b + (\mathbf{v}_a \cdot \mathbf{n}_{ab})(\mathbf{v}_b \cdot \mathbf{n}_{ab})] - \sum_a \sum_b{}' \sum_c{}' \frac{k^2 m_a m_b m_c}{2c^2 r_{ab} r_{ac}},$$

where $r_{ab} = |\mathbf{r}_a - \mathbf{r}_b|$, $\mathbf{n}_{ab}$ is a unit vector along the direction $\mathbf{r}_a - \mathbf{r}_b$, and the prime on the summation sign means that we should omit the term with $b = a$ or $c = a$.

Problems

1. Find the action function for the gravitational field in the Newtonian approximation.

Solution: Using the g_{ik} from (105.3), we find from the general formula (93.3), $G = -\dfrac{2}{c^4} (\nabla \phi)^2$, so that the action for the field is

$$S_g = -\frac{1}{8\pi k} \int\int (\nabla \phi)^2 dV dt.$$

† The equations of motion corresponding to this Lagrangian were first obtained by A. Einstein, L. Infeld and B. Hoffmann (1938) and by A. Eddington and G. Clark (1938).

The total action, for the field plus the masses distributed in space with density μ, is:

$$S = \int\int\left[\frac{\mu v^2}{2} - \mu\phi - \frac{1}{8\pi k}(\nabla\phi)^2\right] dV dt. \tag{1}$$

One easily verifies that variation of S with respect to ϕ gives the Poisson equation (96.2), as it should.

The energy density is found from the Lagrangian density Λ [the integrand in (1)] by using the general formula (32.5), which reduces in the present case (because of the absence of time derivatives of ϕ in Δ) to changing the signs of the second and third terms. Integrating the energy density over all space, where we substitute $\mu\phi = \frac{1}{4\pi k}\phi\Delta\phi$ in the second term and integrate by parts, we finally obtain the total energy of field plus matter in the form

$$\int\left[\frac{\mu v^2}{2} - \frac{1}{8\pi k}(\nabla\phi)^2\right] dV.$$

Consequently the energy density of the gravitational field in the Newtonian theory is $W = -\frac{1}{8\pi k}(\nabla\phi)^2$.†

2. Find the coordinates of the center of inertia of a system of gravitating bodies in the second approximation.

Solution: In view of the complete formal analogy between Newton's law for gravitational interaction and Coulomb's law for electrostatic interaction, the coordinates of the center of inertia are given by the formula

$$\mathbf{R} = \frac{1}{\mathcal{E}}\sum_a \mathbf{r}_a\left(m_a c^2 + \frac{p_a^2}{2m_a} - \frac{km_a}{2}\sum_b{}' \frac{m_b}{r_{ab}}\right),$$

$$\mathcal{E} = \sum_a\left(m_a c^2 + \frac{p_a^2}{2m_a} - \frac{km_a}{2}\sum_b{}' \frac{m_b}{r_{ab}}\right),$$

which is analogous to the formula found in Problem 1 of § 65.

3. Find the secular shift of the perihelion of the orbit of two gravitating bodies of comparable mass (H. Robertson, 1938).

Solution: The Lagrangian of the system of two bodies is

$$L = \frac{m_1 v_1^2}{2} + \frac{m_2 v_2^2}{2} + \frac{km_1 m_2}{r} + \frac{1}{8c^2}(m_1 v_1^4 + m_2 v_2^4) +$$

$$+ \frac{km_1 m_2}{2c^2 r}\left[3(v_1^2+v_2^2) - 7\mathbf{v}_1\cdot\mathbf{v}_2 - (\mathbf{v}_1\cdot\mathbf{n})(\mathbf{v}_2\cdot\mathbf{n})\right] - \frac{k^2 m_1 m_2(m_1+m_2)}{2c^2 r^2}.$$

Going over to the Hamiltonian function and eliminating from it the motion of the center of inertia (see problem 2 in § 65), we get:

$$\mathcal{H} = \frac{p^2}{2}\left(\frac{1}{m_1}+\frac{1}{m_2}\right) - \frac{km_1 m_2}{r} - \frac{p^4}{8c^2}\left(\frac{1}{m_1^3}+\frac{1}{m_2^3}\right) -$$

$$- \frac{k}{2c^2 r}\left[3p^2\left(\frac{m_2}{m_1}+\frac{m_1}{m_2}\right) + 7p^2 + (\mathbf{p}\cdot\mathbf{n})^2\right] + \frac{k^2 m_1 m_2(m_1+m_2)}{2c^2 r^2}, \tag{1}$$

where $\mathbf{p}$ is the momentum of the relative motion.

We determine the radial component of momentum p_r as a function of the variable r and the parameters M (the angular momentum) and $\mathcal{E}$ (the energy). This function is deter-

† To avoid any misunderstanding, we state that this expression is not the same as the component $(-g)\,t_{00}$ of the energy-momentum pseudotensor (as calculated with the g_{ik} from (105.3); there is also a contribution to W from $(-g)\,T_{ik}$.

mined from the equation $\mathcal{H} = \mathcal{E}$ (in which, in the second order terms, we must replace p^2 by its expression from the zero'th approximation):

$$\mathcal{E} = \frac{1}{2}\left(\frac{1}{m_1}+\frac{1}{m_2}\right)\left(p_r^2+\frac{M^2}{r^2}\right)-\frac{km_1m_2}{r}-\frac{1}{8c^2}\left(\frac{1}{m_1^3}+\frac{1}{m_2^3}\right)\left(\frac{2m_1m_2}{m_1+m_2}\right)^2\left(\mathcal{E}+\frac{km_1m_2}{r}\right)^2-$$

$$-\frac{k}{2c^2r}\left[3\left(\frac{m_2}{m_1}+\frac{m_1}{m_2}\right)+7\right]\frac{2m_1m_2}{m_1+m}\left(\mathcal{E}+\frac{km_1m_2}{r}\right)-\frac{k}{2c^2r}p_r^2+\frac{k^2m_1m_2(m_1+m_2)}{2c^2r^2}.$$

The further course of the computations is analogous to that used in § 98. Having determined p_r from the algebraic equation given above, we make a transformation of the variable r in the integral

$$S_r = \int p_r\,dr,$$

so that the term containing M^2 is brought to the form M^2/r^2. Then expanding the expression under the square root in terms of the small relativistic corrections, we obtain:

$$S_r = \int\sqrt{A+\frac{B}{r}-\left(M^2-\frac{6k^2m_1^2m_2^2}{c^2}\right)\frac{1}{r^2}}\,dr$$

[see (98.6)], where A and B are constant coefficients whose explicit computation is not necessary.

As a result we find for the shift in the perihelion of the orbit of the relative motion:

$$\delta\phi = \frac{6\pi k^2m_1^2m_2^2}{c^2M^2} = \frac{6\pi k(m_1+m_2)}{c^2a(1-e^2)}.$$

Comparing with (98.7) we see that for given dimensions and shape of the orbit, the shift in the perihelion will be the same as it would be for the motion of one body in the field of a fixed center of mass m_1+m_2.

CHAPTER 12

COSMOLOGICAL PROBLEMS

§ 106. Isotropic space

The general theory of relativity opens new avenues of approach to the solution of problems related to the properties of the universe on a cosmic scale. It is true that in the present state of both theoretical and astronomical knowledge these questions are far from any final solution. Nevertheless the possibilities which arise from the non-Galilean nature of space-time are already remarkable.

These possibilities are the more important because Newtonian mechanics here leads to contradictions which cannot be avoided within the framework of nonrelativistic theory. Thus, applying the Newtonian formula for the gravitational potential (96.3) to a flat (as it is in Newtonian mechanics) infinite space, we find that the potential becomes infinite at every point. This would lead to infinite forces acting on the matter, which is absurd.

We know that the stars are distributed in space in an extremely nonuniform fashion — they are concentrated in individual star systems (galaxies). But in studying the universe on a "large scale" we should disregard these "local" inhomogeneities which result from the agglomeration of matter into stars and star systems. Thus by the density of mass we must understand the density averaged over regions of space whose dimensions are large compared to the separations between galaxies.

The solutions of the gravitational equations which are considered here (and first found by A. Friedmann, 1922) are based on the assumption that the matter is distributed uniformly over all space.† By its very nature, such an assumption unavoidably has only an approximate validity, because of the averaging which has been performed. Moreover, the available astronomical data are still not sufficient for making any definite judgment concerning the character of the average distribution of the galaxies in space.

However, the isotropic model apparently gives a description of the present state of the universe which is correct in its general features. In particular there is no doubt that it gives a correct explanation of such a fundamental phenomenon as the "red shift" (see § 109).

---

† We shall not consider at all equations containing the so-called cosmological constant, since it is clear at present that there is no physical basis for such a change in the form of the equations of gravitation.

Space uniformly filled with matter is completely homogeneous and isotropic in its properties. This means that we can choose a "world" time so that at every moment the metric of the space is the same at all points and in all directions.

First we take up the study of the metric of the isotropic space as such, disregarding for the moment any possible time dependence. As we did previously, we denote the three-dimensional metric tensor by $\gamma_{\alpha\beta}$, i.e. we write the element of spatial distance in the form

$$dl^2 = \gamma_{\alpha\beta}\, dx^\alpha\, dx^\beta. \tag{106.1}$$

The curvature of the space is completely determined by its three-dimensional curvature tensor, which we shall denote by $P^\alpha_{\beta\gamma\delta}$ in distinction to the four-dimensional tensor R^i_{klm} (the properties of the tensor $P^\alpha_{\beta\gamma\delta}$ are of course completely analogous to those of the tensor R^i_{klm}). In the case of complete isotropy, the tensor $P^\alpha_{\beta\gamma\delta}$ must clearly be expressible in terms of the metric tensor $\gamma_{\alpha\beta}$ alone. It is easy to see from the symmetry properties of $P^\alpha_{\beta\gamma\delta}$ (see §92) that it must have the form:

$$P^\alpha_{\beta\gamma\delta} = \lambda(\delta^\alpha_\gamma \gamma_{\delta\beta} - \delta^\alpha_\delta \gamma_{\gamma\beta}), \tag{106.2}$$

where λ is some constant. The tensor of the second rank, $P_{\alpha\beta} = P^\gamma_{\alpha\gamma\beta}$, is accordingly equal to

$$P_{\alpha\beta} = 2\lambda\gamma_{\alpha\beta} \tag{106.3}$$

and the scalar curvature

$$P = 6\lambda. \tag{106.4}$$

Thus we see that the curvature properties of an isotropic space are determined by just one constant λ. Corresponding to this there are altogether three different possible cases for the spatial metric: (1) the so-called space of constant positive curvature (corresponding to a positive value of λ), (2) space of constant negative curvature (corresponding to values of $\lambda < 0$), and (3) space with zero curvature ($\lambda = 0$). Of these, the last will be a flat, i.e., Euclidean, space.

To investigate the metric it is convenient to start from geometrical analogy, by considering the geometry of isotropic three-dimensional space as the geometry on a hypersurface known to be isotropic, in a fictitious four-dimensional space.† Such a space is a hypersphere; the three-dimensional space corresponding to this has a positive constant curvature. The equation of

† This four-space is understood to have nothing to do with four-dimensional space-time.

a hypersphere of radius a in the four-dimensional space x_1, x_2, x_3, x_4, has the form

$$x_1^2+x_2^2+x_3^2+x_4^2 = a^2,$$

and the element of length on it can be expressed as

$$dl^2 = dx_1^2+dx_2^2+dx_3^2+dx_4^2.$$

Considering x^1, x^2, x^3 as the three space coordinates, and eliminating the fictitious coordinate x^4 with the aid of the first equation, we get the element of spatial distance in the form

$$dl^2 = dx_1^2+dx_2^2+dx_3^2+\frac{(x_1\,dx_1+x_2\,dx_2+x_3\,dx_3)^2}{a^2-x_1^2-x_2^2-x_3^2}. \tag{106.5}$$

From this expression, it is easy to calculate the constant λ in (106.2). Since we know beforehand that $P_{\alpha\beta}$ has the form (106.3) over all space, it is sufficient to calculate it only for points located near the origin, where the $\gamma_{\alpha\beta}$ are equal to

$$\gamma_{\alpha\beta} = \delta_{\alpha\beta}+\frac{x_\alpha x_\beta}{a^2}.$$

Since the first derivatives of the $\gamma_{\alpha\beta}$, which determine the quantities $\Gamma^\alpha_{\beta\gamma}$, vanish at the origin, the calculation from the general formula (92.11) turns out to be very simple and gives the result

$$\lambda = \frac{1}{a^2}. \tag{106.6}$$

We may call the quantity a the "radius of curvature" of the space. We introduce in place of the coordinates x^1, x^2, x^3, the corresponding "spherical" coordinates r, θ, ϕ. Then the line element takes the form

$$dl^2 = \frac{dr^2}{1-\frac{r^2}{a^2}}+r^2\,(\sin^2\theta\,d\phi^2+d\theta^2). \tag{106.7}$$

The coordinate origin can of course be chosen at any point in space. The circumference of a circle in these coordinates is equal to $2\pi r$, and the surface of a sphere to $4\pi r^2$. The "radius" of a circle (or sphere) is equal to

$$\int_0^r \frac{dr}{\sqrt{1-r^2/a^2}} = a\sin^{-1}(r/a),$$

that is, is larger than r. Thus the ratio of circumference to radius in this space is less than 2π.

Another convenient form for the dl^2 in "four-dimensional spherical coordinates" is obtained by introducing in place of the coordinate r the "angle" χ according to $r = a \sin \chi$ (χ goes between the limits 0 to π).† Then

$$dl^2 = a^2[d\chi^2 + \sin^2\chi\,(\sin^2\theta\, d\phi^2 + d\theta^2)]. \tag{106.8}$$

The coordinate χ determines the distance from the origin, given by $a\chi$. The surface of a sphere in these coordinates equals $4\pi a^2 \sin^2 \chi$. We see that as we move away from the origin, the surface of a sphere increases, reaching its maximum value $4\pi a^2$ at a distance of $\pi a/2$. After that it begins to decrease, reducing to a point at the "opposite pole" of the space, at distance πa, the largest distance which can in general exist in such a space [all this is also clear from (106.7) if we note that the coordinate r cannot take on values greater than a].

According to (106.8), the volume of a space with positive curvature is equal to

$$V = \int_0^{2\pi}\int_0^{\pi}\int_0^{\pi} a^3 \sin^2\chi \sin\theta \, d\chi \, d\theta \, d\phi,$$

so that

$$V = 2\pi^2 a^3. \tag{106.9}$$

Thus a space of positive curvature turns out to be "closed on itself". Its volume is finite though of course it has no boundary.

It is interesting to note that in a closed space the total electric charge must be zero. Namely, every closed surface in a finite space encloses on each side of itself a finite region of space. Therefore the flux of the electric field through this surface is equal, on the one hand, to the total charge located in the interior of the surface, and on the other hand to the total charge outside of it, with opposite sign. Consequently, the sum of the charges on the two sides of the surface is zero.

Similarly, from the expression (100.14) for the four-momentum in the form of a surface integral there follows the vanishing of the total four-momentum

† The "cartesian" coordinates x_1, x_2, x_3, x_4 are related to the four-dimensional spherical coordinates a, θ, ϕ, χ by the relations:

$$x_1 = a \sin\chi \sin\theta \cos\phi, \quad x_2 = a \sin\chi \sin\theta \sin\phi,$$

$$x^3 = a \sin\chi \cos\theta, \quad x_4 = a \cos\chi.$$

p^i over all space. Thus the definition of the total four-momentum loses its meaning, since the corresponding conservation law degenerates into the empty identity $0 = 0$.

We now go on to consider geometry of a space having a constant negative curvature. From (106.6) we see that the constant λ is negative if a is imaginary. Therefore all the formulas for a space with negative curvature can be immediately obtained from the preceding ones by replacing a by ia. In other words, the geometry of a space with negative curvature is obtained mathematically as the geometry on a four-dimensional pseudosphere with imaginary radius.

Thus the constant λ is now

$$\lambda = -\frac{1}{a^2}, \tag{106.10}$$

and the element of length in a space of negative curvature has, in coordinates r, θ, ϕ, the form

$$dl^2 = \frac{dr^2}{1+\dfrac{r^2}{a^2}} + r^2(\sin^2\theta\, d\phi^2 + d\theta^2), \tag{106.11}$$

where the coordinate r can go through all values from 0 to ∞. The ratio of the circumference of a circle to its radius is now greater than 2π. The expression for dl^2 corresponding to (106.8) is obtained if we introduce the coordinate χ according to $r = a \sinh \chi$ (χ here goes from 0 to ∞). Then

$$dl^2 = a^2\{d\chi^2 + \sinh^2\chi(\sin^2\theta\, d\phi^2 + d\theta^2)\}. \tag{106.12}$$

The surface of a sphere is now equal to $4\pi a^2 \sinh^2\chi$ and as we move away from the origin (increasing χ), it increases without limit. The volume of a space of negative curvature is, clearly, infinite.

Problem

Transform the element of length (106.7) to a form in which it is proportional to its Euclidean expression.

Solution: The substitution

$$r = \frac{r_1}{1+\dfrac{r_1^2}{4a^2}}$$

leads to the result:

$$dl^2 = \left(1+\frac{r_1^2}{4a^2}\right)^{-2}(dr_1^2 + r_1^2\, d\theta^2 + r_1^2 \sin^2\theta \cdot d\phi^2).$$

§ 107. Space-time metric in the closed isotropic model

Going on now to the study of space-time isotropic metric, we must first of all make a choice of our reference system. The most convenient is a system moving, at each point in space, along with the matter located at that point. One may say that the reference system is just the matter filling the space; the velocity of the matter in this system is by definition zero everywhere ("comoving" reference system.). It is clear that this reference system is reasonable for the isotropic model — for any other choice the direction of the velocity of the matter would lead to an apparent nonequivalence of different directions in space. The time coordinate must be chosen in the manner discussed in the preceding section, i.e., so that at each moment of time the metric is the same over all of the space.

In view of the complete equivalence of all directions, the components $g_{0\alpha}$ of the metric tensor are equal to zero in the reference system we have chosen. Namely, the three components $g_{0\alpha}$ can be considered as the components of a three-dimensional vector which, if it were different from zero, would lead to a nonequivalence of different directions. Thus ds^2 must have the form $ds^2 = -g_{00}\,dx_0^2 - dl^2$. The component g_{00} is here a function only of x^0. Therefore we can always choose the time coordinate so that g_{00} reduces to $-c^2$. Denoting it by τ, we have

$$ds^2 = c^2\,d\tau^2 - dl^2. \tag{107.1}$$

This time τ is clearly the proper time at each point in space.

Let us being with the consideration of a space with positive curvature; from now on we shall, for brevity, refer to the corresponding solution of the equations of gravitation as the "*closed model*". For dl we use the expression (106.8) in which the "radius of curvature" a is, in general, a function of the time. Thus we write ds^2 in the form

$$ds^2 = c^2\,d\tau^2 - a^2(\tau)\{d\chi^2 + \sin^2\chi(d\theta^2 + \sin^2\theta\cdot d\phi^2)\}. \tag{107.2}$$

The function $a(\tau)$ is determined by the equations of the gravitational field. For the solution of these equations it is convenient to use, in place of the time, the quantity η defined by the relation

$$c\,d\tau = a\,d\eta. \tag{107.3}$$

Then ds^2 can be written as

$$ds^2 = a^2(\eta)\{d\eta^2 - d\chi^2 - \sin^2\chi(d\theta^2 + \sin^2\theta\cdot d\phi^2)\}. \tag{107.4}$$

To set up the field equations we must being with the calculation of the components of the tensor R_{ik} (the coordinates x^0, x^1, x^2, x^3 are η, χ, θ, ϕ). Using the values of the components of the metric tensor from (107.4)

$$g_{00} = -a^2, \quad g_{11} = a^2, \quad g_{22} = a^2\sin^2\chi, \quad g_{33} = a^2\sin^2\chi\,\sin^2\theta,$$

we calculate the quantities Γ^i_{kl}:

$$\Gamma^0_{00} = \frac{\dot{a}}{a}, \quad \Gamma^0_{\alpha\beta} = \frac{\dot{a}}{a^3} g_{\alpha\beta}, \quad \Gamma^\alpha_{0\beta} = \frac{\dot{a}}{a}\delta^\alpha_\beta, \quad \Gamma^0_{\alpha 0} = \Gamma^\alpha_{00} = 0,$$

where the dot denotes differentiation with respect to η. (There is no need to compute the components $\Gamma^\alpha_{\beta\gamma}$ explicitly.) Using these values, we find from the general formula (92.11):

$$R^0_0 = \frac{3}{a^4}(a\ddot{a} - \dot{a}^2).$$

From the same symmetry arguments as we used earlier for the $g_{0\alpha}$, it is clear from the start that $R_{0\alpha} = 0$. For the calculation of the components R^β_α we note that if we separate in them the terms containing $g_{\alpha\beta}$ (i.e. only the $\Gamma^\alpha_{\beta\gamma}$), these terms must constitute the components of a three-dimensional tensor P^β_α, whose values are already known from (106.3) and (106.6):

$$R^\beta_\alpha = P^\beta_\alpha + \cdots = \frac{2}{a^2}\delta^\beta_\alpha + \cdots,$$

where the dots represent terms containing g_{00} in addition to the $g_{\alpha\beta}$. From the computation of these latter terms we find:

$$R^\beta_\alpha = \frac{1}{a^4}(2a^2 + \dot{a}^2 + a\ddot{a})\delta^\beta_\alpha,$$

so that

$$R = R^0_0 + R^\alpha_\alpha = \frac{6}{a^3}(a + \ddot{a}).$$

Since the matter is at rest in the frame of reference we are using, $u^\alpha = 0$, $u^0 = 1/a$, and we have from (94.9) $T^0_0 = -\epsilon$, where ϵ is the density of the energy of the matter. Substituting these expressions in the equation

$$R^0_0 - \frac{1}{2}R = \frac{8\pi k}{c^4} T^0_0,$$

we obtain:

$$\frac{8\pi k}{c^4}\epsilon = \frac{3}{a^4}(a^2 + \dot{a}^2). \tag{107.5}$$

Here there enter two unknown functions ϵ and a; therefore we must obtain still another equation. For this it is convenient to choose (in place of the spatial components of the field equations) the equation $T^i_{0;i} = 0$, which is one of the four equations (94.7) contained, as we know, in the equations of gravitation. This equation can also be derived directly with the help of thermodynamic relations, in the following fashion.

When in the field equations we use the expression (94.9) for the energy-momentum tensor, we are neglecting all those processes which involve energy dissipation and lead to an increase in entropy. This neglect is here completely justified, since the auxiliary terms which should be added to T_i^k in connection with such processes of energy dissipation are negligibly small compared with the energy density ϵ, which contains the rest energy of the material bodies.

Thus in deriving the field equations we may consider the total entropy as constant. We now use the well-known thermodynamic relation $d\mathcal{E} = T\,dS - p\,dV$, where $\mathcal{E}$, S, V, are the energy, entropy, and volume of the system, and p, T, its pressure and temperature. For constant entropy, we have simply $d\mathcal{E} = -p\,dV$. Introducing the energy density $\epsilon = \mathcal{E}/V$, we easily find

$$d\epsilon = -(\epsilon+p)\frac{dV}{V}\cdot$$

The volume V of the space is, according to (106.9), proportional to the cube of the radius of curvature a. Therefore $dV/V = 3da/a = 3d(\ln a)$, and we can write

$$-\frac{d\epsilon}{\epsilon+p} = 3d\,(\ln a),$$

or, integrating,

$$3\ln a = -\int \frac{d\epsilon}{p+\epsilon} + \text{const} \tag{107.6}$$

(the lower limit in the integral is constant).†

If the relation between ϵ and p (the "equation of state" of the matter) is known, then Eq. (107.6) determines ϵ as a function of a. Then from (107.5) we can determine η in the form

$$\eta = \pm \int \frac{da}{a\sqrt{\frac{8\pi k}{3c^4}\epsilon a^2 - 1}}. \tag{107.7}$$

Equations (107.6), (107.7) solve, in general form, the problem of determining the metric in the closed isotropic model.

If the material is distributed in space in the form of discrete macroscopic bodies, then to calculate the gravitational field produced by it, we may treat these bodies as material particles having definite masses, and take no account at all of their internal structure. Considering the velocities of the bodies as relatively small (compared with c), we can set $\epsilon = \mu c^2$, where μ is the sum of the masses of the bodies contained in unit volume. For the same reason

† We call attention to the fact that Eq. (107.6) coincides with the Eq. 8 obtained in problem 4, § 97, by integrating the equation $T^i_{0;i} = 0$ in the "comoving" reference system.

the pressure of the "gas" made up of these bodies is small compared with ϵ, and can be neglected (from what we have said, the pressure in the interior of the bodies has nothing to do with the question under consideration). As for the radiation present in space, its amount is relatively small, and its energy and pressure can also be neglected.

Setting $\epsilon = \mu c^2$, $p = 0$ in (107.6), and carrying out the integration, we get

$$\mu a^3 = \text{const.} \tag{107.8}$$

This equation could have been written immediately, since it merely expresses the fact that the sum of the masses of the bodies in all space remains constant (clearly, const $= M/2\pi^2$, where $M = \mu V$ is the total mass in a space of volume $V = 2\pi^2 a^3$). Substituting (107.8) in Eq. (107.7) and carrying out the integration, we obtain

$$a = a_0(1 - \cos\eta), \tag{107.9}$$

where $a_0 = 2kM/3\pi c^2$ is a constant. Finally, for the relation between τ and η we find from (107.3).

$$\tau = \frac{a_0}{c}(\eta - \sin\eta). \tag{107.10}$$

The equations (107.9), (107.10) determine the function $a(\tau)$ in parametric form; the curve described by this relation is a cycloid.

For $\eta = 0, \pm 2\pi, \pm 4\pi \ldots$ a vanishes and μ becomes infinite. But for $\mu \to \infty$, the pressure itself becomes large, and therefore to investigate the metric for values of η near to the values given, we must consider the opposite limiting case of as large pressure as possible (for a given energy density). In § 35, we saw that the maximum pressure is equal to $p = \epsilon/3$ [see (35.6)]. Substituting this in formula (107.6), we get

$$\epsilon a^4 = \text{const}, \tag{107.11}$$

after which (107.7) and (107.3) lead to the relations:

$$a = a_0' \sin\eta, \qquad \tau = \frac{a_0'}{c}(1 - \cos\eta),$$

where the constant a_0' is related in a definite way with the constant in (107.11). Since to consider this solution makes sense only for very small values of a, we can at once write the corresponding approximate formula (obtainable by expanding in powers for $\eta \ll 1$):

$$a = \text{const}\sqrt{\tau}. \tag{107.12}$$

If the sign of τ were changed, the quantity a in (107.12) would become imaginary, and its square negative. All four components g_{ik} in (107.12) would then be negative, and the determinant g positive. But such a metric is physically meaningless. This means that for the values of η given above, the metric actually has singular points. Therefore we must consider values of η only in the interval from 0 to 2π (or, what is the same thing, from 2π to 4π, etc.) and analytic continuation of the metric beyond the ends of this interval has no physical meaning.

§ 108. Space-time metric for the open isotropic model

The solution corresponding to an isotropic space of negative curvature ("*open model*") is obtained by a method completely analogous to the preceding. In place of (107.2), we now have

$$ds^2 = c^2\,d\tau^2 - a^2(\tau)\,\{d\chi^2 + \sinh^2\chi\,(d\theta^2 + \sin^2\theta\,d\phi^2)\}. \qquad (108.1)$$

Again we introduce in place of τ the variable η, according to $c\,d\tau = a\,d\eta$; then we get†

$$ds^2 = a^2(\eta)\,\{d\eta^2 - d\chi^2 - \sinh^2\chi\,(d\theta^2 + \sin^2\theta \cdot d\phi^2)\}. \qquad (108.2)$$

This expression can be obtained formally from (107.4) by changing η, χ, a respectively to $i\eta$, $i\chi$, ia. Therefore the equations of the field can also be gotten directly by this same substitution in Eqs. (107.5) and (107.6). Equation (107.6) retains its previous form:

$$3\ln a = -\int \frac{d\epsilon}{\epsilon + p} + \text{const}, \qquad (108.3)$$

while in place of (107.5), we have

$$\frac{8\pi k}{c^4}\,\epsilon = \frac{3}{a^4}\,(\dot{a}^2 - a^2). \qquad (108.4)$$

Corresponding to this we find, instead of (107.7)

$$\eta = \pm\int \frac{da}{a\sqrt{\dfrac{8\pi k}{3c^4}\,\epsilon a^2 + 1}}. \qquad (108.5)$$

† We note that, by a simple transformation

$$r = Ae^{\eta}\sinh\chi, \qquad ct = Ae^{\eta}\cosh\chi,$$

$$Ae^{\eta} = \sqrt{c^2t^2 - r^2}, \qquad \tanh\chi = \frac{r}{ct},$$

the expression (108.2) is reduced to the "conformal-Galilean" form

$$ds^2 = f(r, t)[c^2\,dt^2 - dr - r^2\,(d\theta^2 + \sin^2\theta\,d\phi^2)].$$

Let us consider first the case of low pressures. Setting $p = 0$, $\epsilon = \mu c^2$ we get the following final formulas:

$$a = a_0 (\cosh\eta - 1), \quad \tau = \frac{a_0}{c} (\sinh\eta - \eta),$$
$$\mu a^3 = \frac{3c^2}{4\pi k} a_0. \tag{108.6}$$

The first two determine the function $a(\tau)$ in parametric form.†

For $\eta = 0$, the radius of curvature $a(\eta)$ vanishes, and μ becomes infinite (the constant of integration in (108.6) was chosen so that $\tau = 0$ corresponds to this value). In contrast to the solution (107.8)–(107.10) this happens here for only one value of η. Near $\eta = 0$, our solution is not applicable, and we must again go over to the case $p = \epsilon/3$. From (108.3) we have as before

$$\epsilon a^4 = \text{const}, \tag{108.7}$$

and for the dependence of a on τ, we find

$$a = a_0' \sinh\eta, \quad \tau = \frac{a_0'}{c} (\cosh\eta - 1).$$

For small η, which is the only case where it makes sense to consider this solution, we again have

$$a = \text{const} \sqrt{\tau}. \tag{108.8}$$

Thus in the case we are considering the metric has a singular point at $\eta = 0$; therefore we must consider all functions either only for $\eta > 0$ or only for $\eta < 0$.

Finally, in the limiting case of the solutions under consideration, corresponding to an infinite radius of curvature of the space, we have a model with a flat (Euclidean) space. The interval ds^2 in the corresponding space-time can be written in the form

$$ds^2 = c^2 d\tau^2 - b^2(\tau) (dx^2 + dy^2 + dz^2) \tag{108.9}$$

(for the space coordinates we have chosen the "cartesian" coordinates x, y, z). The time-dependent factor in the element of spatial distance does not change

† In this case the transformation given in the preceding footnote (with the constant A equal to $a_0/2$) brings ds^2 to the form

$$ds^2 = \left(1 - \frac{a_0}{2\sqrt{c^2t^2 - r^2}}\right)^4 [c^2 dt^2 - dr^2 - r^2 (d\theta^2 + \sin^2\theta \, d\phi^2)]$$

(V. A. Fock, 1955). For large values of $\sqrt{c^2t^2 - r^2}$ (which correspond to $\eta \gg 1$), this metric tends toward a Galilean form, as was to be expected since the radius of curvature tends toward infinity.

In the coordinates r, θ, ϕ, t, the matter is not at rest and its distribution is not uniform; the distribution and motion of the matter turns out to be centrally symmetric about any point of space chosen as the origin of coordinates r, θ, ϕ.

the Euclidean nature of the space metric, since for a given τ this factor is a constant, and can be made unity by a simple coordinate transformation. A calculation similar to those in the previous paragraph leads to the following equations:

$$\frac{8\pi k}{c^2}\epsilon = \frac{3}{b^2}\left(\frac{db}{d\tau}\right)^2, \quad 3 \ln b = -\int \frac{d}{p+\epsilon} + \text{const}.$$

For the case of low pressures, we find

$$\mu b^3 = \text{const}, \ b = \text{const}\, \tau^{\frac{2}{3}}. \tag{108.10}$$

For small τ we must again consider the case $p = \epsilon/3$, for which we find

$$\epsilon b^4 = \text{const}, \quad b = \text{const}\, \sqrt{\tau}. \tag{108.11}$$

Thus in this case also the metric has a singular point ($\tau = 0$).

The main feature of all the solutions considered here is the nonstationary character of the space-time metric: the radius of curvature is a function of the time. A change in the radius of curvature results in a change in all separations between bodies in the space, as is already immediately clear from the fact that the element of spatial distance dl in (106.8) or (106.12) is proportional to a. Thus with increasing a in such a space the bodies "run away" from one another (in the open model, increasing a corresponds to $\eta > 0$, and in the closed model, to $0 < \eta < \pi/2$). From the point of view of an observer located on one of the bodies, it will appear as if all the other bodies were moving in radial directions away from the observer. The speed of this "running away" (at a given moment τ) is proportional to the separation between the bodies.

This prediction of the theory can be related to the astronomically established fact of "recession" of nebulae, as deduced from the Doppler shift of the spectral lines in the light emitted by them (see § 109). We note that the conclusion that the bodies are "running away" can be drawn only when their interaction energy is small compared to the kinetic energy of their "running away"; this condition is always satisfied for sufficiently remote galaxies. In the opposite case the relative separations of the bodies are determined mainly by their interaction; therefore, for example, the effect considered here should have practically no influence on the dimensions of the nebulae themselves, and even less so on the dimensions of stars.

In the treatment of isotropic models, the natural question arises of their stability relative to small perturbations which, in one way or another, disturb the isotropy. The general investigation of this question (E. M. Lifshitz, 1946) leads to the result that an expanding universe is stable and a contracting universe is unstable.†

---

† For the calculations and detailed results for various types of perturbations, see *Journal of Physics USSR*. **10**, 116 (1946).

§ 109. The red shift

Let us consider the propagation of a light ray in an isotropic space. For this purpose it is simplest to use the fact that along the world line of the propagation of a light signal the interval $ds = 0$. We choose the point from which the light emerges as the origin of coordinates χ, θ, ϕ. From symmetry considerations it is clear that the light ray will propagate "radially," i.e., along a line $\theta = \text{const}$, $\phi = \text{const}$. In accordance with this, we set $d\theta = d\phi = 0$ in (107.4) or (108.2) and obtain $ds^2 = a^2(d\eta^2 - d\chi^2)$. Setting this equal to zero, we find $d\eta = \pm d\chi$ or, integrating,

$$\chi = \pm\eta + \text{const}. \tag{109.1}$$

The plus sign applies to a ray going out from the coordinate origin, and the minus sign to a ray approaching the origin. In this form, Eq. (109.1) applies to the open as well as to the closed model. With the help of the formulas of the preceding section, we can from this express the distance traversed by the beam as a function of the time.

In the open model, a ray of light, starting from some point, in the course of its propagation recedes farther and farther from it. In the closed model, a ray of light, starting out from the initial point, can finally arrive at the "conjugate pole" of the space (this corresponds to a change in χ from 0 to π); during the subsequent propagation, the ray begins to approach the initial point. A circuit of the ray "around the space", and return to the initial point, would correspond to a change of χ from 0 to 2π. From (109.1) we see that then η would also have to change by 2π, which is, however, impossible (except for the one case when the light starts at a moment corresponding to $\eta = 0$). Thus a ray of light cannot return to the starting point after a circuit "around the space."

To a ray of light approaching the point of observation (the origin of coordinates), there corresponds the negative sign on η in Eq. (109.1). If the moment of arrival of the ray at this point is $t(\eta_0)$, then for $\eta = \eta_0$ we must have $\chi = 0$, so that the equation of propagation of such rays is

$$\chi = \eta_0 - \eta. \tag{109.2}$$

From this it is clear that for an observer located at the point $\chi = 0$, only those rays of light can reach him at the time $\tau(\eta_0)$, which started from points located at "distances" not exceeding $\chi = \eta_0$.

This result, which applies to the open as well as to the closed model, is very essential. We see that at each given moment of time $\tau(\eta)$, at a given point in space, there is accessible to physical observation not all of space, but only that part of it which corresponds to $\chi \leqslant \eta$. Mathematically speaking, the "visible region" of the space is the section of the four-dimensional space by the light cone. This section turns out to be finite for the open as well as the closed model (the quantity which is infinite for the open model is its section by the hypersurface $\tau = \text{const}$, corresponding to the space where all points are observed at one and the same time τ). In this sense, the difference between the open and closed models turns out to be much less drastic than one might have thought at first glance.

The farther the region observed by the observer at a given moment of time recedes from him, the earlier the moment of time to which it corresponds. Let us look at the spherical surface which is the geometrical locus of the points from which light started out at the time $\tau(\eta-\chi)$ and is observed at the origin at the time $\tau(\eta)$. The area of this surface is $4\pi a^2(\eta-\chi)\sin^2\chi$ (in the closed model), or $4\pi a^2(\eta-\chi)\sinh^2\chi$ (in the open model). As it recedes from the observer, the area of the "visible sphere" at first increases from zero (for $\chi = 0$) and then reaches a maximum, after which it decreases once more, dropping back to zero for $\chi = \eta$ (where $a(\eta-\chi) = a(0) = 0$). This means that the section through the light cone is not only finite but also closed. It is as if it closed at the point "conjugate" to the observer; at this point $\epsilon \to \infty$.

The total amount of *observed* matter is equal in the open model to

$$M_{\text{obs}} = 4\pi \int_0^\eta \mu a^3 \sinh^2\chi \cdot d\chi.$$

Substituting μa^3 from (108.6), we get

$$M_{\text{obs}} = \frac{3c^2 a_0}{2k}(\sinh\eta\cosh\eta - \eta).$$

This quantity increases without limit as $\eta \to \infty$. In the closed model, the increase of M_{obs} is limited by the total mass M; in similar fashion, we find for this case:

$$M_{\text{obs}} = \frac{M}{\pi}(\eta - \sin\eta\cos\eta).$$

As η increases from 0 to π, this quantity increases from 0 to M; the further increase of M_{obs} according to this formula is fictitious, and corresponds simply to the fact that in a "contracting" universe distant bodies would be observed twice (by means of the light "circling the space" in the two directions).

Let us now consider the change in the frequency of light during its propagation in an isotropic space. For this we first point out the following fact. Let there occur at a certain point in space two events, separated by a time interval $d\tau = \frac{1}{c}a(\eta)\,d\eta$. If at the moments of these events light signals are sent out, which are observed at another point in space, then between the moments of their observation there elapses a time interval corresponding to the same change $d\eta$ in the quantity η as for the starting point. This follows immediately from Eq. (109.1), according to which the change in the quantity η during the time of propagation of a light ray from one point to another depends only on the difference in the coordinate χ for these points. But since during the time of propagation the radius of curvature a changes, the time interval τ between the moments of sending out of the two signals and the moments of their observation are different; the ratio of these intervals is equal to the ratio of the corresponding values of a.

From this it follows, in particular, that the periods of light vibrations, measured in terms of the world time τ, also change along the ray, proportionally to a. Thus, during the propagation of a light ray, along its path,

$$\omega a = \text{const.} \tag{109.3}$$

Let us suppose that at the time $\tau(\eta)$ we observe light emitted by a source located at a distance corresponding to a definite value of the coordinate χ. According to (109.1), the moment of emission of this light is $\tau(\eta-\chi)$. If ω_0 is the frequency of the light at the time of emission, then from (109.3), the frequency ω observed by us is

$$\omega = \omega_0 \frac{a(\eta-\chi)}{a(\eta)}. \tag{109.4}$$

Because of the monotonic increase of the function $a(\eta)$, we have $\omega < \omega_0$, that is, a decrease in the light frequency occurs. This means that when we observe the spectrum of light coming toward us, all of its lines must appear to be shifted toward the red compared with the spectrum of the same matter observed under ordinary conditions. This "red shift" phenomenon is essentially the Doppler effect of the bodies' "running away" from each other.

The magnitude of the red shift measured, for example, as the ratio ω/ω_0 of the displaced to the undisplaced frequency, depends (for a given time of observation) on the distance at which the observed source is located [in relation (109.4) there enters the coordinate χ of the light source]. For not too large distances, we can expand $a(\eta-\chi)$ in a power series in χ, limiting ourselves to the first two terms:

$$\frac{\omega}{\omega_0} = 1-\chi\frac{\dot{a}(\eta)}{a(\eta)}$$

(the dot denotes differentiation with respect to η). Further, we note that the product $\chi a(\eta)$ is here just the distance l from the observed source. Namely, the "radial" line element is equal to $dl = a\,d\chi$; in integrating this relation the question arises of how the distance is to be determined by physical observation. In determining this distance we must take the values of a at different points along the path of integration at different moments of time (integration for η = const would correspond to simultaneous observation of all the points along the path, which is physically not feasible). But for "small" distances we can neglect the change in a along the path of integration and write simply $l = a\chi$, with the value of a taken for the moment of observation.

As a result, we find for the percentage change in the frequency the following formula:

$$\frac{\omega-\omega_0}{\omega_0} = -\frac{h}{c}l, \tag{109.5}$$

where we have introduced the notation

$$h = c\frac{\dot{a}(\eta)}{a^2(\eta)}. \tag{109.6}$$

for the so-called "*Hubble constant*". For a given instant of observation, this quantity is independent of l. Thus the relative shift in spectral lines must be proportional to the distance to the observed light source.

Considering the red shift as a result of a Doppler effect, one can determine the corresponding velocity v of recession of the body from the observer. Writing $(\omega-\omega_0)/\omega_0 = -v/c$, and comparing with (109.5), we have

$$v = hl \tag{109.7}$$

(this formula can also be obtained directly by calculating the derivative $v = d(a\chi)\,(d\tau)$.

Astronomical data confirm the law (109.5), but the determination of the value of the Hubble constant is hampered by the uncertainty in the establishment of a scale of cosmic distances suitable for distant galaxies. The latest determinations give the value

$$h \cong 0.8\times 10^{-10}\text{yr}^{-1} = 0.25\times 10^{-17}\,\text{sec}^{-1}. \tag{109.8}$$

It corresponds to an increase in the "velocity of recession" by 25 km/sec for each million light years.

The positive sign of h means that $\dot{a}(\eta) > 0$; in the open model this corresponds to $\eta > 0$, and in the closed model to $0 < \eta < \pi$.

Substituting in Eq. (108.4), $\epsilon = \mu c^2$ and $h = c\dot{a}/a^2$, we get for the open model the following relation:

$$\frac{c^2}{a^2} = h^2 - \frac{8\pi k}{3}\mu. \tag{109.9}$$

Combining this equation with the equality

$$h = \frac{c\sinh\eta}{a(\cosh\eta-1)} = \frac{c}{a}\coth\frac{\eta}{2},$$

we obtain

$$\cosh\frac{\eta}{2} = h\sqrt{\frac{3}{8\pi k\mu}}. \tag{109.10}$$

For the closed model we would get:

$$\frac{c^2}{a^2} = \frac{8\pi k}{3}\mu - h^2, \tag{109.11}$$

$$\cos\frac{\eta}{2} = h\sqrt{\frac{3}{8\pi k\mu}}. \tag{109.12}$$

Comparing (109.9) and (109.11), we see that the curvature of the space is negative or positive accordingly as the difference $(8\pi k/3)\mu - h^2$ is negative or positive. This difference goes to zero for $\mu = \mu_k$, where

$$\mu_k = \frac{3h^2}{8\pi k}. \tag{109.13}$$

With the value (109.8), we get $\mu_k \cong 1\times 10^{-29}$ gm/cm³. In the present state of astronomical knowledge, the value of the average density of matter in space can be estimated only with very low accuracy, and there is no possibility of determining even the sign of $\mu - \mu_k$.

Let us note here a certain inequality which one can obtain for a given value of the quantity h. For the open model we have $h = \dfrac{c \sinh\eta}{a_0(\cosh\eta - 1)^2}$, and therefore

$$\tau = \frac{a_0}{c}(\sinh\eta - \eta) = \frac{\sinh\eta\,(\sinh\eta - \eta)}{h(\cosh\eta - 1)^2}.$$

Since $0 < \eta < \infty$, we must have

$$\frac{2}{3h} < \tau < \frac{1}{h}. \tag{109.14}$$

Similarly, for the closed model we obtain

$$\tau = \frac{\sin\eta(\eta - \sin\eta)}{h(1-\cos\eta)^2}.$$

To the increase of $a(\eta)$ there corresponds the interval $0 < \eta < \pi$; therefore we get

$$0 < \tau < \frac{2}{3h}. \tag{109.15}$$

Next we determine the intensity I of the light arriving at the observer from a source located at a distance corresponding to a definite value of the coordinate χ. The flux density of light energy at the point of observation is inversely proportional to the surface of the sphere, drawn through the point under consideration with center at the location of the source; in a space of negative curvature the area of the surface of the sphere equals $4\pi a^2 \sinh^2\chi$. Light emitted by the source during the interval $d\tau = \frac{1}{c}a(\eta - \chi)d\eta$ will reach the point of observation during a time interval $d\tau \frac{a(\eta)}{a(\eta-\chi)} = \frac{1}{c} a(\eta)\, d\eta$. Since the intensity is defined as the flux of light energy per unit time, there appears in I a factor $a(\eta-\chi)/a(\eta)$. Finally, the energy of a wave packet is proportional to its frequency [see (53.9)]; since the frequency changes during propagation of the light according to the law (109.3), this results in the factor $a(\eta-\chi)/a(\eta)$ appearing in I once more. As a result, we finally obtain the intensity in the form

$$I = \text{const}\, \frac{a^2(\eta-\chi)}{a^4(\eta)\sinh^2\chi}\,. \tag{109.16}$$

For the closed model we would similarly obtain

$$I = \text{const}\, \frac{a^2(\eta-\chi)}{a^4(\eta)\sin^2\chi}\,. \tag{109.17}$$

These formulas determine the dependence of the apparent brightness of an observed object on its distance (for a given absolute brightness). For small χ we can set $a(\eta-\chi) \simeq a(\eta)$, and then $I \sim 1/a^2(\eta)\chi^2 = 1/l^2$, that is, we have the usual law of decrease of intensity inversely as the square of the distance.

Finally, let us consider the question of the so-called proper motions of bodies. In speaking of the density and motion of matter, we have always understood this to be the average density and average motion; in particular, in the system of reference which we have always used, the velocity of the average motion is zero. The actual velocities of the bodies will undergo a certain fluctuation around this average value. In the course of time, the velocities of proper motion of the bodies change. To determine the law of this change, let us consider a freely moving body and choose the origin of coordinates at any point along its trajectory. Then the trajectory will be a radial line, $\theta = \text{const}$, $\phi = \text{const}$. The Hamilton-Jacobi equation (87.6), after substitution of the values of g^{ik}, takes the form

$$\left(\frac{\partial S}{\partial \chi}\right)^2 - \left(\frac{\partial S}{\partial \eta}\right)^2 + m^2c^2a^2(\eta) = 0. \tag{109.18}$$

Since χ does not enter into the coefficients in this equation (i.e., χ is a cyclic coordinate), the conservation law $\partial S/\partial\chi = \text{const}$ is valid. The momentum p of a moving body is equal, by definition, to $p = \partial S/\partial l = \partial S/a\,\partial\chi$. Thus for a moving body the product pa is constant:

$$pa = \text{const}. \tag{109.19}$$

Introducing the velocity v of the proper motion of the body according to

$$p = \frac{mv}{\sqrt{1-\frac{v^2}{c^2}}}\,,$$

we obtain

$$\frac{va}{\sqrt{1-\frac{v^2}{c^2}}} = \text{const.} \qquad (109.20)$$

The law of change of velocity with time is determined by these relations. With increasing a, the velocity v decreases monotonically.

Problems

1. Find the first two terms on the expansion of the apparent brightness of a galaxy as a function of its red shift; the absolute brightness of a galaxy varies with time according to an exponential law, $I_{abs} = \text{const} \cdot e^{\alpha\tau}$ (H. Robertson, 1955).

Solution: The dependence on distance χ of the apparent brightness of a galaxy at the "instant" η, is given (for the closed model) by the formula

$$I = \text{const} \cdot e^{\alpha[\tau(\eta-\chi)-\tau(\eta)]} \frac{a^2(\eta-\chi)}{a^4(\eta)\sin^2\chi}.$$

We define the red shift as the relative change in wave length:

$$z = \frac{\lambda-\lambda_0}{\lambda_0} = \frac{\omega_0-\omega}{\omega} = \frac{a(\eta)-a(\eta-\chi)}{a(\eta-\chi)}.$$

Expanding I and z in powers of χ [using the functions $a(\eta)$ and $\tau(\eta)$ from (107.9) and (107.10)] and then eliminating χ from the resulting equations, we find the result:

$$I = \text{const} \cdot \frac{1}{z^2}\left[1-\left(1-\frac{q}{2}+\frac{ac}{h}d\right)z\right],$$

where we have introduced the notation

$$q = \frac{2}{1+\cos\eta} = \frac{\mu}{\mu_k} > 1.$$

For the open model, we get the same formula with

$$q = \frac{2}{1+\cosh\eta} = \frac{\mu}{\mu_k} < 1.$$

2. Find the leading terms in the expansion of the number of galaxies contained inside a "sphere" of given radius, as a function of the red shift at the boundary of the sphere (where the spatial distribution of galaxies is assumed to be uniform).

Solution: The number N of galaxies at "distances" $\geqslant\chi$ is (in the closed model)

$$N = \text{const} \cdot \int_0^\chi \sin^2\chi\, d\chi \cong \text{const} \cdot \chi^3.$$

Substituting the first two terms in the expansion of the function $\chi(z)$, we obtain:

$$N = \text{const} \cdot z^3\left[1-\frac{3}{4}(2+q)z\right].$$

In this form the formula also holds for the open model.

3. Find the dependence of the apparent angular diameter of a galaxy on distance.

Solution. The angular diameter γ of an object with given absolute linear dimensions R, observed at the moment η, is given by the expression (written for the open model)

$$\gamma = \frac{R}{a(\eta-\chi)\sinh\chi} = \frac{R}{a_0\sinh\chi[\cosh(\eta-\chi)-1]}.$$

As a function of the "distance" χ, this quantity has a minimum for $\chi=\eta/3$. The existence of this minimum is a natural consequence of the decrease of the radius of curvature a corresponding to the decrease of the time $\eta-\chi$ with increasing χ.†

§ 110. The absence of singularities in the general cosmological solution

The assumption of complete homogeneity and isotropy of the distribution of matter in space, which is the basis of the cosmological models treated above, is a very far-reaching assumption from the mathematical point of view, to say nothing of the fact that in the real world it can at best be only approximately correct. In this connection the question arises as to the extent to which this specific assumption is the cause of the important feature of isotropic model — the presence of a time singularity.‡

A natural choice of reference system for studying this question is the synchronous system which, as we saw in § 99, can always be constructed.

It is easy to show, by using the general equations of gravitation, that the determinant g of the metric tensor goes to zero during the course of some finite time.

To do this we turn to Eq. (99.10) and note that the expression on the right is negative for any distribution of matter (or is equal to zero, for empty space):

$$R_0^0=\frac{1}{2c}\frac{\partial}{\partial t}\varkappa_\alpha^\alpha+\tfrac{1}{4}\varkappa_\alpha^\beta\varkappa_\beta^\alpha\leqslant 0. \tag{110.1}$$

In fact, for the energy-momentum tensor (94.9) we have (in the synchronous reference system):

$$T_0^0-\tfrac{1}{2}T=-\tfrac{1}{2}(\epsilon+3p)-(p+\epsilon)u_\alpha u^\alpha,$$

from which it is obvious that this quantity is negative. The same result holds for the energy-momentum tensor of the electromagnetic field (where $T=0$, $-T_0^0$ is the positive energy density of the field).

By virtue of the algebraic inequality§

$$\varkappa_\alpha^\beta\varkappa_\beta^\alpha\geqslant\tfrac{1}{3}(\varkappa_\alpha^\alpha)^2$$

we have from (110.1)

$$\frac{\partial}{\partial t}\varkappa_\alpha^\alpha+\tfrac{1}{6}(\varkappa_\alpha^\alpha)^2\leqslant 0,$$

---

† However, it should be kept in mind that it may happen that the galaxies fuse with one another before this minimum is reached.

‡ The solution of this problem was given in the papers of E. M. Lifshitz and I. M. Khalatnikov, *J. Exptl. Theoret. Phys.* (U.S.S.R.) **39**, 149, 800 (1960); *Soviet Phys. JETP* **12**, 108, 558 (1961); E. M. Lifshitz, V. V Sudakov and I. M. Khalatnikov, *J. Exptl. Theoret. Phys.* (U.S.S.R.) **40**, 1847 (1961); *Soviet Phys. IEPT* **13**, 1298 (1962). We refer the reader to these papers for details of the calculations.

§ Its validity is easily demonstrated by bringing the tensor $\varkappa_\alpha^\beta$ o diagonal form (at any given time).

or

$$\frac{\partial}{\partial t}\frac{1}{\varkappa_\alpha^\alpha} \geqslant \tfrac{1}{6}. \tag{110.2}$$

Suppose, for example, that $\varkappa_\alpha^\alpha > 0$ at some time. Then for decreasing t the quantity $1/\varkappa_\alpha^\alpha$ decreases, always having a finite (nonzero) derivative, so that it must go to zero (from positive values) in the course of a finite time. In other words, $\varkappa_\alpha^\alpha$ goes to ∞, and since $\varkappa_\alpha^\alpha = \partial \ln \sqrt{-g}/c\,\partial t$, this means that the determinant $-g$ goes to zero [no faster than t^6, according to the inequality (110.2)]. If $\varkappa_\alpha^\alpha < 0$ initially, the same thing occurs with increasing time.

However this result still does not by any means prove that there must inevitably be a real singularity in the metric. The only physical singularities are those which are peculiar to the space-time itself and are not related to the character of the reference system. But the singularity which we have shown must inevitably be present in the synchronous system may be fictitious and vanish when we go to some other reference system. The possibility of such a situation is already apparent from the fact that the proof we have presented remains valid for a non-Galilean metric in a flat space-time, for which it is obvious from the start that the singularity is fictitious.

Simple geometrical considerations show that this singularity, which is inevitable in the synchronous reference system, is actually fictitious in general.

We have seen in § 99 that the construction of a synchronous reference system reduces to the construction of a family of geodesics normal to some spacelike hypersurface. But the geodesics of an arbitrary family will in general intersect one another on some enveloping hypersurfaces which are the four-dimensional analogs of the caustic surfaces of geometrical optics. In other words, there is a geometric reason for the appearance of a singularity which is related in an obvious way to the specific properties of the synchronous system and is therefore not physical in character.

An arbitrary metric in four-space also permits the existence of nonintersecting families of timelike geodesic curves. But the property of the curvature of real space-time which is expressed by the inequality $R_0^0 \leqslant 0$ means that the metric permitted by the equations of gravitation excludes the existence of such families, so that the time lines in any synchronous reference system necessarily intersect one another†.

From the analytic point of view this means that the equations of gravitation in the synchronous reference system have a general solution with a fictitious time-singularity.‡ Thus there remains no reason for the

† We have, of course, disregarded the trivial exception where we have bundles of parallel lines in a flat four-space.

‡ In this solution one of the principal values of the tensor $g_{\alpha\beta}$ tends to zero proportionally to the square of the length of the geodesic time curve as measured from its point of tangency to the caustic hypersurface.

existence, in addition to this solution, of still another which would have a true singularity and also be general. By a "general" solution we mean one which permits arbitrary assigment of conditions (distribution of matter and field) at some moment which is chosen as the initial time. Such a solution must contain eight "physically different" arbitrary functions of the space coordinates (cf. the end of § 95).

The geometrical arguments presented here do not, of course, exclude the possible existence of more restricted classes of cosmological solutions of the gravitational equations, having a real singularity. The investigation of the possible types for such singularities leads to the result that the most broad solution with a real singularity is a solution which is the generalization of the metric which we considered in § 102 (Eq. 102.9). In the neighborhood of the singular point (which we choose to be the moment $t = 0$), the leading terms in the expansion of the metric tensor in powers of t have the form

$$g_{\alpha\beta} = t^{2p_1} l_\alpha l_\beta + t^{2p_2} m_\alpha m_\beta + t^{2p_3} n_\alpha n_\beta, \tag{110.3}$$

where $\mathbf{l}$, $\mathbf{m}$ and $\mathbf{n}$ are three vector functions of the (space) coordinates, while p_1, p_2, and p_3 are functions of the coordinates, which are related to one another by the equations

$$p_1 + p_2 + p_3 = p_1^2 + p_2^2 + p_3^2 = 1, \tag{110.4}$$

and we use the convention that $p_1 < p_2 < p_3$. With these expressions, we automatically satisfy the leading terms of Eq. (99.10) for the field in vacuum ($T_i^k = 0$). The three equations (99.11) for $\alpha = 1, 2, 3$, give three relations between the ten arbitrary functions of coordinates which appear in (110.3) (the three components of each of the vectors $\mathbf{l}$, $\mathbf{m}$ and $\mathbf{n}$, and one of the quantities p_1, p_2 and p_3). Satisfying Eq. (99.12) requires that we maintain the condition†

$$\mathbf{l} \cdot \operatorname{curl} \mathbf{l} = 0, \tag{110.5}$$

since otherwise the three-dimensional tensor P_α^β will contain terms of too high order in $1/t$.

Thus we are left with just $10-4 = 6$ independent functions. In addition our choice of reference system still permits arbitrary transformations of the three space coordinates into one another (whereas the choice of the time is fixed by the condition that $t = 0$ at the singular point). As a result, the number of "physically different" arbitrary coordinate functions in the solution is equal to $6-3 = 3$, i.e., it is one less than would be required for the general solution in empty space.

† This condition has a simple geometrical significance: a vector $\mathbf{l}$ which satisfies it can be represented in the form $\mathbf{l} = \psi \operatorname{grad} \phi$ (where ψ and ϕ are two scalar functions), so that $l_\alpha l_\beta \, dx^\alpha dx^\beta = \psi^2 d\phi^2$. This means that the direction of the vector $\mathbf{l}$ at each point in space can be chosen as the direction of the coordinate line x^1 (so that the surfaces $\phi = \text{const}$ will be the surfaces $x^1 = \text{const}$).

In the presence of matter, the form of the metric (110.3) is not changed, but the density and motion of the matter (with the equation of state $p = \epsilon/3$) is determined by the formulas

$$\epsilon = \epsilon^{(0)} t^{-2(1-p_3)}, \qquad u_\alpha = u_\alpha^{(0)} t^{\frac{1-p_3}{2}}, \tag{110.6}$$

which generalize the result obtained in Problem 3 of § 102 (here $\epsilon^{(0)}$, $u_\alpha^{(0)}$ are four arbitrary functions of the coordinates). The back reaction of the matter on the field [whose leading terms are given by the expressions (110.3)] results only in a change in the relations arising from Eqs. (99.11) between the arbitrary functions, which now include $\epsilon^{(0)}$, $u_\alpha^{(0)}$ in addition to **l**, **m** and **n**. In Eqs. (99.10) and (99.12), the right hand sides are quantities of higher order than the leading terms on the left sides, so that they affect only the later terms in the expansion of the metric in powers of t.

Thus the presence of the matter adds four more arbitrary functions of the coordinates to this solution, so that we have all together seven physically different arbitrary functions, which is one less than would be needed for the general solution. Thus this solution, despite its generality, is still only a special case. In other words, it is unstable: there can exist such small perturbations which destroy the behavior described by this solution. Since in the synchronous reference system the singularity cannot disappear completely, this means that under the action of the perturbation it becomes a fictitious singularity.

We should note once again the fact that a solution of the type of (110.3) also exists in the absence of matter (in which case it contains three physically different arbitrary functions). This shows that the general features of the cosmological solutions with respect to singularities already appear for the case of empty space. This result appears reasonable when we note that the gravitational properties of an appropriately selected set of short-wave gravitational waves can imitate the gravitational properties of matter (with the ultrarelativistic equation of state $p = \epsilon/3$). An exceptional case in this sense is the isotropic solution, which does not exist for empty space†. However this exception is related to the fact that the high degree of symmetry (uniformity) in the distribution of matter for this solution cannot be imitated in the fashion described.

Thus we arrive at the fundamental conclusion that the presence of a singularity in time is not a necessary property of the cosmological models of the general theory of relativity, and that the general case of an arbitrary distribution of matter and gravitational field does not lead to the appearance of a singularity.

† We note that this solution is actually a special case of a broader class of solutions (cf. the Problem).

In view of the symmetry of the equations of gravitation with respect to a change in sign of the time, this result applies equally to both time directions. Physically, however, because of the physical nonequivalence of future and past, there is an essential difference between these two cases in the very formulation of the problem. A singularity in the future can have a physical sense only if it occurs under completely arbitrary conditions assigned at some earlier moment in time. It is clear that there is no reason why the distribution of matter and field which is reached in the course of evolution of the universe should correspond to the specific conditions required for the realization of a singular solution of the equations of gravitation, having a true singularity. Moreover, even if we assume that somehow such a distribution is realized at some moment in time, it will inevitably be destroyed later on, simply because of unavoidable fluctuations. Therefore the results presented here exclude the possibility of the existence of a singularity in the future, and mean that a contraction of the universe (if it is to occur at all) must finally give way to an expansion.

To the question the existence of singularity in the past, an investigation based only on the gravitational equations alone can in general give no definite answer. The condition that the singularity should exist for an arbitrary distribution of matter and field, is in this case a priori not obligatory. Such a condition would be equivalent to an assumption that the actual universe is described by some purely accidental solution of the field equations — an assumption which is obviously unsuitable. There can be no doubt that the choince of the solution, which corresponds to the actual universe, is in fact unique and is linked to some basic physical conditions which cannot be found out in the framework of the existing theory of gravitation alone. It will become possible to elucidate these conditions only in the course of further synthesis of the physical theories. Only then could it become possible to find out unambiguously whether there is a singularity in the specific solution which satisfies these conditons.

Problem

Find the solution of the gravitational equations in which a contraction of space proceeds "quasiuniformly", i.e. so that all the components $g_{\alpha\beta}$ (in the synchronous reference system) tend to zero according to the same law. The space is filled with matter with the equation of state $p = \epsilon/3$.

Solution. We look for a solution in the neighborhood of the singular point ($t = 0$) in the form

$$g_{\alpha\beta} = ta_{\alpha\beta}+t^2b_{\alpha\beta}+\dots, \tag{1}$$

† The isotropic model corresponds to the special choice of the function $a_{\alpha\beta}$ giving a space of constant curvature.

where $a_{\alpha\beta}$ and $b_{\alpha\beta}$ are functions of the (space) coordinates.† The inverse tensor is

$$g^{\alpha\beta} = \frac{1}{t} a^{\alpha\beta} - b^{\alpha\beta},$$

where the tensor $a^{\alpha\beta}$ is inverse to $a_{\alpha\beta}$, and $b^{\alpha\beta} = a^{\alpha\gamma} a^{\beta\delta} b_{\gamma\delta}$; in the following, all operations of raising indices and covariant differentiation are carried out using the metric $a_{\alpha\beta}$ which is independent of the time.

Computing the left sides of Eqs. (99.10) and (99.11) to second and to first order in $1/t$, respectively, we obtain (setting $c = 1$):

$$-\frac{3}{4t^2} + \frac{b}{2t} = \frac{8\pi k}{3}\epsilon(-4u_0^2+1), \quad \tfrac{1}{2}(b_{;\alpha} - b^{\beta}_{\alpha;\beta}) = -\frac{32\pi k}{3}\epsilon u_\alpha u_0,$$

where $b = b^{\alpha}_{\alpha}$. Also using the identity

$$-1 = u_i u^i \cong -u_0^2 + \frac{1}{t} u_\alpha u_\beta a^{\alpha\beta},$$

we then find:

$$8\pi k\epsilon = \frac{3}{4t^2} - \frac{b}{2t}, \tag{2}$$

$$u_\alpha = \frac{t^2}{2}(b_{;\alpha} - b^{\beta}_{\alpha;\beta}). \tag{3}$$

The three-dimensional Christoffel symbols and with them the tensor $P_{\alpha\beta}$ are independent of the time in the first approximation in $1/t$; here $P_{\alpha\beta}$ coincides with the expressions which are obtained by computing simply with the metric $a_{\alpha\beta}$. Taking this into account, we find that the terms of order t^{-2} in Eq. (99.12) cancel, while the terms $\sim 1/t$ give

$$P^{\beta}_{\alpha} + \frac{3}{4} b^{\beta}_{\alpha} + \frac{5}{12}\delta^{\beta}_{\alpha} b = 0,$$

from which

$$b^{\beta}_{\alpha} - \frac{4}{3} P^{\beta}_{\alpha} + \frac{5}{18}\delta^{\beta}_{\alpha} P \tag{4}$$

(where $P^{\beta}_{\alpha} = a^{\beta\gamma} P_{\alpha\gamma}$). In view of the identity

$$P^{\beta}_{\alpha;\beta} - \frac{1}{2} P_{;\alpha} = 0$$

[cf. (95.10)], the relation

$$b^{\beta}_{\alpha;\beta} = \frac{7}{9} b_{;\alpha}$$

holds, so that (3) can be rewritten in the form

$$u_\alpha = \frac{t^2}{9} b_{;\alpha}. \tag{5}$$

Thus all six of the functions $a_{\alpha\beta}$ are arbitrary, and the coefficients $b_{\alpha\beta}$ of the next term in the expansion (1) can be determined from them. The choice of the time in the metric (1) is completely fixed by the requirement that $t = 0$ at the singular point; but the space coordinates still permit of an arbitrary transformation which leaves the time alone (so that we can, for example, bring the tensor $a_{\alpha\beta}$ to diagonal form). Thus the solution we have obtained contains altogether three physically different arbitrary functions.

We note that in this solution the spatial metric is inhomogeneous and anisotropic, while the matter distribution tends to uniformity as $t \to 0$. In the approximation (5) the curl of the three-dimensional velocity **v** is equal to zero, while its magnitude tends to zero according to the law:

$$v^2 = v_\alpha v_\beta g^{\alpha\beta} \sim t^3.$$

INDEX

COURSE OF THEORETICAL PHYSICS

Vol. 1. *Mechanics*

Vol. 3. *Quantum Mechanics—Non-relativistic Theory*

Vol. 4. *Relativistic Quantum Theory*

Vol. 5. *Statistical Physics*

Vol. 6. *Fluid Mechanics*

Vol. 7. *Theory of Elasticity*

Vol. 8. *Electrodynamics of Continuous Media*

Vol. 9. *Physical Kinetics*

207886